EXPERIMENTAL ENDOCRINOLOGY

A SOURCEBOOK OF BASIC TECHNIQUES

EXPERIMENTAL ENDOCRINOLOGY

A SOURCEBOOK OF BASIC TECHNIQUES

by

M. X. ZARROW
Department of Biological Sciences
Purdue University
Lafayette, Indiana

J. M. YOCHIM
Department of Comparative
Biochemistry and Physiology
University of Kansas
Lawrence, Kansas

J. L. McCARTHY
Department of Biology
Southern Methodist University
Dallas, Texas

WITH A CHAPTER ON INVERTEBRATE HORMONES BY

R. C. SANBORN
Department of Biological Sciences
Purdue University
Lafayette, Indiana

1964

ACADEMIC PRESS
New York and London

ACADEMIC PRESS INC.
111 Fifth Avenue, New York, New York 10003

United Kingdom Edition published by
ACADEMIC PRESS INC. (LONDON) LTD.
Berkeley Square House, London W.1

LIBRARY OF CONGRESS CATALOG CARD NUMBER: **64-23025**

Third Printing, 1968

PRINTED IN THE UNITED STATES OF AMERICA.

Dedicated to our respective wives, whose aid and encouragement was of inestimable value in the completion of this book.

Preface

Endocrinology is a subject that has come to the fore only since the third decade of the twentieth century. As a result, this discipline has borrowed concepts and methods from areas in the biological sciences that were well established at the time of its infancy. At one time or another endocrinology has been taught as part of formal courses in anatomy, physiology, biochemistry, pharmacology, internal medicine, and other subjects. Indeed, it is part of all of these areas, but our knowledge has so increased that endocrinology can no longer be taught adequately as part of another course. To permit the student to synthesize concepts from the vast array of experimental data requires a study of the subject as such, and not as a part of one of the older disciplines. One might say that endocrinology has come of age.

Houssay, Nobel Laureate in Medicine, has stated that physiology can be taught properly only by practical and individual teaching. Indeed, this is also true of endocrinology. A discipline that has borrowed techniques from so many areas of science offers a wide variety of experiences and experiments for the student. Only by working in the laboratory with the hormone, the animal, the cell, and the test tube can the student truly learn to appreciate the role of the hormones in the regulation of physiological events. In this respect, the present text is dedicated to the appreciation and understanding of the whole organism and its interrelationship with the environment.

This book, based on a laboratory course that was first taught in Professor F. L. Hisaw's laboratory in 1946, is designed as a textbook and manual for use in an advanced course or for use by the individual student in a project course. Therefore, the student should possess some basic knowledge in the areas of physiology, biochemistry, histology, and endocrinology. Furthermore, the inclusion of an extensive list of references is designed to give the student an opportunity to examine the literature pertinent to the laboratory work he is doing, and to utilize this literature in the preparation of his written reports.

The practical goal of the book has been to include, in addition to those exercises which have been tried at classroom level, some techniques not commonly used in the classroom, but nonetheless applicable. An attempt also has been made to include more exercises than can be used in a one-semester course. This should permit the student or instructor to select those exercises best suited to the student's goal and within the means of the laboratory.

Finally, it should be noted that not all of these experiments will be successful in different laboratories. Such factors as strain of animals, environmental conditions, nutritional state, etc., may influence results. It may be necessary to change treatment schedules, dosages, etc., but regardless of results, the laboratory experience should be of inestimable value. Under the direction of the authors, about 85 per cent of these experiments have worked successfully at the student level.

M. X. ZARROW

April, 1964

Contents

a

CONTENTS

Experiment 2–12. Extraction and Purification of Estrogens
from Urine 52
Experiment 2–13. Modified Kober Reaction for Use with
Purified Extracts Prepared in Experiment 2–12 . . . 55
Experiment 2–14. Extraction of Estrogens from Urine of
Pregnancy (Simplified Procedure) 56
Experiment 2–15. Colorimetric Estimation of Urinary Estrogens
by the Kober Reaction (Simplified Procedure) . . . 57
Experiment 2–16. Fluorometric Estimation of Estrogens
(Simplified Procedure) 59
References 60

Chapter 3 THE PROGESTOGENS

Sites of Progestogen Formation 65
Nature of the Progestogens 67
Action of the Progestogens 67
The Assay of Progestogens 78
Biogenesis, Metabolism, and Mechanism of Action . . . 83
Experiment 3–1. The Induction of Pseudopregnancy . . 86
Experiment 3–2. The Decidual Cell Reaction 87
Experiment 3–3. Assay of Progesterone by the Decidual
Cell Response 89
Experiment 3–4. The Assay of Progesterone by Measures of
Endometrial Proliferation 92
Experiment 3–5. The Assay of Progestogens by Stromal Cell
Hypertrophy of the Mouse Uterus 94
Experiment 3–6. Assay of Progesterone by Estimation of
Carbonic Anhydrase of the Uterus 96
Experiment 3–7. Effects of Estrogen and Progesterone on the
Maintenance of Gestation 100
Experiment 3–8. Extraction and Estimation of Pregnanediol
from Urine 101
References 103

Chapter 4 RELAXIN

Sites of Relaxin Formation 109
Nature of Relaxin 110
Action of Relaxin 112
The Assay of Relaxin 115
Biogenesis, Metabolism, and Mechanism of Action . . . 115
Experiment 4–1. Relaxation of the Pubic Symphysis of the
Guinea Pig 116
Experiment 4–2. The Action of Relaxin on the Interpubic
Ligament of the Mouse 117
Experiment 4–3. Measurement of the Interpubic Ligament of
the Mouse during Gestation 119
Experiment 4–4. Inhibition of Contractions of the Uterus . 120
References 120

Chapter 14   THE INVERTEBRATE HORMONES

APPENDIX

CHAPTER 1

Introduction

During the early history of endocrinology, it became apparent that a similar approach was used by many investigators in studies on the identification of glands of internal secretion and their secretory products. This classical approach consisted of three steps: ablation, replacement therapy, and chemical isolation and purification.

Ablation, the surgical removal of the tissue or gland in question, was the initial step and, if successful, usually resulted in a specific syndrome or deficiency state directly ascribable to the loss of the gland. Once the deficiency state was induced experimentally, *replacement therapy* was instituted in an effort to prevent the syndrome. This was effected by the reimplantation of the gland in question back into an animal. Thus, the testes, for example, removed from their normal location, were immediately reintroduced into another part of the body, thus preventing ·the appearance of castration symptoms. Such an experiment was first described in the classical work of Berthold. It is now possible, by utilizing highly inbred strains of animals, to permit the deficiency symptoms to develop following ablation and then to alleviate the state by the implantation of a similar gland from a genetically similar animal. A final stage in this step was to prepare a crude extract of the gland which could be injected into the animal after ablation. The third step in the identification of an endocrine gland and its secretory products was the *isolation* of the stimulating substance from the gland, and its *purification.*

Sources of the Hormones

The classical development of the experimental method described above provided all the necessary criteria by which a substance could be identified as a hormone. According to the original definition, a hormone is a specific chemical entity that is secreted into the blood by a well defined group of cells and is transported via the vascular system to a site distant from its point of origin, where its action takes place. Similarly, the endocrine gland was described as a well defined group of cells that

1

secretes a unique organic chemical product directly into the circulation rather than through a series of ducts, as do digestive glands such as the salivary gland or the exocrine pancreas.

Thus, the endocrine system and its hormones was thought to be a system for control and integration of physiological processes analogous to, but separate and distinct from, the other great integrative mechanism in the organism—the nervous system. Unlike the nervous system, which is almost entirely of ectodermal origin, the endocrine system is composed of organs that vary widely in embryological origin, being derived from all three primitive layers, ectoderm, mesoderm, and endoderm (see Table 1-1). Again unlike the nervous system, whose action is rapid and ephemeral, the endocrine system exerts its effects over prolonged periods of time, sometimes for weeks or months.

TABLE 1–1

THE EMBRYONIC DERIVATION OF THE DUCTLESS GLANDS AND THE
TYPES OF HORMONES PRODUCED

Embryonic source of gland	Derivation of gland	Gland	Type of secretion
Endoderm	Pharyngeal pouches	Thyroid Parathyroid	Iodinated amino acids Proteins or polypeptides
	Intestine	Islets of Langerhans	Protein
Mesoderm	Mesenchyme from dorsal mesentery	Adrenal cortex	Steroids
	Genital ridge	Ovary, testis	Steroids, protein, or polypeptide
Ectoderm	Neural crest material, chromaffin tissue of primitive sympathetic nervous system	Adrenal medulla	Cathechol amines
	Stomadeum	Adenohypophysis	Proteins
	Diencephalon	Neurohypophysis	Polypeptides

However, it soon became apparent that both the nervous system and the endocrine system were not entirely distinct and that each utilized "methods" of the other. For example, the adrenal medulla might be considered as an extension of the nervous system. This group of cells (within the adrenal gland in mammals) originates from nervous tissue, receives an abundant preganglionic autonomic nerve supply, and when stimulated secretes into the circulation epinephrine and norepinephrine. Norepinephrine is identical in structure and function to the substance released by most postganglionic sympathetic nerve fibers. If, however, norepinephrine is accepted as a hormone, its alternate tissue source, the postganglionic sympathetic nerve ending should be considered an endocrine structure; and if so, one is tempted in addition to admit acetylcholine into the realm of hormones.

Indeed, recent findings indicate that the hormones vasopressin and oxytocin are stored in the posterior pituitary gland but originate in certain neurons of the hypothalamus. These hormones then pass from the hypothalamus to the neurohypophysis by way of the axons of the hypothalamic-hypophyseal nerve tract. Such an origin of certain hormones in neural tissue has long been recognized in insects and crustaceans. In mammals, it is now postulated that a number of hypophyseal releasing factors are formed in the hypothalamus, pass directly to the anterior pituitary gland via a *portal circulatory system,* and influence the release of such hormones as the gonadotropins, adrenocorticotropin, and thyrotropin. It is apparent that the cells of the nervous system in many different species, ranging from mammals to the arthropods, possess the ability to produce both hormones and other substances that affect and control the release of hormones from endocrine glands.

Thus, it appears that a substance may be classified as a hormone even though (a) it is secreted by the nervous system, (b) it does not act at a site distant from its point of origin, and (c) it is not transported by the vascular system. Once these original restrictions are lifted, it appears that there exist a large number of naturally occurring substances, sometimes called tissue hormones, that frequently are disregarded in the study of the endocrine system. These are such substances as renin, histamine, heparin, and serotonin. Obviously many more data of a physiological nature are needed before one can attempt to classify such compounds and the "ductless glands" from which they come. But it must be remembered that classifications are simply aids to an understanding of knowledge. Definitions must continue to remain flexible and open to revision as new information is made available. In the light of new findings and the need for definitions broad enough to encompass them, a hormone might now be defined as a physiological organic substance that is secreted by living cells in relatively restricted areas of the organism and that diffuses or is transported to a site in the same organism, where it brings about an adjustment that tends to integrate the component parts and actions of the organism.

Recently a new subdivision of endocrinology made its appearance; it is growing with amazing rapidity. This is neuroendocrinology, which concerns itself with (a) the interaction of the nervous system with the endocrine system, (b) the secretion of hormones or neurohormones by the nervous system, and (c) the influence of hormones on the nervous system. In addition, the classical approach to the study of endocrinology has been amplified in recent years by studies concerned with the biogenesis, metabolism, and mechanisms of action of the hormones and with the integrative actions of groups or combinations of hormones. These new approaches and the kinds of information they yield are described below.

Nature of the Hormones

Compounds that exhibit hormone action may be found in many molecular sizes and shapes. However, the hormones may be classified generally into three groups on the basis of their chemical structures: amino acids or their derivatives, such as epinephrine, norepinephrine, acetylcholine, and the iodothyronines; steroids related to cholesterol, such as testosterone, progesterone, corticosterone, and estrone; and polypeptides and proteins, with or without an additional carbohydrate moiety attached, such as corticotropin, melanocyte stimulating hormone, relaxin, follicle stimulating hormone, insulin, and parathormone.

Many hormones are normally bound to plasma proteins and circulate with them. This includes both steroid and nonsteroid hormones. In the case of the estrogens, for instance, a specific complex is formed with blood protein (estroprotein complex) which appears to be of major importance in the transport and activity of the hormone. If the binding of the estrogen is prevented by subtotal hepatectomy, activity is lost.

It has long been known that thyroxine is bound to the α-globulin fraction of blood and to albumin. Actually, one of the chemical tests for circulating thyroxine level is based on the determination of protein-bound iodine (PBI). The protein-bound thyroxine is inactive as such and must be in the free state before it can act at the cellular level. During pregnancy in the human being, the thyroxine level of the blood increases markedly whereas the basal metabolic rate remains normal. It is apparent that the hormone is not acting at the cellular level under these circumstances, either as a result of a decreased rate of diffusion of the hormone into the tissues, a control of the mechanism responsible for splitting the thyroid-protein complex, or an increase in thyroid hormone catabolism or excretion to keep pace with its increased synthesis.

Hormones also appear to show selectivity for certain tissues and are bound by these tissues. Thus, insulin is rapidly bound by muscle and by adipose and mammary tissue, and to a limited extent thyroid stimulating hormone is bound by the thyroid gland, and the gonadotropins appear to be trapped by the gonads.

Several general characteristics seem to apply to all compounds that have been classed as hormones to date. These compounds (a) act in trace amounts; (b) are not sources of energy for biological reactions; (c) regulate rates of chemical reactions, but do not initiate new reactions; (d) require a latent period before an effect is apparent; (e) are rapidly removed from the circulation and metabolized by the tissues, sometimes within minutes; (f) appear to be active only in tissues that can respond or are sensitive to their action, i.e., have a specificity of action dependent in great part on tissue sensitivity.

Many of these characteristics also apply to the vitamins and to enzymes. However, all the hormones, unlike many vitamins, are produced within the animal and thus cannot be considered akin to the non energy-supplying dietary requirements of the organism, such as the vitamins. Hormones differ from the enzymes in that they appear to be more highly tissue specific, are produced in relatively localized areas by specialized tissues (compared to many enzymes that are universally present in almost all tissues), and tend to cause physiological adjustments that are observable at the organismic level rather than at the intracellular level. Recent research however, has provided clues which suggest that the hormones do work in conjunction with enzymes, acting as cofactors, to regulate reaction rates within the cell.

Action of the Hormones

The actions of the hormones in the living organism may be classified under three general headings: morphogenesis, homeostasis, and functional integration.

A. MORPHOGENESIS

Morphogenesis encompasses the growth, differentiation, and maturation of the organism. Nearly all the hormones (with the possible exception of the posterior pituitary hormones, pressor amines, and neurohumors) possess some morphogenetic activity. Somatotropin (STH) provides an outstanding example of this type of action since it stimulates the overall growth of the organism. Similarly, thyroxine stimulates growth, differentiation, and maturation of specific tissues, such as the nervous system, as well as a general metamorphosis in some animals. Testosterone, a protein anabolic hormone, stimulates both general protein synthesis and growth of the male reproductive tract. Estradiol is a hormone primarily responsible for the growth and development of the female reproductive tract.

B. HOMEOSTASIS

Homeostasis refers to the maintenance of a steady, but dynamic equilibrium of all the components of the internal environment of an animal. This active process is facilitated to a large extent by the hormones. Among hormones of major importance in this activity are insulin, parathormone, the adrenal corticoids, and the antidiuretic hormone. Thus, although a chemical turnover is occurring constantly in the internal environment, the hormones tend to stabilize and buffer the change. For example, circulating sugar is being constantly drained and utilized for the production of energy and is periodically increased after food ingestion. The variations in blood sugar levels are none-the-less kept within physiologically tolerable limits, primarily through the action of hormones such as insulin, glucagon, and certain of the adrenal corticoids. This kind of homeostatic activity is observed not only for blood sugar, but for many other substances, e.g., sodium, calcium, and potassium.

Among the actions of many hormones must be included the homeostatic regulation of their own secretion. The methods of regulation of secretion of an endocrine gland are quite varied, and a number of mechanisms may be involved in an individual instance. The *servomechanism* or *feedback system* is evidenced primarily between the tropic or stimulating hormones of the pituitary gland and the target endocrine glands upon which the tropic hormones act. The concept is a relatively simple one involving mutual control of secretion rates of the tropic hormone and target gland hormones by the levels of these substances in circulation. For example, thyrotropin (TSH) stimulates the release of thyroxine from the thyroid gland and thyroxine in turn acts back on the pituitary gland to inhibit further release of TSH. Evidence for such a concept is easily obtained. TSH is necessary for the physiological and morphological states of the thyroid gland. In the absence of TSH, the thyroid gland undergoes atrophy and produces little to no hormone. In the presence of excess thyroxine, the thyroid gland involutes and is comparable to that seen after hypophysectomy or lack of TSH. Thus, the concentration of thyroxine in the blood apparently determines the rate of release of TSH from the pituitary gland. If the blood level of thyroxine falls, the pituitary gland secretes more TSH; and if the blood level of thyroxine rises, the release of TSH is suppressed. Comparable systems have been described for corticotropin (ACTH) and the adrenal corticoids, and for the gonadotropins and the ovarian estrogens. Whether or not the target gland hormones act directly on the hypophysis or via the hypothalamus (or both) is still a moot point in many instances.

It is apparent that, in a feedback system, the rate of utilization and excretion of the target gland hormone is a critical factor which determines the level of that hormone in circulation. This, in turn, modifies the activity of the servomechanism. If the hormone is rapidly lost from the circulation either through utilization, degradation, or excretion, then the level drops rapidly and more tropic hormone is released; if on the other hand less of the hormone is removed, its blood titer increases until a level is reached that inhibits release of the tropic hormone. An example of this type of relationship may be obtained by exposing a mammal to a change in season. As the temperature drops, there may be observed an increased heat production and increased thyroxine utilization with a subsequent decrease in thyroxine blood level. The change in circulating thyroxine level stimulates an increased release of TSH, leading to a hypertrophy and hyperplasia of the thyroid gland and an increased thyroxine synthesis and release. On exposure to high temperature, the reverse occurs.

A second method of regulation is a modified type of feedback mechanism in which a blood metabolite level, controlled by the hormone, influences the rate of hormone secretion. Examples of this type of control are noted in the regulation of insulin secretion by blood glucose levels and of parathormone release by serum calcium levels. In these cases, the blood concentration of a substance controlled by the hormone influences the rate of release of the hormones.

The maintenance of a homeostatic condition by hormones need not be a result of *internal* cues such as blood glucose or calcium levels. The external environment also provides cues for physiologic adjustments via hormone secretion. In fact, a third method of regulation of hormone secretion involves a *neural* or *neurohumoral* mechanism. A classical example is the effect of the external environment on reproductive activity, in which such factors as light may affect the growth and development of the gonads. The pathway involves the retina, optic nerve, hypothalamus, and hypophysis, an observation well documented in some seasonal breeders. Exteroceptive stimuli of a visual, auditory, tactile, or olfactory nature are all quite effective as stimulators or inhibitors of endocrine activity. Probably one of the best examples of endocrine inhibition by exteroceptive stimuli is the effect of stressors on reproduction.

C. INTEGRATION

The integration of physiological events in the animal is the third major action of the hormones. As mentioned above, the two major integrative systems that exist in the organism are the nervous system and the endocrine system. At one time physiologists believed that these systems acted independently of each other. Differences in both their modes of action and their methods of transmission suggested this concept. Nervous system regulation is characterized by its rapid speed of transmission and highly specific pathways and points of response; the endocrine system, on the other hand, is characterized by a much slower speed of transmission and by a diffuse delivery of the message, i.e., to the entire organism, relying on the presence of specific target tissues sensitive to the changes in blood hormone levels. While the characteristics described above are true in a general way for the two systems, both the nervous system and the endocrines are highly integrated, depend upon one another, and complement each other in their actions.

In many activities the two systems act in a highly coordinated manner. Ovulation in the rabbit or in any nonspontaneous ovulator is a classical example of this type of coordination. Release of the ovum from the ovary is triggered in the following manner: a coital stimulus to the vaginal wall and cervix is transmitted, via the nervous system, to the hypothalamus, which in turn appears to stimulate or permit the release of luteinizing hormone (LH) from the anterior pituitary gland. LH, transported by the circulatory system, acts on the ovary to cause ovulation.

Examples of the integrative action of the endocrine system itself may be seen in many of the aspects of reproduction. For example, sexual receptivity in the infraprimate female occurs around the time of ovulation and permits copulation (and successful ovum fertilization) to occur. The fertilized egg, as it moves down the oviduct to the uterus, begins its cell division and is transformed into a free floating blastocyst in the uterus. During this sequence of events, the corpus luteum of the ovary (recently formed after ovulation) becomes active and secretes progestogens. These hormones transform the uterus into a structure that permits implantation of the blastocyst. If these two series of events are not synchronized in time, blastocyst implantation may fail to occur, and pregnancy will not obtain.

The Assay of Hormones

A. BIOLOGICAL INDICATORS

In considering the actions of the hormones, it becomes evident that each group of hormones possesses the ability to alter some morphogenetic, homeostatic, or integrative mechanism in the organism and that each such action is relatively unique. Thus, the gonadotropins stimulate gonadal changes, thyrotropin acts on the thyroid gland, the adrenal steroids maintain carbohydrate and salt balance, and insulin regulates blood sugar level, to mention a few. These relatively specific biological responses are all naturally occurring events or changes in structure that may be indicative of the presence of specific hormones. As such they may be good biological indicators of hormones and, thus, may be used to measure hormone activity if they meet certain criteria.

However, many hormones have actions that are apparently similar, e.g., the actions of the adrenal steroids on blood sugar and the actions of epinephrine or glucagon on this parameter. To be useful, a biological indicator should be unique to the hormone; the more specific the hormone is for the event, the more reliable is the indicator. Such an indicator also should be readily apparent and easily measured in a quantitative manner. In general, the biological indicators for the sex steroids are more apparent and more easily recognizable than those for the other hormones. Highly specific indicators for testosterone are the comb in the bird, claspers in fish, and thumb pads and dorsal crest in certain amphibians. In the mammal, the size of the prostate and seminal vesicles, viable sperm, and other criteria are specific indexes of androgenic activity. Hair distribution in the primate is a good indicator of the sex steroids, but it suffers from the fact that it cannot be quantified. Body configuration is another sex indicator, but it is highly subjective as well as difficult to standardize. Reliable and specific biological indicators can be utilized as quantitative methods for hormone assay.

B. The Bioassay and the Chemical Assay

The bioassay serves two useful purposes. It provides a means of measuring the concentration of the hormone or its specific activity in the bodily fluids or tissues, and it also serves as a method of determining the relative potency of various natural and synthetic hormones. Although the bioassay can determine the relative activities of different substances, it cannot distinguish between an impure, but potent substance and a pure but less active substance. Establishment of the purity of a substance remains in the realm of chemistry. The bioassay, however, is a necessary aid in the laboratory for deciding which steps are important in the process of obtaining a pure substance.

In the normal course of events, the bioassay is usually superseded by a chemical assay. This development occurs after sufficient purity has been established so that the chemical characteristics, and usually the structure of the compound, are known. In general, the chemical assay is to be preferred since it eliminates animal variation, which is frequently a large source of error. Furthermore, the chemical assay is more readily standardized, and because interfering substances are removed it usually gives results that are more reproducible. Nevertheless, the bioassay plays a very necessary role in various stages of extract preparation, comparison of specific potencies, and determination of the concentration of hormones in tissues. Frequently, the bioassay is the more sensitive of the two methods and can be used to advantage when only small amounts of material are available.

The development of a good bioassay depends on the available biological indicators. Such indicators are preferred that meet the following conditions:

1. Accuracy of response: the measured response to the hormone approaches reasonably well the true response to the hormone.

2. Objectivity of end point: the response to the hormone can be measured by instruments and need not be evaluated subjectively.

3. Specificity of response: the response to the hormone is peculiar to that hormone alone under rigidly defined conditions.

4. Sensitivity of response: the response to the hormone can be obtained with relatively small amounts of the hormone.

5. Precision of response: the response to the hormone is readily reproducible and gives a good dose-response relationship. Such a relationship usually exhibits two desirable qualities: the slope of the dose-response line is steep, and the standard error is small. These qualities are expressed as an index of precision, lambda (λ), the ratio of the standard error to the slope. The index of precision is in the range of 0.3 or less in useful assays.

The response to a hormone—and thus the bioassay—is influenced by the species and strain of animal, the nutritional state, the route of administration of the hormone, the vehicle used, and, of course, any changes in the molecule. As most of the hormones are inactive orally, they are usually injected intramuscularly or subcutaneously. The intravenous route is utilized only for an immediate response or in cases where a transient, high blood level is desired; usually the steroids are not given in this manner. The vehicle used may influence markedly the degree of response by affecting the rate of absorption. This is especially true in the case of the steroid hormones. Consequently, pellet implantation of a steroid is superior to an injection since the hormone is slowly and continuously absorbed from the pellet, whereas the injected material is rapidly removed from its vehicle. Many different vehicles have been suggested; in general, the vehicle that permits slow absorption into the circulation gives a more marked and consistent effect. Oil vehicles are therefore superior to aqueous ones. Recently, it has been shown that a suspension of the proteinaceous hormones, like relaxin and ACTH, in a beeswax-oil mixture is far superior to multiple injections of the hormone in water. Injection of certain hormones in an aqueous medium containing a vital dye may also increase the effectiveness of the hormone by delaying absorption. Changes in the molecule (such as an esterification) that do not interfere with the type of activity of a hormone also may increase its effectiveness markedly. This action may be by an interference in the rate of absorption, metabolism, degradation, or excretion. On the other hand, molecular modification can also decrease the effectiveness of the preparation, even though the rates of absorption and metabolism are changed.

Biosynthesis, Metabolism, and Mechanisms of Action of Hormones

Experiments that elucidate the pathways of formation and metabolism of the hormones all parallel each other in methods of attack. A prime requisite for studies of this kind is the availability of a chemically pure hormone. Thus, the preliminary techniques always involve extraction, bioassay, and finally, chemical analysis to determine the homogeneity of the extract and the optimal methods of obtaining it. Early during these experiments, preliminary evidence of the chemical nature of the compound is collected, i.e., whether it is a glycoprotein, phenolic steroid, iodinated tyrosine derivative, or other. Also, these procedures may provide clues concerning those parts of the molecule that are necessary for activity, such as the carbohydrate moiety of a protein, the presence of an unsaturated ring in a steroid, or the presence of iodine on the molecule. Finally, the chemically pure compound is analyzed for the presence and percentage of various elements (carbon, nitrogen, sulfur, etc.); if it is a protein, the relative amino acid composition is obtained (e.g., 5% phenylalanine, no tryptophan, trace of arginine). It is during this stage that tentative structures may be assigned. For example, after careful analysis of insulin, a four-stranded protein structure, connected by disulfide linkages, was first postulated. This theoretical model was later modified to a two-stranded complex, a modification which has since been confirmed and agrees well with estimates of the molecular weight of insulin. Often, in the analysis of hormone structure, an indication of its method of synthesis can be gained. Thus, the similarity in structure of the posterior pituitary hormones oxytocin and vasopressin, and the similarity in structure of melanocyte stimulating hormone (MSH) to part of the ACTH molecule, suggest that, in each case, the hormones may have common biosynthetic pathways.

Until the early 1950's, the methods of determination of biosynthetic pathways were rather limited in scope. Since that time—with the development of ultrasensitive methods of electrophoresis; of paper, column, and thin layer chromatography; of countercurrent extraction techniques; of the use of radioactive tracer techniques; and, quite recently, of gas chromatography—many advances have been made in a few areas of hormone biosynthesis. More often than not, several of these methods are used simultaneously to gain the necessary information. Tissues of origin are extracted for the hormone and related compounds. These related compounds are of especial interest. They are purified, and their relative concentration is measured. Often, from this information, indications of major pathways of synthesis are obtained. The techniques of electrophoresis, chromatography, and countercurrent extraction are useful in this regard.

By the use of tracer techniques, one can administer suspected precursors to the animal (or to the excised tissue maintained *in vitro*) and at selected intervals measure radioactivity of various fractions of the extracted, purified, and identified yield. The knowledge of the structures of hormone precursors and degradation products is useful in determining the kinds of enzymes that may be present and necessary to effect these changes. Enzymatic studies can confirm these postulations and offer information on alternate routes of synthesis by the tissue. Often, microorganisms are useful in research involving different routes of synthesis and degradation.

Probably the most marked advances in analysis of hormone biosynthesis have been made with the thyroid hormones and the adrenal and gonadal steroids. The bioassays and chemical assays have been invaluable in this regard. Unfortunately, much less is known of the other hormones; in most cases, these structures are quite complex, and in many instances they have not been purified sufficiently.

Finally, the analysis of excretory products by bioassay and chemical determination yields additional information on possible routes of degradation and relative activity of the excreted material. From all this information, generalizations can be made on the kind of molecule, its molecular configuration, and possible modifications that will produce hormone activity. Thus, unique compounds with slightly altered structures can be synthesized in the laboratory and tried in the animal. In these studies, the bioassay is of prime importance.

Probably the least understood of the various aspects of endocrinology (although much basic information has been accumulated) are the mechanisms of action of the hormones. During early studies, this area could not be considered in detail, and discussions of mechanism of action (if it was discussed at all) were confined to the "gross aspects" of hormone action: estrogen acts by causing behavioral estrus, by increasing uterine water content and muscle protein, and by increasing uterine contractions, among other things. As experimental methods became more sophisticated and more data were obtained, questions of mechanism of action became more detailed: How does estrogen alter membrane permeability to affect water uptake? How is the action of estrogen on uterine contractility related to muscle transmembrane potentials? How does estrogen manifest its action on ATP and acto-myosin of uterine muscle? By what method does estrogen act in the nervous system to affect behavior? These are but a few of the questions currently under investigation.

Since the hormones vary in chemical construction, it would be surprising to find the same kind of mechanism involved for all hormones. Indeed, the variety of actions that may be ascribable to a single hormone, such as estradiol, indicate that several mechanisms of action may exist for a single hormone. Sufficient evidence has been accumulated to suggest that hormones directly affect enzyme systems within the cell. One paramount question still unanswered is how this action occurs. There is also evidence indicative that hormones act directly on the cell membrane to alter permeability, thereby indirectly influencing the reactions of the cell by changing substrate levels within the cell. Furthermore, there is evidence suggestive of a relationship between the vitamins and the hormones. Exactly what are these relationships has not been elucidated.

Insulin has been shown to promote the transfer of glucose into the cells of certain tissues, such as muscle and fat. The cell membrane apparently acts as a barrier to the free entry of the sugar molecule, but in the presence of insulin, sugar is readily admitted. How insulin effects this change in permeability is not understood; the insulin molecule may attach itself to specific areas or points on the surface of the cell membrane and modify the membrane characteristics to permit the entry of the glucose molecule. After the sugar has entered the cell, it can then be acted upon by the intracellular enzymes. However, changes in cell permeability need not be the only mechanism of action of insulin. Some investigators have observed that, in liver tissue, insulin acts directly on intracellular enzymes. Probable points of action in various metabolic pathways have been suggested for the hormone.

Modifications of the theory that the cell membrane is the site of action of hormones have been proposed. These are based on findings with the electron microscope. In addition to the cell itself being delimited by a surface membrane, a large number of membrane-limited structures exist within the cell: mitochondria, nucleus, nucleolus, reticular material, etc. It is believed that many of the enzyme systems are confined to specific compartments, such as the mitochondria, and are thus isolated from the rest of the cell by a semipermeable membrane. The hormones then may be involved in the activity of these cytoplasmic and nuclear structures and, by changing membrane permeability, may act to liberate certain enzyme systems, or make sufficient substrate available for the enzyme systems to act.

An example of a direct action of a hormone on an enzyme system has been noted for estradiol. It has been shown that estradiol may serve in placental and endometrial tissue as a coenzyme for a transhydrogenation reaction between reduced nicotinamide adenine dinucleotide phosphate (NADPH; old terminology, TPNH) and nicotinamide adenine dinucleotide (NAD; old terminology, DPN) increasing the amount of nicotinamide adenine dinucleotide phosphate (NADP) available as a hydrogen acceptor. Electron transfer by means of such an estrogen-sensitive transhydrogenase system would result in an increased availability of NADP for other NADP-dependent reactions.

Finally, relationships between the vitamins and hormones that have been observed in many areas of endocrinology suggest that a mechanism of hormone action may also involve the vitamins. For example, the actions of estrogen have been shown to be dependent upon the presence in the animal of folic acid. Lack of this vitamin, or its inhibition by administration of a folic acid antagonist such as aminopterin, effectively inhibits estrogenic action. In some animals, an antisterility factor, vitamin E, has been found necessary for normal reproductive activity. Lack of the vitamin results in sterility. A relationship between intestinal absorption of calcium, the presence of the vitamins D, and parathormone has been recognized for some time. Quantitative relationships have been observed between ACTH secretion and adrenal ascorbic acid content (vitamin C), and LH secretion and ovarian ascorbic acid content. In most instances the relationship between vitamin and hormone is still obscure, but enough information has been accumulated to suggest that it is more than casual.

Thus, the mechanisms of action of hormones may be through an effect on cell-membrane permeability, on hormone-sensitive enzyme systems, and, most probably, through other means as well, such as activation of nuclear mechanisms to stimulate cell division, change in transmembrane potentials by binding ions to inhibit or facilitate muscle contraction, etc. These actions result in critical changes in biochemical activity, which in most instances are manifested as a morphogenetic, metabolic, or integrative shift in the physiology of the whole organism. Such gross changes in homeostasis are thus a result of the peculiar specificity that each of certain critical tissues contains for the unique structure of its stimulating hormone.

Useful References in Endocrinology

Allen, E., Danforth, C. H., and Doisy, E. A. (eds.). 1939. "Sex and Internal Secretions," 2nd ed. Williams & Wilkins, Baltimore, Maryland.

Burn, J. H., Finney, D. J., and Goodwin, L. G. 1950. "Biological Standardization." Oxford Univ. Press, London and New York.

Cole, H. H., and Cupps, P. T. 1959. "Reproduction in Domestic Animals." Academic Press, New York.

Dorfman, R. I. (ed.). 1962. "Methods in Hormone Research," Vols. 1 and 2. Academic Press, New York.

Dorfman, R. I., and Shipley, R. A. 1956. "Androgens." Wiley, New York.

Emmens, C. W. (ed.). 1950. "Hormone Assay." Academic Press, New York.

Gorbman, A. (ed.). 1959. "Comparative Endocrinology." Wiley, New York.

Gorbman, A., and Bern, H. A. 1962. "A Textbook of Comparative Endocrinology." Wiley, New York.

Hafez, E. S. E. (ed.). 1962. "Reproduction in Farm Animals." Lea & Febiger, Philadelphia, Pennsylvania.

Harris, G. W. 1955. "Neural Control of the Pituitary Gland." Arnold, London.

Heller, H. 1957. "The Neurohypophysis." Butterworths, London.

Lloyd, C. W. (ed.). 1959. *Recent Progr. Endocrinol. Reprod. Proc. Conf. Syracuse, 1958.*

Nalbandov, A. V. 1958. "Reproductive Physiology." Freeman, San Francisco, California.

Parkes, A. S. (ed.). 1952–1957. "Marshall's Physiology of Reproduction." Longmans, Green, New York.

Pincus, G., and Thimann, K. V. (eds.). "The Hormones," Vol. 1, 1948; Vol. 2, 1950; Vol. 3, 1955. Academic Press, New York.

Pitt-Rivers, R., and Tata, J. R. 1959. "The Thyroid Hormones." Pergamon Press, New York.

Selye, H. 1952. "Textbook of Endocrinology," 2nd ed. Acta Endocrinologica, Montreal, Canada.

Turner, C. D. 1960. "General Endocrinology," 3rd ed. Saunders, Philadelphia, Pennsylvania.

Velardo, J. T. (ed.). 1958. "Endocrinology of Reproduction." Oxford Univ. Press, London and New York.

Wigglesworth, V. B. 1954. "The Physiology of Insect Metamorphosis." Monographs in Biology, No. 1, Cambridge Univ. Press, London and New York.

Williams, R. H. (ed.). 1962. "A Textbook of Endocrinology." Saunders, Philadelphia, Pennsylvania.

Young, W. C. (ed.). 1961. "Sex and Internal Secretions," 3rd ed. Williams & Wilkins, Baltimore, Maryland.

Zuckerman, S. (ed.). 1962. "The Ovary," Vols. 1 and 2. Academic Press, New York.

CHAPTER 2

The Estrogens

The reproductive periodicity observed in the adult female mammal is a direct result of cyclic changes that occur in the ovary. The hormones secreted by this gland effect changes in general morphology (as evidenced during puberty), regulate the metabolic activity of the uterus and other sex accessory tissues, control certain aspects of behavior, and, in general, support those physiological activities essential for reproduction of the species.

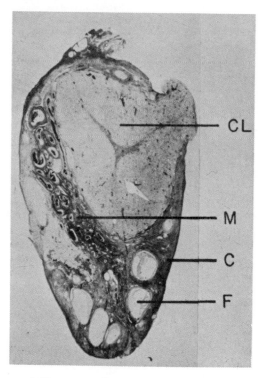

Fig. 2-1. Ovary of *Macaca mulata* (rhesus monkey). *C*, cortex; *M*, medulla; *F*, atretic follicle; *CL*, corpus luteum.

17

Sites of Estrogen Formation

In most mammals, the ovary is located posterior to the kidney and dorsolateral to most of the other abdominal organs in the pelvic region and is the major site of production of the estrogenic hormones. Grossly, the ovary is composed of an inner medulla and an outer cortex (Fig. 2-1). The medulla consists primarily of a loose fibromuscular stroma within which is embedded an extensive vascular network composed of small branches of the ovarian artery and a larger network of veins. The cortex is composed externally of a single layer of germinal epithelium, either cuboidal or columnar in shape, beneath which may be found follicles in various stages of development and atresia (Fig. 2-2). In

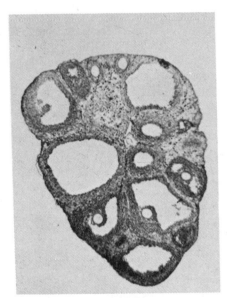 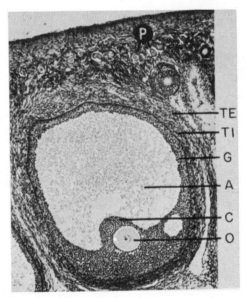

Fig. 2-2. *Left:* Ovary of the rat with several maturing follicles. *Right:* Maturing follicle in ovary of *Macaca mulata. A,* antrum of follicle containing follicular fluid; *C,* cumulus oophorus; *G,* granulosa; *O,* ovum; *P,* primordial follicle; *TE,* theca externa; *TI,* theca interna.

adult animals, corpora hemorrhagica, corpora lutea, and corpora albicantia may be present. The connective tissue stroma of the cortex is rather densely packed in comparison to that of the medulla. The layer directly beneath the germinal epithelium is known as the tunica albuginea.

The site of production of the estrogenic hormones is thought to be the relatively vascular theca interna of the mature Graafian follicle (Fig. 2-2). These cells contain extractable estrogens, exhibit the characteristic histochemical reactions indicative of the presence of such hormones, and, in general, exhibit maximum cytological activity during the estrogenic phase of the reproductive cycle. The follicular fluid is a rich source of estrogens and is thought to accumulate the hormones through diffusion from the surrounding thecal cells or capillary network.

Nature of the Estrogens

The natural estrogens of animal origin are usually characterized by a basic steroid structure, a cyclopentanoperhydrophenanthrene nucleus. Although it has become apparent that estrogenic activity is not dependent upon this structure, most of the natural estrogens (28) are steroids or very closely related to steroids in structure. Table 2–1 depicts the structures of several estrogens, natural and synthetic, and their sources. It should be noted that the synthetic estrogens and those that occur in certain forage crops are not steroids.

Action of the Estrogens

Many physiological processes are modified by estrogens. These modifications generally result in increased growth or metabolism of tissues receptive to the hormone, and in a characteristic sexual behavior pattern. Estrogen-sensitive tissues include the reproductive tract and associated pelvic structures, the mammary gland, secondary sexual structures, the thyroid gland, thymus gland, hypophysis, and the long bones. Response at the organismic level usually involves an excitatory behavior pattern that permits mating. Some of the actions of estrogens are described below.

A. Reproductive Cycles

The estrogens effect the first visible signs of puberty in the female mammal and maintain throughout the reproductive life span those structures necessary for pregnancy. Senescence is evidenced by involution of these structures and a decreased secretion of estrogen. During the reproductive life span, the female mammal exhibits cyclic changes in the ovary which may lead, periodically, to ovulation. This activity, which affects the entire reproductive tract and other accessory tissues, is dependent on endocrine factors and in the infraprimates is referred to as the estrous cycle. In general, seasonal cycles of reproductive activity may involve only one estrous period during the year (monestrous), or, as in certain animals such as the rat, mouse, or cow, reproduction is

TABLE 2–1
MOLECULES THAT EXHIBIT ESTROGENIC ACTIVITY

Estrogen	Structure	Source
Estradiol-17β (isomeric form, estradiol-17α)		Ovary, placenta, testis (stallion), urine (mare)
Estrone		Urine (mare, human being), ovary, placenta, adrenal gland, palm kernel
Estriol (isomeric form, 16-epiestriol)		Urine (human being)
16α-Hydroxyestrone (isomeric form, 16β-hydroxyestrone		Urine (human being)
Equilin		Urine (mare)
Equilenin		Urine (mare)

possible throughout the entire year (polyestrous). Seasonal breeders
may be monestrous or polyestrous, whereas the continuous breeders are

TABLE 2-1 (*Continued*)

Estrogen	Structure	Source
Genistein	HO, OH, O, OH	Ladino clover, strawberry clover, alfalfa (22)
Coumestrol	HO, O, O, OH, O	Forage crops, soybean oil meal, subterranean clover (14)
Diethylstilbestrol (*cis* isomer and *trans* isomer)	HO—C=C—OH, CH_2 CH_2, CH_3 CH_3	Synthetic
Benzestrol	H H H, C—C—C, CH_2 CH_2 CH_2, CH_3 CH_3, HO OH	Synthetic
Hexestrol	HO—C—C—OH, H H, CH_2 CH_2, CH_3 CH_3	Synthetic
Dienestrol	HO—C—C—OH, CH CH, CH_3 CH_3	Synthetic

all polyestrous animals. Estrus, or psychic heat, is brought on by the estrogens.

A second type of sexual cycle is observed in the primates and is referred to as the menstrual cycle. This cycle is distinguished by a

TABLE 2–1 (*Continued*)

Estrogen	Structure	Source
Triphenylethylene		Synthetic
Tri-*p*-anisyl chloroethylene		Synthetic

period of uterine desquamation and bleeding (Table 2–2). Although a definite period of sexual receptivity or estrus is present in animals with an estrous cycle, the primates show no clear period of psychic heat during the menstrual cycle. In both types of cycles, ovulation occurs at a well defined period and may bring with it changes in the reproductive tract which permit implantation of the fertilized egg. These changes are effected by the hormones of the ovary, which in turn are under the control of the pituitary gland.

TABLE 2–2

THE MENSTRUAL CYCLE OF THE MACAQUE

Time (days)	Stage	Uterine change	Ovary
1–3	Menstrual	Desquamation and hemorrhage; a few small tubular glands present at the termination of this period	Quiescent
4–12	Proliferative (follicular)	Growth of uterine mucosa; glands straight and long, nuclei take up most of cell space	Ripening of Graafian follicle. Preovulatory
12–28	Progestational (luteal)	Glands grow faster than stroma, convolution occurs. Release of glandular secretions into lumen. Clear vacuolar spaces seen in the cells.	Postovulatory corpus luteum formed and active

Table 2–3 lists the characteristic cycle lengths and periods of ovulation in various common mammals (58).

TABLE 2–3
Cyclic Activity of Various Mammals

Species[a]	Cycle Type[b]	Cycle Length (days)	Duration of estrus[c]	Ovulation Type[d]	Ovulation Time	Luteal phase in absence of coitus
Cat	S, P	14	4 days	I	24–30 hours after coitus	No
Cow	C, P	21	13–14 hours	Sp	12–16 hours after end of estrus	Yes
Dog	S, M	60	7–9 days	Sp	1–3 days after onset of estrus	Yes
Ewe	S, P	16	30–36 hours	Sp	12–24 hours prior to end of estrus	Yes
Ferret	S	—	Continuous	I	30 hours after coitus	No
Fox	S, M	90	1–5 days	Sp	1–2 days after onset of estrus	Yes
Goat	S, P	20–21	39 hours	Sp	30–36 hours after onset of estrus	Yes
Ground squirrel (*Citellus tridecemlineatus*)	S, P	14–28	3 days	I	8–12 hours after coitus	No
Guinea pig	C, P	16	6–11 hours	Sp	10 hours after onset of estrus	Yes
Hamster	C, P	4	20 hours	Sp	8–12 hours after onset of estrus	No
Man	C, Mn	28	None	Sp	14 days prior to onset of menses	Yes
Mare	S, P	19–23	4–7 days	Sp	6 days after onset of estrus	Yes
Mink	S, P	8–9	2 days	I	40–50 hours after coitus	No
Monkey (macaque)	C, Mn	28	None	Sp	11–14 days after onset of menses	Yes
Mouse	C, P	4	10 hours	Sp	2–3 hours after onset of estrus	No
Rabbit	C	—	Continuous	I	10 hours after coitus	No
Rat	C, P	4–5	13–15 hours	Sp	8–10 hours after onset of estrus	No
Sow	C, P	21	2–3 days	Sp	36 hours after onset of estrus	Yes

[a] Species either domesticated or in captivity.

[b] Cycle types: C, continuous, nonseasonal, will breed reasonably well during any part of the year; S, seasonal, cyclic activity occurs during specific time(s) of year; P, polyestrous, more than one period of heat during the season; M, monestrous, one period of heat during the season; Mn, menstrual cycle.

[c] Duration of estrus: Restricted time of the cycle during which the male may be accepted.

[d] Type of ovulation: I, induced; Sp., spontaneous.

B. THE VAGINAL EPITHELIUM

Marked changes occur in the vaginal epithelium during both the estrous and menstrual cycles. These changes have been correlated with changes in the ovary and uterus and in some instances are good indicators of the stage of the cycle. A typical estrous cycle, as evidenced in the guinea pig or the sow is characterized by two phases, a preovulatory follicular phase and a postovulatory luteal phase. Vaginal smears obtained from these animals at different times of the cycle show, respectively: nucleated epithelial cells during the preovulatory stage (proestrus); cornified epithelial cells during estrus; a mixture of cornified and nucleated epithelial cells with an infiltration of leukocytes during the postovulatory stage (metestrus); mucus and leukocytes during the luteal or progestational phase; and a sparse smear of leukocytes and a few epithelial cells during diestrus. In contrast to the estrous cycle of the guinea pig is that of the rat and mouse. In these animals, no luteal phase is present, owing to the absence of functional corpora lutea. Hence, only a metestrus and short diestrus occur. Figure 2-3 and Table 2–4 depict the various stages of the estrous cycle in the rat as

TABLE 2–4

THE ESTROUS CYCLE OF THE RAT

Time (days)	Stage	Vaginal smear	Vaginal histology
1/2–1	Proestrus (E)	Many epithelial cells, granular cytoplasm, cells round or spindle	Rapid epithelial growth
1–2	Estrus (C)	Remnants of epithelial cells, large cornified cells flat and irregular	Maximum growth
1	Metestrus (C, E, L)	Many cornified and epithelial cells; infiltration of leukocytes	Desquamation
1–2	Diestrus (L, E)	Few epithelial cells; few to many leukocytes	Quiescence. Only a few layers of epithelial cells present

observed by vaginal smears. These changes are relatively obvious and have been shown to be under the direct influence of estrogen. Similar changes, although not as well correlated with events occurring in the ovary, may be observed in vaginal smears taken during various phases of the menstrual cycles of human beings and monkeys.

C. The Uterine Cervix, Pubic Symphysis, and Related Structures

Estrogen has been shown to "feminize" the bony structure of the pelvis and pubic symphysis in many mammals (39, 72, 73). A breakdown of symphyseal bone and cartilage to connective tissue has been observed, and in some species a complete resorption of ventral pubic structures occurs coincident with puberty and estrogen secretion (49). The uterine cervix (as the vagina) increases in size, in water content, and in secretory activity under estrogen domination. A decrease in both the tensile strength and percentage of collagen of the cervix is noted, and during pregnancy a slight increase in dilatability occurs, after estrogen administration. Pretreatment with estrogen is necessary for the successful action of relaxin on the symphysis pubis and cervix uteri (see Chapter 4).

D. The Uterus

The action of estrogens on the uterus in the mammal results in hyperemia (5), followed by an increase in both wet and dry weight, amino acid incorporation, nitrogen deposition, nucleic acid synthesis, phosphorus uptake, and glycogen deposition (62). An increase in enzyme activity (52, 62) and oxidative metabolism occurs, resulting in a generalized hypertrophy and hyperplasia of both the endometrium and myometrium. The uterus under estrogen domination exhibits an increased spontaneous rhythmic motility (63), a characteristic contraction pattern during electrical stimulation (24, 65), an altered ionic balance across the cell membrane (40), and an increased sensitivity to extracts of the posterior pituitary gland (61, 65). The action of other hormones of ovarian origin (i.e., progestogens, relaxin, etc.) upon the uterus usually requires a preliminary priming of this tissue by estrogen. Thus, the estrogens may have a synergizing effect on the action of other hormones by establishing a morphological and physiological substrate sensitive to these hormones.

E. Psychic Heat

In animals which exhibit an estrous cycle, the period prior to and during ovulation is often coincident with the period designated as psychic heat. Although "estrus" may occur without ovulation and ovulation without any manifestation of sexual receptivity, the two periods are often erroneously linked. It is currently thought that the psychic manifestations that are observed coincident to the time of ovulation (i.e., increased spontaneous activity, mating behavior, sexual receptivity, etc.) are under the influence of estrogen (and progestogen),

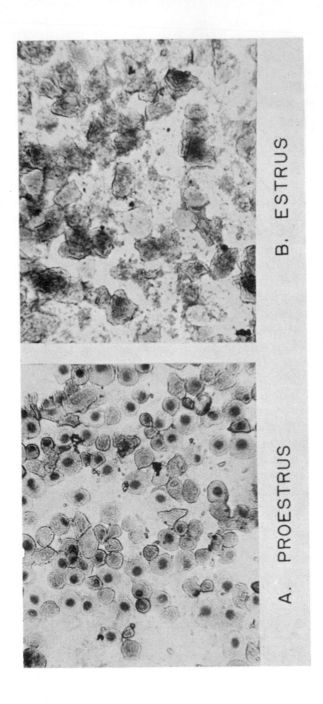

B. ESTRUS

A. PROESTRUS

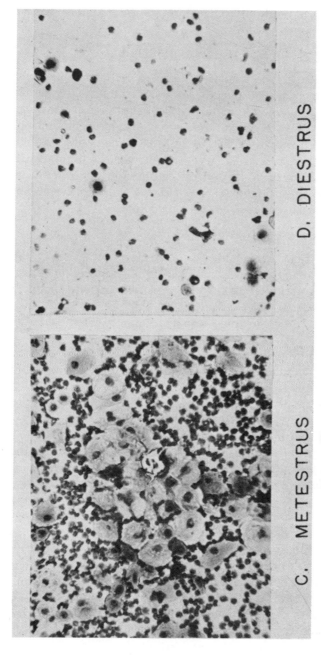

Fig. 2-3. Vagina smears obtained during four phases of the estrous cycle of the rat. (A) Proestrus. (B) Estrus. (C) Metestrus. (D) Diestrus.

possibly through an action on the hypothalamus (43). Ovulation, on the other hand, is a result of the actions of the pituitary gonadotropins (Chapter 10).

F. MAMMARY GLAND

The response of the mammary gland to estrogen stimulation varies among the mammals. An increase in length, branching, and size of the duct system, proliferation of nonductile adipose and other connective tissues, and some increase in size and pigmentation of the nipple and areola occur. In some mammals (e.g., guinea pig, cow, goat) estrogen causes an increase in alveolar development whereas in others this effect is not observed. As with other tissues sensitive to the ovarian hormones, the mammary gland requires pretreatment with estrogen before the effects of progestogens and relaxin are noted.

G. OTHER ACTIONS OF THE ESTROGENS

1. Feminization of somatotype (increase in fat depots in certain areas, closure of epiphyseal-diaphyseal synchondroses in growing animals, thinning of epidermis, regulation of hair pattern, feather pattern, and coloring, etc.)
2. Increase in actomyosin formation and ATPase activity in the myometrium
3. Retention of calcium
4. Stimulation of ovarian tissue, growth of follicle, and maintenance of corpora lutea
5. Increase in alkaline phosphatase and β-glucuronidase in the vagina and uterus
6. Stimulation of oviduct
7. Synergism with progesterone in the maintenance of pregnancy
8. Increased water retention, edema of skin (sex skin of monkey)
9. Vasodilation
10. Tumorigenesis (uterus, cervix, vagina, mammary gland, etc.)

The Assay of Estrogen

Any one of the actions of estrogen listed above may be considered, under strict experimental conditions, to be a qualitative indicator of the presence or absence of estrogen. However, not all these effects are peculiar to estrogen. Thus, increased water retention, vasodilation, retention of calcium can be obtained with substances that do not cause vaginal cornification, growth of the mammary gland, or psychic heat. Conversely, not all the activities attributed to estrogen occur in all mammals. In addition, certain effects may be due to an indirect action of the estrogen; and finally, all responses are not similarly affected by different dose levels of estrogenic hormones. In general, the best biological indicators are consistently demonstrated under definite physiological conditions and best observed in one or two species. The effects are usually the result of a direct and specific action of the hormone and can be observed and quantified easily. Several biological indicators have been developed into standard bioassays for the estrogens. These are cornification of the vaginal epithelium or increase in weight of the uterus of the ovariectomized rat or mouse, vaginal opening in immature rodents or in immature or ovariectomized guinea pigs, and increase in weight of the chick oviduct.

The response to any single preparation thought to contain an estrogen is influenced by (a) the vehicle used for administration and the route of administration, (b) the speed with which the hormone is absorbed, metabolized, and excreted, and (c) the sensitivity of the end point used to measure potency (36).

A. THE EFFECT OF VEHICLE AND ROUTE OF ADMINISTRATION

Table 2–5 illustrates the effect of vehicle and method of administration on the comparative potency of estradiol, estrone, and estriol in an assay using the vaginal smear response of the mouse. It will be noted that 50% aqueous glycerin is a more effective vehicle for the intravaginal

TABLE 2–5

MEDIAN EFFECTIVE DOSE OF THE ESTROGENS
WHEN APPLIED INTRAVAGINALLY IN 3 APPLICATIONS[a]

Hormone	Effective dose in olive oil (μg)	Effective dose in 50% aqueous glycerin (μg)	Comparison of intravaginal to subcutaneous when applied in	
			Oil	Glycerin
Estradiol	0.0075	0.0005	1:6	1:100
Estrone	0.025	0.00025	1:4	1:400
Estriol	0.5	0.00075	1:2	1:1200

[a] Adapted from Muhlbock (59).

application of the three hormones than is olive oil. Furthermore, the relative increase in estrogenic potency is greatest with estriol and least with estradiol when glycerin is substituted for oil, thus making all three estrogens almost equally efficacious. The oil vehicle results in a decreasing order of effectiveness: estradiol the most potent and estriol the least potent.

Using estrone as a standard (activity of estrone rated as 1.0), the ratios, shown in the accompanying tabulation, of potency of estradiol: estrone:estriol have been observed with the vaginal cornification assay of the rat.

Nature of vehicle used for injection	Ratio estradiol:estrone:estriol
Oil	3–12:1.0:0.22–0.01
Aqueous	7:1.0:1.0–0.004

The wide variation in relative potencies is probably a result of the different slopes of the dose response curves of each of the hormones. Similar results are obtained when the uterine weight assay is used. Of the synthetic estrogens, diethylstilbestrol, hexestrol, and dienestrol have been found to have a potency between that of injected estrone and estradiol.

B. FACTORS THAT AFFECT ABSORPTION, METABOLISM, AND EXCRETION

Esterification of the steroid molecule with an aliphatic or cyclic side chain results in a prolongation of the action of the hormone after injection. This type of activity seems to be a function of the length of the chain. Hence, estradiol monobenzoate acts for a greater length of time than the diacetate, which in turn is effective over a longer period than estradiol. A single injection of estradiol cyclopentylpropionate is effective for periods as long as 3 weeks. There is little to no effect of esterification on duration of action when these substances are administered orally, intravaginally, or intravenously. The effect of esterification tends to delay absorption of the hormone from its site of injection and to decrease the rate of degradation, thus prolonging its action. However, an increase in the minimal dose required to effect stimulation may be necessary (35).

C. SENSITIVITY OF POTENCY ESTIMATES

The end points used to measure the potency of various estrogens differ in their sensitivities to the hormone. Table 2–6 illustrates the wide range of sensitivities observed with several of the more common bioassay techniques.

In assaying for the potency of estrogenic substances, care must be utilized in maintaining proper controls. Many of the vegetable oils used in the diet or as vehicles for application of the hormone exhibit some

TABLE 2–6
SENSITIVITY OF VARIOUS BIOASSAYS FOR ESTROGENS

Test animal	Route of administration of hormone	End point measured	Threshold dose estradiol (μg)	Reference
Chick	Subcutaneous	Weight of oviduct	400	(29)
Mouse	Subcutaneous	Vaginal smear	2.5×10^{-2}	(2)
Rat	Subcutaneous	Uterine weight	2.5×10^{-2}	(20)
Rat	Subcutaneous	Uterine water	6.2×10^{-3}	(5)
Guinea pig	Subcutaneous (area of vulva)	Vaginal opening	4.0×10^{-4}	(44)
Mouse	Intravaginal	Vaginal smear	5.0×10^{-6}	(70)
Rat	Intrauterine	Golgi apparatus	2.0×10^{-5}	(34)
Rat	Intrauterine	Osmiophilic reaction in the uterine endometrium	2.0×10^{-6}	(48)

estrogenic properties. Tables 2–7 and 2–8 (15) illustrate the effects of some of these oils when fed or injected into immature mice.

TABLE 2–7
EFFECT OF INJECTED CORN AND OLIVE OILS ON THE UTERINE WEIGHT OF IMMATURE MICE[a]

Material	Total volume injected subcutaneously (four 0.1-ml injections)	Mean uterine weight (mg)
None	—	9.9
0.9% saline	0.4	10.3
Corn oil (sample 1)	0.4	13.2
Corn oil (sample 2)	0.4	16.8
Olive oil	0.4	12.5

[a] From Booth *et al.* (15).

Similarly, contamination of laboratory feed with plant and animal products which contain estrogenic activity (see Table 2–1) can interfere with assays for estrogen. Table 2–9 illustrates the effects of an extract of commercial feed on the uterine weight of ovariectomized mice (84).

Of the physicochemical methods that have been employed for the estimation of estrogenic potency, four involve spectrophotometric procedures and require a relatively high degree of sample purity (8, 16, 27).

Infrared spectrophotometry can be used with crystalline ketonic estrogens and usually requires a 1.0 ml sample containing about 1000 μg

TABLE 2–8
EFFECT ON UTERINE WEIGHT OF FEEDING VARIOUS OILS[a]

Kind of oil	Level fed in diet (%) (total oil consumed, 1 gm)	Mean uterine weight (mg)
None, control diet	—	9.5
Mineral	10	8.6
Castor, refined	10	9.4
Cottonseed, refined	10	10.1
Safflower, refined	10	13.6
Cod liver, refined	10	13.9
Corn, refined	10	14.2
Linseed	10	14.6
Wheat germ	10	15.0
Peanut, refined	10	15.9
Olive, refined	10	16.7
Soybean, refined	10	17.7
Coconut, crude	10	19.0
Rice bran, refined	10	22.5
Sesame, refined[b]	—	—

[a] From Booth et al. (15).
[b] Similar to rice bran oil in estrogenic activity.

TABLE 2–9
EFFECT OF COMMERCIAL ANIMAL FEED EXTRACT ON UTERINE WEIGHT[a]

Treatment after ovariectomy		Body weight (gm)	Uterine weight (mg)
None		28.6	11.2
Estradiol:	0.002 μg	30.5	23.1
	0.005 μg	29.2	24.2
	0.01 μg	31.5	40.0
	0.1 μg	29.2	97.3
Food extract:	0.05 ml	29.1	24.6
	0.1 ml	28.7	53.6

[a] From Zarrow et al. (84).

of estrogen. Quantitative absorption measurements are made between 10 and 11 μ.

Ultraviolet spectrophotometry, also used with pure crystalline compounds, requires a 1–3 ml sample containing 12–100 μg of estrogen. Measurements are obtained on an ultraviolet (UV) spectrophotometer in the range of the spectrum between 280 and 293 mμ.

The *Kober reaction* is a rather useful colorimetric assay dependent upon the development of a red color evolved as a result of a reaction between estrogen and concentrated sulfuric or phosphoric acid. The reaction seems to be specific for the phenolic grouping in ring A of the natural estrogens but requires correction for nonspecific pigments when urinary extracts of estrogens are used. Samples of 5–10 ml are generally employed at a concentration of 10–60 μg of estrogen per sample. Absorbancy is measured between 480 and 520 mμ.

Fluorometric procedures have been evolved from the first stage of the Kober reaction. This stage results in the conversion of phenolic steroids to orange-yellow compounds that emit a greenish fluorescence. The fluorescence intensity, as measured with a yellow glass photocell filter, requires a sample of 5–10 ml at a concentration of 1–5 μg per sample. With an interference type photocell filter, concentrations of 0.1–1.0 μg per sample are required. A light source with a 436 mμ wavelength effects maximum fluorescence of wavelengths between 440 and 490 mμ, depending upon the estrogen being measured.

Biogenesis, Metabolism, and Mechanism of Action

The normal pathway of estrogen synthesis is still a matter of conjecture. It is currently thought that either androgens may represent a precursor of these hormones or the hormones are synthesized from smaller units such as acetate (Fig. 2-4) (38, 45–47, 75). It is fairly well established (28, 55) that estradiol and estrone are interconvertible *in vivo* and that estriol is a final product of estrogen metabolism in many

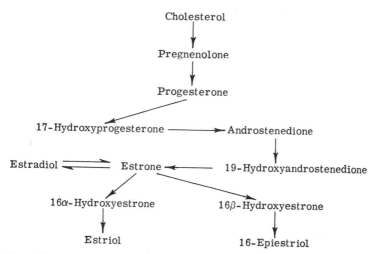

Fig. 2-4. Possible mode of biosynthesis and metabolism of estrogens.

mammals, being formed most probably from 16-hydroxyestrone. These hormones, which are found both free and protein bound in the circulation, appear to be both activated and inactivated by the liver, the latter process by conjugation, esterification, or degradation. The products and the hormone are excreted in the urine in the free form or conjugated as glucuronides and as sulfates.

TABLE 2–10

LEVELS OF ESTROGENS IN THE URINE OF THE HUMAN BEING DURING THE MENSTRUAL CYCLE, PREGNANCY, AND THE POSTMENOPAUSAL PERIOD[a]

Time measurement	Estrogen excreted per 24 hours				
	Estriol	Estrone	Estradiol	16-Epi-estriol	16α-Hydroxy-estrone
Onset of menstruation	6 μg	5 μg	2 μg	—	—
Ovulation peak	27 μg	20 μg	9 μg	—	—
Luteal maximum	22 μg	14 μg	7 μg	—	—
Pregnancy, 160 days	7 mg	0.7 mg	0.2 mg	—	—
Pregnancy, term	30 mg	2.0 mg	0.75 mg	0.75 mg	2.0 mg
Postmenopause	3.3 μg	2.5 μg	0.6 μg	—	—

[a] Data from Brown (17–19).

Table 2–10 depicts the approximate levels of several of the urinary estrogens of the human being as determined by the Kober reaction during the menstrual cycle, pregnancy, and the postmenopausal period (17–19). It will be noted that two peaks in the urinary concentration of estrogens occur during the menstrual cycle: one around the time of ovulation and the second during the luteal phase. The latter rise probably reflects an increased secretion of estrogens by the theca lutein cells of the corpus luteum. The major source of estrogens in postmenopausal women is most probably the adrenal cortex.

Recent evidence suggests that the estrogens may serve as a coenzyme in a transhydrogenation reaction in the placenta and the endometrium between reduced nicotinamide adenine dinucleotide phosphate (NADPH; old terminology, TPNH) and nicotinamide adenine dinucleotide (NAD; old terminology, DPN), increasing the amount of NADP available as a hydrogen acceptor (41, 77, 78). This reaction would increase the rate of NADP-dependent reactions such as those involving cytoplasmic isocitric dehydrogenase and glucose 6-phosphate dehydrogenase (Fig. 2-5). The overall result would tend to increase the amount of substrate metabolized by the cell with a resultant increase in "bio-

$$\text{Isocitrate} + \text{NAD}^+ \rightleftharpoons \text{NADH} + \text{H}^+ + \alpha\text{-Ketoglutarate} + CO_2$$

$$\text{NAD}^+ + \text{Estradiol} \rightleftharpoons \text{NADH} + \text{H}^+ + \text{Estrone}$$

$$\text{NADPH} + \text{H}^+ + \text{Estrone} \rightleftharpoons \text{NADP}^+ + \text{Estradiol}$$

$$\text{NADP}^+ + \text{Isocitrate} \rightleftharpoons \text{NADPH} + \text{H}^+ + \alpha\text{-Ketoglutarate} + CO_2$$

Fig. 2-5. Possible effect of estrogens on the pyridine nucleotide systems of the placenta. Adapted from Villee (78).

logically useful" energy, i.e., energy for protein and nucleic acid synthesis, water uptake, etc. These reactions appear to result in a reversible oxidation-reduction of estradiol ⇌ estrone. However, they are inhibited by some of the metabolic products of estradiol and by diethylstilbestrol. In addition, diethylstilbestrol is without effect in these reactions, and hence the reaction cannot explain the action of all estrogens.

Estrogen increases the amount of contractile protein, creatine phosphate, and adenosine triphosphate (ATP) in myometrium (23, 25). These changes result in an increase in the maximum tension that can be developed by the uterus. Coincident with the increase in actomyosin, there are observed changes in the membrane potential of the myometrial cell (40, 50, 56, 57). This potential is increased from 30–35 mv (in the rabbit) under minimum estrogen stimulation to about 45 mv after sufficient treatment with the hormone. Concomitantly, an increase in rhythmicity of action potentials and of spontaneous contractions is noted. The myometrium under estrogen domination becomes sensitive to external calcium concentration. Lack of calcium abolishes normal excitability. It has been suggested (40) that effective triggering of myometrial activity may depend upon the stability of calcium which participates in the formation of excitable structures and that this stability may be regulated by the hormones.

Thus, the mechanism of action of estrogens on contraction of the uterus seems to be twofold: through an increase in contractile protein and energy-rich phosphate sources within the cell, and through regulation of ionic and electrical balance across the membrane.

Antihormones

Many substances are known to inhibit specific actions of the estrogens. Recently, it has been shown that progesterone, deoxycorticosterone acetate (DCA), and estriol restrict the stimulation of lactic dehydrogenase-NADH oxidase by estradiol-17β in the uterus (13). Similarly, stilbestrol, estradiol-17α, and estriol inhibit an estradiol-17β-sensitive transhydrogenase system of the placenta which transfers hydrogen from NADPH to NAD (79). The inhibition of the transhydrogenase reaction can be reversed by the addition of large amounts of estradiol-17β.

Estrogen-sensitive tissues appear to require the presence of folic acid. The increase in nucleic acid phospholipids, acid-soluble phosphate, and protein nitrogen that occurs in the uterus of the rat after estrogen stimulation can be inhibited by folic acid deficiency or folic acid antagonists (aminopterin) (26). The lack of folic acid in the primate prevents the inhibition of menstruation by estradiol (83). Table 2–11 lists several

TABLE 2–11

COMPOUNDS THAT INHIBIT ESTRADIOL-INDUCED REACTIONS

Vaginal cornification		Uterine water, subcutaneous administration	Uterine weight, subcutaneous administration
Intravaginal application	Subcutaneous administration		
Dimethylstilbestrol	19-Nortestosterone	Hydrocortisone	DCA[b]
Ethylstilbestrol	Testosterone	Cortisone	Cortisone acetate
n-Propylstilbestrol	17-Ethyl-19-	MER-25[a]	Testosterone
Mesobutestrol	nortestosterone		Testosterone
19-Nortestosterone			propionate
17-Ethyl-19-	17-Ethynyl-19-		Progesterone
nortestosterone	nortestosterone		17-Ethyl-19-
17-Ethynyl-19-	MER-25[a]		nortestosterone
nortestosterone			MER-25[a]
			Estriol
			Cortisone
			Hydrocortisone

[a] MER-25: 1-(p-2-diethylaminoethoxyphenyl)-1-phenyl-2-p-methoxyphenylethanol.
[b] DCA: deoxycorticosterone acetate.

compounds that inhibit estradiol-induced vaginal cornification, uterine water increase, and uterine weight increase (30, 37, 53, 71, 76). It will be noted that many of these substances are steroidal in nature and that some of them have estrogenic activity in their own right.

EXPERIMENT 2–1

The Estrous Cycle*

The existence of a typical estrous cycle in the guinea pig and the associated changes in vaginal cytology were first reported by Stockard and Papanicolaou in 1917. Shortly thereafter, similar phenomena were

* Cf. references (1–3, 54, 68, 81).

reported in the rat and mouse. Vaginal smears obtained from these animals were found to correlate well with changes occurring in the reproductive tract and with the secretion of the ovarian hormones.

Examine stained slides of vaginal smears of the rat. Observe the three types of cells and mucus, if present:

1. Polymorphonuclear leukocytes
2. Nucleated epithelial cells
3. Large squamous epithelial cells, commonly called cornified cells. Nucleus present or absent
4. Mucus

Procedure

Technique of Obtaining a Vaginal Smear

Place a drop of water in the vagina of the rat with a medicine dropper. Aspirate this several times and then transfer the liquid to a slide. It is sometimes convenient to divide the slide into six squares with a wax pencil (Fig. 2-6) and to stain the preparation after vaginal smears have

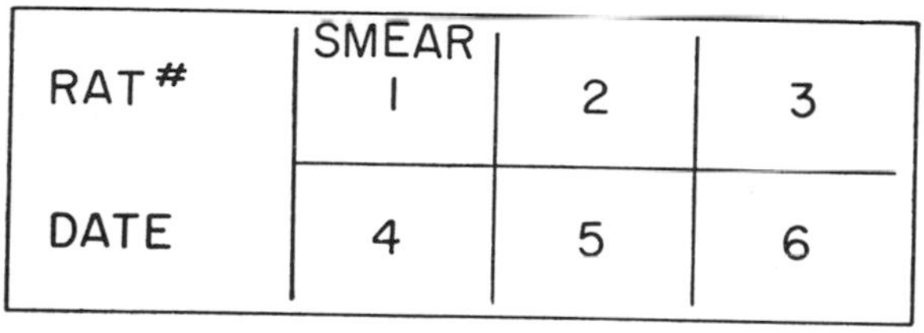

RAT #	SMEAR 1	2	3
DATE	4	5	6

Fig. 2-6. Preparation of slide for observation of the estrous cycle by means of vaginal changes.

been obtained for 6 days. This has the advantage of permitting the observer to note the sequence of events on a single slide. Observe the wet smear under the microscope and compare with samples that have been stained.

Staining Vaginal Smears

1. Dry the smear.
2. Place in absolute methyl alcohol (5 seconds).
3. Dry in air at room temperature.
4. Place in Giemsa solution (1:20) for 30 minutes.
5. Rinse in water.
6. Dry and observe under microscope.

Experimental

1. Follow the estrous cycle of four rats through three to four complete cycles using the flow sheet (Fig. 2-7) for recording the data.

Rat No.	smear date									
_____	smear date									
	smear date									
Rat No.	smear date									
_____	smear date									
	smear date									
Rat No.	smear date									
_____	smear date									
	smear date									
Rat No.	smear date									
_____	smear date									
	smear date									
Rat No.	smear date									
_____	smear date									
	smear date									
Rat No.	smear date									
_____	smear date									
	smear date									
Rat No.	smear date									
_____	smear date									
	smear date									

Fig. 2-7. Flow sheet for data on vaginal smears.

2. Draw representative examples of cells seen in the vaginal smear.

3. Draw the typical smear seen during diestrus, proestrus, estrus, and metestrus.

4. Plot a frequency distribution of the number of times of occurrence of cycles of 4, 5, and 6 days' duration. Graph the pattern of cyclic activity of several rats.

5. Observe under the microscope typical cross sections of a mammalian ovary. Note ovum, follicle, corpora lutea, and stromal tissue.

EXPERIMENT 2–2

Cyclic Running Activity and the Estrous Cycle*

It has been known since 1923 that an increase in the spontaneous running activity of the rat occurs during estrus. This cyclic phenomenon has been shown to be diurnal as well as under the influence of the estrogenic hormones. It is reduced during pseudopregnancy, pregnancy, and lactation, and after ovariectomy.

Procedure

1. Place a prepubertal female rat in an activity cage for several weeks.† After puberty, record the stage of the estrous cycle and the number of revolutions of the wheel each day. Follow the diurnal rhythm of the animal through several cycles by recording spontaneous activity in the morning and evening.

2. Ovariectomize the rat (see Experiment 2–3). Repeat the observations for several weeks and then treat the rat with pellets‡ of (a) estrogen, (b) progesterone, (c) testosterone. Always remove the old pellet prior to implanting a new one.

3. Adrenalectomize the rat (see Experiment 7–1) and measure activity after treatment with (a) 1% NaCl as drinking water, (b) plain drinking water, (c) plain drinking water and injections of deoxycorticosterone acetate.

EXPERIMENT 2–3

Ovariectomy: Rat, Mouse, Guinea Pig

Procedure

The animal is placed in a large jar and anesthesia is induced with ether. When the animal has ceased to move or struggle, it is removed and placed on an operating board; anesthesia is continued with an ether cone. The hair may then be clipped from the back, although it is not

---

* Cf. references (64, 66, 69, 80, 82).

† Best results are obtained if the rats are acclimated to the activity cage prior to the onset of puberty.

‡ Pellets may be easily implanted by anesthetizing the rat with ether and inserting the material subcutaneously through a small incision made on the back of the neck. Daily injections may be substituted for pellets: (a) 1.0 μg estradiol, (b) 2.0 mg progesterone, (c) 1.0 mg testosterone.

essential to do so. The area is cleansed with 1:1000 Zephiran,* and an incision from 1.0 to 1.5 cm long is made in the skin midway between the last rib and the knee about 1 cm lateral to the spinal muscles (Fig. 2-8,

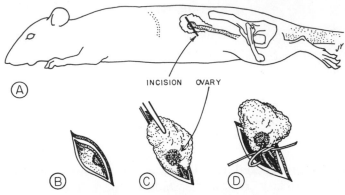

INCISION   OVARY

Fig. 2-8. Ovariectomy of the rat.

A). A second incision is made through the muscle layer and into the peritoneal cavity. If the incision is correctly placed, the ovary will be seen immediately underneath, embedded in a mass of fat (Fig. 2-8, B). The fat is withdrawn, and the ovary is separated and tied off with a silk ligature (Fig. 2-8, C, D). It may then be cut away and the uterus returned to the peritoneal cavity. The incision through the muscle is then closed with one or more sutures and the skin with two or more stitches. The ovary on the opposite side may then be removed through a separate incision.

In cases where mice or young rats are used, it may not be necessary to tie off the ovary as hemorrhage is insignificant. It is only necessary to pinch the fallopian tube and vessels present at the point where the cut will be made. This can be done with a mosquito hemostat or fine forceps of the watchmaker type. One may also simply sew the skin and disregard the incision through the muscle, if the latter is not too long.

EXPERIMENT 2–4

Bioassay of Estrogens by the Vaginal Smear Technique†

There are two methods commonly employed for the bioassay of the estrogenic hormones. These are concerned with changes in the vaginal

---

* Operating instruments should be kept in Zephiran (benzalkonium chloride) for all operations on rats, mice, and guinea pigs.
† Cf. references (21, 59, 70).

smear and with the increase in the weight of the uterus of the rat and mouse. Both procedures require the use of ovariectomized animals. In the first procedure, the hormone may be injected systemically or applied locally. The systemic application gives results which are more consistent, whereas the local application results in a marked increase in sensitivity. Experiments using the latter method of treatment demonstrate the importance of the solvent used and the increased effectiveness of all the estrogens, especially estriol.

Procedure

1. Ovariectomy and verification of operation—1st week: Castrate the animals and take vaginal smears daily for 5 days to confirm the completeness of the operations. Discard all animals showing estrous smears on the last 3 days.

2. Priming—2nd week: Inject all mice once with 2 μg of estradiol in oil and obtain vaginal smears twice daily on days 2, 3, and 4. Discard all mice failing to show a positive reaction: a response characterized by nucleated epithelial cells or cornified cells. Start "Experimental" test at third week.

Experimental

1. Distribute the animals into 6 groups of 10 mice each and inject various dosages of the standard estradiol into four groups and two dosages of the unknown sample in the other two groups. A standard curve is to be established at 4 dose levels using ten mice per group, as follows:

Group 1: 0.05 μg/0.3 ml total dose
Group 2: 0.02 μg/0.3 ml total dose
Group 3: 0.015 μg/0.3 ml total dose
Group 4: 0.005 μg/0.3 ml total dose

2. Two dilutions of the unknown are to be used, one dilution per group. Use the flow sheet (Fig. 2-9) for recording the data. The scheme of injections and vaginal smears is as follows:

Injections	Day 1	5 PM—0.1 ml
	Day 2	9 AM—0.1 ml
		5 PM—0.1 ml
Vaginal smears	Day 3	5 PM—1st smear
	Day 4	9 AM—2nd smear
		5 PM—3rd smear
	Day 5	9 AM—4th smear

3. The smears are stained and a dose-response curve is established for the standard estrogenic preparation. By comparison of this curve with

Animal no.	Total dose	Time of injection			Smears			
		Day 1	Day 2		Day 3	Day 4		Day 5
		5 PM	9 AM	5 PM	5 PM	9 AM	5 PM	9 AM

Fig. 2-9. Flow sheet for the assay of estrogen by vaginal cornification.

the response obtained from the unknown sample, determine the potency of the unknown in terms of micrograms of estradiol.

The crossover test is used by many laboratories to increase the accuracy of the assay (51). In this procedure, the assay is repeated with the groups reversed; i.e., the mice that received the standard are injected with the unknown, and vice versa. This procedure, the crossover test, is to be used after a tentative idea of the potency of the unknown has been established. Then comparable groups of the unknown sample and the standard are used. Figure 2-10 depicts a typical dose-response curve using the vaginal smear assay in the mouse.

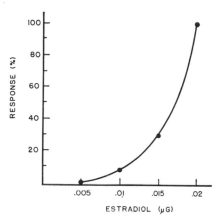

Fig. 2-10. The effect of estradiol on the vaginal smear of the ovariectomized mouse.

EXPERIMENT 2–5

Uterine Atrophy Following Castration

The secretions of estrogens by the ovary, although cyclic in nature, maintain the reproductive tract in a state that is somewhat greater than "basal." Removal of the ovary leads eventually to involution and atrophy of the reproductive tract and associated estrogen-maintained structures to states that, in some instances, are infantile. The present experiment is designed to demonstrate the rate at which atrophy occurs in the uterus following ovariectomy.

Procedure

Female mice or rats are castrated and uterine weights are obtained at definite intervals following the operation. The schedule suggested below will yield a good uterine atrophy curve.

Day	Postoperative days	Number of mice
1	0	4
3	2	3
5	4	3
8	7	3
10	9	3
15	14	3
22	21	3

Note the time required for the castration effect to be complete and plot the data both on an absolute (milligrams uterine weight) and relative (milligrams per 100 gm body weight) scale. Figure 2-11 depicts a typical atrophy curve obtained from ovariectomized mice.

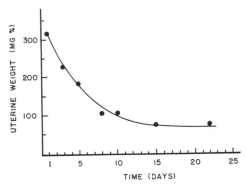

Fig. 2-11. Atrophy of the uterus of the mouse following ovariectomy.

EXPERIMENT 2–6

Bioassay of Estrogens by the Increase in Uterine Weight*

Replacement therapy with estrogens restores the reproductive tract of ovariectomized animals to the precastrate state. The degree of growth of the uterus under such therapy is proportional to the dose of hormone administered, within limits. Thus, the increase in uterine weight serves as a convenient bioassay for estrogens.

* Cf. references (5, 6).

Castrated mice used in the experiment on the assay of estrogens by the vaginal smear procedure may be used in this experiment. A 2-week rest period (see Fig. 2-11) is the minimum time requirement to permit the reproductive tract to return to a baseline.

Procedure

1. The mice are distributed into six groups of 10 animals each, and are injected subcutaneously each day for 7 days.

2. The animals are killed with ether on the 8th day, i.e., 24 hours after the last injection; the uteri are removed, trimmed of fat, and weighed rapidly on a torsion balance to the nearest 0.1 mg.

Experimental

1. A standard curve is to be established for estradiol as follows:

Group	Daily dose (μg)	Total dose (7 days) (μg)
1	0.0	0.0
2	0.001	0.007
3	0.002	0.014
4	0.005	0.035
5	0.010	0.070
6	0.020	0.140

2. As in the assay by the vaginal smear procedure, two dilutions of an unknown sample are to be injected into two groups of 10 mice each.

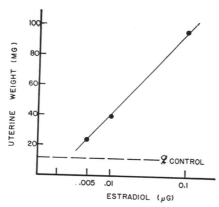

Fig. 2-12. Response of the uteri of ovariectomized mice to daily injections of estradiol (84).

3. Establish a dose-response curve and determine the potency of the unknown sample in terms of micrograms estradiol. Compare the sensitivity of this procedure with that of the vaginal assay. Note the difference in time and total dosage used. Plot the standard curve as log dose-response. Figure 2-12 depicts a typical dose-response curve for estradiol.

EXPERIMENT 2–7

The Effect of Estrogen on Oviduct Weight of the Immature Bird*

The immature chick offers several advantages as a test animal for estrogen although the assay is not as sensitive as other assays (see Table 2–6). The birds are inexpensive, hence large numbers can be used, thus increasing the precision of the measurement; no surgery is required; if necessary, weighings may be done on a triple beam balance (although accuracy is lost) since oviduct weights range from 0.1 gm to 1.5 gm.

Procedure

1. Immature female chicks (16-day-old White Leghorn) are injected for 7 days (intramuscular), using a daily volume of 0.1 ml of stilbestrol in the dosages suggested below.

2. The animals are weighed and killed on the 8th day and the oviducts are removed and weighed to the nearest 0.5 mg. The entire genital tract, from the infundibulum to the cloaca, is included as oviduct weight.

Experimental

1. Establish a dose response-curve for stilbestrol as follows:

Number of birds	Daily dosage of stilbestrol (mg)
10	0.0
10	0.05
10	0.10
10	0.20
10	0.50
10	1.00

2. Express the results as milligrams per 100 grams body weight.

* Cf. references (29, 85).

3. Establish the potency of an unknown sample. Figure 2-13 depicts a typical dose-response curve for stilbestrol.

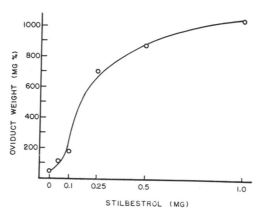

Fig. 2-13. Effect of diethylstilbestrol on weight of the oviduct in the chick (85).

EXPERIMENT 2–8

A Microbioassay of Estrogen*

Effects of estrogen on the endometrium of the uterus include a depletion of basal phospholipid and a hypertrophy of the Golgi apparatus of the endometrial cell. These effects seem to be specific to estrogen and have been used as a microbioassay.

Procedure

1. Female rats (180–200 gm) which have been ovariectomized, are rested for 2 weeks prior to treatment.

2. A 2.0 microliter (μl) volume of solution is injected by a microsyringe (see Chapter 3, Experiment 3–5, for technique of injection) into the lumen of a 10-mm segment of one uterine horn.

3. After 48 hours, the animals are killed and the injected uterine segment is removed and divided into two pieces. Two samples are also obtained from the contralateral (uninjected) horn.

4. One piece from each horn is processed by a direct silver method for Golgi apparatus (31), embedded in paraffin, and sectioned at 5 μ. The slide of the Golgi apparatus is available for study immediately after the sections have been cleared.

° Cf. reference (34).

5. The other pair of tissues is fixed overnight in dichromate–sublimate, embedded in paraffin, and sectioned at $5\,\mu$ (32). These are ready for visualization of phospholipids after staining with Sudan black B in 70% alcohol (33).

Experimental

The following dosages of estradiol benzoate are to be injected, each in a volume of $2\,\mu$l of solution:

(a) 2.0 μg
(b) 0.2 μg
(c) 0.02 μg
(d) 0.002 μg
(e) 0.0002 μg
(f) 0.00002 μg
(g) control (no treatment)

An increase in the size of the Golgi apparatus (located just above the nucleus of the endometrial cell) may be observed with as little as $0.00002\,\mu$g estradiol benzoate. A depletion of phospholipid (noted just below the nucleus of the endometrial cell) may be observed with similar dosages of estradiol benzoate.

EXPERIMENT 2–9

Suppressive Action of Various Steroids on Estradiol-Induced Uterine Growth*

Several of the steroid hormones inhibit the action of estrogen on the reproductive tract (see Table 2–11). However, some of these hormones may also have uterotropic effects observable at higher dose levels. The present experiment demonstrates the effect on the uterus of treatment with testosterone and cortisone, as well as the antiestrogenic action of these steroids.

Procedure

1. Rats which have been ovariectomized are rested for 2 weeks prior to treatment.

2. Six animals are used as controls. Three of these are injected once daily for 3 days with 0.1 μg estradiol.

3. Table 2–12 lists the doses of testosterone and cortisone that are

* Cf. reference (76).

injected alone or with 0.1 μg estradiol daily for 3 days. At least three ovariectomized rats should be used at each dose level.

4. The animals are autopsied 24 hours after the last injection. Uteri are dissected free, trimmed, and quickly weighed on a torsion balance to the nearest 0.1 mg.

TABLE 2–12

Dosages (in Milligrams) of Testosterone and Cortisone for Demonstration of Uterotropic and Antiestrogenic Action

Testosterone	Testosterone + 0.1 μg estradiol	Cortisone	Cortisone + 0.1 μg estradiol
0.1	0.1	0.1	0.1
1.0	1.0	1.0	1.0
2.0	2.0	2.0	2.0
4.0	4.0	4.0	4.0

5. Plot on separate graphs the effect of increasing doses of the (a) androgen and (b) corticosteroid on the uterine weight of the rat, with and without concomitant treatment with estradiol. Establish for each curve the baselines of uterine weight obtained in (i) the ovariectomized and estrogen-primed rat, and (ii) the ovariectomized control rats.

EXPERIMENT 2–10

Weight, Water Content, and Spontaneous Activity of the Uterus during the Estrous Cycle*

Because of the cyclic nature of estrogen secretion in animals such as the rat and mouse, the uterus exhibits changes in secretory and contractile activity, depending upon the stage of the estrous cycle.

Procedure and Experimental

1. Follow the estrous cycle of rats until observations of the vaginal smears leave no doubt as to the stage of the cycle.

2. Divide the animals into four groups of at least four each, as follows:

Group 1:	proestrus
Group 2:	estrus
Group 3:	metestrus
Group 4:	diestrus

* Cf. references (6, 42, 60).

3. The uterine horns from three rats in each group are to be removed in one piece, trimmed, opened longitudinally, blotted gently on moist filter paper, and weighed to the nearest 0.1 mg on a torsion balance.

4. These are then to be dried *in vacuo* at 60°C for at least 24 hours and until constant dry weights are obtained. Observe the state of the uterus at the time of removal from the animal, i.e., whether vascularized, fluid filled, colorless, etc.

5. Relate the visual observations, changes in dry weight, wet weight, and per cent water to the stage of the estrous cycle.

6. A uterine horn from the fourth animal of each group is to be removed; of this a 1.5-cm section is to be attached to a kymograph lever system and placed in an oxygenated mammalian Ringer solution at a constant temperature of 37°C. A sample experimental setup is depicted in Fig. 2-14. See Appendix A–8 for preparation of Ringer solution.

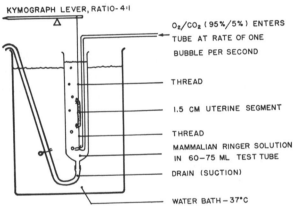

Fig. 2-14. Diagram of apparatus used for measurement of spontaneous uterine contractions.

7. Record on the kymogram the spontaneous activity of the uterine section. Determine the rate of contraction and observe the amplitude and degree of rhythmicity. Relate these observations to the stage of the estrous cycle.

EXPERIMENT 2–11

The Action of Estrogen on Serum Calcium Levels*

Blood levels of calcium seem to be regulated primarily by the hormone of the parathyroid gland, while calcium absorption from the gastro-

* Cf. references (7, 74).

intestinal tract may be promoted by vitamin D. However, in some animals, particularly birds, e.g., the domestic hen and the bobwhite quail, a pronounced rise in blood calcium is observed prior to ovulation. This is probably a result of increased estrogen secretion. There is also evidence that estrogen has an action on skeletal calcium.

Procedure and Experimental

Determine the serum calcium levels (by the method described in Experiment 12–3) of the following animals under the conditions described:

A. Chicken
(1) Nonovulating
(2) Ovulating
(3) Nonovulating, treated daily for 7 days as follows:

> (a) stilbestrol, 0.5 mg
> (b) stilbestrol, 1.0 mg
> (c) stilbestrol, 2.0 mg
> (d) stilbestrol, 4.0 mg

Blood samples are to be taken 24 hours after the last injection of stilbestrol. (For methods of withdrawing blood from the chicken, see Experiment 12–2.)

B. Rabbit
(1) Control, no treatment
(2) Treated, 2 mg stilbestrol daily, for 7 days

Blood samples are to be taken 24 hours after the last injection of stilbestrol. (For methods of withdrawing blood from the rabbit, see Experiment 12–2.)

C. Turtle (Pseudemys scripta troostii)
(1) Control
(2) Treated, 50 mg estrone (intramuscular injection). Kill 5 days after injection

D. Frog (Rana catesbiana)
(1) Control
(2) Treated, 10 mg estrone (intramuscular injection). Kill 5 days after injection

E. Fish (Paralabrax clathratus), bass
(1) Control

(2) Treated, 10 mg estrone (intramuscular injection). Kill 5 days after injection

---

EXPERIMENT 2–12

Extraction and Purification of Estrogens from Urine*

This method of fractionation and purification yields estrogens relatively free of contaminating substances that interfere with the Kober reaction. Quantities of the order of 5–10 μg estrogen per 24-hour urine sample can be measured. The method thus provides a sample sufficiently pure for demonstration of the variations in urinary estrogens during the menstrual cycle. However, meticulous care must be taken to ensure that reagents are of high purity and that glassware, reagent bottles, joints, air jets, etc., are free of contamination. A detailed discussion of precautions is given by Bauld (12).

Procedure and Experimental

A complete 24-hour urine specimen is collected without preservative and, if necessary, stored at 4°C; analyses are begun within 48 hours.

Hydrolysis

1. The 24-hour urine specimen is diluted to 2.5 liters with distilled water and mixed thoroughly. Two 500-ml portions are placed in 1000-ml round-bottom flasks. The samples are brought to the boiling point under reflux condensers, 75 ml of concentrated HCl is added, and boiling is continued for 1 hour.

Separation of the Acid Fraction

2. The cooled solutions are extracted with ether (1 × 150 ml, 3 × 125 ml), interfacial solid residues being discarded after vigorous shaking of the combined extracts. The ether solutions are submitted to the procedures described under Steps 3–5.

3. Wash with 100 ml of concentrated carbonate solution (pH 10.5). Discard carbonate solution.

4. Shake with 25 ml of 2 N NaOH. The aqueous phase, without removal from the separating funnel, is partially neutralized with 100 ml of 1 M NaHCO$_3$. The ether and aqueous phases are again shaken, and the aqueous phase is discarded.

5. Wash the ether extract with 1 M NaHCO$_3$ (1 × 25 ml) and then

* Cf. references (1, 12).

with water (1×12.5 ml); both aqueous phases are discarded. The ether solutions are then distilled to dryness. If the 24-hour urine volume is 1250 ml or less, one-half of the quantities given above are used.

Separation of Estriol

6. The residues are dissolved in 1.5 ml of ethanol and transferred to separatory funnels with 25 ml of benzene. The solutions are washed with water (2×25 ml, 2×12.5 ml), giving an aqueous phase that contains estriol.

7. The benzene is removed *in vacuo*, giving the estrone-estradiol-neutral fraction.

Preliminary Purification of the Aqueous Phase (Containing Estriol)

8. The aqueous washings are treated with 7.5 ml of $10\,N$ NaOH, boiled for 30 minutes under reflux, and extracted with 100 ml of ether. The ether extract is discarded.

9. The aqueous phase is brought to pH 9.3–9.5 by passing CO_2 from a manifold into separatory funnels containing the extracts. One limb of the manifold is led into a similar funnel containing 75 ml of water and 7.5 ml of $10\,N$ NaOH and thymolphthalein; this separate funnel serves as an indicator for the partial neutralization of the funnels containing urine extracts. With a manifold diameter of 1 inch, and capillary-glass tubing of 1 mm bore, the rate of gas flow into the funnels is sufficiently uniform that no further check of the pH is required.

10. These solutions are then extracted with ether (4×40 ml), and the combined extracts are washed with $1\,M$ NaHCO$_3$ (1×5 ml) and water (2×5 ml).

11. The ether is then distilled, leaving the impure estriol fraction.

Chromatography of the Impure Estriol Fraction

12. Chromatograph columns are prepared by the method of Bauld (1955) (11), with the following characteristics: mobile phase, ethylene dichloride; stationary phase, 70% methanol; columns, 1 cm $\times$ 10 cm, are packed from a slurry containing 1 ml of stationary phase per gram of Celite; diameter of holes in packing plunger, 0.7 mm; temperature $18 \pm 0.5°$; percolation rate of solvent, 10–12 ml per hour. The residues from Step 11 are dissolved in 1 ml of mobile phase, transferred by pipettes carefully to the tops of the chromatographs, and allowed to pass through the column until the top is just dry. The transfer procedure is repeated twice with 1-ml washings of mobile phase. When the second wash enters the chromatogram, collection of eluate is begun and a

reservoir containing mobile phase is fitted to the top of the column. The eluate from 0 to 14 ml* is discarded; the next 16 ml* is collected, giving the estriol fraction. The solvent is removed *in vacuo,* the residue is dissolved in 3 ml of ethanol, and a 2-ml portion is transferred to a color reaction tube. Quinol (50 ± 5 mg) is added, and the solvent is removed by heating in a boiling water bath with a stream of filtered air directed onto the surface of the solution.

Chromatography of the Estrone-Estradiol-Neutral Fraction

12a. Chromatographs are prepared by the method of Bauld (1955) (11), with the following characteristics: mobile phase, benzene; stationary phase, $0.8 N$ NaOH; columns, 1 cm $\times$ 12 cm, are packed from a slurry containing 0.8 ml of stationary phase per gram of Celite; diameter of holes in packing plunger, 1.00 mm; temperature $18 \pm 0.5°$; percolation rate of solvent, 10–12 ml per hour. The residues from Step 7 are applied to the chromatograms as described above for chromatography of the impure estriol fraction. The eluate from 0 to 10 ml* (neutral fraction) is discarded, the end of the column is rinsed with a stream of benzene, and the eluate from 10 to 30 ml* is collected, giving the impure estrone fraction. The next 10 ml* is discarded and the mobile phase is changed to ethylene dichloride:benzene (3:1, v/v); 50 ml* is collected, giving the impure estradiol fraction.

Final Purification of the Impure Estrone Fraction

13. The estrone fraction from Step 12a is evaporated to dryness *in vacuo,* boiled under reflux for 30 minutes with 10 ml of $1 N$ NaOH, acidified with 1 ml of $12 N$ H_2SO_4, and extracted with benzene $(1 \times 20$ ml$)$.

14. The extracts are washed with $0.5 M$ Na_2CO_3 $(1 \times 4$ ml$)$ and water $(2 \times 4$ ml$)$ and transferred to color reaction tubes. Quinol (50 ± 5 mg) is added, and the solvent is removed by heating at 80–90° in a stream of filtered air. This gives the estrone fraction.

Final Purification of the Impure Estradiol Fraction

15. The impure estradiol fraction (from Step 12a) is treated exactly as described above for the impure estrone fraction (Steps 13 and 14). This gives the purified estradiol fraction.

The estrogens prepared by this method are biologically active.

---

* Slight variations are inevitable in the packing technique of different workers. Therefore, the exact elution pattern of the estrogens should be determined by this method, and fractions taken accordingly.

Experimental

1. Prepare a 24-hour urine sample obtained from a woman during pregnancy or during the proliferative phase of the menstrual cycle.

2. Determine the estrogenic activity by the vaginal smear or uterine weight assay procedures.

EXPERIMENT 2–13

Modified Kober Reaction for Use with Purified Extracts Prepared in Experiment 2–12*

The colorimetric methods for determination of estrogens are based upon the presence of a phenolic grouping in ring A of the steroid. Thus, all the natural estrogens of animal origin can be detected by these methods. Some of the synthetic and plant estrogens, however, do not contain this grouping and hence cannot be determined by the colorimetric procedure. The following modification of the Kober reaction may be used to measure the potency of extracts of urine (during the menstrual cycle and pregnancy) prepared as described in Experiment 2–12. Although a high degree of purification of these extracts is attempted in order to minimize interference from nonestrogenic urinary chromogens, nonetheless, a correction factor must be applied to account for remaining interfering substances.

Procedure

Reagents

1. *Reagent for estradiol-17β.* NaNO₃ (10 mg) and quinone (certified chemical, 20 mg) in 1.0 liter of H_2SO_4 (60%, v/v) are warmed (at approximately 50°) until the solution turns light green and opalescent. Quinol (20 gm reagent grade) is added and dissolved by further warming and shaking; the solution (after cooling) is filtered through sintered glass (porosity no. 4, fine).

2. *Reagent for estrone and estriol.* These reagents are prepared as above, but with 66% (v/v) and 76% (v/v) H_2SO_4, respectively, as solvents.

Color Development of Purified Extracts Obtained in Experiment 2–12

1. The appropriate reagent (2.6 ml for estradiol-17β and estriol; 3.0 ml for estrone) is added to the estrogen and quinol residues contained in test tubes (23 mm × 150 mm).

* Cf. reference (12).

2. The test tubes are heated for 20 minutes; they are shaken twice during this time to ensure adequate mixing and solution of the quinol. The solutions are then cooled in a bath of cold water (approximately 15°). Quinol, 50 ± 5 mg, is added, and dilution is carried out as follows:

(a) estradiol-17β: 0.7 ml reagent
(b) estriol: 0.7 ml water
(c) estrone: 0.3 ml water

3. The tubes are shaken 5–10 times, then reheated for 15 minutes with two shakings during this time to dissolve the quinol. The cooled solutions are transferred to 1-cm cuvettes, and their optical densities are measured at:

(a) 480, 512.5, and 545 mμ for estrone
(b) 480, 512.5, and 545 mμ for estriol
(c) 480, 515,   and 550 mμ for estradiol

The measurements can be made on a Beckman DU spectrophotometer, or on a Beckman model B spectrophotometer if the line voltage is stabilized. Optical-density readings (D) are corrected by applying the following equations (4):

$$\left.\begin{array}{r}\text{estriol}\\ \text{and}\\ \text{estrone}\end{array}\right\} \text{ corrected } = D_{512.5\ m\mu} - 1/2(D_{480\ m\mu} + D_{545\ m\mu})$$

$$\text{estradiol corrected } = D_{515\ m\mu} - 1/2(D_{480\ m\mu} + D_{550\ m\mu})$$

A calibration curve may be established for each of the estrogens by plotting the corrected absorption values of standard estrogen solutions containing between 1 and 10 μg of hormone per sample.

Experimental

Prepare a 24-hour urine sample obtained from a woman during pregnancy or other stages of the reproductive cycle according to the procedure listed in Experiment 2–12 and determine the estrogen content using the Kober reaction.

EXPERIMENT 2–14

Extraction of Estrogens from Urine of Pregnancy*
(Simplified Procedure)

This procedure is a simplified extraction method in which the final product contains all the ether-soluble phenolic products of urine. It is adequate for measuring total estrogenic material contained in pregnancy

* Cf. reference (67).

urine but is not suitable for estimation of urinary estrogen levels during the menstrual cycle, as impurities tend to obscure the results obtained from extracts with low levels of estrogen.

Procedure

Open Flask Hydrolysis

1. A 24-hour urine specimen is collected under toluene and diluted to a volume of 2.5 liters.

2. Heat 100 ml of diluted urine to boiling under reflux conditions. As the sample comes to a boil, add 15 ml of 10 N HCl down the condenser. Boiling is continued for 30 minutes.

Extraction of Estrogens from Acid-Hydrolyzed Urine

1. Cool the sample of acid-hydrolyzed urine (100 ml). Extract once with 100 ml and twice with 50 ml of purified ethyl ether.

2. Combine the extracts and wash three times with 25-ml portions of 5% (w/v) $NaHCO_3$.

3. Combine washings. Back-extract these once with 20 ml of ether.

4. Ether extract is combined with back-extract and evaporated to dryness.

5. Residue is warmed with about 3 ml ethanol, and 100 ml benzene is added.

6. Benzene solution is extracted once with 50 ml and twice with 25 ml of N NaOH.

7. Extracts are combined, acidified with 15 ml of 10 N HCl, and extracted once with 100 ml and twice with 50 ml of ether.

8. The combined extract is washed twice with 20-ml portions of 5% (w/v) $NaHCO_3$. Washings are back-extracted once with 20 ml of ether.

9. Ether extract and back-extract are combined and washed three times with 20-ml portions of water. Evaporate the ether extract to dryness.

The residue contains the total ether-soluble phenolic fraction of hydrolyzed urine and may be dissolved in ethanol and measured out for assay.

EXPERIMENT 2–15

Colorimetric Estimation of Urinary Estrogens by the Kober Reaction* (Simplified Procedure)

This method of colorimetric assay gives adequate values for total

* Cf. reference (67).

estrogen (expressed as estriol) in urine of pregnancy. It is not suitable for urine obtained during normal menstrual cycles, as the method of correction for impurities is less accurate for samples containing small quantities of estrogens. Urine samples extracted by the procedure described in Experiment 2–14 may be analyzed by this method.

Procedure

Preparation of Kober Reagent

1. Pure concentrated H_2SO_4, 5.6 parts by volume, is added slowly to 3.6 parts by volume of freshly redistilled phenol (at 60°C), and mixed in a dry, well stoppered bottle. The reagents are measured by pipettes, and time must be allowed for prolonged draining due to the viscosities of the substances. The resulting solution must be kept as protected from water as possible. The reagent should be checked weekly with an estriol standard (1 ml = 30 μg).

Assay

1. Measured samples of the solution of urinary phenolic fraction (10–80 μg estrogen, and not more than 2% of a 24-hour specimen)[*] are evaporated to dryness in a stream of air in test tubes, about 2 cm in diameter, with graduations at 8 and 15 ml.

2. To the dry residues, 3-ml portions of Kober reagent are added; the tubes are heated in boiling water for 20 minutes. Cool in an ice–salt freezing mixture.

3. Add 3 ml water and mix thoroughly.

4. Heat tubes for 3 minutes in boiling water.

5. Cool to room temperature by immersion in water.

6. Dilute to 15-ml mark with 10% (v/v) H_2SO_4.

7. Read the intensity of absorption at 520 mμ on 7-ml portions of the final solutions in a photoelectric colorimeter.

8. Heat the 8-ml portions in boiling water for 1.5 hours to fade the pink color. Cool, replace lost water, and read in colorimeter at 520 mμ. The amount of estrogen (as estriol) obtained from the difference between the initial and final readings is referred to an estriol calibration curve.

An estriol calibration curve may be established by measuring the

---

[*] When an amount of the phenolic fraction of more than 2% of the 24-hour urine sample is used, precipitates may form during the subsequent fading procedure.

absorption of standard solutions containing between 10 μg and 80 μg estriol per sample tube.

Fluorometric Estimation of Estrogens*
(Simplified Procedure)

The urinary estrogen fractions from Experiment 2–14 may be estimated by this method.

Procedure

1. Test samples and standard preparations are diluted to contain 0.1–5.0 μg† per 0.1 or 0.2 ml, using ethanol, toluene, or water.

2. Samples of 0.1 ml of aqueous or 0.2 ml of ethanol or toluene solutions are accurately pipetted into separate fluorometer tubes. Samples of the same size and in the same solvent are used for both the standard and unknown.

3. H_2SO_4, 1.0 ml of 90% (v/v), is added to each tube and the tube is shaken. All tubes are placed in a water bath at 80° ± 5°C for 10–20 minutes.

* Cf. references (9, 10).

† For maximum sensitivity, a sample size as low as 0.1–0.5 μg estrone equivalent per sample may be used if the following filter combinations are used:

A { Activating lamp filter: Maximum transmission at 365 mμ
    Photocell filter: 89% transmission over 380 mμ
                                 or
B { Activating lamp: 422 mμ
    Photocell filter   More than 80% transmission over 450 mμ

Filter combination B is recommended for urine extracts.

For maximum specificity, sample size of 1–5 μg estrone equivalent are required with the following filter combinations:

Activating lamp filter: Interference filter, transmission at 420 mμ
Photocell filter: Interference filter, transmission in region
                                of 500–520 mμ
                                Auxiliary filter with more than 80% transmission over 450 mμ

When this filter combination is used, nonestrogenic steroids show less than 5% fluorescence (estrone equivalent to 100%).

A calibration curve for estrone may be prepared with concentrations between 0.1 and 5.0 μg per 0.1 or 0.2 ml (10 μg per tube, maximum concentration).

4. The tubes are removed from the bath, and 6 ml of 65% (v/v) H_2SO_4 is added. Mix thoroughly using a flattened, spirally tipped stirring rod. After the tubes have stood for several minutes to permit bubbles to disappear, the relative fluorescence of the standard and unknown is determined using a fluorometer.

Notes: (a) Sample must be measured accurately. (b) Final volume must be the same in all tubes. (c) The concentration of H_2SO_4 during the 10-minute heating period (i.e., after dilution by the sample) must be the same in both the standards and the unknowns—between 70% and 85% H_2SO_4 by volume. If the acid concentration is 80%, only 10 minutes' heating is necessary. If 70%, 20 minutes' heating is required. The reaction can tolerate heating up to 1 hour. (d) Temperature is not a critical factor. (e) Dilution of the heated sample with 65% acid will maintain the stability of the reaction for several days.

References

1. Allen, E. 1922. The estrous cycle of the mouse. *Am. J. Anat.* **30:** 297–371.
2. Allen, E., and Doisy, E. A. 1923. An ovarian hormone; preliminary report on its localization, extraction and partial purification and action in test animals. *J. Am. Med. Assoc.* **81:** 819–821.
3. Allen, E., Francis, B. F., Robertson, L. L., Colgate, C. E., Johnston, C. G., Doisy, E. A., Kountz, W. B., and Gibson, H. V. 1924. The hormone of the ovarian follicle, its localization and action in test animals, and additional points bearing upon the internal secretion of the ovary. *Am. J. Anat.* **34:** 133–181.
4. Allen, W. M. 1950. A simple method for analyzing complicated absorption curves, of use in the colorimetric determination of urinary steroids. *J. Clin. Endocrinol.* **10:** 71–83.
5. Astwood, E. B. 1938. A six-hour assay for the quantitative determination of estrogen. *Endocrinology* **23:** 25–31.
6. Astwood, E. B. 1939. Changes in the weight and water content of the uterus of the normal adult rat. *Am. J. Physiol.* **126:** 162–170.
7. Baldini, J. T., and Zarrow, M. X. 1952. Estrogen and serum calcium level in the bobwhite quail. *Poultry Sci.* **31:** 800–804.
8. Bates, R. W. 1954. Spectrophotometric methods for determination of estrogenic steroids. *Recent Progr. Hormone Res.* **9:** 95–112.
9. Bates, R. W., and Cohen, H. 1950. Experimental basis for selecting the optimal conditions for quantitative fluorometry of natural estrogens. *Endocrinology* **47:** 166–181.
10. Bates, R. W., and Cohen, H. 1950. Fluorescence spectra of natural estrogens and their application to biological extracts. *Endocrinology* **47:** 182–192.
11. Bauld, W. S. 1955. Separation of oestrogens in urinary extracts by partition chromatography. *Biochem. J.* **59:** 294–300.
12. Bauld, W. S. 1956. A method for the determination of oestriol, oestrone and oestradiol-17b in human urine by partition chromatography and colorimetric estimation. *Biochem. J.* **63:** 488–495.

13. Bever, A. T. 1959. Steroid influences on the lactic dehydrogenase-DPNH oxidase system of the rat uterus. *Ann. N. Y. Acad. Sci.* **75**: 472–490.

14. Bickoff, E. M., Booth, A. N., Lyman, R. L., Livingston, A. L., Thompson, C. R., and De Eds, F. 1957. Coumestrol, a new estrogen isolated from forage crops. *Science* **126**: 969–970.

15. Booth, A. N., Bickoff, E. M., and Kohler, G. O. 1960. Estrogenlike activity in vegetable oils and mill by-products. *Science* **131**: 1807–1808.

16. Brown, J. B. 1952. Some observations on the Kober colour and fluorescence reactions of the natural oestrogens. *J. Endocrinol.* **8**: 196–210.

17. Brown, J. B. 1955. Urinary excretion of oestrogens during the menstrual cycle. *Lancet* **i**: 320–323.

18. Brown, J. B. 1955. A new method for the determination of oestrogens in urine and its application to a study of the oestrogen excretion in the menstrual cycle. *Mem. Soc. Endocrinol.* **3**: 1–10.

19. Brown, J. B. 1956. Urinary excretion of oestrogens during pregnancy, lactation, and the re-establishment of menstruation. *Lancet* **i**: 704.

20. Bulbring, E., and Burn, J. H. 1935. The estimation of oestrin and of male hormone in oily solution. *J. Physiol.* **85**: 320.

21. Burn, J. H., Finney, D. J., and Goodwin, L. G. 1950. "Biological Standardization," Chap. 9, pp. 240–256. Oxford Univ. Press, London and New York.

22. Cheng, E., Yoder, L., Story, C. D., and Burroughs, W. 1954. Estrogenic activity of some isoflavone derivatives. *Science* **120**: 575–576.

23. Csapo, A. 1950. Actomyosin formation by estrogen action. *Am. J. Physiol.* **162**: 406–410.

24. Csapo, A., and Corner, G. W. 1952. The antagonistic effects of estrogen and progesterone on the staircase phenomenon in uterine muscle. *Endocrinology* **51**: 378–385.

25. Csapo, A., and Corner, G. W. 1953. Effect of estrogen on the isometric tension of rabbit uterine strips. *Science* **117**: 162–164.

26. Davis, J. S., Meyer, R. K., and McShan, W. H. 1956. The effects of aminopterin and estrogen on the phosphate metabolism of rat uterus. *Endocrinology* **59**: 505–515.

27. Diczfalusy, E. 1953. Chorionic gonadotrophin and oestrogens in the human placenta. *Acta Endocrinol. Suppl.* **12**.

28. Dorfman, R. I. 1955. Steroid hormone metabolism, *in* "The Hormones" (G. Pincus and K. V. Thimann, eds.), Vol. 2, pp. 589–664. Academic Press, New York.

29. Dorfman, R. I., and Dorfman, A. S. 1948. Studies on the bioassay of hormones—the assay of estrogens by a chick oviduct method. *Endocrinology* **42**: 85–92.

30. Edgren, R. A., and Calhoun, D. W. 1957. Estrogen antagonisms: Inhibition of estrone-induced uterine growth by testosterone propionate, progesterone and 17 ethyl-19-nortestosterone. *Proc. Soc. Exptl. Biol. Med.* **94**: 537–539.

31. Elftman, H. 1952. A direct silver method for the Golgi apparatus. *Stain Technol.* **27**: 47–52.

32. Elftman, H. 1957. Phospholipid fixation by dichromate-sublimate. *Stain Technol.* **32**: 29–31.

33. Elftman, H. 1958. Effects of fixation on lipoid histochemistry. *J. Histochem. Cytochem.* **6**: 317–321.

34. Elftman, H. 1960. A micro-bioassay for estrogen. *Proc. Soc. Exptl. Biol. Med.* **105**: 19–21.

35. Emmens, C. W. 1939. The duration of action of certain natural and synthetic oestrogens when administered orally or by injection. *J. Endocrinol.* **1**: 142–146.
36. Emmens, C. W. 1950. Estrogens, in "Hormone Assay" (C. W. Emmens, ed.), pp. 391–417. Academic Press, New York.
37. Emmens, C. W., Cox, R. I., and Martin, L. 1960. Oestrogen inhibition by steroids and other substances. *J. Endocrinol.* **20**: 198–209.
38. Engel, L. L. 1957. The biosynthesis of estrogens. *Cancer* **10**: 711–715.
39. Gardner, W. U. 1936. Sexual dimorphism of the pelvis of the mouse, the effect of estrogenic hormones upon the pelvis and upon the development of scrotal hernias. *Am. J. Anat.* **59**: 459–483.
40. Goto, M., and Csapo, A. 1959. The effect of the ovarian steroids on the membrane potential of uterine muscle. *J. Gen. Physiol.* **43**: 455–466.
41. Hagerman, D. D., and Villee, C. A. 1959. Metabolic studies of the mechanism of action of estrogens, *Recent Progr. Endocrinol. Reproduction, Proc. Conf. Syracuse, 1958,* pp. 317–333.
42. Harne, O. G. 1931. A study of spontaneous activity in the excised uterine horns of the rat by an improved method. *Am. J. Physiol.* **99**: 227–236.
43. Harris, G. W. 1959. The nervous system—follicular ripening, ovulation, and estrous behavior, *Recent Progr. Endocrinol. Reproduction, Proc. Conf. Syracuse, 1958,* pp. 21–43.
44. Hartman, C. G., Littrell, J. L., and Tom, J. 1946. The weanling guinea pig as test object for estrogen assays. *Endocrinology* **39**: 120–130.
45. Heard, R. D. H., Jacobs, R., O'Donnell, V., Peron, F. G., Saffron, J. C., Solomon, S. S., Thompson, L. M., Willoughby, H., and Yates, C. H. 1954. The application of C^{14} to the study of the metabolism of the sterols and steroid hormones. *Recent Progr. Hormone Res.* **9**: 383–410.
46. Heard, R. D. H., Jellink, P. H., and O'Donnell, V. J. 1955. Biogenesis of estrogens; the conversion of testosterone-4-C^{14} to estrone in the pregnant mare. *Endocrinology* **57**: 200–204.
47. Heard, R. D. H., and O'Donnell, V. J. 1954. Biogenesis of the estrogens: the failure of cholesterol-4-C^{14} to give rise to estrone in the pregnant mare. *Endocrinology* **54**: 209–215.
48. Heimlich, A. 1957. Ph.D. Thesis, Purdue University.
49. Hisaw, F. L. 1925. The influence of the ovary on the resorption of the pubic bones of the pocket gopher, *Geomys bursarius* (Shaw). *J. Exptl. Zool.* **42**: 411–441.
50. Kuriyama, H. A., and Csapo, A. I. 1959. The "evolution" of membrane and myoplasmic activity of uterine muscle. *Biol. Bull.* **117**: 417–418.
51. Laqueur, E. 1935. Zur Eichung brunstgebender Stoffe. *Klin. Wochschr.* **14**: 339–341.
52. Leathem, J. H. 1959. Some biochemical aspects of the uterus. *Ann. N. Y. Acad. Sci.* **75**: 463–471.
53. Lerner, L. J., Holthaus, F. J., Jr., and Thompson, C. R. 1958. A non-steroidal estrogen antagonist 1-(p-2-diethylaminoethoxyphenyl)-1-phenyl-2-p-methoxyphenyl ethanol. *Endocrinology* **63**: 295–318.
54. Long, J. A., and Evans, H. M. 1922. The estrous cycle in the rat and its associated phenomena. *Mem. Univ. Calif.* **6**: 1–128.
55. Marrian, G. F. 1957. The urinary estrogens and their quantitative determination. *Cancer* **10**: 704–706.

56. Marshall, J. M. 1959. Effects of estrogen and progesterone on single uterine muscle fibers in the rat. *Am. J. Physiol.* **197**: 935–942.

57. Marshall, J. M., and Csapo, A. I. 1959. The effects of calcium deficiency and oxytocin on the membrane activity of uterine muscle as measured by the "Sucrose Gap" method. *Biol. Bull.* **117**: 419.

58. A. S. Parkes (ed.). 1956. "Marshall's Physiology of Reproduction," Vol. 1. Longmans, Green, New York.

59. Muhlbock, O. 1940. Die intravaginale Verabreichung oestrogener Hormone bie kastrierten Mausen. *Acta Brevia Neerl. Physiol. Pharmacol. Microbiol.* **10**: 42.

60. Painter, E. E., and Harne, O. G. 1934. Analysis of contraction types of excised uterus of rat. *Am. J. Physiol.* **108**: 33–41.

61. Parkes, A. S. 1930. On the synergism between oestrin and oxytocin. *J. Physiol.* (*London*) **69**: 463–472.

62. Pincus, G. 1955. The Physiology of the Ovarian and Testis Hormones, *in* "The Hormones" (G. Pincus and K. V. Thimann, eds.), pp. 665–684. Academic Press, New York.

63. Reynolds, S. R. M. 1949. "Physiology of the Uterus." Harper (Hoeber), New York.

64. Richter, C. P., and Hartman, C. G. 1934. The effect of injections of amniotin on the spontaneous activity of gonadectomized rats. *Am. J. Physiol.* **108**: 136–143.

65. Schofield, B. M. 1957. The hormonal control of myometrial function during pregnancy. *J. Physiol.* (*London*) **138**: 1–10.

66. Slonaker, J. R. 1924. The effect of pubescence, oestruation, and menopause on the voluntary activity in the albino rat. *Am. J. Physiol.* **68**: 294–315.

67. Stevenson, M. F., and Marrian, G. F. 1947. The determination of oestrogens in human pregnancy urine. A new method of correcting for the brown colour developed in the Kober reaction by non-oestrogenic substances. *Biochem. J.* **41**: 507–511.

68. Stockard, C. R., and Papanicolaou, G. N. 1917. The existence of a typical oestrous cycle in the guinea pig with a study of its histological and physiological changes. *Am. J. Anat.* **22**: 225–283.

69. Stone, C. P. 1939. Sex drive, *in* "Sex and Internal Secretion" (E. Allen, C. H. Danforth, and E. A. Doisy, eds.), 2nd ed., Chap. 23. Williams & Wilkins, Baltimore, Maryland.

70. Sulman, F. G. 1952. Intravaginal assay of estrogens. *Endocrinology* **50**: 61–67.

71. Szego, C. M. 1952. Pituitary-adrenal cortical antagonism to estrogenic stimulation of the uterus of the ovariectomized rat. Observations on structural specificity of crystalline steroids. *Endocrinology* **50**: 429–441.

72. Talmage, R. V. 1946. Histological effects of estradiol, progesterone and relaxin on the symphysis pubis of the guinea pig. *Anat. Record* **96**: 528.

73. Talmage, R. V. 1947. Changes produced in the symphysis pubis of the guinea pig by the sex steroids and relaxin. *Anat. Record* **99**: 91–111.

74. Urist, M. R., and Schjeide, A. O. 1961. The partition of calcium and protein in the blood of oviparous vertebrates during estrus. *J. Gen. Physiol.* **44**: 743–756.

75. Vande Wiele, R. L., and Jailer, J. W. 1959. Placental steroids. *Ann. N. Y. Acad. Sci.* **75**: 889–894.

76. Velardo, J. T. 1959. Steroid hormones and uterine growth. *Ann. N. Y. Acad. Sci.* **75**: 441–462.

77. Velardo, J. T. 1960. Pacemaker action of ovarian hormones in reproductive proc-

esses: II. The estrogens and progesterones during pregnancy. *Fertility Sterility* **11:** 343–369.

78. Villee, C. A. 1959. Estrogens and uterine enzymes. *Ann. N. Y. Acad. Sci.* **75:** 524–534.
79. Villee, C. A., and Hagerman, D. D. 1957. Compounds with an anti-estrogenic activity *in vitro. Endocrinology* **60:** 552–558.
80. Wang, G. H. 1923. The relation between "spontaneous activity" and the oestrous cycle in the white rat. *Comp. Psychol. Monographs* **2:** No. 6.
81. Young, W. C., Boling, J. C., and Blandau, R. J. 1941. The vaginal smear picture, sexual receptivity and time of ovulation in the albino rat. *Anat. Record* **80:** 37–45.
82. Young, W. C., and Fish, W. R. 1945. The ovarian hormones and spontaneous running activity in the female rat. *Endocrinology* **36:** 181–189.
83. Zarrow, M. X., Hisaw, F. L., and Salhanick, H. A. 1954. Differential effect of aminopterin on the action of estradiol and progesterone in monkeys. *Am. J. Obstet. Gynecol.* **67:** 1139–1147.
84. Zarrow, M. X., Lazo-Wasem, E. A., and Shoger, R. L. 1953. Estrogenic activity in a commercial animal ration. *Science* **118:** 650–651.
85. Zarrow, M. X., Peters, L. E., and Caldwell, A. L., Jr. 1960. Comparative potency of several progestogenic compounds in a battery of different biological tests. *Ann. N. Y. Acad. Sci.* **71:** 532–541.

CHAPTER 3

The Progestogens

It has been shown that, in the mammalian female, action by the estrogens leads to sexual maturity, growth of the uterus, the drive for mating, and other phenomena essential for the early phases of reproductive activity. If any generalization can be made about the progestogenic hormones, it is that they are essential for the continuation of reproductive processes in the female mammal: the nidation of the blastocyst in the uterus, the maintenance of the gravid state, the morphological development of the mammary gland and other phenomena related to gestation and lactation.

Sites of Progestogen Formation

Progestogens have been isolated from four major sources in the mammal: the ovary, the placenta, the testis, and the cortex of the adrenal

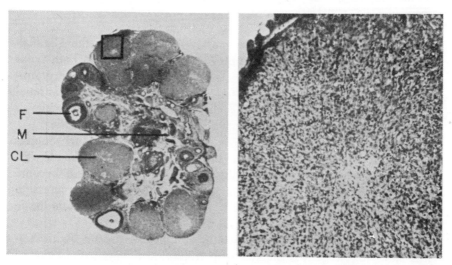

Fig. 3-1. *Left:* Ovary of the rat on the fourth day of pseudopregnancy. *CL*, corpus luteum; *F*, follicle; *M*, medulla of ovary. *Right:* Corpus luteum, rat. Taken from section delimited by square on left (50× magnification).

gland. The hormone from the ovary has been extracted from the corpus luteum and is thought to be produced by the theca-lutein or granulosa-lutein cells of this structure (Figs. 3-1 and 3-2). These cells begin form-

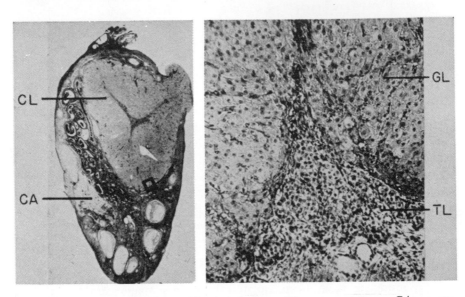

Fig. 3-2. *Left:* Ovary of *Macaca mulata. CL,* corpus luteum; *CA,* corpus albicans. *Right:* Corpus luteum of human being. *TL,* theca lutein cells; *GL,* granulosa lutein cells (100× magnification).

ing from cells of the theca interna and the granulosa of the Graafian follicle at about the time of ovulation. In their mature state, both types of cells exhibit histochemical evidence of steroid secretions. The granulosa-lutein cells are rather large, tend to resemble cells of the adrenal cortex, and contain a rounded, somewhat vesicular nucleus with an easily discernible nucleolus.

As the corpus luteum ages, histological changes occur that suggest degeneration. The granulosa-lutein cell becomes highly vacuolated, with a dark, pycnotic nucleus. A fatty degeneration ensues, the cells become shrunken in size and connective tissue invades the area. This regression continues until the entire structure has become a small connective tissue scar in the ovary, called a corpus albicans (Fig. 3-2).

That portion of the placenta which is thought to secrete both estrogens and progestogens is the syncytial trophoblast. This tissue begins to form from the cellular trophoblast at the time of implantation of the blastocyst and is actually part of the "advancing edge" of the blastocyst as it penetrates the endometrium of the uterus. In the well developed placenta (human being), the syncytial trophoblast forms an outer covering over each villus, thus being in contact with maternal circulation. This tissue, embryonic in origin, also exhibits histochemical reactions indicative of the presence and metabolism of steroids.

Progestogens that have been isolated from the testis are thought to be secreted by the interstitial cells of Leydig. These hormones may represent precursors or metabolites of the androgens (see Chapter 5). Similarly, progestogens extracted from the cortical cells of the adrenal gland are believed to represent precursors of the adrenal corticosteroids (see Chapter 7).

Nature of the Progestogens

The natural progestogens of animal origin are steroidal in structure and differ slightly from the estrogens. The basic structure of the progestogen molecule is the pregnane nucleus (see Appendix A–4). It will be noted that, in contrast to the estrogens, ring A is saturated, C-10 contains a methyl group, and a 2-carbon side chain is present on C-17.

Table 3–1 depicts the structures and sources of several compounds classified as progestogens. Many of these compounds are similar to androgens in structure, and hence possess androgenic activity. Some of these steroids also possess estrogenic and corticosteroid-like activity.

Action of the Progestogens

Evidence for the existence of a corpus luteum hormone dates back to the original work of Fraenkel (23), who reported a failure to maintain pregnancy in the rabbit after removal of the corpus luteum. These results have since been confirmed in many laboratories and in many different species of mammal (5, 14, 19, 33, 34, 57, 62, 99). It was not until 1929 (3, 4, 5), however, that a lipoidal extract of the corpus luteum was shown to induce progestational proliferation in the rabbit uterus; in 1934 a similar extract was obtained from the placenta (1). Purification and crystallization of progesterone isolated from corpora lutea was achieved in the laboratory of Allen and Wintersteiner in 1934 (6).

The actions of progestogens are as varied as those of the estrogens and involve the same end organs and tissues. The relationship between these two groups of hormones is interesting and somewhat complex. Many of the responses of tissues to progestogenic hormones can be elicited with massive doses of progestogen alone (77); few of the responses can be elicited with estrogen alone. Administration of small doses of estrogen concomitantly with or prior to the progestogen treatment lessens considerably the dosage requirement of the latter. Hence, estrogen

TABLE 3–1

MOLECULES THAT EXHIBIT PROGESTOGENIC ACTIVITY

Progestogen	Structure	Source
Progesterone (Δ⁴-pregnene-3, 20-dione)		Corpus luteum, placenta, adrenal gland, cow testis
17α-Hydroxy-progesterone		Follicular fluid, human being, mare
17α-Hydroxy-progesterone-caproate		Synthetic
11β-Hydroxy-progesterone		Synthetic
9α-Fluoro-11β-hydroxy-progesterone		Synthetic

and progesterone are considered to act *synergistically* in their effects on sensitive tissues. However, progestogens inhibit many actions of estrogens, and estrogen is capable of inhibiting progestogenic activity. In

TABLE 3–1 (*Continued*)

Progestogen	Structure	Source
17α-Ethynyl-19-nor-testosterone		Synthetic
17α-Ethynyl-tetosterone		Synthetic
17α-Ethynyl-17-hydroxy-5(10)-estren-3-one		Synthetic
17α-Ethyl-19-nor-testosterone		Synthetic
Pregnanediol (3, 20α)		Urine, male and female, human being, placenta, human being Bile, pregnant cow (3, 20β form)

these instances, the hormones are considered to act *antagonistically.* Whether or not a synergistic or antagonistic effect is observed is more often than not dependent upon the ratio of doses (or levels) of the two hormones. Thus one may speak of *estrogenic dominance* or *progestogenic dominance,* depending on whether the effect observed is a result of

TABLE 3–1 (*Continued*)

Progestogen	Structure	Source
19-Nor- progesterone		Synthetic
6α-Methyl- 17α-acetoxy- progesterone		Synthetic
Δ⁴-3-Ketopregnen- 20α-ol and its 20β-ol isomer (20α- and 20β- hydroxyprogest- erone)		Corpus luteum, human being; placenta, human being; ovary, rabbit

estrogen predominance, or progestogen predominance. Some of the effects of progestogens are discussed below, but it must be remembered that many of these, in the normal animal, may be effects observed as a result of the synergistic or antagonistic ratios of both steroids rather than of either one alone. *Apparent inconsistencies of response to hormone stimulation may merely be a result of different ratios of the two hormones.*

A. REPRODUCTIVE CYCLES

The presence of a functional corpus luteum, and hence the secretion of progesterone, generally tends to delay the onset of the next estrous period in animals with an estrous cycle. Vaginal cornification is inhibited, ovulation is repressed, sexual activity is repressed, and hence the cycle is prolonged. In mammals which normally display functional corpora lutea during their cycles (see Chapter 2), this phase is known as the luteal, progestational, or secretory phase. In other mammals, such as the rat and mouse, functional corpora lutea are not formed unless coitus (or some mechanical stimulation of the uterine cervix) is effected. Hence these animals exhibit a short diestrous phase before the next cycle begins. After cervical stimulation, however, the cycle is prolonged, with the same characteristics observed in other mammals. This phase, although identical in all respects to the normal progestational phase, is sometimes referred to as "pseudopregnancy." Normal cyclic activity, as in animals with a "built-in" luteal phase, resumes after regression of the corpus luteum. Thus, the reproductive cycles of the mammals may be classified as shown in Fig. 3-3. It is currently thought that the induction of the

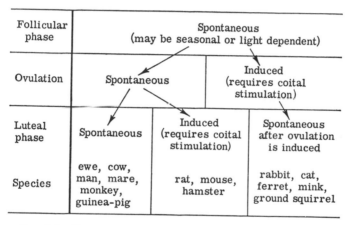

Fig. 3-3. Classification of reproductive cycles of mammals.

luteal phase by cervical stimulation is mediated by the nervous system, through the hypothalamus, to the anterior pituitary gland (see Chapter 10).

B. THE VAGINA, CERVIX, AND PUBIC SYMPHYSIS

The vaginal epithelium, under progestogen domination, is relatively thin, columnar in shape, and contains goblet cells. The vaginal smears show a rather sparse, cellular population consisting of some nucleated epithelial cells and many leukocytes. Mucus may be present, indicating the presence of synergizing levels of estrogen; however, progesterone in large doses is also capable of causing mucification (56). The arborization patterns of dried cervical mucus have been used as an index of progestogen:estrogen activity during pregnancy in the human being (43). Progesterone causes changes in the water content of the rat vagina (104), and a decrease in estrogen-induced β-glucuronidase (32). An inhibition of cervical dilation is observed in normal pregnant rats treated with progesterone (82). Progesterone, in combination with estrogen is capable of causing relaxation of the pubic symphysis in the guinea pig, but the uterus must be present for this action to be manifest. The effect is most striking when estrogen, progestogen, and relaxin are administered simultaneously (38, 84). In the latter instance the uterus need not be present.

C. THE UTERUS: EFFECTS ON THE ENDOMETRIUM AND UNDERLYING STROMA

Progestogens act in conjunction with estrogens on the endometrium of the uterus. Although progestogens may inhibit the overall rise in uterine weight produced by estrogens, an increase in the luminal surface areas occurs as a result of growth of the endometrium. Increased glandular complexity and secretory activity are also observed. Glycogen content (human being) (102, 103), carbonic anhydrase (rabbit, mouse) (50, 60), acid phosphatase and glycoprotein (52) are all elevated during the secretory or luteal phase or after administration of progesterone. The degree of complexity and glandular proliferation of the rabbit endometrium has been used as the basis of several bioassays for progesterone. Similarly, changes in the shape of the nuclei of the stromal cells in the uterus have been utilized as a very sensitive bioassay for progestogens. The test animal used in this instance is the immature or ovariectomized mouse.

The endometrial-stromal complex under progestogen domination may be in a physiological condition optimal for implantation of a blastocyst (4, 14). The adhesive mechanism (12) seems, in part, to be progestogen dependent (11, 28) and is inhibited by estrogen (27). In some mammals (guinea pig, rat, mouse, rabbit, hamster) the uterus reacts rather violently to the implanting embryo or to traumatic mechanical or chemical stimuli. The antimesometrial portion of the uterus is the first to respond in this respect (46). In the pseudopregnant rat, sensitivity of the uterus to trauma is greatest on the fourth day after estrus and thereafter declines rapidly. The response of the rat uterus to traumatic stimuli is by a rapid growth of stromal components to form a structure similar histologically to the maternal portion of the placenta. This structure has been referred to as the "deciduoma," or "placentoma," and is dependent upon the presence of synergizing ratios of estrogens and progestogens (73, 93). The decidual cell reaction reaches maximum growth about the fifth day after traumatization in the rat and declines after about the seventh day (Fig. 3-4). At the point of maximum size

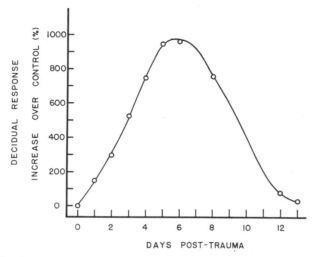

Fig. 3-4. Decidual cell response during pseudopregnancy (rat).

there is observed an increase in glycogen and water content of the uterus. The vaginal smear of the rat, however, continues to show a predominant picture of leukocytes, with a few epithelial cells, for a total of about 18–21 days from the time of last cornification, indicating the presence of corpora lutea which are functional for a period comparable to the length of gestation. Thus, the implantation reaction of the uterus of the rat triggers a response that results in a prolongation of the life-span of the corpus luteum over that observed during normal pseudo-pregnancy. The decidual cell reaction of the rat (and mouse) has been used as a bioassay of progestogens (7).

At the termination of the functional phase of the corpus luteum during a normal cycle, a regression of all those structures that have been built up by progestogen is observed. The endometrium and sub-endometrial stroma involute to a basal state and the cycle begins again. In primates, this regression manifests itself in a sloughing of all that uterine tissue maintained by progestogen and a discharge of this material through the vagina. This period in the primate cycle is termed menstruation.

D. The Uterus: Effects on the Myometrium

Synergizing doses of estrogen and progestogen restore the ability of the uterus of ovariectomized rats to utilize various substrates for energy of contraction (92). The uterus, under progestogen domination, generally exhibits a decreased, arrhythmic, spontaneous motility (71), a contraction pattern during electrical stimulation which is opposite to that of estrogen domination (15, 76), a decreased sensitivity to extracts of the posterior pituitary gland (9, 24, 71, 76, 80, 81), and an altered ionic balance and increased electrical potential across the membrane of the myometrial cell (16, 26, 54). Figure 3-5 illustrates the effect of

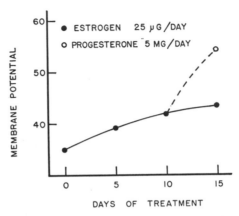

Fig. 3-5. Effect of estradiol and progesterone on the membrane potential of the myometrial cell of the rabbit uterus. Adapted from Csapo (16).

progesterone on the membrane potential of the estrogen-primed myometrium of the rabbit uterus. Progesterone antagonizes the effect of estradiol and relaxin on glycogen, and in turn is partly prevented by these hormones from depressing alkaline phosphatase activity (30, 31). Progestogen increases the lactic dehydrogenase activity of the rat uterus, but restricts the estradiol-induced increase of NADH oxidase (10).

E. THE OVARY AND OVIDUCT

The major effect of progestogen on the ovary is mediated through the action of the hormone on the secretory activity of the anterior pituitary gland. Progestogen in small doses promotes ovulation through its effect on LH release from the pituitary gland. This action is thought to occur during the normal cyclic activity of many mammals, i.e., a preovulatory release of progestogen by the Graafian follicle which promotes release of gonadotropin from the pituitary gland and facilitates ovulation. Progesterone injected into restricted areas of the hypothalamus of the hen also results in ovulation (69). Larger doses of the luteal hormone inhibit the release of pituitary gonadotropins, thus inhibiting ovulation. Thus large doses of progesterone over a prolonged period of time inhibit follicular development and cause atrophy of the ovary (see Chapter 10 for detailed discussion). Progesterone causes a decreased motility of the oviduct and in the chick inhibits the increase in weight of the oviduct caused by estrogen.

F. Psychic Manifestations

The promotion of estrus behavior (mating) has been shown to be under the influence of progestogen as well as estrogen (72, 95, 96). The introduction of progesterone into the lateral ventricle of the brain of the estrone-primed hamster (44), or subcutaneous injection into guinea pigs or mice results in psychic estrus. The response has been suggested for use as a bioassay of progesterone. Progesterone also plays a role in maternal behavior in the rabbit.

G. Mammary Gland

In general, administration of progestogen results in an increase of the lobuloalveolar system of the mammary gland subsequent to preliminary priming with estrogen. In several species, large amounts of progestogen are capable of producing full differentiation in the absence of estrogen priming (78). Relaxin potentiates the effect of the steroids on the lobuloalveolar system. Progestogens may inhibit lactation (in combination with estrogen) (8, 55), perhaps by direct action on the mammary gland.

H. The Maintenance of Gestation

The physiological basis of gestation is founded upon the development and maintenance of an intrauterine environment suitable for implantation and the growth and development of the embryo. Obviously the endocrine requirements for the pregnant animal are different from those in the nonpregnant animal. Hence, changes in rates of secretions of almost all the endocrine glands may occur. These changes affect mineral and carbohydrate metabolism (regulated by the adrenal gland and pancreas), calcium and phosphorus metabolism (ovary and parathyroid glands), general metabolic rate (pituitary gland and thyroid gland), etc. The endocrine glands concerned chiefly with the maintenance of an optimal uterine environment for gestation are the pituitary gland, the ovary, and the placenta. Of primary importance are the secretions of progestogens from the ovary and the placenta.

Progestogens are absolutely essential for the maintenance of pregnancy in all mammals. In many animals (rat, rabbit, mouse) ovariectomy at any time during pregnancy immediately terminates gestation. In other animals it does not, but it has been established that the placenta is a primary source of progesterone in these mammals (monkey, human being). In still other animals (sheep, guinea pig) ovariectomy, if performed during the first half of gestation, results in abortion. During the latter part of pregnancy, the placenta secretes enough hormone to maintain pregnancy. In general, those animals which are primarily monotocous can maintain pregnancy during most of the gestation period in the absence of the ovaries. In polytocous mammals, an ovarian source of progestogen is usually required during the greater portion of pregnancy.

As necessary as the requirement of progestogen for maintenance of pregnancy, is the requirement of small, but effective, levels of estrogen for optimum conditions for pregnancy. Progestogen alone does not seem to be capable of supporting gestation to the same extent as a synergizing combination of the two steroids. Table 3–2 depicts the effects of

TABLE 3–2

THE EFFECT OF ESTRADIOL AND PROGESTERONE ON FETAL SURVIVAL[a]
IN THE RAT OVARIECTOMIZED ON DAY 12 OF GESTATION[b]

Dose of progesterone (mg)	Dose of estradiol				
	0 μg	0.04 μg	0.1 μg	0.2 μg	0.4 μg
0.5	—	—	—	61.3	42.0
1.0	2.6	55.7	69.6	96.6	58.0
2.0	74.1	95.2	90.0	90.0	82.5
3.0	61.7	—	70.6	90.3	92.2

Control, untreated, pregnant rats: 92.8%

[a] Values stated as percentages of fetuses alive on day 20.
[b] From Yochim and Zarrow (94).

various combinations of estradiol and progesterone on the survival of fetuses in the pregnant, ovariectomized rat (94). It will be noted that the effect of progesterone on fetal survival is potentiated as well as inhibited by estrogen. High doses of progestogen may have a masculinizing effect on the fetus (70).

Although the inception, maintenance and termination of pregnancy among mammals is based upon almost identical endocrine mechanisms, the lengths of gestation vary considerably among and within the species. Generally, the longer gestation periods occur in mammals which produce either larger or more mature offspring at birth. Table 3–3 lists the duration of pregnancy in several mammals (41).

TABLE 3–3

DURATION OF GESTATION IN MAMMALS[a]

Animal	Length of pregnancy (days)
Opossum (Marsupial)	12–13
Golden hamster	14–18
Mouse	21
Rat	22
Hedgehog	31
Rabbit	31–33
Giant kangaroo (marsupial)	39
Beaver	42
Fox	60
Guinea pig	62–69
Dog	63
Cat	63
Lion	105–112
Pig	119–130
Lemur	130
Sheep	147–154
Goat	147
Tiger	155
Monkey (*Macaca*)	180
Bear	180–187
Mountain goat	180–187
Hippopotamus	210–240
Chimpanzee	270
Cattle	270
Man	270
Deer	300
Whale	315
Horse	330
Camel	390
Giraffe	420–450
Rhinoceros	540
Elephant	600–630

[a] Adapted from Huettner (41).

I. OTHER EFFECTS OF PROGESTOGENS

Other known effects include (a) inhibition of parturition; (b) inhibition of estrogen-induced tumors; (c) androgenic and antiandrogenic effects (azoospermia); (d) anesthetic effect; (e) corticosteroid-like activity.

The Assay of Progestogens

Many of the tests for progestogens are based on responses of the uterus to the hormone (21). These include: endometrial growth of the rabbit uterus, stromal cell changes of the mouse uterus, decidual cell response of the rat and mouse, increase in carbonic anhydrase of the uterus of the rabbit, and inhibition of the estrogen-induced weight increase of the rat and mouse uterus and chick oviduct. Other tests include: the maintenance of gestation in the rat, mouse, and rabbit and the mating response of suitably primed hamsters and guinea pigs. The end points used for the assays of progestogens are not all specific for the progestogen molecule; they are generally considered to be responses that result from the action of progesterone. Compounds considered to be predominantly androgenic may possess slight progestational activity; these compounds can be rated in terms of "progesterone equivalents" in the same manner that nonsteroidal estrogens can be rated in terms of estradiol or estrone equivalents when assayed against estradiol or estrone. In the course of assaying a new preparation of a progestogen, often a battery of tests is run in which a standard, such as progesterone, is used for comparison. In almost all the assays, estrogen may either synergize or antagonize the effect of the progestogen.

As with the estrogens, the potency of progestogenic preparations is influenced by the vehicle used for administration; the route of administration; factors that affect rates of absorption, metabolism, and excretion; and the sensitivity of the end point used to measure potency. Table 3–4 depicts the effect of vehicle on progestogenic activity using the rat

TABLE 3–4

EFFECT OF PROGESTERONE ON THE DECIDUAL CELL RESPONSE[a] OF THE RAT[b]

Dose (mg)	Oil	Aqueous suspension
0.2	131.1	—
0.5	175.7	—
1.0	379.7	181.1
2.0	476.8	267.6

[a] Measured as uterine weight in milligrams.
[b] From Zarrow et al. (101).

decidual cell response as the assay method (101). Using this response, injection of progesterone in oil seems more effective than injection as an aqueous suspension.

In a similar fashion, the route of administration has an effect on potency. Table 3–5 depicts the relative doses of progesterone necessary to produce comparable reactions using different routes of administration of the hormone. The assay used was a measure of progestational proliferation in the rabbit.

TABLE 3–5

APPROXIMATE RELATIVE DOSES OF PROGESTERONE ADMINISTERED
BY DIFFERENT ROUTES TO PRODUCE COMPARABLE PROGESTATIONAL
PROLIFERATION OF THE RABBIT ENDOMETRIUM

Intrauterine	Subcutaneous	Intramuscular	Oral
1	100	1000	10,000

Changes in the progestogen molecule can seriously affect its potency by affecting the rate of absorption and metabolism of the compound. Thus 17α-hydroxyprogesterone is about 60 times more active than progesterone by the stromal cell hypertrophy assay (74, 100), but relatively inactive by the progestational proliferation assay. Esterification of the molecule to 17α-hydroxyprogesterone 17-n-caproate produces a compound, about 2–5 times as active as progesterone assayed by endometrial proliferation (200 times as active as its nonesterified precursor) (45), which is a long-acting steroid with detectable effects for almost 3 weeks after administration. However, there may be a delay in the onset of activity.

The various assays for progestogens differ in their sensitivity to the hormone. Table 3–6 lists several of the more common bioassays and their respective sensitivities to progesterone.

One of the difficulties involved in assaying the potency of progestational agents is the varying degree in which estrogen is required as a preliminary or auxiliary treatment. The potency of progestogens may therefore be dependent upon whether synergizing or antagonizing ratios of the two hormones are present. Because many of the synthetic progestational steroids are also slightly estrogenic, the inherent estrogenic properties of these molecules may preclude a progestational effect by one assay method which is extremely sensitive to estrogen, but potentiate it by another which is not. Hence, it is difficult to "carry over" from one effect to another; i.e., the fact that a steroid is capable of producing significant endometrial proliferation in the rabbit uterus is no criterion of how it will maintain pregnancy in the same animal. This is not true of the estrogens. (If one estrogen is more potent than another in one respect, it will usually be more potent in many other respects.) Thus,

TABLE 3–6

SENSITIVITY OF VARIOUS BIOASSAYS FOR PROGESTERONE

Test animal	Route of administration of hormone	End point measured[a]	Progesterone (*total* threshold dose)	Reference
Rat	Subcutaneous	Decidual response	2.0 mg	(101)
Mouse	Subcutaneous	Decidual response	1.6 mg	(101)
Rabbit	Subcutaneous	Endometrial proliferation	0.5 mg	(75)
Rabbit	Intrauterine	Endometrial proliferation	0.5 μg	(75)
Mouse	Intrauterine	Stromal cell hypertrophy	0.0002 μg	(101)
Rabbit	Subcutaneous	Carbonic anhydrase (M)	0.125 mg	(61)
Rabbit	Subcutaneous	Carbonic anhydrase (C)	0.5 mg	
Rat	Subcutaneous	Inhibition of uterine weight	1.5 mg	(85)
Chick	Intramuscular	Inhibition of oviduct weight	1.4 mg	(101)
Mouse	Subcutaneous	Inhibition of uterine weight	1.5 mg	(18)
Hamster	Lateral ventricle of brain	Sex receptivity	0.025 mg	(44)
Guinea pig	Subcutaneous	Sex receptivity	0.05 mg	(36)

[a] (M) manometric determination; (C) colorimetric determination.

the bioassay of progestogens is complicated by the fact that the biological reactions involved are sensitive to estrogen:progestogen ratios. All the responses listed in Table 3–6 either require a preliminary or auxiliary treatment with estrogen or are extremely sensitive to the presence of this hormone. The progestogenic potency of several steroids is roughly compared, in Table 3–7, to that of progesterone or norprogesterone administered by different methods.

Several chemical and physicochemical tests for progesterone have been devised, but these have the following disadvantages; they are usually tedious, require a high degree of sample purity, may not be entirely specific, and may require relatively large amounts of starting material. One of the earliest chemical tests for progesterone involves the determination of its metabolite, pregnanediol glucuronide, in the urine. The determination is made either gravimetrically or colorimetrically after preliminary hydrolysis, extraction, and filtration of the extract from urine (25, 79, 83, 87, 90). The gravimetric technique requires about 5 mg pregnanediol per urine sample, and the colorimetric procedure is sensitive to 0.5 mg per 24-hour sample.

Spectrophotometric estimations of progesterone may be accomplished by measuring the absorption (at 240 mμ) of highly purified extracts. Extraction of progesterone is made with organic solvents after hydrolysis, and the material is purified usually by a combination of countercurrent distribution methods and chromatography (63). These methods can easily measure 8–9 μg per milliliter of extract.

TABLE 3–7

Compounds That Exhibit Progestational Activity

Compound[a]	Activity[b]			Test of activity
	Intra-uterine	Subcutaneous	Oral	
PROGESTERONE	100	100	(5)	STANDARDS
19-NORPROGESTERONE	(30–100)	(1000)	100	
11β-Hydroxyprogesterone	1.5	—	—	Stromal cell response, mouse
	—	1	—	Endometrial proliferation, rabbit
9α-Fluoro-11β-hydroxy-progesterone	—	5–10	—	Endometrial proliferation, rabbit
11-Dehydroprogesterone	—	200	—	Endometrial proliferation, rabbit
	—	200	—	Decidual response, rat
	—	250	—	Oviduct inhibition, chick
	100	—	—	Stromal cell response, mouse
17α-Hydroxyprogesterone	<1	<1	—	Endometrial proliferation, rabbit
	—	<2	—	Decidual response, rat
	—	<4	—	Decidual response, mouse
	—	15	—	Oviduct inhibition, chick
	6000	—	—	Stromal cell response, mouse
17α-Hydroxyprogesterone caproate (Delalutin)	—	200–500	—	Endometrial proliferation, rabbit
	—	2	—	Decidual response, rat
	—	<4	—	Decidual response, mouse
	—	8	—	Oviduct inhibition, chick
	—	<2	—	Pregnancy maintenance, rat
	—	125	—	Pregnancy maintenance, rabbit
17α-Hydroxyprogesterone acetate	—	500	10–20	Endometrial proliferation, rabbit
(17α-acetoxypro-gesterone; Prodox)	—	<1	—	Pregnancy maintenance, rat

TABLE 3–7 (*Continued*)

Compound[a]	Activity[b]			Test of activity
	Intra-uterine	Subcutaneous	Oral	
6α-Methyl-17α-hydroxy progesterone acetate (medroxyprogesterone acetate; Provera)	—	2000–5000	1000	Endometrial proliferation, rabbit
	—	2000	—	Pregnancy maintenance, rat
	—	400–500	—	Pregnancy maintenance, rabbit
Δ^4-3-Ketopregnen-20α-ol	—	30–50	—	Endometrial proliferation, rabbit
	20	—	—	Stromal cell response, mouse
Δ^4-3-Ketopregnen-20β-ol	—	10–20	—	Endometrial proliferation, rabbit
	200	—	—	Stromal cell response, mouse
17α-Ethynyltestosterone (Pregneninolone; ethisterone; anhydro-hydroxyprogesterone; Pranone)	—	10	5–50	Endometrial proliferation, rabbit
	—	<4	—	Pregnancy maintenance, rat
	<1	—	—	Stromal cell response, mouse
17α-Ethynyl-19-nor-testosterone (norethindrone; Norlutin)	<1	50–1000	100	Endometrial proliferation, rabbit
	—	70	—	Decidual response, rat
	—	<50	—	Decidual response, mouse
	—	1500	—	Oviduct inhibition, chick
	—	0	—	Pregnancy maintenance, rat, rabbit
17α-Ethynyl-$\Delta^{5,10}$-estrenolone (norethynodrel; Enovid)	<1	0–25	25	Endometrial proliferation, rabbit
	—	0	0	Pregnancy maintenance, rat, rabbit
17α-ethyl-19-nortestosterone (Nilevar)	25	500–1000	250	Endometrial proliferation, rabbit
	—	40	—	Decidual response, rat
	—	180	—	Decidual response, mouse

TABLE 3–7 (*Continued*)

Compound[a]	Activity[b]			Test of activity
	Intra-uterine	Subcutaneous	Oral	
17α-Ethyl-19-nortestosterone (Nilevar)	—	180	—	Oviduct inhibition, chick
	—	70	0	Pregnancy maintenance, rabbit
	—	200	—	Pregnancy maintenance, rat
17-(1-Methallyl)-19-nortestosterone	—	100	—	Pregnancy maintenance, rabbit
	1000	500	100	Endometrial proliferation, rabbit
17-(2-Methallyl)-19-nortestosterone	—	2500	—	Endometrial proliferation, rabbit
	—	100–200	100	Pregnancy maintenance, rat
	—	100	—	Pregnancy maintenance, rabbit

[a] Names in parentheses: synonyms, trivial names, or clinical preparations that contain these substances.

[b] Comparisons should be made against progesterone for the "Intrauterine" and "Subcutaneous" columns, and against norprogesterone for the "oral" column for similar tests of activity only.

Analysis of small samples of blood which contain progesterone can be made by polarographic methods after the Girard ketone derivative of the hormone has been obtained by column partition chromatography (13). The sensitivity of these methods is about 0.1 μg/ml using plasma volumes of 2 ml.

Table 3–8 depicts the concentrations of progesterone and pregnanediol obtained from the human female and estimated by various chemical methods.

Biogenesis, Metabolism, and Mechanism of Action

Progesterone may be synthesized *in vivo* from a degradation of cholesterol according to the steps outlined in Fig. 3-6. The compound is converted by the liver (and kidney) to various metabolites which may be recovered from feces or urine, depending on the species. It has been calculated (64) that the turnover time (the time needed to replace the total blood pool) for progesterone in the human being is about 3

TABLE 3–8

CONCENTRATION OF PROGESTERONE AND PREGNANEDIOL IN THE HUMAN FEMALE

	Progesterone	Pregnanediol
Follicular phase, menstrual cycle	(from follicles of of ovary) (98)	(urine) (25, 89)
Day 1	—	0.5 mg
5	0	0.3 mg
10	0	0.1 mg
12	2–3 μg	—
13	60 μg	—
14 (ovulation)	50 μg	—
Luteal phase, menstrual cycle	(from corpora lutea) (98)	(urine) (25)
Day 15	—	1.0 mg
16	25 μg	—
20	60 μg	2–3 mg
22	80 μg	—
25	40 μg	2–3 mg
29 (1)	6–8 μg	0.5 mg
Gestation	(from placenta) (47)	(urine/24 hrs.) (88)
80 days	50 μg	10 mg
160	100 μg	25 mg
200	300 μg	55 mg
240	500 μg	75 mg
270	800 μg	85 mg
Placental blood, term (66)	0.4 μg/ml	—
Peripheral blood, postparturient (13, 63)	0.1 μg/ml	—
Umbilical blood (13)	0–1.3 μg/ml	—
Placenta (17, 59, 65)	1–1.5 mg/kg	—

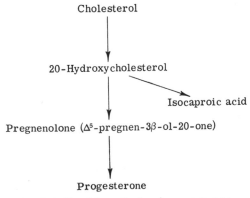

Cholesterol

↓

20-Hydroxycholesterol   → Isocaproic acid

↓

Pregnenolone (Δ^5-pregnen-3β-ol-20-one)

↓

Progesterone

Fig. 3-6. The biosynthesis of progesterone.

minutes during the latter part of pregnancy. Thus, synthesis, metabolism, and inactivation of circulating progesterone occurs very rapidly. Some of the active hormone is taken up by fatty tissue, which tends to delay reabsorption into blood and subsequent metabolism and excretion. In contrast to the relatively high rate of production of large amounts of progesterone, is the relatively small amount usually found in target tissues, an observation indicating that small concentrations of the hormone near the target cells may be sufficient for activity.

Evidence is being accumulated to suggest that the uterus may govern the synthesis of progesterone by luteal tissue (20). *In vitro* studies indicate that when luteal tissue is incubated with endometrial cells from a uterus in the early secretory phase, a significant increase in progesterone synthesis is observed. This effect is not observed when gonadotropins (pregnant mare serum, human chorionic gonadotropin, luteotropin), oxytocin, or pituitary homogenates are incubated with luteal tissue. Extracts prepared from uterine tissue in the late diestrual phase (sow) inhibit progesterone synthesis. Conversely, hysterectomy during the latter part of the progestational phase of the cycle tends to prolong the functional activity of the corpus luteum in the rat, sow, guinea pig, rabbit, cow, and sheep.

The metabolism of progesterone has been studied extensively in the human being. The most abundant metabolites found in the urine are pregnane-3α,20α-diol (pregnanediol), pregnan-3α-ol-20-one (pregnanolone), and allopregnanediol. Metabolites with a 3α-hydroxy group (such as pregnanediol) are excreted mainly as glucuronides, conjugation occurring in the liver. Figure 3-7 depicts the probable relationship between progesterone and some of its 3α-hydroxy metabolites in the human being (97). In the rat, the main excretory pattern is through the fecal material.

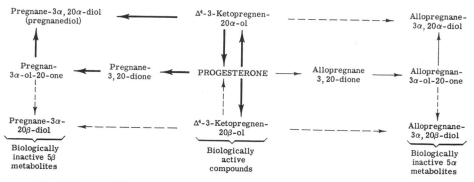

Fig. 3-7. Probable metabolic pathway of progesterone in the human being (97).
→, major path in human being; ----→, hypothetical; →, proved *in vivo* and *in vitro*.

The mechanism of action of progesterone is obscure. Because the hormone (and other related steroids) are reduced by enzymes that require the nicotinamide adenine nucleotides, it has been thought that progesterone may act by stimulating reactions requiring these cofactors. However, there seems as yet to be no relation between endocrine activity and the above-mentioned observations.

The effects of progesterone on the excitability of the myometrium may be related to its ability to increase the membrane potential by altering the environmental ionic concentrations at the cell membrane. These changes may, in part, explain the relative membrane stability and suppression of contractile activity observed in the progestogen-dominated uterus.

EXPERIMENT 3–1

The Induction of Pseudopregnancy*

Although the corpus luteum of the rat may initially secrete some progesterone, it does not maintain a functional existence for any appreciable length of time during the normal estrous cycle. However, during the period of estrus, and to some extent during diestrus, stimuli applied to the uterine cervix can elicit a response in the animal that enables the corpus luteum to maintain a functional existence for periods up to 2 weeks. A typical progestational state, characterized by a quiescent uterus and a vaginal smear containing leukocytes, mucus, and perhaps a few nucleated epithelial cells, is observed. This progestational or pseudopregnant reaction can be completely inhibited by administration of ether or barbiturate anesthesia prior to stimulation of the cervix, or by pelvic nerve neurectomy, an indication that the mediation of the response is by neurohumoral mechanisms.

Procedure and Experimental

1. Stimulate the uterine cervix of a rat in estrus with a thin glass rod (2–3 mm in diameter) by manually introducing the rod into the vagina and tapping the cervix gently but rapidly. (A thin metal rod, 2–3 mm in diameter, inserted into an electric vibrator tool is an excellent means of effecting cervical stimulation.) The typical response noted is a severe lordosis, accompanied usually by tremors of the abdomen and mild squeaking. Pseudopregnancy may also be obtained by mating the animal to a vasectomized male or by applying an electrical stimulus of 5 volts to the uterine cervix. The latter method is used very commonly.

* Cf. references (29, 42, 49, 91).

2. Observe vaginal smears daily until the return of a normal estrous cycle.

3. Determine the length of pseudopregnancy as the number of days from the first day of metestrus observed after cervical stimulation to the first day of vaginal cornification after cervical stimulation.

4. Anesthetize a rat in estrus with ether and stimulate the uterine cervix. Determine whether pseudopregnancy can be induced under these conditions.

5. Anesthetize a rat in estrus with Nembutal (25 mg per kilogram body weight) administered intraperitoneally. Stimulate the uterine cervix of the rat as above after anesthesia has developed and determine whether pseudopregnancy has occurred.

EXPERIMENT 3–2

The Decidual Cell Reaction*

It has been recognized since the original experiments of Loeb (1908) (48) that a functional corpus luteum is essential for the development of the maternal portion of the placenta. During the fourth day of pseudopregnancy in the rat, the endometrium of the uterus is sensitive to mechanical and chemical stimuli and will respond by producing a growth similar in appearance to the maternal placenta. This reaction is dependent upon synergizing levels of estrogen and progestogen from the ovary. The growth reaches maximal size by the ninth or tenth day of pseudopregnancy (Fig. 3-4), 5–6 days after uterine traumatization.

Procedure

Pseudopregnancy

1. Stimulate the uterine cervices of rats (200–250 gm body weight) in estrus with a glass rod or by electric shock as described in Experiment 3-1. Day 1 of pseudopregnancy is designated as the first day that the vaginal smear contains predominantly leukocytes. Discard all animals showing proestrous smears on day 4.

2. All animals are traumatized during the afternoon† on the days designated below, and killed 5 days after traumatization.

---

* Cf. references (16a, 22, 46, 48, 78, 86, 93).

† Using a standard diurnal photoperiod of 10 hours of darkness and 14 hours of daylight, optimal time of traumatization is on day 4 of pseudopregnancy, 6–10 hours after the lights are turned on.

3. Uteri are dissected out and stretched to a standard length (5 cm); the diameter is measured.

4. Each uterine horn is weighed separately on a torsion balance to the nearest 0.1 mg.

Mechanical Traumatization with a Burred Needle (Fig. 3-8)

1. The rat is anesthetized with ether and a longitudinal incision 3 cm in length is made on the ventral surface of the lower abdomen.

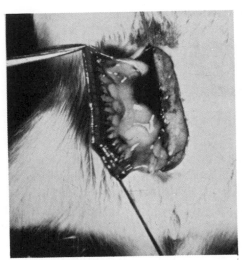 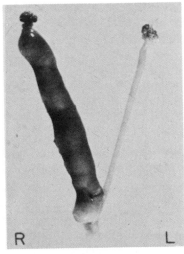

Fig. 3-8. *Left:* Method of mechanical traumatization. From DeFeo (16a).
Right: Deciduoma in right horn (R) of the uterus of a rat on the ninth day of pseudopregnancy. Left horn (L), control. From Yochim and DeFeo (93).

2. One uterine horn is exposed, and a small incision is made with a fine scissors just above the uterine-cervical junction.

3. A blunt needle with a burr at the tip is inserted into the uterine lumen at this point and carefully extended up to the tubal end of the uterus.

4. While grasping the tubal end of the uterus with a fine forceps, gently withdraw the needle, ensuring that the burr is against the anti-mesometrial surface all along the length of the horn. This can be done by pulling gently on the horn with the needle as it is withdrawn.

5. Replace the uterus in the abdominal cavity, take several sutures in the muscle wall (close enough so that the intestine is not eviscerated), and close the skin incision with sutures or wound clips. The other horn of the uterus is used as a control. It must not be touched during the operation.

Similar results may be obtained by looping a thread through the uterine lumen several times and tying it loosely on the outside of the uterine horn. However, the completeness of traumatization in this case will depend upon how many loops are made along the length of the uterus.

Chemical Traumatization

Histamine dihydrochloride, 1.0 mg in 0.1 ml saline, may be injected into the uterus via the tubal end. The operation is carried out using the same procedure as for ovariectomy.

Experimental

1. Using the above procedures, the following experiments are to be performed:

Group I: cervical stimulation during estrus:

    3 rats: needle trauma day 3 of pseudopregnancy
    3 rats: needle trauma day 4 of pseudopregnancy
    3 rats: needle trauma day 5 of pseudopregnancy
    2 rats: needle trauma day 4 of pseudopregnancy; ovariectomy day 4
       of pseudopregnancy

Group II: cervical stimulation during estrus:

    2 rats: histamine injection day 4 of pseudopregnancy
    2 rats: thread loops day 4 of pseudopregnancy
    2 rats: needle trauma day 4 of pseudopregnancy; follow vaginal smears
       until first day of cornification, then autopsy

2. Compare the weights of uteri traumatized on days 3, 4, and 5 of pseudopregnancy, and on day 4 by different methods of traumatization. Express results as per cent increase of traumatized horn over control horn. Compare the lengths of pseudopregnancy in traumatized animals with those in Experiment 3–1.

EXPERIMENT 3–3

Assay of Progesterone by the Decidual Cell Response*

The decidual cell response in the rat (and mouse) has been used as an assay for progestogen. The assay is extremely sensitive to estrogens. For this reason, assay of progestogens with inherent estrogenic activity may tend to obscure results. The assay may be performed in several ways: either with castrated rats primed with estrone, or with animals in

* Cf. references (7, 37, 93, 101).

estrus, ovariectomized on the day of traumatization. Various end points have been measured; a subjective grading of the magnitude of the response; a measurement of the diameter of the uterine horn after stretching it to a standard length; or a measurement of the increase in weight of the traumatized horn compared with a nontraumatized control horn.

Procedure and Experimental

A. Assay Using Ovariectomized Rats

1. Rats should be ovariectomized for 1 week and then injected subcutaneously as follows: 1 μg estrone per day for 5 days; x mg progesterone per day for 9 days.

2. On the 5th day of progesterone treatment, the animals are laparotomized, and one uterine horn is exposed for needle traumatization as described in Experiment 3–2.

3. The incision is closed and the animals are treated with progesterone for 4 more days.

4. Kill 24 hours after the last injection. Remove the uterine horns, clean off adhering fat, blot on moist filter paper, and weigh separately on a torsion balance to the nearest 0.1 mg. The data are expressed as the percentage increase in weight of traumatized horn over control horn:

$$\frac{\text{weight trauma horn} - \text{weight control horn}}{\text{weight control horn}} \times 100$$

B. Assay Using Rats in Estrus

1. Rats whose vaginal smears show cornified cells are made pseudopregnant by stimulating the uterine cervices by one of the methods described in Experiment 3–1. The first day of *metestrus* is designated as day 1 of pseudopregnancy.

2. On day 4 of pseudopregnancy, unilateral traumatization of the uterus is effected by the method described under Section A of this experiment.

3. At this time, bilateral ovariectomy is performed; the animals are injected daily with progesterone through day 8 of pseudopregnancy.

4. The animals are killed on day 9 (24 hours after the last injection of progesterone), and the uteri are dissected free and weighed as described in Section A of this experiment.*

* These experiments may be shortened by injecting the progestogen for 3 days after traumatization and killing on day 4. However, a proportionate decrease in the magnitude of response will be observed.

Develop a standard dose-response curve by injecting into each rat (5 rats per group) the following daily doses of progesterone:

Group   I: 0.0 mg
Group   II: 0.25 mg
Group   III: 0.5 mg
Group   IV: 1.0 mg
Group   V: 2.0 mg
Group   VI: 4.0 mg

C. Effect of Estrogen on Progesterone-Maintained Deciduomata

Rats prepared as in Section B of this experiment are injected in the following manner from day 4 through day 8 of pseudopregnancy:

Group   I: 0.1 μg estrone, 2.0 mg progesterone
Group   II: 0.2 μg estrone, 2.0 mg progesterone
Group   III: 0.5 μg estrone, 2.0 mg progesterone
Group   IV: 1.0 μg estrone, 2.0 mg progesterone
Group   V: 2.0 μg estrone, 2.0 mg progesterone
Group   VI: 10.0 μg estrone, 2.0 mg progesterone

In this experiment, the animals may be bilaterally traumatized. Express results as milligrams uterine weight. Figure 3-9 shows a typical graph of the results.

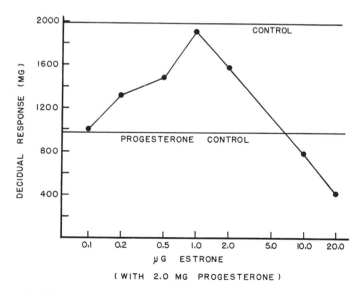

Fig. 3-9. Effect of estrone on progesterone-maintained deciduomata. From Yochim and DeFeo (93).

Compare the effects obtained using combinations of estrogen and progesterone with those obtained using progesterone alone.

EXPERIMENT 3-4

The Assay of Progesterone by Measures of Endometrial Proliferation*

The rabbit is the standard assay animal used in these experiments because the change in the complexity of the endometrium after progesterone administration is very marked. Immature or ovariectomized rabbits of the Dutch-Belted or New Zealand White strain are often used. This response is also sensitive to estrogens as is noted in the decidual cell response. Grading of the results is accomplished by comparing histological sections of the uterus subjectively on the basis of degree of endometrial complexity, or by determining the ratio of areas of the glandularis to the total mucosa of the uterus (G:M ratio).

Procedure

Immature, or ovariectomized female rabbits (1–1.5 kg) are injected subcutaneously for 6 days with 5.0 μg estradiol per day. The test compound may be administered orally or by subcutaneous or intramuscular injection, or by intrauterine injection, as follows:

A. Oral, Subcutaneous, or Intramuscular Injection

1. Administer the compound daily for 5 days after the priming with estradiol (total time of treatment, 11 days).

2. Animals are killed on day 12, at 24 hours after the last progestogen treatment. The uteri are removed, fixed in Bouin's solution, sectioned at 6 μ, and stained with hematoxylin and eosin for grading.

3. If the rabbits are killed by breaking the neck and cutting the carotid arteries to exsanguinate the carcass, some of the tissue may be used for carbonic anhydrase determination by the method of Experiment 3–6. Daily dosages of progesterone to establish a standard scale for the subcutaneous and intramuscular technique are: 0.025 mg, 0.05 mg, 0.1 mg, 0.2 mg, 0.4 mg.

B. Intrauterine Technique

1. After the estradiol priming, the animal is anesthetized on the seventh day, the abdomen is opened, and a uterine horn is exposed.

* Cf. references (51, 53, 68).

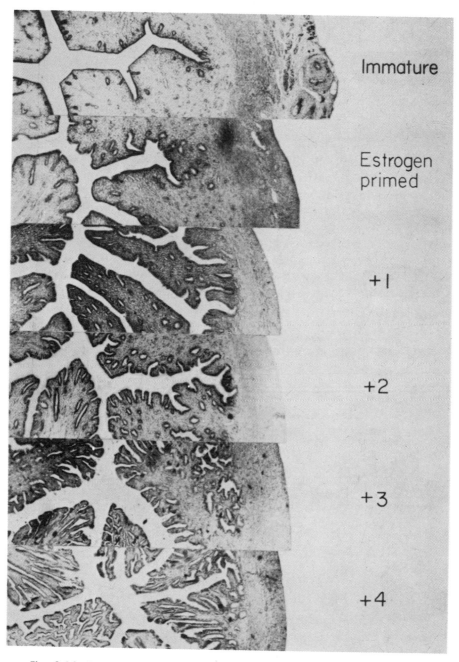

Fig. 3-10. Progestational proliferation of the uterus of the rabbit graded by the method of McPhail.

2. Two ligatures are placed around a segment of the uterus 3–4 cm long, leaving the major blood vessels outside the ties.

3. The upper ligature is tied tightly, the lower one is left loose.

4. Cut the uterine horn below the second ligature and inject the test compound (or progesterone)in 0.1 ml oil into the segment with a tuberculin syringe and blunted needle.

5. As the hormone is injected, the ligature is tightened and held tight so that the needle can be withdrawn without loss of fluid. Secure the second ligature and close the abdomen.

6. Animals are killed 72 hours after the injection. Histological preparations are made as above. Dosages of progesterone necessary to establish a standard scale are: 0.5 μg, 1.0 μg, 2.0 μg, 4.0 μg.

The responses may be graded in a fashion similar to that depicted in Fig. 3-10. As the grading is highly subjective, variations are likely to occur between different laboratories. Grading by the method of G:M ratio involves measuring the projected images of the areas of the glandular (G) portion and the total endometrial-stromal mucosa (M) of uterine sections with a planimeter, and dividing the former measurement by the latter.

EXPERIMENT 3–5

The Assay of Progestogens by Stromal Cell Hypertrophy of the Mouse Uterus*

This is a bioassay for minute amounts of progestogen and as such has been found useful for estimating progestogen content of small samples of tissues and blood. It is specific for only three or four progestogens: progesterone, Δ^4-3-ketopregnen-20α-ol and its 20β-ol isomer, 17α-hydroxyprogesterone, 11-dehydroprogesterone, and perhaps a few others. Quantitative grading is difficult. The minimal effective dose has been described as the least amount of hormone which will induce a positive response in the stromal nuclei of the uterus. To be graded positive, the stromal nucleus must be smooth and ovoid in outline, enlarged, slightly elongated, with fine and even chromatin particles and a conspicuous nucleolus. All these conditions must be met. By contrast, the negative response depicts nuclei that are shrunken, fusiform in appearance, with clumped chromatin and no recognizable nucleolus (Fig. 3-12).

* Cf. references (39, 40, 100).

Procedure

1. A highly inbred strain of mice (e.g., CHI strain of Strong, Purdue Swiss) should be used.

2. Animals are ovariectomized and rested at least 16 days. The assay is performed by administering, by intrauterine injection, progesterone or the test substance while the animal is under anesthesia.

3. Animals are killed 48 hours after the injection, and the uteri are removed and fixed in Landowsky's fluid.

4. Paraffin sections are cut 6 μ thick and stained with hematoxylin and eosin for grading.

Technique of Intrauterine Injection

1. A microliter syringe is affixed to a micrometer caliper as shown in Fig. 3-11. Graduations on the syringe should be checked by calibrating

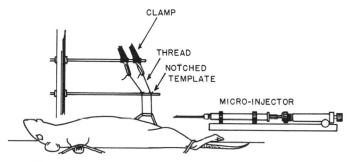

Fig. 3-11. Technique of microinjection in mouse uterus.

with the micrometer caliper. This may be done by extruding mercury from the syringe with the caliper and weighing the mercury. If the syringe is inaccurate, calibrate directly with the caliper, disregarding the syringe calibrations.

2. Anesthetize the mouse with Nembutal and ether. Expose one uterine horn through a midventral incision.

3. Anchor the horn by passing a needle under it through the meso-metrium to keep it from being retracted back into the body.

4. One tight ligature is placed near the tubal end of the horn (leaving the major blood vessels free). A second thread is loosely placed with an overhand knot 5 mm caudal to the first.

5. The ends of both threads are passed through a template with notches 5.0 mm apart and secured with small clamps. (The template is

clamped on a stand and lies 1.5 cm above the animal in such a manner that the threads are held vertically and tightly.) The uterus should now be suspended in a horizontal position by two vertical threads, one 5.0 mm caudal to the other.

6. Ensure that the syringe needle is filled with fluid. Grasp the uterus with fine forceps about 2 mm caudal to the posterior ligature and insert the needle (bevel up) into the uterine lumen immediately cranial to the forceps.

7. Extend the needle forward almost to the anterior ligature. Inject 0.0006 ml of fluid into the lumen.

8. As the needle is withdrawn, tension is put on the caudal thread to make a sharp angle in the horn when the needle is removed. The tension is maintained until the caudal knot is drawn tight.

9. After the threads have been cut, the second horn is similarly injected, if desired.

The minimum effective dose of progesterone depends upon the time of autopsy:

(a) 6 hours after injection: 0.0008 μg
(b) 24 hours after injection: 0.0004 μg
(c) 48 hours after injection: 0.0002 μg

The assay is commonly run for 48 hours.

Determine the threshold dose to produce a positive response (Fig. 3-12) using the following dosages of progesterone (threshold dose of progesterone varies with the strain of mice used):

(a) 6 mice: 0.0001 μg/0.0006 ml
(b) 6 mice: 0.0002 μg/0.0006 ml
(c) 6 mice: 0.0004 μg/0.0006 ml
(d) 6 mice: 0.0006 μg/0.0006 ml

EXPERIMENT 3–6

Assay of Progesterone by Estimation of Carbonic Anhydrase of the Uterus*

It has been demonstrated that the carbonic anhydrase concentration of the rabbit uterus is hormone dependent. Several methods for the assay of progesterone have been developed; they are based upon the estimation of carbonic anhydrase in suitably primed rabbits. These methods include a colorimetric assay in which the rapidity of a pH change in solutions containing the enzyme are compared to a standard curve, and

* Cf. references (60, 61, 67).

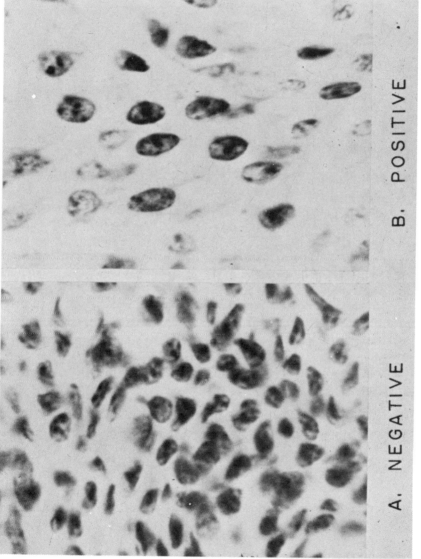

A. NEGATIVE   B. POSITIVE

Fig. 3-12. The stromal cell hypertrophy reaction. From Hooker and Forbes (39). (A) negative, (B) positive.

a manometric procedure which measures the evolution of carbon dioxide from a reaction mixture after a standard time.

Procedure

Reagents

1. *0.1 M phosphate buffer* (300 ml of 0.1 M Na_2HPO_4 + 200 ml of 0.1 M KH_2PO_4)
2. *0.1 M NaHCO₃*
3. *Standard carbonic anhydrase preparation,*[*] or tissue extract

Technique of the Manometric Assay

1. Warburg flasks (15 ml capacity) are used. These flasks are modified to have a side arm but no center well. A magnetic stirrer is positioned to turn two stirring bars, one in the reaction flask and the other in an ice-water bath.

2. Into the main compartment of the Warburg flask add 2.0 ml of the phosphate buffer. Add to this 0.2 ml of the carbonic anhydrase solution or tissue extracts.

3. Into the side arm add 1.0 ml of the bicarbonate solution.

4. The flasks are then placed in the ice bath and the stirrer is engaged at moderate speed.

5. After equilibrium is established, empty the contents of the side arm of the flask into the main chamber, set the stirrer at high speed.

6. Determine the volume of CO_2 evolved after exactly 2 minutes. The change in pressure of CO_2 within the closed system is corrected for changes in the thermobarometer. In order to maintain a constant rate of stirring during the 2-minute period, a voltage stabilizer may be necessary.

Relation of CO_2 Output to Carbonic Anhydrase

1. Using the following aqueous solutions of standard carbonic anhydrase (in Enzyme Units, EU, per 0.2 ml of solution), determine the CO_2 evolution after the reaction has proceeded for 2 minutes:

Solution 1:	0.25 EU
Solution 2:	0.50 EU
Solution 3:	1.0 EU
Solution 4:	2.0 EU

2. Establish a standard curve, plotting concentration of carbonic anhydrase against microliters CO_2. Determine the slope of the line (see below).

[*] K & K Laboratories, Inc., Jamaica, New York.

$$y = a + bx$$

where y = ordinate = microliters of CO_2; x = abscissa = EU; a = y-intercept of curve; b = slope of line.

Relation of Carbonic Anhydrase to Progesterone Dosage

1. To establish the standard progesterone curve, immature rabbits are primed with estradiol much as they are for the assay of progesterone by endometrial proliferation (Experiment 3–4). Progesterone is injected subcutaneously for 5 days in the concentrations stated in Table 3–9.

TABLE 3–9

DOSE-RESPONSE RELATION BETWEEN PROGESTERONE
AND CARBONIC ANHYDRASE CONCENTRATION[a]

Progesterone		Enzyme units of carbonic anhydrase per gram tissue
Daily dose (mg)	Total dose (5 days) (mg)	
0.00	0.00	157.8
0.025	0.125	314.1
0.05	0.25	476.2
0.10	0.50	726.2
0.20	1.00	952.6
0.40	2.00	1078.5
0.80	4.00	1130.3

[a] From Ogawa and Pincus (61).

2. At 24 hours after the last injection the animals are killed by breaking the neck and cutting the carotid arteries to exsanguinate as completely as possible.

3. The uterus is quickly isolated, weighed, and rinsed in cold saline solution. (The tissue may be stored, frozen, in the refrigerator for several days without loss of activity.)

4. Split the uterus longitudinally, dissect out the endometrium and grind it with a tenfold volume of distilled water in a TenBroeck homogenizer. This procedure should be carried out in an ice-water bath.

5. Transfer the homogenate to 15-ml graduated centrifuge tubes and centrifuge at 1500 rpm for 15 minutes. Record the volumes of fluid, decant, and use the supernatant liquid for determination of enzyme activity by the method described above.

6. Plot a standard curve of total dose, progesterone vs. Enzyme Units per gram tissue. [Using the mathematical expression for the slope of the curve obtained in Step 2 of preceding section, translate CO_2 evolution of

the progesterone curve into Enzyme Units; $x = (y\text{-}a)/b$; plot against dose of progesterone.]

Experimental

1. Determine the carbonic anhydrase levels of the uterus of rabbit during pseudopregnancy and in the castrated or immature rabbit pretreated with estrogen and various concentrations of progesterone.

2. Determine the progestogenic potency of an unknown sample by the carbonic anhydrase method.

EXPERIMENT 3–7

Effects of Estrogen and Progesterone on the Maintenance of Gestation*

Unlike the case in the human being and other primates, the presence of the ovaries is essential throughout gestation in many mammals. This has been found to be true in the rat, mouse, ground squirrel, and rabbit, for example. The rat, mouse, and rabbit are ideal animals for the study of the effects of the ovarian hormones on pregnancy and fetal survival.

Procedure and Experimental

Two adult male rats (each 250–500 gm weight) are placed in a cage containing 10 female rats (each 180–250 gm weight) at 6:00 PM and removed from the cage the following morning at 8:00 AM. Vaginal smears taken of each rat at this time are to be observed under the microscope for the presence of spermatozoa. Pregnancy is dated as "day 0" the morning that spermatozoa are found.

Five groups of rats thus inseminated are to be treated as follows:

Group   I: Autopsy at parturition. Record increase in maternal weight daily. Record total number of fetuses, number of live fetuses, fetal weights, and number of sites of implantation in the uterus.

Group II: Ovariectomize on day 11 of gestation and inject 0.1 μg estradiol twice daily (8:00 AM and 8:00 PM). Autopsy on day 19 and record the total number of fetuses, number of live fetuses, number of implantation sites, and fetal weights. Record maternal weight daily.

Group III: Ovariectomize on day 11 of gestation and inject 0.5 mg progesterone twice daily (8:00 AM and 8:00 PM). Autopsy on day 19 and record as above.

Group IV: Ovariectomize on day 11 of gestation and inject 0.5 mg proges-

* Cf. references (2, 35, 47, 58, 94).

terone and 0.1 μg estradiol twice daily (8:00 AM and 8:00 PM).
Autopsy on day 19 and record as above.

Group V: Control group. Autopsy normal pregnant rats on day 19 of gestation and record as above.

Express fetal survival as per cent survival of litters:

$$\frac{\text{No. live fetuses}}{\text{No. implantation sites}} \times 100$$

EXPERIMENT 3–8

Extraction and Estimation of Pregnanediol from Urine*

The following procedure for the extraction and estimation of pregnanediol from urine is a colorimetric method capable of accurately measuring more than 0.4 mg of material in a fifth of a 24-hour sample of human urine. Thus it is applicable for determinations of pregnanediol content during the menstrual cycle as well as during pregnancy.

Procedure and Experimental

A 24-hour specimen of urine collected with 5 ml toluene as preservative is made up to 2500 ml, and duplicate 500-ml samples are removed. Each sample is treated as follows:

1. Place sample in a 1000-ml flask and after the addition of 100 ml of toluene, bring to a boil in a reflux condenser. Add down the condenser to the boiling mixture 50 ml of concentrated HCl and continue the boiling for exactly 10 minutes.

2. The flask is rapidly cooled in cold water and the contents are transferred to a separatory funnel of 750-ml capacity. After shaking and allowing the urine layer to separate, the urine layer is run off into the original flask and the layer of toluene and emulsion is filtered with gentle suction through a Whatman no. 1 paper on a Büchner filter funnel. The urine layer is then returned to the separatory funnel and extracted twice more with 100-ml portions of toluene, each toluene and emulsion layer being filtered in succession through the same filter funnel.

3. The combined filtrates are then transferred to a clean separatory funnel; after the small urine layer that separates out has been run off, the toluene extract is washed twice with 100-ml portions of N NaOH and twice with 100-ml portions of water. The washed toluene extract is run into a 500-ml round-bottom flask and is evaporated to dryness over a steam bath under a fume hood.

* Cf. reference (79).

4. The dry residue is transferred quantitatively with warm ethanol to a 20-ml conical centrifuge tube, and the ethanolic solution is evaporated to dryness in a water bath under a stream of air.

5. To the residue in the tube add exactly 4.0 ml of ethanol; place tube in a beaker of water maintained at 75°C. After stirring with a glass rod for 1 minute to obtain complete solution, 16.0 ml of $0.1 N$ NaOH is added dropwise from a burette during a 3-minute period with stirring, the last 1 ml being used to wash down the stirring rod into the tube.

6. After a further 1 minute at 75°C, the beaker of water containing the tube is transferred to an incubator at 37°C and left overnight. Approximately 8–10 mg of Hyflo-Super Cel (Johns-Manville Co., Ltd.) is added, and the mixture is stirred with a glass rod. The rod is washed down into the tube with 1 ml of a 1:4 (v/v) ethanol-water mixture; the tube is then centrifuged for 1 hour (1500 rpm; radius of centrifuge head, 15 cm). The supernatant solution is finally sucked from the precipitate with the aid of a fine glass tube attached to a slowly running water pump.

7. Repeat Step 5, but use water instead of NaOH.

8. Repeat Step 6, but incubate only 2 hours and do not add Hyflo-Super Cel.

9. Repeat Steps 7 and 8.

10. To the final precipitate in the centrifuge tube add 5 ml of ethanol and dissolve the pregnanediol by warming at about 75°C with stirring. Norite charcoal (1–2 mg) is then added, and warming is continued for 2 minutes. The mixture is filtered through a small filter (Whatman no. 1 paper) into a test tube of 1 inch diameter, the centrifuge tube and filter being washed three times with 2-ml portions of warm ethanol.

11. The filtrate and washings in the tube are evaporated in a water bath under a stream of air, and the residue is dried by leaving the tube in a vacuum desiccator over calcium chloride for several hours.

12. The color reaction is carried out with not more than about 0.5 mg of the finally purified product. If the amount of pregnanediol appears on inspection to be in excess of 0.5 mg, a suitable aliquot portion is removed after solution in a known volume of ethanol. To the dry pregnanediol, 10.0 ml of concentrated H_2SO_4 is added from a burette, and the tube is left in a water bath at 25°C for 20 minutes and occasionally shaken. The intensity of the yellow color produced is measured in a Spekker photoelectric absorptiometer using a "spectrum violet" no. 601 light filter.

The absorptiometer readings are interpreted by reference to a calibration curve made with known amounts of pure pregnane-$3\alpha,20\alpha$-diol varying from 0.1 to 0.5 mg. It is advisable to construct a fresh calibration curve for each batch of unknowns.

References

1. Adler, A. A., de Fremery, P., and Tausk, M. 1934. Progestin in placental extract. *Nature* **133**: 293.
2. Alexander, D. P., Frazer, J. F. D., and Lee, J. 1955. The effects of steroids on the maintenance of pregnancy in the spayed rat. *J. Physiol. (London)* **130**: 148–155.
3. Allen, W. M. 1930. VI. The production of progestational proliferation of the endometrium of the immature rabbit by progestin (an extract of the corpus luteum) after preliminary treatment with oestrin. *Am. J. Physiol.* **92**: 612–618.
4. Allen, W. M., and Corner, G. W. 1929. Physiology of the corpus luteum. III. Normal growth and implantation of embryos after very early ablation of the ovaries, under the influence of extracts of the corpus luteum. *Am. J. Physiol.* **88**: 340–346.
5. Allen, W. M., and Corner, G. W. 1929. Physiology of the corpus luteum. VII. Maintenance of pregnancy in rabbit after very early castration, by corpus luteum extracts. *Proc. Soc. Exptl. Biol. Med.* **27**: 403–405.
6. Allen, W. M., and Wintersteiner, O. 1934. Crystalline progesterone. *Science* **80**: 190–191.
7. Astwood, E. B. 1939. An assay method for progesterone based upon the decidual cell reaction in the rat. *J. Endocrinol.* **1**: 49–55.
8. Benson, G. K., Cowie, A. T., Folley, S. J., and Tindall, J. S. 1959. Recent developments in endocrine studies on mammary growth and lactation. *Recent Progr. Endocrinol. Reprod. Proc. Conf. Syracuse, 1958*, pp. 457–496.
9. Berde, B., and Cerletti, A. 1958. Quantitative comparison of substances related to oxytocin: a new test. *Acta Endocrinol.* **27**: 314–324.
10. Bever, A. T. 1959. Steroid influences on the lactic dehydrogenase-DPNH oxidase system of the rat uterus. *Ann. N. Y. Acad. Sci.* **75**: 472–490.
11. Boving, B. G. 1959. Implantation. *Ann. N. Y. Acad. Sci.* **75**: 700–725.
12. Boving, B. G. 1959. Endocrine influences on implantation. *Recent Progr. Endocrinol. Reprod. Proc. Conf. Syracuse, 1958*, pp. 205–226.
13. Butt, W. R., Morris, P., Morris, C. J. O. R., and Williams, D. C. 1951. The polarographic estimation of steroid hormones. *Biochem. J.* **49**: 434–438.
14. Corner, G. W. 1928. Physiology of the corpus luteum. I. The effect of very early ablation of the corpus luteum upon embryo and uterus. *Am. J. Physiol.* **86**: 74–81.
15. Csapo, A., and Corner, G. W. 1952. The antagonistic effects of estrogen and progesterone on the staircase phenomenon in uterine muscle. *Endocrinology* **51**: 378–385.
16. Csapo, A. 1961. The role of progesterone in the maintenance and termination of pregnancy. *In* "Brook-Lodge Symposium on Progesterone" (A. C. Barnes, ed.), pp. 7–22. Brook Lodge Press, Augusta, Michigan.
16a. DeFeo, V. J. 1963. The temporal aspect of uterine sensitivity in the pseudopregnant or pregnant rat. *Endocrinology* **72**: 305–316.
17. Diczfalusy, E. 1952. Progesterone in human placental tissue. *Acta Endocrinol.* **10**: 373–389.
18. Dorfman, R. I., Kincl, F. A., and Ringold, H. J. 1961. Antiestrogen assay of neutral steroids administered by subcutaneous injection. *Endocrinology* **68**: 17–24.

19. Drummond-Robinson, G., and Asdell, S. A. 1926. The relation between the corpus luteum and the mammary gland. *J. Physiol.* (*London*) **61**: 608–614.
20. Duncan, G. W., Bowerman, A. M., Anderson, L. L., Hearn, W. R., and Melampy, R. M. 1961. Factors influencing *in vitro* synthesis of progesterone. *Endocrinology* **68**: 199–207.
21. Emmens, C. W. 1950. Hormones of the corpus luteum. *In* "Hormone Assay" (C. W. Emmens, ed.), Chap. 17, pp. 419–441. Academic Press, New York.
22. Ershoff, B. H., and Deuel, H. J., Jr. 1943. Prolongation of pseudopregnancy by induction of deciduomata in the rat. *Proc. Soc. Exptl. Biol. Med.* **54**: 167–168.
23. Fraenkel, L. 1903. Die Funktion des Corpus-luteum. *Arch. Gynaekol.* **68**: 438–545.
24. Fuchs, F., and Fuchs, A. 1958. Induction and inhibition of labour in the rabbit. *Acta Endocrinol.* **29**: 615–624.
25. Goldfine, M. M., and Cohen, S. L. 1953. Glucuronidase hydrolysis for pregnanediol assays. *Endocrinology* **52**: 597–604.
26. Goto, M., and Csapo, A. 1959. The effect of the ovarian steroids on the membrane potential of uterine muscle. *J. Gen. Physiol.* **43**: 455–466.
27. Greenwald, G. S. 1957. Interruption of pregnancy in the rabbit by the administration of estrogen. *J. Exptl. Zool.* **135**: 461–482.
28. Greenwald, G. S. 1958. Endocrine regulation of the secretion of mucin in the tubal epithelium of the rabbit. *Anat. Record* **130**: 477–496.
29. Greep, R. O., and Hisaw, F. L. 1938. Pseudopregnancy from electrical stimulation of the cervix in the diestrum. *Proc. Soc. Exptl. Biol. Med.* **39**: 359–360.
30. Hall, K. 1960. Modification by relaxin of the response of the reproductive tract of mice to oestradiol and progesterone. *J. Endocrinol.* **20**: 355–364.
31. Hall, K. 1960. A microscopical study of the effect of relaxin in modifying the action of oestradiol and progesterone on the uterine tract of mice. *J. Physiol.* (*London*) **152**: 42P.
32. Harris, R. S., and Cohen, S. L. 1951. The influence of ovarian hormones on the enzymatic activities of tissues. *Endocrinology* **48**: 264–272.
33. Harris, R. G., and Pfiffner, J. J. 1929. Extracts of corpora lutea in relation to pregnancy. *Anat. Record* **44**: 205 (abstr.).
34. Hartman, C. G. 1925. The interruption of pregnancy by ovariectomy in the aplacental opossum: a study in the physiology of implantation. *Am. J. Physiol.* **71**: 436–454.
35. Herrick, E. H. 1928. The duration of pregnancy in guinea pigs after removal and also after transplantation of ovaries. *Anat. Record* **39**: 193–200.
36. Hertz, R., Meyer, R. K., and Spielman, M. A. 1937. The specificity of progesterone in inducing sexual receptivity in the ovariectomized guinea pig. *Endocrinology* **21**: 533–535.
37. Hisaw, F. L., and Velardo, J. T. 1951. Inhibition of progesterone in decidual development by steroid compounds. *Endocrinology* **49**: 732–741.
38. Hisaw, F. L., Zarrow, M. X., Talmage, R. V. N., Money, W. L., and Abramowitz, A. A. 1942. Relation of progesterone to relaxin formation. *Anat. Record* **84**: 457 (abstr.).
39. Hooker, C. W., and Forbes, T. R. 1947. Bioassay for minute amounts of progesterone. *Endocrinology* **41**: 158–169.
40. Hooker, C. W., and Forbes, T. R. 1949. Specificity of bioassay for progesterone. *Endocrinology* **45**: 71–74.

41. Huettner, A. F. 1949. "Fundamentals of Comparative Embryology of the Vertebrates," revised ed. Macmillan, New York.
42. Jacobson, A., Salhanick, H. A., and Zarrow, M. X. 1950. Production of pseudopregnancy and its inhibition by various drugs. *Am. J. Physiol.* **161:** 522–527.
43. Jacobson, B. D. 1960. Abortion, its prediction and management: evaluation of newer progestational agents. *Fertility Sterility* **11:** 399–413.
44. Kent, G. C., and Leiberman, M. J. 1949. Induction of psychic estrus in the hamster with progesterone administered via the lateral brain ventricle. *Endocrinology* **45:** 29–32.
45. Kessler, W. B., and Borman, A. 1958. Some biological activities of certain progestogens: I. 17-α-hydroxyprogesterone 17-n-caproate. *Ann. N. Y. Acad. Sci.* **71:** 486–493.
46. Krehbiel, R. H. 1937. Cytological studies of the decidual reaction in the rat during early pregnancy and in the production of deciduomata. *Physiol. Zool.* **10:** 212–233.
47. Kroc, R. L., Steinetz, B. G., and Beach, V. L. 1959. The effects of estrogens, progestogens and relaxin in pregnant and nonpregnant laboratory rodents. *Ann. N. Y. Acad. Sci.* **75:** 942–980.
48. Loeb, L. 1908. The experimental production of part of the placenta in the rabbit. *Proc. Soc. Exptl. Biol. Med.* **5:** 102–104.
49. Long, J. A., and Evans, H. M. 1922. The estrous cycle in the rat and its associated phenomena. *Mem. Univ. Calif.* **6:** 1–128.
50. Lutwak-Mann, C. 1955. Carbonic anhydrase in the female reproductive tract. Occurrence, distribution and hormonal dependence. *J. Endocrinol.* **13:** 26–38.
51. McGinty, D. A., Anderson, C. P., and McCullough, N. B. 1939. Effect of local application of progesterone on the rabbit uterus. *Endocrinology* **24:** 829–832.
52. McKay, D. G., Hertig, A. T., Bardawil, W. A., and Velardo, J. T. 1956. Histochemical observations on the endometrium: I. Normal endometrium. *Obstet. Gynecol.* **8:** 22–39.
53. McPhail, M. K. 1934. The assay of progestin. *J. Physiol. (London)* **83:** 145–156.
54. Marshall, J. M. 1959. Effects of estrogen and progesterone on single uterine muscle fibers in the rat. *Am. J. Physiol.* **197:** 935–942.
55. Meites, J., and Sgouris, J. T. 1954. Effects of altering the balance between prolactin and ovarian hormones on initiation of lactation in rabbits. *Endocrinology* **55:** 530–534.
56. Meyer, R. K., and Allen, W. M. 1933. The production of mucified cells in the vaginal epithelium of certain rodents by oestrin and by corpus luteum extracts. *Anat. Record* **56:** 321–343.
57. Nelson, W. O., and Haterius, H. O. 1930. An experimental study of ovariectomy and transplantation in the pregnant albino rat. *Physiol. Zool.* **3:** 231–241.
58. Nelson, W. O., Pfiffner, J. J., and Haterius, H. O. 1930. The prolongation of pregnancy by extracts of corpus luteum. *Am. J. Physiol.* **91:** 690–695.
59. Noall, M. W., Salhanick, H. A., Neher, G. M., and Zarrow, M. X. 1953. Method for the isolation of progesterone from human placentae. *J. Biol. Chem.* **201:** 321–328.
60. Ogawa, Y., and Pincus, G. 1960. Micro determination of carbonic anhydrase in animal tissue. *Endocrinology* **67:** 551–558.
61. Ogawa, Y., and Pincus, G. 1961. Further studies on progestin bioassay using the endometrial response in the rabbit. *Endocrinology* **68:** 680–686.

62. Parkes, A. S. 1928. The role of the corpus luteum in the maintenance of pregnancy. *J. Physiol.* (*London*) **65**: 341–349.
63. Pearlman, W. H. 1954. Recent experiences in the detection, estimation and isolation of progesterone and related C$_{21}$ steroids. *Recent Progr. Hormone Res.* **9**: 27–44.
64. Pearlman, W. H. 1957. Circulating steroid hormone levels in relation to steroid hormone production. *Ciba Found. Colloq. Endocrinol.* **11**: 233–251.
65. Pearlman, W. H., and Cerceo, E. 1952. The isolation of progesterone from human placenta. *J. Biol. Chem.* **198**: 79–83.
66. Pearlman, W. H., and Thomas, M. 1953. The progesterone content of human placental blood. *Endocrinology* **52**: 590–596.
67. Pincus, G., Miyake, T., Merrill, A. P., and Longo, P. 1957. The bioassay of progesterone. *Endocrinology* **61**: 528–533.
68. Pincus, G., and Werthessen, N. T. 1937. A quantitative method for the bioassay of progestin. *Am. J. Physiol.* **120**: 100–104.
69. Ralph, C. L., and Fraps, R. M. 1960. Induction of ovulation in the hen by injection of progesterone into the brain. *Endocrinology* **66**: 269–272.
70. Revesz, C., Chappel, C. I., and Gaudry, R. 1960. Masculinization of female fetuses in the rat by progestational compounds. *Endocrinology* **66**: 140 (notes and comments).
71. Reynolds, S. R. M. 1949. "Physiology of the Uterus." Harper (Hoeber), New York.
72. Ring, J. R. 1944. The estrogen-progesterone induction of sexual receptivity in the spayed female mouse. *Endocrinology* **34**: 269–275.
73. Rothchild, I., Meyer, R. K., and Spielman, M. A. 1940. A quantitative study of oestrogen-progesterone interaction in the formation of placentomata in the castrate rat. *Am. J. Physiol.* **128**: 213–224.
74. Salhanick, H. A., Holmstrom, E. G., and Zarrow, M. X. 1957. Biological activity of 17-α-hydroxyprogesterone in the mouse, rabbit and human being. *J. Clin. Endocrinol. Metab.* **17**: 667–672.
75. Saunders, F. J., and Drill, V. A. 1958. Some biological activities of 17-ethynyl and 17-alkyl derivatives of 17-hydroxyestrenones. *Ann. N. Y. Acad. Sci.* **71**: 517–531.
76. Schofield, B. M. 1957. The hormonal control of myometrial function during pregnancy. *J. Physiol.* (*London*) **138**: 1–10.
77. Selye, H. 1940. Effect of chronic progesterone overdosage on the female accessory sex organs of normal, ovariectomized and hypophysectomized rats. *Anat. Record* **78**: 253–271.
78. Shelesnyak, M. C. 1957. Some experimental studies on the mechanism of ova-implantation in the rat. *Recent Progr. Hormone Res.* **13**: 269–322.
79. Sommerville, I. F., Gough, N., and Marrian, G. F. 1948. The quantitative determination of small amounts of pregnanediol in human urine. *J. Endocrinol.* **5**: 247–257.
80. Steinetz, B. G., Beach, V., and Kroc, R. L. 1956. The influence of estrogen, progesterone and relaxin on the response of the 19 day pregnant mouse to oxytocin. *Anat. Record* **124**: 365 (abstr.).
81. Steinetz, B. G., Beach, V. L., and Kroc, R. L. 1957. The influence of progesterone, relaxin and estrogen on some structural and functional changes in the pre-parturient mouse. *Endocrinology* **61**: 271–280.

82. Steinetz, B. G., Beach, V. L., and Kroc, R. L. 1959. The physiology of relaxin in laboratory animals. *Recent Progr. Endocrinol. Reprod. Proc. Conf. Syracuse, 1958,* pp. 390–427.

83. Talbot, N. B., Berman, R. A., MacLachlan, E. A., and Wolfe, J. K. 1941. The colorimetric determination of neutral steroids (hormones) in a 24-hour sample of human urine (pregnanediol; total, alpha and beta alcoholic, and non-alcoholic 17-ketosteroids). *J. Clin. Endocrinol.* **1:** 668–673.

84. Talmage, R. V. 1947. Changes produced in the symphysis pubis of the guinea pig by the sex steroids and relaxin. *Anat. Record* **99:** 91–111.

85. Velardo, J. T. 1958. Biological action of 17-α-hydroxyprogesterone 17-*n*-caproate on the reproductive processes of the rat. *Ann. N. Y. Acad. Sci.* **71:** 542–554.

86. Velardo, J. T., Olsen, A. G., Hisaw, F. L., and Dawson, A. B. 1953. The influence of decidual tissue upon pseudopregnancy. *Endocrinology* **53:** 216–220.

87. Venning, E. H. 1938. Further studies on the estimation of small amounts of sodium pregnanediol glucuronidate in urine. *J. Biol. Chem.* **126:** 595–602.

88. Venning, E. H. 1955. Endocrine changes in normal pregnancy. *Am. J. Med.* **19:** 721–723.

89. Venning, E., and Browne, J. S. L. 1937. Urinary excretion of sodium pregnanediol glucuronidate in the menstrual cycle (an excretion product of progesterone). *Am. J. Physiol.* **119:** 417P.

90. Venning, E. H., and Browne, J. S. L. 1940. A study of the metabolism of crystalline progesterone. *Endocrinology* **27:** 707–720.

91. Wang, G. H. 1923. The relation between "spontaneous activity" and the oestrous cycle in white rat. *Comp. Psychol. Monograph* **2:** No. 6.

92. West, T. C., Jones, D. M., and Loomis, T. A. 1953. Effect of ovarian hormones on contractile energy of rat uterus. *Am. J. Physiol.* **172:** 541–546.

93. Yochim, J. M., and DeFeo, V. J. 1962. Control of decidual growth in the rat by steroid hormones of the ovary. *Endocrinology* **71:** 134–142.

94. Yochim, J., and Zarrow, M. X. 1961. Action of estradiol, progesterone, and relaxin in the maintenance of gestation in the castrated pregnant rat. *Fertility Sterility* **12:** 263–276.

95. Young, W. C. 1941. Observations and experiments on mating behavior in female mammals. *Quart. Rev. Biol.* **16:** 135–156.

96. Young, W. C. 1941. Observations and experiments on mating behavior in female mammals. *Quart. Rev. Biol.* **16:** 311–335.

97. Zander, J. 1961. The chemical estimation of progesterone and its metabolites in body fluids and target organs. *In* "Brook-Lodge Symposium on Progesterone" (A. C. Barnes, ed.), pp. 77–89. Brook Lodge Press, Augusta, Michigan.

98. Zander, J., Forbes, T. R., von Münstermann, A. M., and Neher, R. 1958. Δ⁴-3-ketopregnen-20-α-ol and Δ⁴-3-ketopregnen-20-β-ol, two naturally occurring metabolites of progesterone. Isolation, identification, biologic activity and concentration in human tissues. *J. Clin. Endocrinol. Metab.* **18:** 337–353.

99. Zarrow, M. X., and Neher, G. M. 1955. Concentration of progestin in the serum of the rabbit during pregnancy, the puerperium and following castration. *Endocrinology* **56:** 1–8.

100. Zarrow, M. X., Neher, G. M., Lazo-Wasem, E. A., and Salhanick, H. A. 1957. Biological activity of certain progesterone-like compounds as determined by the Hooker-Forbes bioassay. *J. Clin. Endocrinol. Metab.* **17:** 658–666.

101. Zarrow, M. X., Peters, L. E., and Caldwell, A. L., Jr. 1958. The comparative potency of several progestogenic compounds in a battery of different biological tests. *Ann. N. Y. Acad. Sci.* **71:** 532–541.
102. Zondek, B., and Hestrin, S. 1947. Phosphorylase activity in human endometrium. *Am. J. Obstet. Gynecol.* **54:** 173–175.
103. Zondek, B., and Stein, L. 1940. Glycogen content of the human uterine mucosa. Glycopenia uteri. *Endocrinology* **27:** 395–399.
104. Zuckerman, S., Palmer, A., and Hanson, D. A. 1950. The effect of steroid hormones on the water content of tissues. *J. Endocrinol.* **6:** 261–276.

CHAPTER 4

Relaxin

Relaxin is a water-soluble hormone of the ovary and reproductive tract discovered by Hisaw in 1926 (21). It is considered to be a hormone of pregnancy with an active role in the preparation of certain tissues for delivery of the young, although it appears to affect different tissues in different species of mammals. Thus, relaxin stimulates pubic relaxation in the guinea pig, but not in the rabbit. The ability of the hormone to inhibit uterine contractions in estrous animals has been observed in all animals tested thus far, although only a limited number have been examined.

Sites of Relaxin Formation

Relaxin is secreted primarily by the ovaries, especially the ovaries of pregnancy. It has been found in the blood and ovaries of a wide variety of species including the guinea pig, rabbit, rat, cat, horse, sheep, cow, whale, and human being (25, 34). Analysis of blood indicates that the hormone is found consistently only during pregnancy. The concentration rises from a very low level early in gestation to a peak or plateau during the latter part of pregnancy, and then falls precipitously after parturition. This pattern has been noted in the rabbit and the human being (31, 46). Figure 4-1 shows the values obtained for the concentration of relaxin throughout pregnancy in the rabbit. The concentration of relaxin in the blood has been measured also in the pregnant guinea pig (42) and pregnant cow (38). In these two animals, a slight drop occurs prior to parturition; after delivery, the hormone is not detectable.

A major source of relaxin during pregnancy appears to be the corpus luteum. The concentration of relaxin in the ovary of the sow rises rapidly during pregnancy to a level of 10,000 guinea pig units (GPU) per gram fresh tissue (24). High levels of relaxin have also been found in the ovary of the pregnant rat, mouse, and whale (5, 34). Additional studies in the gestating rabbit reveal the presence of relaxin in the placenta and the uterine endometrium. Ovariectomy of a pregnant rabbit followed by

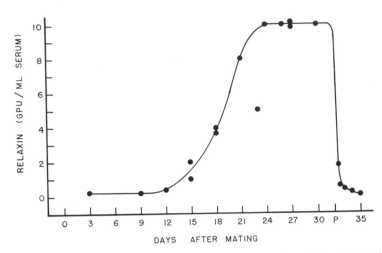

Fig. 4-1. Relaxin content of blood during gestation in the rabbit. Adapted from Marder and Money (31).

progesterone replacement therapy to maintain pregnancy does not alter the concentration of relaxin in the blood, an indication that the placenta and uterus can supply the normal relaxin requirements during pregnancy (49). Treatment of both the rabbit and the guinea pig with progesterone causes the release of relaxin in minimal amounts by the uterus (26, 27). Table 4–1 lists some of the sources of relaxin and the approximate concentration of the hormone.

Nature of Relaxin

Relaxin is a water-soluble polypeptide or protein of molecular weight less than 10,000. The hormone is stable to heat but is inactivated by agents such as cysteine, an indication of the presence of a sulfhydril linkage essential for the biological activity of the hormone (9, 10). The hormone is also inactivated by hot alkali and proteolytic enzymes. The molecule contains 12.7% nitrogen and 10.5% reducing sugars (partly in the form of hexoseamine). In addition, cysteine, guanidine, and arginine have been found. A molecular weight of approximately 5000 has been suggested for the hormone.

Separation of relaxin into several different components has been effected by the use of countercurrent distribution procedures utilizing a butanol-trichloroacetic acid system (11). Four compounds have been isolated, each containing relaxin activity. Thus, it appears that relaxin is actually composed of at least four active components.

TABLE 4–1

RELAXIN CONTENT OF VARIOUS TISSUES IN DIFFERENT SPECIES

Species	Tissue	State of cycle or type of treatment	Relaxin content (GPU)	References
Sow	Ovary	Immature	<1.0/gm	(24)
	Ovary	Follicular	<1.0/gm	(24)
	Ovary	Luteal	2.5–5.0/gm	(24)
	Ovary	Nonpregnant	3.0–10/gm	(3)
	Ovary	Pregnant	10,000–15,000/gm	(24)
	Ovary	Pregnant	3,000–96,000/gm	(3)
	Placenta	Pregnant	0.5–2.5/gm	(24)
	Uterus	Pregnant	<1.0/gm	(24)
	Serum	Pregnant	2.0/ml	(24)
Guinea pig	Serum	Nonpregnant	Negative	(42)
	Serum	Pregnant	0.5/ml	(42)
	Uterus	Estradiol/Progesterone	10.0/gm	(41)
Rabbit	Serum	Nonpregnant	Negative	(31)
	Serum	Pregnant	10.0/ml	(31)
	Serum	Pseudopregnant	0.2/ml	(26)
	Serum	Progesterone	0.2/ml	(26)
	Uterus	Pregnant	10.0/gm	(49)
	Placenta	Pregnant	50–75/gm	(49)
	Ovary	Pregnant	25–30/gm	(49)
	Maternal placenta	Pregnant	250–350/gm	(49)
	Fetal placenta	Pregnant	10–25/gm	(49)
Human	Serum	Pregnant (first 6 months)	Present	(2, 32)
Dog	Serum	Pregnant	Present	(22)
	Serum	Estrous	0.3/ml	(34)
Cat	Serum	Pregnant	Present	(22)
Mare	Serum	Pregnant	Present	(22)
Chicken	Ovary	—	10/gm	(25)
Mouse	Ovary	Pregnant, day 16	114/gm	(34)
	Ovary	Pregnant, day 19	200/gm	(34)
	Uterus	Pregnant	Negative	(34)
	Placenta	Pregnant	Negative	(34)
Rat	Ovary	Pregnant, day 13	290	(34)
	Ovary	Pregnant, day 21	720	(34)
	Ovary	Pregnant	Present	(5)
Whale	Corpus luteum	—	536/gm	(34)
Shark	Ovary	Pregnant	Present	(34)
Rooster	Testes	—	Present	(34)
Cow	Blood	Pregnant, second half	0.1–1.0/ml	(38)
	Blood	Ovarian cyst	0.1–0.6/ml	(38)

Action of Relaxin

Relaxin appears to be a hormone the utilization of which has evolved along several pathways in different species. Two generalizations can be made with regard to the action of the hormone: (a) relaxin appears to be peculiarly adapted by the species for its particular requirements for parturition; (b) relaxin acts on a tissue after it has been pretreated or exposed to estrogen. Thus, whether the action is to produce pelvic relaxation, inhibition of uterine contractions, or dilation of the uterine cervix, it is manifest only if the various tissues have been exposed previously to estrogen.

Of the various actions of the hormone, symphyseal relaxation has been demonstrated only in the guinea pig, mouse, deermouse, and Skomer vole. Negative results have been reported in the rabbit, ewe, rat, and pig. Cervical dilation has been reported in the mouse, rat, cow, pig, and human being. It is not presently known whether other species show this effect. Inhibition of uterine contractions by relaxin has been observed in the guinea pig, rat, and mouse.

A. RELAXATION OF THE PELVIC JOINT

Separation of the pubic symphysis has been described in the guinea pig, mouse, deermouse, and Skomer vole. In all instances, to produce the effect, the castrated animal must be pretreated with estrogen. The reaction occurs within 4–6 hours after administration of relaxin in the guinea pig, and after 24–36 hours in the mouse. Symphyseal separation in the guinea pig can also be induced by estrogen alone or by estrogen followed by progesterone. However, the action observed after prolonged treatment with estrogen is the result of growth and proliferation of the symphyseal pad and resorption of the bone whereas the observed action of relaxin is the result of a breakdown and dissolution of the symphyseal cartilage and the collagenous connective tissue fibers. The relaxation of the pubic symphysis of the guinea pig induced by progesterone is comparable to that seen after relaxin treatment (36, 37) and is apparently a result of the secretion of relaxin by the uterus (41, 42).

Changes in the interpubic ligament in the mouse (14, 15, 18, 19) and the deermouse (45) have been described fully. Hall and her colleagues have demonstrated, in the mouse, a marked increase in the length of the interpubic ligament during the latter part of pregnancy. This effect can be reproduced in the nonpregnant, ovariectomized, estrogen-primed mouse by administration of relaxin; it is presently the basis of an assay for the hormone. Progesterone does not appear to induce the secretion of relaxin in the mouse and actually inhibits interpubic separation (16, 34). The situation in the deermouse is comparable to that seen in the mouse. Interpubic separation begins between the tenth and fifteenth day of gestation and thereafter increases rapidly to a level of 4 mm at parturition (Fig. 4-2).

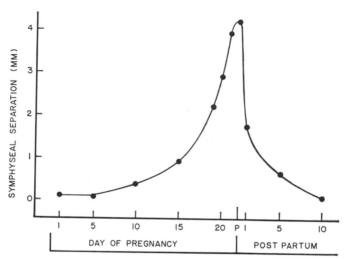

Fig. 4-2. Pubic separation during gestation in a substrain of deermouse (*Peromyscus maniculatus*). Adapted from Zarrow *et al.* (45).

B. INHIBITION OF MYOMETRIAL ACTIVITY

Inhibition of spontaneous activity of the uterine myometrium by relaxin has been described in the guinea pig, rat, and mouse both *in vivo* and *in vitro* (29, 33, 39). In general, relaxin inhibits spontaneous uterine contractions in an estrogenized or estrous animal but does not interfere with the action of oxytocin or acetylcholine. Tachyphylaxis has been shown to occur following repeated administration of the hormone.

C. RELAXATION OF THE UTERINE CERVIX

The uterine cervix shows both morphological and physiological changes during different phases of the estrous cycle and pregnancy. Among the changes observed are a softening and dilation of the cervix prior to parturition. Such a phenomenon is well known in the human being and has also been observed in the cow, pig, rat, mouse, and monkey. Experimental studies on the hormonal control of cervical dilation indicate that relaxin, following an initial priming with estrogen, is the agent responsible for dilation in these animals (4, 7, 13, 24, 34, 48, 50,

51). Measurements of changes in the cervix of the rat reveal a progressive decrease in tensile strength with advancing pregnancy (Fig. 4-3);

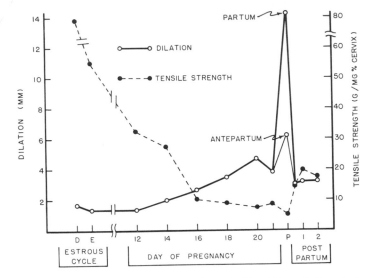

Fig. 4-3. Changes in the tensile strength and dilatability of the uterine cervix of the rat during pregnancy. Adapted from Zarrow and Yochim (51).

these changes can be reproduced in ovariectomized animals treated with estrogen, progestogen, and relaxin. The increase in cervical dilatability observed in the pregnant rat can also be reproduced after ovariectomy by treatment with estrogen, progestogen, and relaxin.

D. GESTATION

Relaxin affects the maintenance of pregnancy in both mice and rats. The hormone was shown to have a progesterone-sparing action in mice (17); i.e., less of the luteal hormone was needed to maintain pregnancy in the castrated mouse if relaxin was also given. In the rat, however, relaxin appears to potentiate the action of estrogen on maintenance of pregnancy. Thus, if relaxin is administered, less estrogen is required for optimal maintenance of pregnancy, but with increasing estrogen, fetal survival is impaired if relaxin is given (40).

E. PARTURITION

Relaxin facilitates delivery of the young in mice. This appears to be due to an increased sensitivity of the uterus to oxytocin. In addition, separation of the pubic symphysis and dilation of the uterine cervix, events concerned with parturition in many species, also are actions of relaxin.

F. The Mammary Gland

The original observation of a synergism between relaxin, estradiol, and progesterone on lobuloalveolar growth in the rat has been confirmed in the rabbit and guinea pig (12, 20).

G. Other Effects

An increase in water content of the uterus has been observed as a direct effect of relaxin (6). The hormone also synergizes with estrogen, inducing a number of biochemical changes in the uterus (30): an increase in water content, dry weight, total glycogen, and alkaline phosphatase. Potentiation of progesterone by relaxin has been noted in the uterus of the rabbit (44). Relaxin has also been shown to synergize with estrogen on vaginal cornification (6a).

The Assay of Relaxin

Several bioassays have been devised to test for relaxin activity. Among these are measures of separation of the pubic symphysis and inhibition of uterine motility. The guinea pig (21, 29) and the mouse (15, 19, 28, 30) have been used as assay animals. The unit of relaxin activity, as determined by the guinea pig pubic symphysis separation test, has been defined as the minimal amount of hormone necessary to cause appreciable separation of the symphysis (measured by manual palpation) in nine of twelve estrogen-primed, virgin animals. More objective tests have utilized X-ray measurement of the symphysis of the mouse (15, 28) or direct measurement of the length of the inter-pubic ligament in the mouse (30, 35). Inhibition of spontaneous uterine motility of the estrous mouse (or rat) has also been used as an objective assay of relaxin (33, 39). As with all impure extracts, several dose levels of the hormone must be used, and a standard preparation of known potency must be run simultaneously for purposes of comparison.

Biogenesis, Metabolism, and Mechanism of Action

Little is known of the biogenesis and metabolism of relaxin. Concerning its mechanism of action, one generalization can be made: relaxin produces its most striking effects on an estrogenized substrate. This seems to be true for uterine motility, pubic symphysis separation, dilation of the uterine cervix, and other changes. With respect to the pubic symphysis, relaxin appears to cause a depolymerization of connective tissue ground substance. Its motility-inhibiting activity may be a result of the action of the hormone on the membrane potential of the myometrial cell.

As with other hormones, relaxin is rapidly absorbed from the site of injection and is rapidly lost from the blood. More than 50% of the hormone disappears from the blood within 1 hour following an intravenous injection, and 96% is lost after 12 hours (47). Only 1–4% of the injected hormone has been found in the urine.

Although early data failed to show any antigenic activity with relaxin, antibodies to the hormone have been produced following treatment of rabbits with relaxin in Freund's adjuvant. The rabbit antiserum can prevent the action of the hormone on the pubic symphysis of the mouse.

EXPERIMENT 4–1

Relaxation of the Pubic Symphysis of the Guinea Pig*

The first assays described for the determination of relaxin involved the use of the pubic ligament of the ovariectomized guinea pig. Initially a qualitative test was established to determine the presence or absence of pubic relaxation. This was modified for assay purposes by using serial dilutions. The unit was originally defined as the minimal amount of hormone necessary to relax the pelvic ligament in 12 hours. The definition was later modified in an effort to quantitate the response: the minimal amount of hormone necessary to elicit appreciable symphyseal separation in two-thirds to three-fourths of the group of animals tested.

Procedure

1. Intact, virgin guinea pigs (each weighing 350–400 gm) are used in this experiment. Inject 5 μg estradiol cyclopentylpropionate (ECP) subcutaneously on the first day of treatment.

2. On day 5, inject subcutaneously 1.0 ml of a standard relaxin preparation (3.0 GPU/1.0 ml saline).

3. Palpate the pubic symphysis for mobility at 6 hours and 12 hours after the injection.† If no response occurs, repeat Steps 1 and 2 the following week (day 1: 5.0 μg ECP; day 5: relaxin standard; palpate at 6 and 12 hours). Two to four weeks are usually required for the response to occur.

Animals which respond to the above treatment should be used for the assay on the week after the response occurs.

* Cf. references (1, 21, 30, 34).
† See footnote* p. 117.

Assay Procedure

1. Prime the animals with 5.0 μg ECP on day 1.

2. On day 5, inject (in 1.0 ml saline) the following doses of standard: 0.25, 0.5, 1.0, and 2.0 GPU. (Four groups of animals, 6 guinea pigs per group, will yield a crude standard curve suitable for preliminary testing of the unknown.)

3. Serial dilutions of unknown potency are injected into another series of ECP-primed animals. Palpate the pubic symphysis for mobility 6 hours after the injection.*

4. The responses are graded 0 to 6; responses of 4–6 are considered positive, i.e., an appreciable amount of symphyseal separation is observed by means of manual palpation.

For assay purposes, 60 guinea pigs should be distributed into equal groups, allowing one group for each of two or three dose levels of standard and of unknown in order to obtain statistical significance. (Dose levels of unknown are determined from the preliminary assay in Steps 2 and 3 above.) Thus, each group should contain either 10 or 15 animals, depending upon the numbers of groups used.

EXPERIMENT 4–2

The Action of Relaxin on the Interpubic Ligament of the Mouse†

Measurement of the separation of the pubic symphysis of the mouse was first carried out by X-ray of the interpubic distance (18, 28). This was followed by the direct measurement of the interpubic ligament with a calibrated micrometer eyepiece, using a binocular microscope at a total magnification of 13 times. Visualization was facilitated by trans-illumination of the ligament (Fig. 4-4) with a Lucite rod and a light (30, 35).

Procedure

1. Virgin, immature female mice (age, 28 days; weight, 14–18 gm) are used.

---

* Palpation is accomplished in the following manner. The animal, ventral side up, is held between the knees of the seated examiner. The examiner grasps the pubic symphysis and crest of the ischium firmly between thumbs and forefingers (holding the legs with the other fingers) so that each half of the pelvis may be moved independently. Mobility of the symphysis is determined by alternately moving each half back and forth.

† Cf. references (18, 28, 30, 35).

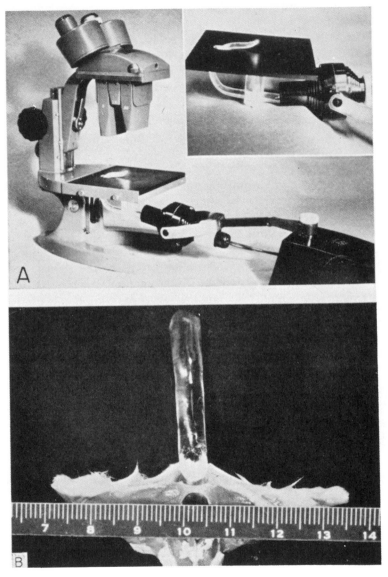

Fig. 4-4. (A) Apparatus for measuring interpubic ligament length in the mouse. (B) Interpubic ligament as viewed through the microscope. Taken from Kroc *et al.* (30).

2. The animals are primed on day 1 with a subcutaneous injection of 5.0 μg estradiol cyclopentylpropionate (ECP). The hormone is dissolved in peanut oil (or sesame oil) and injected in a volume of 0.1 ml.

3. On day 8, the animals are injected subcutaneously with relaxin. The hormone is dissolved in a 1% solution of benzopurpurine 4B and injected in a volume of 0.1 ml. The dosages of standard should range from 0.1 to 1.0 GPU relaxin (i.e., 0.1, 0.2, 0.4, 0.8, 1.0 GPU).

4. Autopsies are performed 36 hours after the injection of relaxin. The symphyseal tissue is exposed, and after removal of the rectum, vagina, and surrounding connective tissue, the interpubic ligament is measured at a magnification of 13 times. Visualization with a binocular dissecting microscope is facilitated if the ligament is illuminated from below by use of a Lucite rod which carries the light from the light source (Fig. 4-4). Figure 4-5 depicts the size of the interpubic ligament obtained under these conditions.

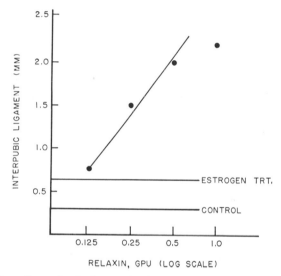

Fig. 4-5. The effect of relaxin on the length of the interpubic ligament of the mouse.

EXPERIMENT 4–3

Measurement of the Interpubic Ligament of the Mouse during Gestation

Procedure and Experimental

Using the method described in Experiment 4-2, measure the change in length of the interpubic ligament throughout gestation in the mouse. Using a minimum of two mice per point, autopsy the animals on the following days of pregnancy: 1, 5, 10, 15, 18, 20, 21 (parturition), days 1, 2, 3, 4, post-partum. Plot a graph showing changes in length of the ligament with time and at parturition.

EXPERIMENT 4–4

Inhibition of Contractions of the Uterus*

The discovery of the inhibition of spontaneous uterine contractions by relaxin (8, 33) led to the development of an assay for this hormone in the estrous mouse (30). Uterine horns from young adult mice (during estrus) are placed in a constant-temperature bath of approximately 25 ml of modified Ringer's solution at 37°C. A comparable *in vitro* assay for relaxin using the rat has also been suggested.

Procedure

1. Remove the uterine horns from a mouse (or rat) in estrus and place in a constant temperature bath at 37°C. (Discard the uterus if it shows the "ballooning" typical of proestrus.) See Experiment 2-10 for details. A Ringer–Locke solution or a Tyrode's solution (see Appendix A–8) may be used for the bath; aerate with 95% O_2 and 5% CO_2.

2. Attach one horn to an isotonic lever and record contractions on a smoked-drum kymograph or with an ink-writing system.

3. Obtain a tracing for an initial control period of 15 minutes.

4. Add relaxin to the water bath at 5-minute intervals in increments that double the concentration in the bath until contractions are inhibited (i.e., 0.05, 0.1, 0.2, 0.4, 0.8, 1.6, 3.2 GPU).

5. Add oxytocin to the bath after uterine contractions are inhibited by relaxin (see Experiment 11–1).

What happens to the system after the hormones have been removed by flushing the bath with clean solution?

References

1. Abramowitz, A. A., Money, W. L., Zarrow, M. X., Talmage, R. V. N., Kleinholz, L. H., and Hisaw, F. L. 1944. Preparation, biological assay and properties of relaxin. *Endocrinology* **34**: 103–114.
2. Abramson, D., Hurwitt, E., and Lesnick, G. 1937. Relaxin in human serum as a test of pregnancy. *Surg. Gynecol. Obstet.* **65**: 335–340.
3. Albert, A., Money, W. L., and Zarrow, M. X. 1947. An improved method of extraction and purification of relaxin from fresh whole ovaries of the sow. *Endocrinology* **40**: 370–374.

* Cf. references (5, 29, 30, 33).

4. Birnberg, C. H., and Abitbol, M. 1958. The use of cervilaxin in term labor. *Ann. N. Y. Acad. Sci.* **75**: 1016–1022.

5. Bloom, G., Paul, K. G., and Wiqvist, N. 1958. A uterine relaxing factor in the pregnant rat. *Acta Endocrinol.* **28**: 112–118.

6. Brennan, D. M., and Zarrow, M. X. 1959. Water and electrolyte content of the uterus of the intact and adrenalectomized rat treated with relaxin and various steroid hormones. *Endocrinology* **64**: 907–913.

6a. Dewar, A. D., Hall, K., and Newton, W. H. 1946. Potentiation of the vaginal response to oestrone by the "relaxin" fraction of pregnant rabbit serum. *J. Physiol. (London)* **105**: 37P–38P.

7. Eichner, E., Waltner, C., Goodman, M., and Post, S. 1956. Relaxin, the third ovarian hormone: its experimental use in women. *Am. J. Obstet. Gynecol.* **71**: 1035–1048.

8. Felton, L. C., Frieden, E. H., and Bryant, H. H. 1953. The effects of ovarian extracts upon activity of the guinea pig uterus *in situ. J. Pharmacol. Exptl. Therap.* **107**: 160–164.

9. Frieden, E. H., and Hisaw, F. L. 1951. The mechanism of symphysial relaxation; the distribution of reducing groups, hexoseamine and proteins in symphyses of normal and relaxed guinea-pigs. *Endocrinology* **48**: 88–97.

10. Frieden, E. H., and Hisaw, F. L. 1953. The biochemistry of relaxin. *Recent Progr. Hormone Res.* **8**: 333–378.

11. Frieden, E. H., Stone, N. R., and Layman, N. W. 1960. The properties of relaxin in preparations purified by counter current distribution. *J. Biol. Chem.* **235**: 2267–2271.

12. Garrett, F. A., and Talmage, R. V. 1952. The influence of relaxin on mammary gland development in guinea-pigs and rabbits. *J. Endocrinol.* **8**: 336–340.

13. Graham, E. F., and Dracy, A. E. 1953. The effect of relaxin and mechanical dilation on the bovine cervix. *J. Dairy Sci.* **36**: 772–777.

14. Hall, K. 1947. Effects of pregnancy and relaxin on histology of the pubic symphysis in the mouse. *J. Endocrinol.* **5**: 174–182.

15. Hall, K. 1948. Further notes on the action of relaxin and oestrone on the pelvis of the spayed mouse, including a single dose test of potency of relaxin. *J. Endocrinol.* **5**: 314–321.

16. Hall, K. 1949. The role of progesterone on the mechanism of pelvic relaxation in the mouse. *Quart. J. Exptl. Physiol.* **35**: 65–75.

17. Hall, K. 1957. The effect of relaxin extracts, progesterone and oestradiol on maintenance of pregnancy, parturition and rearing of young after ovariectomy in mice. *J. Endocrinol.* **15**: 108–117.

18. Hall, K., and Newton, W. H. 1946. The normal course of separation of the pubes of pregnant mice. *J. Physiol. (London)* **104**: 346–352.

19. Hall, K., and Newton, W. H. 1947. The effect of oestrone and relaxin on the X-ray appearance of the pelvis of the mouse. *J. Physiol. (London)* **106**: 18–27.

20. Hamolsky, M., and Sparrow, R. C. 1945. Influence of relaxin on mammary development in sexually immature female rats. *Proc. Soc. Exptl. Biol. Med.* **60**: 8–9.

21. Hisaw, F. L. 1926. Experimental relaxation of pubic ligament of guinea-pig. *Proc. Soc. Exptl. Biol. Med.* **23**: 661–663.

22. Hisaw, F. L. 1929. The corpus luteum hormone. I. Experimental relaxation of the pelvic ligaments of the guinea pig. *Physiol. Zool.* **2**: 59–79.

23. Hisaw, F. L. 1959. Discussion, after paper by Steinetz *et al. Recent Progr. Endocrinol. Reprod., Proc. Conf. Syracuse, 1958*, p. 426.

24. Hisaw, F. L., and Zarrow, M. X. 1948. Relaxin in the ovary of the domestic sow. *Proc. Soc. Exptl. Biol. Med.* **69**: 395–398.

25. Hisaw, F. L., and Zarrow, M. X. 1950. The physiology of relaxin. *Vitamins Hormones* **8**: 151–178.

26. Hisaw, F. L., Zarrow, M. X., Money, W. L., Talmage, R. V. N., and Abramowitz, A. A. 1944. Importance of the female reproductive tract in the formation of relaxin. *Endocrinology* **34**: 122–134.

27. Hisaw, F. L., Zarrow, M. X., Talmage, R. V. N., Money, W. L., and Abramowitz, A. A. 1942. Relation of progesterone to relaxin formation. *Anat. Record* **84**: 457.

28. Kliman, B., Salhanick, H. A., and Zarrow, M. X. 1953. The response of the pubic symphysis of the mouse to extracts of pregnant rabbit serum and pregnant sow ovaries and its application as an assay method. *Endocrinology* **53**: 391–402.

29. Krantz, J. C., Bryant, H. H., and Carr, C. J. 1950. The action of aqueous corpus luteum extract upon uterine activity. *Surg. Gynecol. Obstet.* **90**: 372–375.

30. Kroc, R. L., Steinetz, B. G., and Beach, V. L. 1959. The effects of estrogens, progestogens and relaxin in pregnant and nonpregnant laboratory rodents. *Ann. N. Y. Acad. Sci.* **75**: 942–980.

31. Marder, S. N., and Money, W. L. 1944. Concentration of relaxin in the blood serum of pregnant and postpartum rabbits. *Endocrinology* **34**: 115–121.

32. Pomerenke, W. T. 1934. Experimental ligamentous relaxation in the guinea pig pelvis. *Am. J. Obstet. Gynecol.* **27**: 708–713.

33. Sawyer, W. H., Frieden, E. H., and Martin, A. S. 1953. *In vitro* inhibition of spontaneous contractions of the rat uterus by relaxin containing extracts of sow ovaries. *Am. J. Physiol.* **172**: 547–552.

34. Steinetz, B. G., Beach, V. L., and Kroc, R. L. 1959. The physiology of relaxin in laboratory animals. *Recent Progr. Endocrinol. Reprod., Proc. Conf. Syracuse, 1958*, pp. 389–427.

35. Steinetz, B. G., Beach, V. L., Kroc, R. L., Stasilli, N. R., Nussbaum, R. E., Nemith, P. J., and Dun, R. K. 1960. Bioassay of relaxin using a reference standard: a simple and reliable method utilizing direct measurement of interpubic ligament formation in mice. *Endocrinology* **67**: 102–115.

36. Talmage, R. V. 1947. A histological study of the effects of relaxin on the symphysis pubis of the guinea pig. *J. Exptl. Zool.* **106**: 281–298.

37. Talmage, R. V. 1947. Changes produced in the symphysis pubis of the guinea pig by the sex steroids and relaxin. *Anat. Record* **99**: 91–113.

38. Wada, H., and Yuhara, M. 1961. Concentration of relaxin in the blood serum of pregnant cow and cow with ovarian cyst. *Proc. Silver Jubilee, Kyoto Univ.* pp. 61–66.

39. Wiqvist, N. 1959. Immediate and prolonged effects of relaxin on the spontaneous activity of the mouse and rat uterus. *Acta Endocrinol. Suppl.* **46**: 1–32.

40. Yochim, J., and Zarrow, M. X. 1961. Action of estradiol, progesterone and relaxin in the maintenance of gestation in the castrated pregnant rat. *Fertility Sterility* **12**: 263–276.

41. Zarrow, M. X. 1946. Relaxation in the symphysis pubis of the guinea pig produced by estradiol and progesterone. *Anat. Record* **96**: 528.

42. Zarrow, M. X. 1947. Relaxin content of blood, urine and other tissues of pregnant and postpartum guinea pigs. *Proc. Soc. Exptl. Biol. Med.* **66**: 488–491.

43. Zarrow, M. X. 1949. The antidiuretic action of relaxin-containing preparations. *Proc. Soc. Exptl. Biol. Med.* **71:** 705–707.

44. Zarrow, M. X., and Brennan, D. M. 1959. The action of relaxin on the uterus of the rat, mouse and rabbit. *Ann. N. Y. Acad. Sci.* **75:** 981–990.

45. Zarrow, M. X., Eleftheriou, B. E., Whitecotten, G. L., and King, J. A. 1961. Separation of the pubic symphysis during pregnancy and after treatment with relaxin in two subspecies of *Peromyscus maniculatus. Gen. Comp. Endocrinol.* **1:** 386–391.

46. Zarrow, M. X., Holmstrom, E. G., and Salhanick, H. A. 1955. The concentration of relaxin in the blood serum and other tissues of women during pregnancy. *J. Clin. Endocrinol. Metab.* **15:** 22–27.

47. Zarrow, M. X., and Money, W. L. 1948. Some studies on the pharmacology of relaxin. *J. Pharmacol. Exptl. Therap.* **93:** 180–187.

48. Zarrow, M. X., Neher, G. M., Sikes, D., Brennan, D. M., and Bullard, J. F. 1956. Dilation of the uterine cervix of the sow following treatment with relaxin. *Am. J. Obstet. Gynecol.* **72:** 260–264.

49. Zarrow, M. X., and Rosenberg, B. 1953. Sources of relaxin in the rabbit. *Endocrinology* **53:** 593–598.

50. Zarrow, M. X., Sikes, D., and Neher, G. M. 1954. Changes in uterus, cervix and vulva of gilt following treatment with relaxin. *J. Clin. Endocrinol. Metab.* **14:** 798.

51. Zarrow, M. X., and Yochim, J. 1961. Dilation of the uterine cervix of the rat and accompanying changes during the estrous cycle, pregnancy and following treatment with estradiol, progesterone and relaxin. *Endocrinology* **69:** 292–304.

CHAPTER 5

The Androgens

The testis of the vertebrate performs two functions: (a) the production of sperm, and (b) the production of the male sex hormones, the androgens. Androgens control the secondary sexual characteristics of the male and the secretion of seminal plasma. Contrary to the obvious cyclic nature of ovulation in the female, spermatogenesis and androgen production are either continuous throughout the year in year-round breeders or throughout the season in seasonal breeders.

Sites of Androgen Production

The testes are located in the lower part of the abdomen or in a scrotal sac, if present. The size of the sac is controlled by testosterone; the sac appears to have a role in thermoregulation of the testis. The scrotal testis is, in fact, very sensitive to heat since a temperature equivalent to that of the body causes aspermia. Under normal conditions, the internal temperature of the scrotal sac is approximately 2°C lower than the body temperature. The regulation of testicular temperature is effected by relaxation or contraction of scrotal musculature, the distance of the gland from the body being controlled thereby.

The hormones of the testis are secreted by the cells of Leydig, also known as the interstitial cells in mammals (1) and the interlobular cells in birds. These cells are found interspersed among the seminiferous tubules (Fig. 5-1) and arise from the mesenchymal cells present in the interstitium. Spermatogonia, the male germ cells, line the basement membrane of the seminiferous tubules. These cells give rise through a series of divisions to adult sperm, a process referred to as spermatogenesis. Spermatogenesis has been described as occurring in waves. The remaining major cellular element of the testis are the Sertoli cells. These cells also line the basement membrane of the seminiferous tubules and are thought to play a sustentacular and nutritive role to the developing sperm.

Both functions of the testis are under the control of the pituitary

125

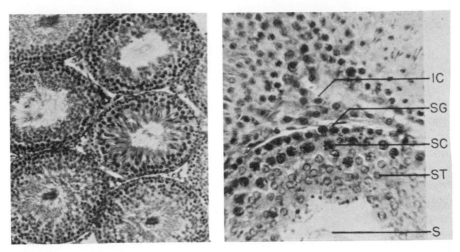

Fig. 5-1. Cross section of a normal testis. *Left:* Cross section of seminiferous tubules of rat testis (from 50× magnification). *Right:* Seminiferous tubules (from 430× magnification). *IC*, interstitial cells (Leydig cells); *SG*, spermatogonia; *SC*, spermatocyte; *ST*, spermatid; *S*, spermatozoa.

gonadotropins: follicle stimulating hormone (FSH) and luteinizing hormone (LH). FSH stimulates spermatogenesis and LH stimulates synthesis and release of testosterone. In the absence of the gonadotropins, spermatogenesis ceases, the Leydig cells fail to secrete androgen, and testicular atrophy occurs. In general, it is assumed that, for the control of androgen release, a feedback mechanism exists that is analogous to the mechanism for the pituitary-thyroid and pituitary-adrenal systems. In the case of testosterone, this is not as clearly seen, although injection of testosterone will cause testicular atrophy. However, the direct application of small amounts of testosterone to the hypothalamus has been found to inhibit both spermatogenesis and androgen release (3). Genetic factors also play a role in the postpubertal activity of the testis (36).

Additional sites of androgen production are the adrenal cortex, the ovary, and probably the placenta. Of these three, the adrenal gland produces the most significant amount of androgens. Under pathological conditions, large amounts of androgen also may be released from the ovary (15).

Nature of the Androgens

Testosterone is the principal androgen of the testis and belongs to the class of hormones known as the steroids. It is a 17β-hydroxylated C_{19} steroid and is related to the androstane series (Fig. 5-2). The hormone apparently is not stored in the body but released to the blood stream, where it circulates, bound loosely to the blood proteins. The

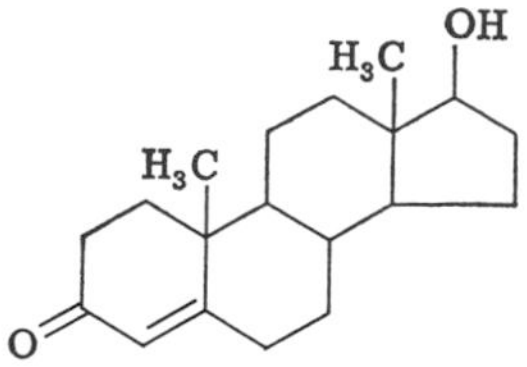

Fig. 5-2. Structure of testosterone.

binding is such that the hormone does not readily filter through the kidney glomeruli but is easily available for utilization by the tissue.

Action of the Androgens

The main endocrine function of the androgens is to maintain the integrity of the reproductive tract and the secondary sex characteristics of the male (Table 5–1). Like estradiol, testosterone causes an increased blood flow and stimulates growth of the target tissues. Although small doses of testosterone inhibit spermatogenesis, presumably acting via the pituitary and the hypothalamus, large doses of the androgen stimulate the testis directly (37). Both the motility and life span of epididymal sperm are influenced by testosterone. The sperm motility in guinea pigs may be increased from a period of 30 days after castration to 70 days in castrated androgen-treated animals. The effect of testosterone on the production of seminal fluid can be shown readily by the electroejaculatory test (13, 28).

Testosterone promotes growth, development, and secretory activity of such accessory sexual tissues as the prostate gland, seminal vesicles, coagulating, bulbourethral, and preputial glands and the growth of the penis, vas deferens, and scrotum (6, 28, 29). Marked atrophy of all these structures occurs after castration. Normally, in the rodent, castration atrophy is completed in about 2 weeks after orchidectomy. Treatment with androgens will either prevent the castration atrophy or return the atrophied glands to normal, including the secretory activity of the glands, as shown by the electroejaculatory test (13, 28).

Testosterone influences a variety of secondary sexual characteristics (31). The distribution of facial, body, and pubic hair in man is a function of androgen secretion. Part of the general body configuration characteristic of the male is attributed to the action of testosterone, i.e., the closure of epiphyseal cartilage plates of long bones is advanced, but not as rapidly as with estrogen. Testosterone also influences the pitch of the voice in man. In other animals, e.g., the rooster, the action of androgen may be seen in the comb, wattles, and spurs. In amphibians, the size of the clasping pads is stimulated by androgens. The hormonal activity of the testis influences both aggressive and male sex behavior (2). Castration has been found to reduce fighting among male experimental animals, and castrated animals are generally more docile. Sexual behavior is markedly reduced by castration or other treatments that reduce the function of the testis; such animals show a decreased tendency to undertake mating activity (16, 38). However, that many other factors also influence behavior is demonstrated by the fact that prepubertal and postpubertal castration do not necessarily induce similar behavioral changes (2). A summary of the physiological actions of testosterone is given in Table 5–1.

TABLE 5–1

SUMMARY OF PHYSIOLOGICAL ACTIONS OF TESTOSTERONE

A. Spermatogenesis
   1. Inhibition via the pituitary and/or hypothalamus
   2. Direct stimulation of spermatogenesis
   3. Prolongation of epididymal sperm life
B. Accessory glands and tissue
   1. Stimulation of growth and secretory activity of seminal vesicles, prostate, coagulating, bulbourethral, and preputial glands
   2. Stimulation of growth of penis and scrotum
C. Secondary sex characteristics
   1. Distribution of body hair
   2. Configuration of body
   3. Comb, wattles, spurs, feathers of birds, clasping pads of amphibia, markings, dorsal spine of certain fishes
   4. Pitch of voice
   5. Behavior, sexual and aggressive
D. Metabolism
   1. Promotes nitrogen retention; protein anabolic action, enzyme synthesis
   2. Increased storage of creatine

PROTEIN ANABOLIC ACTION

Many hormones influence body growth in terms of linear change and body weight. Among these may be listed the pituitary growth hormone, thyroid hormones, and the three groups of steroids, i.e., androgens, estrogens, and corticosteroids. In 1935, a urinary extract with androgenic activity was found to cause nitrogen retention in castrated dogs (18). The active substance was shown to be testosterone, and the protein anabolic action of the male sex hormone has since been demonstrated in rats, dogs, and human beings (20). The nitrogen-retaining effects of testosterone are evidenced by an increased weight gain which is the result of hypertrophy of certain internal organs and an increase in the mass of the general musculature following hormone administration. The attempts to utilize the protein anabolic action of the hormone clinically have been limited by the androgenic side effects of testosterone. A number of new steroids have been synthesized in an effort to obtain a substance with greater anabolic action and little or no androgenicity. Among this group are derivatives of 19-nortestosterone that possess an anabolic activity equal to that of the parent hormone but have only one-tenth the androgenicity (8).

Testosterone also has been shown to influence linear growth prior to epiphyseal fusion. Small doses of the hormone can increase the width of the epiphyseal cartilage whereas large doses are ineffective. In addition, testosterone synergizes with STH in stimulation of the epiphyseal cartilage plate, but once again large doses of the androgen inhibit the action of growth hormone (11, 32, 34). There is some evidence that insulin must be present for testosterone to exert its protein anabolic effect.

The Assay of Androgens

The bioassay of androgens is generally based on the response of the secondary and accessory sexual tissues to treatment with the hormone. Thus, the increase in weight of the ventral prostate and the seminal vesicles of the immature or castrated rat (Fig. 5-3) and the weight or

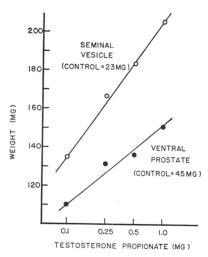

Fig. 5-3. Response of the seminal vesicles and ventral prostate gland of the rat to testosterone propionate.

size of the comb of the castrated cock or immature cockerel have become standard measures of androgenic activity. The enlargement of the levator ani muscle of the rat is used as a test of the protein anabolic action of androgens. A modification of this test has been developed which measures the uptake of α-aminoisobutyric acid-C^{14} by the levator ani muscle (24). This assay is thought to be a more sensitive and reliable test of protein anabolism. In addition, techniques are available for the determination of testosterone in plasma using chromatographic and fluorometric methods (9).

Although testosterone is the most active natural androgen, other substances of steroidal nature possess androgenic activity. The potencies of some of these steroids are compared in Table 5–2. Except for testosterone and ethynyltestosterone, all the compounds cited are found in the urine and may be considered to be degradation products of testosterone. The synthetic steroid ethynyltestosterone (17) is a rather weak androgen and also possesses some measure of progestogenic activity. In the latter aspect, the substance is three to five times as active as progesterone when given orally and about one-fifth as effective parenterally.

The specific biological effectiveness of a steroid can be altered both qualitatively and quantitatively by changes in the chemical structure of the molecule. Because of their structural similarity, some of the progestogens and adrenal steroids also possess a degree of androgenic activity (12). Esterification of the molecule is one method by which biological effectiveness can be changed (25). Testosterone propionate is somewhat more active than testosterone, and the effect of the propionate derivative lasts longer. Other esters, such as the cyclopentyl propionate, have even greater activity. The route of administration also plays an important role in determining the effectiveness of a hormone. Most steroids are least effective when given orally and most effective when given by pellet implantation. The intramuscular and subcutaneous routes of administration are the most common ones for the steroids. These routes are far more effective than the oral route but not as effective as pellet administration. Although most of the androgenic steroids are relatively inactive when administered orally, methyltestosterone is quite potent when given by this route. A comparison of oral activity of some steroids is listed in Table 5–3.

The systemic effect following percutaneous application of steroid hormones was first demonstrated with androgens and estrogens. The application of testosterone, suspended in an ointment, to the shaved backs of castrated guinea pigs and rats resulted in excellent stimulation of the prostate glands and seminal vesicles in both species (29). Daily

TABLE 5–2

COMPARISON OF SOME ANDROGENS BASED ON THE CAPON COMB ASSAY

Substance	Structure	Equiv. to 1.0 IU of androgen [a] (μg)	Comparison of activity [b]
Testosterone		13–17	100
Androsterone		100	6.7
Isoandrosterone		700	46.7
Dehydroiso-androsterone		200–300	16.7
Ethynyl-testosterone		9	600
Etiocholanolone		Inactive	–

[a] 1.0 IU of androgen is equivalent to 100μg of crystalline androsterone.

[b] A value of 100 was assigned to testosterone.

TABLE 5–3

COMPARISON OF THE ORAL ACTIVITY OF VARIOUS ANDROGENS
IN CASTRATED RATS TREATED FOR 10 DAYS[a]

Substance[b]	Weight of seminal vesicles (mg) after treatment		Weight of prostate (mg) after treatment	
	1 mg daily	5 mg daily	1 mg daily	5 mg daily
Methyltestosterone	35	180	90	210
Testosterone	20	59	57	74
Testosterone propionate	15	22	50	65
Androsterone	12	18	42	60
Controls	14	14	40	40

[a] From data of Miescher and Tschopp (23).

[b] Compounds were dissolved in 50% ethyl alcohol.

treatment with 0.6 mg of hormone maintained the weights of the accessory reproductive organs in the castrated animals comparable to that seen in the untreated normal controls. The presence of hair interfered with the percutaneous absorption of the hormone only to a slight degree. Untreated, castrated animals, housed together with the treated animals, also showed stimulation of the seminal vesicles and prostate glands. Thus in experimental work, animals receiving hormone treatment must be caged separately from those which are untreated or those given different doses of the steroids. Leakage of the steroid-containing vehicle from an injection site may contaminate animals on other treatments and influence biological response. While local application is an effective method of administration, the technique is especially usable in only a limited number of instances, such as treatment of the comb of the capon or vagina of the mammal, where the hormone may be applied directly to the target structure.

Biogenesis, Metabolism, and Mechanism of Action

The biosynthetic pathway for the androgens is illustrated in Fig. 5-4. Acetate and cholesterol are the basic precursors, and both pregnenolone and progesterone are important intermediates in the synthesis of testosterone. The hormone is rapidly degraded or metabolized in the liver and to a smaller extent in the kidney. The relatively inactive metabolites of testosterone are excreted in the urine or in the bile and feces in the form of 17-ketosteroids. These urinary androgens are present as water-soluble glucuronides and sulfates. Androsterone, epiandrosterone, and etiocholanolone are the principal ketosteroids present in the urine (Fig. 5-5).

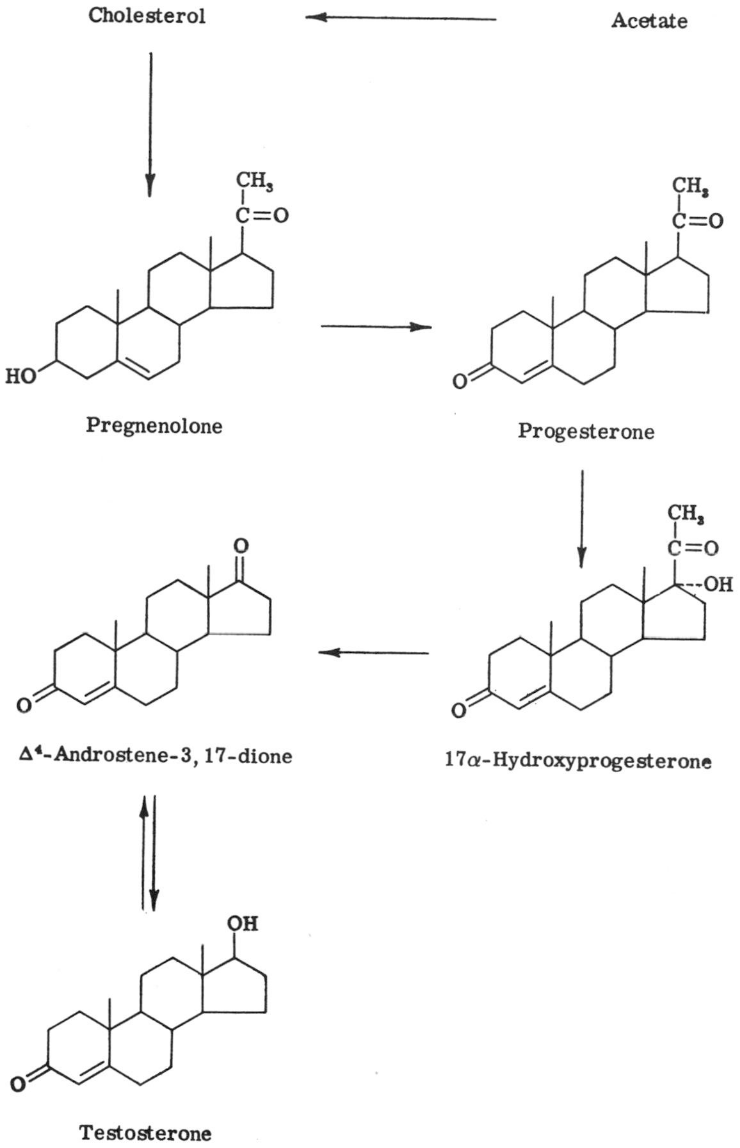

Fig. 5-4. Scheme for the biosynthesis of testosterone (5, 33).

The mechanism of action of androgens is poorly understood at the present time. As with the other hormones, a number of mechanisms are probably involved, depending on the response studied and the target tissue or tissues used. Androgens maintain the primary and accessory

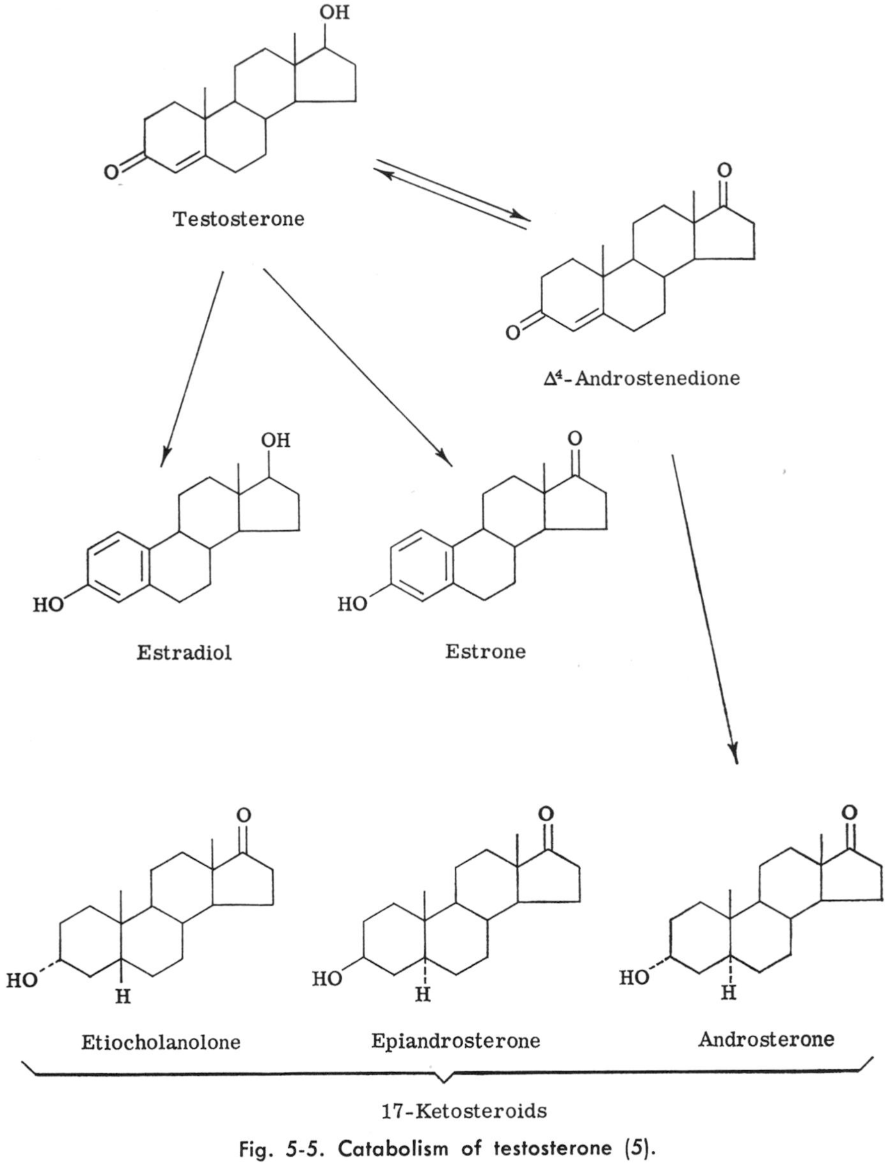

Fig. 5-5. Catabolism of testosterone (5).

sexual tissues, the sex characteristics, and also influence protein metabolism, electrolyte balance and some enzyme concentrations in both sexual and nonsexual tissues. Because the androgens show this variety of actions, a single mechanism accounting for all the responses is difficult to visualize. One suggestion for a possible mechanism deals with the regulation of the rate of synthesis of specific enzyme systems, thus placing the focal point at the level of protein synthesis (5). The increase in the effective concentration of certain enzymes in specific tissues give support to this hypothesis. Androgen treatment results in an increased concentration of the following enzymes in rodents: β-glucuronidase, D-aminooxidase, arginase in kidney, aldolase in prostate, and succinic dehydrogenase in prostate and seminal vesicles. These responses to testosterone represent a true *de novo* synthesis of the enzyme (5). The following hypothesis is suggested: (a) A tissue is in a quiescent state since certain essential enzymes are present in inadequate concentrations. (b) Androgens increase rates of synthesis of essential enzymes to concentrations that permit growth and development. (c) Androgens present specificity of action by selective stimulation of an enzyme in one tissue but not another. (d) The action of the androgen is at the level of control of the rate of enzyme synthesis.

Antiandrogens

Estrogens are usually cited as the typical inhibitors of androgen action; however, other compounds in this category include: progesterone, methylcholanthrene, dehydroepiandrosterone, and 20-methyl-Δ^5-pregnene-3β,20-diol. The relationship of the estrogens to androgens in action

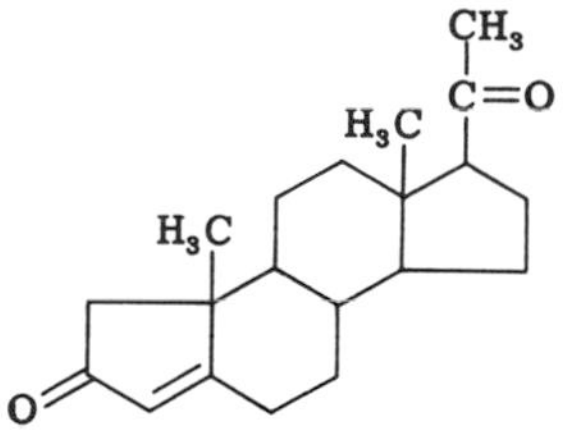

A-Norprogesterone

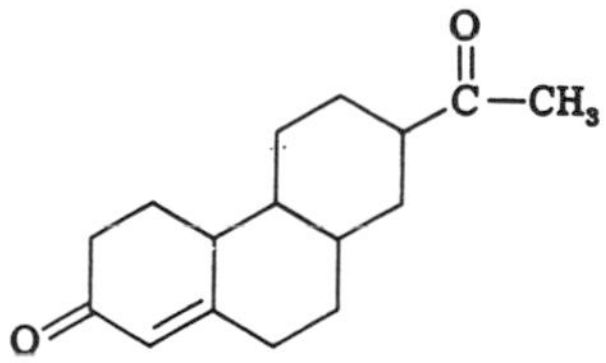

2-Acetyl-7-oxo-1, 2, 3, 4, 4α,4β,5, 6, 7, 9, 10, 10α- dodecahydrophenanthrene

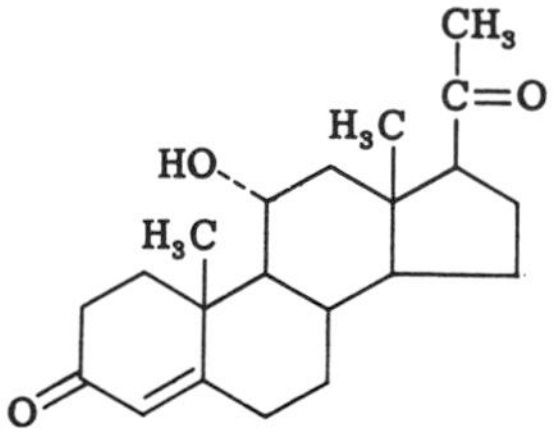

11α-Hydroxyprogesterone

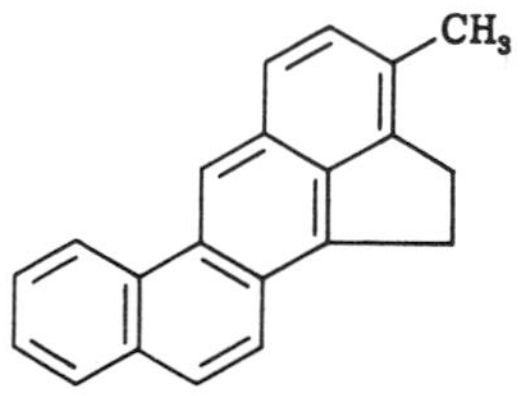

Methylcholanthrene

Fig. 5-6. Structure of some antiandrogens.

on the accessory sexual tissue is a complex one. In the intact rat, large doses of estrogen inhibit the action of testosterone, probably the result of direct antagonism of testosterone at the tissue level as well as inhibition of the pituitary gland. Smaller doses of estrogen, however, cause an increase in the weight of the seminal vesicle and produce an additive effect when given simultaneously with testosterone. Such an effect is clearly seen after treatment of prepubertal or castrated rats. Estrogen causes hypertrophy of the fibromuscular elements in the seminal vesicles whereas the androgens stimulate secretory epithelium. Seminal vesicles of the mouse or hamster do not respond in such a manner.

The synthesis of A-norprogesterone and the nonsteroidal phenanthrene derivative, 2-acetyl-7-oxo-1,2,3,4,4α,4β,5,6,7,9,10,10α-dodecahydrophenanthrene (Fig. 5-6), led to the discovery that these compounds possess antiandrogenic activity (4, 22). The phenanthrene derivative is of special interest since this nonsteroidal compound inhibits the action of testosterone in the rat androgen and chick comb assays, yet is itself devoid of hormonal effects (7).

EXPERIMENT 5-1

Orchidectomy in the Rodent*

Castration in the male is a rather simple operation, especially in animals with external testes. In such animals, the testes are usually removed through a small incision made in the scrotum. Orchidectomy results in changes in protein and fat metabolism of the organism as well as in atrophy of the accessory and modification of the secondary sexual characteristics and sex behavior patterns.

Procedure

After anesthesia has been induced with ether, place the animal on an operating board, on its back. The hind legs then may be tied down and, if desired, the hair overlying the scrotal area clipped. Cleanse the skin with Zephiran. An incision is made through the skin of the scrotum, and the testis on one side is separated from the surrounding tissue by blunt dissection. A second incision is then made through the transparent tunica vaginalis. This enables the tunica to be retracted and the testis to be exposed. A ligature is made around the tunica vaginalis and spermatic cord, thus interrupting the blood supply and leaving the entire testis exposed. The gland is removed by a cut close to the ligature. The second testis is then removed in the same manner and the skin incision

* Cf. references (2, 21).

is closed with two or three sutures. Care must be taken not to interfere with the function of the rectum and anus.

Experimental

Castrate one group of adult male rats or mice and keep a second group as controls.

Kill several animals according to the following schedule and weigh the ventral prostate, seminal vesicles, and coagulating gland: day 1 (day of operation), day 3 or 4, day 8, day 15, and day 21. Record total and relative weight (mg/100 gm). Tabulate and graph data to show change in accessory gland weight as a function of time after castration.

See Fig. 5-7 for diagram of male reproductive tract.

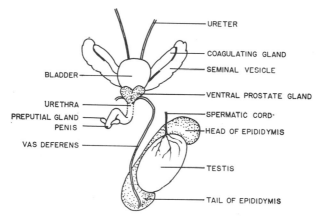

Fig. 5-7. Diagram of the reproductive tract of the male rat.

EXPERIMENT 5-2

Caponization of the Cockerel

Though the bird does not have a scrotal testis, castration in this animal is nevertheless rather simple procedure. The operation may be performed without anesthesia, observing the usual aseptic techniques.

Procedure

Grasp the bird and fold the wings, one under the other, on the dorsal side. Restrain the bird by holding the wings and legs and applying slight traction in opposite directions. The bird may be placed on a V-shaped operating board and restrained by tying the legs and placing a strap across the body. With the bird lying on its side, an incision is made in the last intercostal space just ventral to the uncinate process of the 6th vertebral rib. A rib spreader is inserted, and the exposed air sacs are punctured with a surgical hook. Deflation of the air sacs will expose the testes lying at the anterior pole of each kidney. The gonads are shaped like small elongated beans; they may be yellow, gray, black, or any combination of these colors. The testis is grasped with a broad forceps (Pratt-Smith or Pennington hemostatic) and removed with gentle traction. If the testis is grasped too close to the point of attachment, fatal hemorrhage may occur as a result of disruption of the posterior vena cava. Both testes may be removed through one incision, but often the operation will be performed more easily if incisions are made on each side. Suturing the incision after removal of the gonad is unnecessary.

A 12-hour precastration starvation period will greatly facilitate the operation. Postoperatively, an occasional bird may "balloon" (wind puff) if the skin incision heals more rapidly than the air sacs. Incising the skin to allow the air to escape corrects the condition. The deflation may have to be repeated two or three times. Birds 6–8 weeks old, weighing about a pound, are the best surgical risks.

Experimental

Castrate one group of cockerels and leave a second group as controls.

Kill several birds from each group weekly over a 4-week period and weigh the combs. The combs are to be cut off at the base of the head with a sharp razor.

Compare the growth curve of the combs in the two groups of birds.

EXPERIMENT 5–3

The Bioassay of Androgens by the Chick Comb Method*

It has been stated previously that testosterone influences the secondary sex characteristics of male animals. The crest of lizards and combs of birds are under androgen influence. In the preceding experiment (5–2), changes in the comb of birds may be noted after castration. The direct application of androgenic hormones to the comb is a case in which local action of the hormone may be seen.

Procedure and Experimental

Single-comb cockerels are distributed into groups of 10 animals each,

* Cf. references (4–6, 27, 31).

and a dose-response curve is to be established for several androgens. The chicks are kept in a temperature-controlled brooder with a controlled photoperiod. Although the different treatment groups should be housed separately, combined groups may be maintained in one tier of the brooder and the groups marked with dyes of various colors. Treatment is started when the birds are 48–72 hours of age. The hormones are dissolved in ether, and the solution is applied to the lateral surface of the comb, using a 27-gauge needle and 0.25-ml tuberculin syringe. The treatment is continued for 7 days; the birds are killed and autopsied on the eighth day. The combs are dissected out (cut off with sharp scalpel or razor blade close to the surface of the head) and weighed. The results are expressed as milligrams per 100 gm of body weight.

Various androgens may be dissolved in ether and the following concentration ranges prepared: testosterone, 5–20 μg/ml; androsterone, 50–200 μg/ml; ethynyltestosterone, 1–10 μg/ml. Apply 0.2 ml of steroid solution to the comb daily for 7 days. Plot the dose response curve for each androgen tested. At least 10 chicks must be used at each dose level of a given steroid.

EXPERIMENT 5–4

The Bioassay of Androgens in the Rat or Mouse*

A classical technique used for the assay of androgens in the rodent is based on the responses of the seminal vesicles and prostate glands in immature or castrated males (Fig. 5-3). If castrated animals are used, a period of 2 weeks must elapse after orchidectomy in order to ensure that involution of accessory organs is complete; a baseline is then established from which the responses to androgens can be quantified. If the results are to be expressed in terms of the international standard, then crystalline androsterone must be assayed at the same same to compare the results. One international unit of androgen is defined as the biological activity equivalent to 100 μg of crystalline androsterone. Since crystalline testosterone is also readily available now, results may be expressed in milligram equivalents of testosterone.

Statistical analysis of data is an important aspect of biological assay, especially since a variability of response to a single dose of a given compound is characteristic of living organisms. Thus information on the confidence limits of the data or standard errors of the means aid in estimating the significance of the results. It would be a valuable adjunct to this experiment if the results were to be subjected to a very elemen-

* Cf. references (6, 12, 21, 27, 28, 38).

tary statistical analysis. Texts on statistical analysis will provide information for undertaking the students' t test. While this test is suggested as an introduction to the use of statistics in biological problems, it should be recognized that more sophisticated analyses are available.

Procedure and Experimental

Six groups of 10 mice each are castrated, and 10 additional mice are retained as normal controls. The animals are rested for 2 weeks following surgery to allow for castration atrophy.

The assay of androgen is to be performed using testosterone propionate. The animals are injected daily for 7 days by the subcutaneous route. The assigned dose of hormone is administered in 0.1 ml oil solution. Only the vehicle, 0.1 ml oil, is given to control groups. Each treatment group must be placed in separate cages. On day 8, 24 hours after the last injection, all animals are killed. The seminal vesicles, ventral prostate, adrenal and pituitary glands are removed, cleaned of adhering fat, and weighed on a torsion balance to the nearest 0.1 mg.

For *each group*, record body and gland weight of the individual animals in tabular form. Prepare tables and graphs of the data both as absolute weights and as percentages of body weights. Apply a statistical analysis to the results. See tabulation for assigned daily dosages of testosterone propionate for each group.

Group 1	Noncastrated	Controls
Group 2	Castrated	Controls
Group 3	Castrated	100 μg
Group 4	Castrated	200 μg
Group 5	Castrated	500 μg
Group 6	Castrated	1.0 mg
Group 7	Castrated	2.5 mg

EXPERIMENT 5–5

Androgenic Activity of Different Steroids*

Steroids of the testis, ovary, and adrenal gland show some similarity in action because of similarities in chemical structure of the molecules. Some of the steroid hormones of the ovary and adrenal gland are known to possess androgenic activity. In the adrenal gland, active androgens may be secreted. Masculinization in females has been observed as a result of tumors of the adrenal gland.

* Cf. references (5, 6, 12, 15, 27).

Procedure and Experimental

Three male rats are castrated for each of 8 groups and 3 normal rats are maintained as controls. After a 2-week rest period to permit castration atrophy, the treatments indicated in the accompanying tabulation are initiated.

Group 1	Normal control	0.1 ml oil, subcutaneous (sc)
Group 2	Castrated control	0.1 ml oil, sc
Group 3	Estradiol	0.1 mg, sc
Group 4	Progesterone	0.5 mg, sc
Group 5	DCA	0.5 mg, sc
Group 6	Testosterone propionate	0.1 mg, sc
Group 7	Stilbestrol	0.1 mg, sc
Group 8	Testosterone propionate	0.1 mg, oral, by stomach tube
Group 9	Methyltestosterone	0.1 mg, oral, by stomach tube

The animals are treated with the hormones in 0.1 ml oil daily for 7 days.* A complete endocrine postmortem examination is to be performed 24 hours after the last injection. The following glands and organs are to be dissected out and weighed: pituitary, thyroid, ventral prostate, seminal vesicles, coagulating and adrenal glands, kidney, and thymus. The thymus gland can be readily visualized by exposing the gland and placing a drop or two of Carnoy's fluid on it (see Appendix A-9).

EXPERIMENT 5–6

Total Neutral 17-Ketosteroid Determination†

Since testosterone is degraded and excreted in the urine in the form of 17-ketosteroids (17-KS), determination of the levels of these materials in urine gives some indication of the state of gonadal function. However, the adrenal glands also produce steroids that contribute to the 17-KS excretion level. Therefore, this determination is nonspecific for the testes but is of diagnostic and experimental value.

Dehydroisoandrosterone serves as the standard for such determinations. While the procedure outlined is primarily based on urine samples from human beings and other larger animals, pooled urine samples

---

* Although this assay is based on a 7-day treatment schedule, it is possible to use a much shorter schedule. However, a decrease in the number of daily treatments would require an increase in the daily dosage of hormone to yield significant results.

† Cf. references (6, 23).

from smaller animals may be used. For this experiment, 24-hour urine samples from students in the class may be used.

Procedure

Reagents

1. *HCl, concentrated*
2. *Absolute ether*
3. *NaOH 10% aqueous*
4. *KOH, 5 N*
5. *m-Dinitrobenzene, recrystallized, 2% in ethanol*
6. *Ethanol, absolute*
7. *Ethanol, 75%*
8. *Amyl acetate*
9. *Dehydroisoandrosterone* (20 μg/0.2 ml absolute alcohol)

Determination

1. Place 10 ml of urine in a test tube.
2. Add 3 ml concentrated HCl.
3. Place tube in water bath at 80°–85°C for 10 minutes.
4. Cool hydrolyzed urine rapidly and place 10 ml in a separatory funnel.
5. Extract with 40 ml of absolute ether (shake for 30 seconds).
6. Wash ether extract with 20 ml of 10% NaOH.
7. Wash ether extract with 20 ml distilled H_2O.
8. Six aliquots of the ether extract (5 ml each) are pipetted into test tubes and evaporated to dryness in water bath.
9. To each of three of the tubes from Step 8 add 0.2 ml of absolute alcohol, 0.3 ml of 5 N KOH, and 0.2 ml of 2% m-dinitrobenzene in absolute alcohol. Save the other three tubes for standardization (Step 9a).
10. Shake and place in the dark in water bath at 27°C for 90 minutes.
11. Remove tubes, add 1 ml of 75% alcohol to each tube, and shake.
12. Add 1 ml of amyl acetate.
13. Shake and swirl the tubes vigorously for 10 seconds.
14. Place in the dark for 8 minutes.
15. Transfer amyl acetate-alcohol layer (supernatant) into a cuvette.
16. Read the optical density immediately in a Beckman spectrophotometer at 510 mμ.
17. Repeat for the other two tubes.

Standardization

9a. Add 0.2 ml of standard solution (dehydroisoandrosterone, 20 μg/

0.2 ml) in place of the absolute alcohol to the three remaining aliquots from Step 8 and run through as above. The difference between the readings on these two types of aliquots is the standard value.

Note 1: In actual practice, stagger the tubes at 2-minute intervals starting with the addition of the *m*-dinitrobenzene (Step 9).

Note 2: The colorimetric determination is made on three aliquots. The remaining three aliquots are used for the standard.

Experimental

Compare the 24-hour excretion of urinary ketosteroids in several individuals, including males, females, and different age groups.

EXPERIMENT 5-7

Myotropic Action of Androgens as Demonstrated by the Levator Ani Test*

The levator ani assay was developed following observations on the myotropic and nitrogen-retaining properties of steroids. The compounds that were found to possess the greatest protein anabolic activity as determined by the classical nitrogen retention methods also were found to show marked ability to increase the weight of the levator ani muscle. Though the response follows a satisfactory relation for an assay, the test has been criticized with respect to its validity in regard to general body anabolism. Some investigators feel that the levator ani test only reflects the action of androgens on general body anabolism. Nevertheless the test has been used extensively in the screening of compounds. Anabolic agents tested by this method have been shown to induce positive nitrogen balance in human beings though other metabolic side affects also have been detected. The levator ani test may be carried out by treating immature castrated male rats for 1 week and then dissecting out and weighing the levator ani muscle (Fig. 5-8).

Procedure and Experimental

Male rats (21 days old) are castrated; treatment is started at the time of castration. The rats are given daily subcutaneous injections of 0.1 ml of the steroid solution in oil for 7 days. On the 8th day, 24 hours after the last injection, the animals are killed. Depending on the number of rats available, treatment groups (see tabulation) can be established; at least 5 animals should be in each treatment group.

° Cf. references (8, 14, 18, 20, 24, 30, 34, 39).

Group 1	Injected control	0.1 ml oil
Group 2	Testosterone propionate	0.1 mg
Group 3	Testosterone propionate	0.25 mg
Group 4	Testosterone propionate	0.5 mg
Group 5	Testosterone propionate	1.0 mg
Group 6	Testosterone propionate	2.5 mg
Group 7	Testosterone propionate	5 mg

If sufficient animals are available, a second assay should be carried out with methylandrostenediol or some other steroid with marked protein anabolic activity.

At the time of postmortem, the seminal vesicles and prostate glands can be removed with the levator ani, and the action of testosterone on these structures can be examined (see Experiment 5–4). The levator

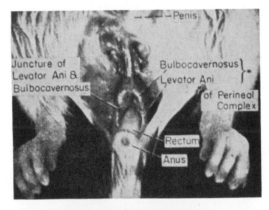

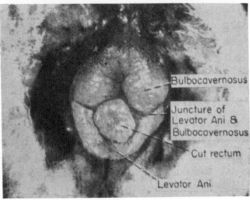

Fig. 5-8. Dissection of the levator ani muscle of the rat. From Herschberger *et al.* (14).

ani muscle is dissected out by removing the skin from the scrotal area between the base of the penis and the anus. The perineal area is then cleared of fat and connective tissue. Thus the perineal complex is disclosed, including the constriction indicating the point at which the levator ani joins the bulbocavernosus muscle (Fig. 5-8). The rectum is then transected caudal to the levator ani; the muscle is freed from the rectum, removed, and weighed on a torsion balance.

EXPERIMENT 5–8

The Effect of Androgens on Renal β-Glucuronidase*

Androgens possess the ability to induce hypertrophy of the kidney and to increase the renal β-glucuronidase. In recent years, data have been presented to indicate that this response is specific for androgens. The question has been raised whether this response is related to the masculinizing action or the protein anabolic action of the androgens or to neither of these. The animal of choice for this response is the mouse. Since different strains show various degrees of response, the strain should be carefully selected and tested against an androgen standard.

Procedure†

Reagents

1. *Phenolphthalein monoglucuronide cinchonidine.* Prepare as directed by Talalay *et al.*† or purchase sodium salt from a biochemical supply company.

2. *Acetate buffer, 0.1 M.* To 5.785 gm sodium acetate (3 H_2O) in water, add 3.25 ml glacial acetic acid; make up to 1 liter with distilled water.

3. *Glycine buffer.* To glycine, 16.30 gm, and NaCl, 12.65 gm, dissolved in water, add 10.9 ml of concentrated NaOH (100 gm NaOH in 100 ml water); make up to 1 liter. The pH of this solution should be 10.45.

4. *Phenolphthalein.* Phenolphthalein (100 mg) dissolved in 100 ml of 80% ethyl alcohol.

5. *Ethyl acetate*

6. *Hydrochloric acid, 0.2 N*

7. *NaOH, 0.1 N*

* Cf. references (6, 10, 19).

† Cf. P. Talalay, W. H. Fishman, and C. Huggins, *J. Biol. Chem.* **166**: 757–772 (1946).

Preparation of Substrate

Mix 0.788 gm phenolphthalein glucuronide cinchonidine with 0.2 N HCl in a separatory funnel. Extract the mixture with ethyl acetate by shaking. Draw off the ethyl acetate layer and evaporate to dryness *in vacuo* to provide phenolphthalein glucuronic acid. Neutralize the salt by adding 0.1 N NaOH. The final solution should contain the neutralized salt in 100 ml distilled water. Store the solution in the refrigerator.

Assay

Grind the tissue to be assayed (15–30 mg) in an ice-chilled homogenizer with 5 ml of ice-cold water. The grinding should be complete within 1–2 minutes. Transfer the homogenate to a centrifuge tube and centrifuge it. The supernatant is decanted, and aliquots of the liquid (0.5 ml) are assayed for β-glucuronidase.

1. Transfer 4 ml of 0.1 M acetate buffer into all glass-stoppered test tubes. Add 0.5 ml of 0.01% sodium phenolphthalein glucuronide to the experimental tubes, *not* to the controls. Put samples in a water bath at 38°C and allow tubes to come to temperature.

2. At timed intervals, add 0.5 ml of enzyme solution (supernatant liquid from tissue extract) to the experimental tubes. Mix the solutions, stopper, and incubate for *exactly* 60 minutes.

3. At the end of the incubation period, add 5 ml of 0.4 M glycine buffer to each *experimental* tube. Add 5 ml of the glycine buffer to the control tube, then add 0.5 ml substrate (sodium phenolphthalein glucuronide). At this point, it may be necessary to centrifuge the experimental tubes for 5–10 minutes to remove any precipitated tissue protein.

4. Read samples in colorimeter at 540 mμ, using the control tubes to set the instrument to 100% transmission (or zero absorbancy).

5. Calibration: Prepare 1-ml dilutions of phenolphthalein containing 5–60 μg of the indicator. Prepare tubes as follows:

> (a) 4.0 ml of 0.1 M acetate buffer
> (b) 5.0 ml of 0.4 M glycine buffer
> (c) 1.0 ml of phenolphthalein dilution

Read samples against distilled water in a colorimeter set at 540 mμ.

6. The unit for glucuronidase: 1 unit of β-glucuronidase liberates 1 μg of phenolphthalein from the test substrate in 1 hour at 38°C. The phenolphthalein released by the experimental tubes may be determined by reading from a graph of the calibration values (absorbancy of phenolphthalein vs. micrograms phenolphthalein): micrograms phenolphthalein $\times$ 10 = micrograms phenolphthalein released by enzyme in

total weight of tissue; this is equivalent to units of β-glucuronidase in total weight of tissue.

Experimental

Five groups, 3 male mice in each, are to be used in this experiment. The animals may be castrated or not. All mice are to be given daily subcutaneous injections of the test substance, in 0.1 ml oil, for 14 days (see tabulations).

Group 1	Oil controls	
Group 2	Testosterone propionate	0.05 mg/day
Group 3	Testosterone propionate	0.1 mg/day
Group 4	Testosterone propionate	0.15 mg/day
Group 5	Testosterone propionate	0.20 mg/day

On day 15, 24 hours after the last injection, the animals are to be killed by cervical fracture and weighed. The kidneys are removed, weighed, and analyzed for β-glucuronidase.

EXPERIMENT 5–9

Electroejaculatory Test*

In 1930, electrical stimulation was found to induce ejaculation in the guinea pig. A similar response has been obtained in the ram, rat, and other animals. The response has been utilized as a test for the functional status of the seminal vesicles. No ejaculate can be secured in the castrated animal, but treatment with testosterone will bring back the response. A quantitative measure may also be obtained by allowing the ejaculate to coagulate and then weighing the material.

Procedure

The ejaculatory test is carried out on the adult anesthetized rat tied to an animal board, ventral side down. Place clip electrodes on the ear and tongue. (*Note:* as an alternate, electrodes may be placed on the ear and in the rectum.) Three successive electric shocks are to be administered at intervals 1 minute apart. If a stimulator is not available, a Powerstat or Variac may be used. Small alligator clips may be attached to the ends of an electric cord and the male end of the cord inserted into the output socket of the Powerstat. The instrument is then connected to a 110-volt alternating current source. Each of the three shocks should be administered for 10 seconds at 30 volts.

* Cf. references (13, 28).

Examine the animal for the presence of coagulated ejaculate. If an ejaculate is present, obtain the weight of the material. Tabulate the effects of the various treatments on ejaculation of the male rat.

Experimental

Place adult male rats on treatment (see tabulation) and carry out the electroejaculatory test on days 1, 7, and 14.

Normal	—	
Castrated	Oil	
Castrated	Testosterone propionate	0.2 mg/day
Castrated	Testosterone propionate	0.5 mg/day
Castrated	Testosterone propionate	1.0 mg/day
Castrated	Testosterone propionate	2.0 mg/day
Castrated	Estradiol	10 μg/day
Normal	Estradiol	10 μg/day

EXPERIMENT 5–10

Male Sexual Behavior*

Sexual behavior in the male varies with the species but can be observed readily in almost all animals. These responses may include such precopulatory phenomena as sniffing, nuzzling, or general excitement in the presence of a female. In addition to showing general interest in the female, e.g., following her about, the animal may attempt to mount with or without intromission and copulation. Interference with the functioning of the testes modifies the normal mating responses of most animals. However, the psychological factors involved in such responses must be recognized, for a variety of other conditions, in addition to endocrine physiology, will influence the mating behavior of a particular animal. Although prepubertal castration generally leads to reduced sexual and aggressive activity, conflicting data have been obtained from behavioral studies after postpubertal orchidectomy. Testosterone treatment leads to precocious sexual activity.

Procedure and Experimental

Select at least 9 adult male rats and distribute the animals into treatment groups (see tabulation). At the end of 2 weeks, begin the mating activity test.

Group 1: Normal controls, oil injected
Group 2: Castrated, allow 2 weeks for castration atrophy

* Cf. references (2, 16, 35).

Group 3: Castrate and immediately initiate testosterone propionate therapy (1.0 mg/0.1 ml oil per day) (*Note:* if possible treat other animals with different dosages of testosterone propionate.)

The mating activity test should be carried out at least 3 hours after the onset of the dark phase of the photoperiod of the animal room and should be performed in subdued light. Obtain several female rats in natural proestrus as determined by vaginal smears. Enough female animals should be available so that, should copulation occur, the female may be removed from the experiment.

Construct a confinement about 2×2 feet square, 12 inches high. The bottom of the confinement, the animal room floor, may be covered with brown paper or bedding material. Place the test male in the confinement and allow 5 minutes for the animal to become accustomed to the area. Introduce the female and record the responses of the male during the next 5 minutes. Note whether the male shows interest in the female, following her, sniffing, etc. Secondly, note if the male attempts to or does mount the female and whether intromission occurs. Record the types of responses for each treatment group. (Observe the actions of the female also during the time of copulation; quivering of ears, lordosis, lifting of tail, etc.)

EXPERIMENT 5–11

Fighting Behavior in Male Mice*

It was readily recognized in ancient times that castration led to numerous changes. Among these changes, it was noted that castrated animals became more docile. In recent times, many studies have been carried out to determine the effect of testosterone on the aggressive behavior of male animals. Most experimenters readily note the aggressive behavior of some strains of mice when a strange male is introduced into a cage with other male mice. It has been found that androgens are in a large measure responsible for this activity. However, castrated adult males do not necessarily become more tractable.

Procedure and Experimental

A group of 9 adult male mice are to be treated as indicated in the tabulation. (*Note:* Marking the fur of *each* animal with picric acid solution would be of value at the time of the test.)

Group 1: Normal, oil-injected controls
Group 2: Castrated, allow 2 weeks for castration atrophy

* Cf. reference (2).

Group 3: Castrate and immediately initiate testosterone propionate injections,
    0.5 mg/day

Immediately after surgery, isolate all animals by housing each mouse in a separate cage. At the end of the 30-day period, use a separate cage to test the fighting response. Simultaneously place into the cage 2 normal controls and observe for 5 minutes. Note whether signs of aggression are evident and which animal is the more belligerent. Test each control animal against other control mice. Then proceed to test each castrated mouse and each castrated testosterone-treated animal against members of the respective groups. Finally initiate between-group testing, i.e., test normal animals against castrated animals (groups 1 vs. 2, 1 vs. 3, and 2 vs. 3). Establish a hierarchy of response. Which group or individual is most aggressive?

References

1. Ancel, P., and Bouin, P. 1903. Histogenèsis de la glande interstitielle du testicule chez le porc. *Compt. Rend. Soc. Biol.* **55**: 1680–1682.
2. Beach, F. A. 1948. "Hormones and Behavior." Harper (Hoeber), New York.
3. Davidson, J. M., and Sawyer, C. H. 1961. Evidence for an hypothalamic focus on inhibition of gonadotropin by androgen in the male. *Proc. Soc. Exptl. Biol. Med.* **107**: 4–7.
4. Dorfman, R. I. 1959. The anti-androgenic activity of a phenanthrene derivative in the chick. *Endocrinology* **64**: 464–466.
5. Dorfman, R. I. 1961. Mechanism of Action of Steroid Hormones: Androgens, *in* "Mechanism of Action of Steroid Hormones," (C. A. Villee and L. L. Engle, eds.). Pergamon Press, New York.
6. Dorfman, R. I., and Shipley, R. A. 1956. "Androgens Biochemistry, Physiology and Clinical Significance." Wiley, New York.
7. Dorfman, R. I., and Stevens, D. 1960. Some biological properties of a perhydro-phenanthrene derivative. *Endocrinology* **67**: 394–406.
8. Eisenberg, E., and Gordan, G. S. 1950. The levator ani muscle of the rat as an index of myotropic activity of steroidal hormones. *J. Pharmacol. Exptl. Therap.* **99**: 38–44.
9. Finkelstein, M., Forchielli, E., and Dorfman, R. I. 1961. Estimation of testosterone in human plasma. *J. Clin. Endocrinol. Metab.* **21**: 98–101.
10. Fishman, W. H. 1951. β-Glucuronidase and the action of steroid hormones. *Ann. N. Y. Acad. Sci.* **54**: 548–557.
11. Geschwind, I. I., and Li, C. H. 1955. The tibia test for growth hormone, *in* "Hypophyseal Growth Hormone" (R. W. Smith, O. H. Gaebler, and C. N. H. Long, eds.), pp. 28–53. McGraw-Hill, New York.
12. Greene, R. R., Burrill, M. W., and Thomson, D. M. 1940. Further studies on the androgenicity of progesterone. *Endocrinology* **27**: 469–472.
13. Gunn, R. M. C. 1936. Fertility in sheep: Artificial production of seminal ejaculation and the characters of the spermatozoa contained therein. *Bull. Council Sci. Ind. Res. Australia* **94**: 116.
14. Herschberger, L. G., Shipley, E. G., and Meyer, R. K. 1953. Myotropic activity of 19-nortestosterone and other steroids determined by modified levator ani muscle method. *Proc. Soc. Exptl. Biol. Med.* **85**: 175–180.

15. Hill, R. T., and Strong, M. T. 1940. Ovaries secrete male hormone. *Endocrinology* **27**: 79–82.

16. Hupp, E. W., Pace, H. B., Furchtgott, E., and Murphree, R. L. 1960. Effect of fetal irradiation on mating activity in male rats. *Psychol. Rept.* **7**: 289–294.

17. Inhoffen, H. H., and Holweg, W. 1938. Neue per os-wirksame weibliche Keimdrüsen-Derivate: 17-Aethinyl-Oestradiol und Pregnen-in-on-3-ol-17-ol-17. *Naturwissenschaften* **26**: 96.

18. Kochakian, C. D., and Murlin, J. R. 1935. The effect of male hormone on the protein and energy metabolism of castrate dogs. *J. Nutr.* **10**: 437–459.

19. Kochakian, C. D. 1946. The role of hydrolytic enzymes in some of the metabolic activities of steroid hormones. *Recent Progr. Hormone Res.* **1**: 177–214.

20. Kochakian, C. D. 1946. The protein anabolic effects of steroid hormones. *Vitamins Hormones* **4**: 255–310.

21. Korenchevsky, V. 1950. The influence of cryptochidism and castration on body weight, fat deposition and the sexual and endocrine organs of male rats. *J. Pathol. Bacteriol.* **33**: 607–636.

22. Lerner, L. J., Bianchi, A., and Borman, A. 1960. A norprogesterone, an androgen antagonist. *Proc. Soc. Exptl. Biol. Med.* **103**: 172–175.

23. Masuda, M., and Thuline, H. C. 1953. An improved method for determination of urinary 17-ketosteroids. *J. Clin. Endocrinol. Metab.* **13**: 581–586.

24. Metcalf, W., and Broich, T. 1961. A rapid reproducible and sensitive levator ani test for anabolic activity. *Proc. Soc. Exptl. Biol. Med.* **107**: 744–748.

25. Miescher, K., Wettstein, A., and Tschopp, E. 1936. The activation of the male sex hormones. *Biochem. J.* **30**: 1970–1977 and 1977–1989.

26. Miescher, K., and Tschopp, E. 1938. Über orale Wirksamkeit mannlicher Sexual-Hormon. *Schweiz. Med. Wochschr.* **68**: 1258.

27. Moore, C. R. 1939. Biology of the testis. *In* "Sex and Internal Secretions" (E. Allen, C. H. Danforth, and E. A. Doisy, eds.), 2nd ed., Chap. 7. Williams and Wilkins, Baltimore, Maryland.

28. Moore, C. R., and Gallagher, T. F. 1930. Seminal vesicle and prostate function as a testis hormone indicator: the electric ejaculation test. *Am. J. Anat.* **45**: 39–69.

29. Moore, C. R., Lamar, J. K., and Back, N. 1938. Cutaneous absorption of sex hormones. *J. Am. Med. Assoc.* **111**: 11–14.

30. Nimni, M. E., and Bavettov, L. A. 1961. Effect of testosterone propionate on the tissue protein synthesis in the castrated male rat. *Proc. Soc. Exptl. Biol. Med.* **106**: 738–740.

31. Pezard, A. 1920. Secondary sexual characteristics and endocrinology. *Endocrinology* **4**: 527–540.

32. Reiss, H., Fernandes, J. E., and Bola, Y. M. L. 1946. The peripheral inhibitory influence of large doses of testosterone on epiphyseal cartilaginous growth. *Endocrinology* **38**: 65–70.

33. Savard, K., and Goldzieher, J. W. 1960. Biosynthesis of steroids in stallion testis tissue. *Endocrinology* **66**: 617–624.

34. Simpson, M. W., Marx, E., Becks, H., and Evans, H. M. 1944. The effect of testosterone propionate on the body weight and skeletal system of hypophysectomized rats, synergism with pituitary growth hormone. *Endocrinology* **35**: 309–316.

35. Stone, C. 1940. Precocious copulatory activity induced in male rats by subcutaneous injections of testosterone propionate. *Endocrinology* **26**: 511–515.

36. Vilar, O., and Hertz, R. 1958. Postnatal histogenesis and endocrine functions of abnormal testes in the A × C rat. *Proc. Soc. Exptl. Biol. Med.* **98**: 553–557.
37. Wakeling, A. 1959. The effect of gonadotrophins and androgen on spermiogenesis in the immature rat. *J. Endocrinol.* **19**: 263–273.
38. Witschi, E., Levine, W. T., and Hill, R. T. 1932. Endocrine reactions of X-ray sterilized males. *Proc. Soc. Exptl. Biol. Med.* **29**: 1024–1026.
39. Werner, M., Hitz, A., Thoehen, H., and Bauman, H. R. 1961. Stoffwechseluntersuchungen am Menschen mit einem anabolen Steroid (Methandrostenolon). *Klin. Wochschr.* **39**: 998–106.

CHAPTER 6

Epinephrine and Norepinephrine

The concept that the adrenal medulla secreted a substance or substances with a catechol nucleus developed from the report by Vulpian in 1856 that this tissue developed a color upon treatment with ferric chloride. The exact nature of the substance and its action were not known until 1895, when Oliver and Shafer reported a marked rise in blood pressure following the injection of extracts of the adrenal medulla. Finally in 1902, Abel (1) prepared from medullary tissue an active crystalline compound which was called epinephrine. Subsequently a second amine, norepinephrine, was isolated. In the ensuing years, a vast amount of information on the action of the pressor amines of the medulla has been accumulated.

Sites of Formation

The medullary hormones are secreted primarily by the chromaffin tissue of the adrenal medulla. In addition, the adrenergic terminal nerve endings of the sympathetic nervous system release norepinephrine and to a very slight degree epinephrine. Since adrenomedullated animals live quite well under controlled conditions, it is obvious that the adrenal medulla is not essential for life.

The medulla is ectodermal in origin and differentiates from the cells of the neural crest in conjunction with the sympathetic ganglia. The cells of the medulla are modified postganglionic cells and maintain contact with the preganglionic fibers of the sympathetic nervous system in the adult. Secretory activity is largely regulated by the splanchnic nerves. Stimulation of these nerves causes release of the hormones, whereas sectioning of the nerves or direct application of nicotine to the medulla prevent the release of the hormones.

The adrenal gland of the mammal is a compound gland composed of a peripheral cortex and central medulla (Fig. 7-1). The cells of the medulla are irregular in shape and arranged in small rounded groups or short cords surrounded by venules and capillaries. The secretory cells contain fine granules that react with chromate (the chromaffin reaction), hence the reference to this tissue as chromaffin tissue. The cells also give a green color after treatment with ferric chloride. In addition to the secretory cells, the medulla contains single sympathetic ganglion cells, or clusters of them, and groups of small round cells, which are probably lymphocytes. The vascular system of the adrenal medulla consists of a rich capillary network around the cell groups. This capillary network arises from major arterial vessels that pass through the cortex or the hilus. The capillaries drain into the same venous system as the cortex, uniting to form the central veins, which emerge as the suprarenal vein.

The adrenal glands of the mammal are paired structures located at the anterior poles of the kidneys and slightly medial. If the gland is cut in half, it presents peripherally a yellow to reddish brown zone, the cortex, and a central, thin gray zone, the medulla. The two adrenal structures, i.e., the cortex and medulla, differ in embryogenesis, phylogenesis, structure, and function. In fish and reptiles, the adrenal structures are intermingled, with groups of chromaffin tissue surrounded by cortical tissue; in amphibians, the two components are either in juxtaposition or intermingled. In cyclostomes, elasmobranchs, and teleosts, the chromaffin tissue is spatially distinct from the adrenal cortex (or interrenal bodies). In these species, strands of chromaffin tissue are present along the dorsal aorta and in association with the sympathetic ganglia.

Chromaffin cells that resemble the medullary cells in staining reaction, in origin, and in the presence of an epinephrine-like activity are also found widely dispersed throughout the body of the vertebrate and invertebrate. The sites include the mouths of certain mollusks, the nervous system of the leech, and the skin of some amphibians. In the mammal, tissues such as the paraganglia found within or adjacent to the sympathetic ganglia, the carotid glands, the organs of Zuckerkandl near the origin of the inferior mesenteric artery, and scattered cells within the liver, kidney, gonads, etc., also possess properties similar to chromaffin cells. Evidence is still lacking, however, to prove that these extramedullary chromaffin cells are truly part of the endocrine system.

Histochemical studies have indicated that the medullary hormones are contained in the cytoplasmic granules of the chromaffin cells (26). These granules appear to possess a high level of amine material, and they discharge their contents following stimulation. Whether the same cells produce both epinephrine and norepinephrine, or whether separate cells produce single hormones is still in question. However, a preponderance of physiological evidence indicates the presence of two specific types of medullary cells with regard to endocrine function: (a) Injection of insulin causes an increased release of epinephrine while the intravenous injection of glucose diminishes the output of epinephrine without affecting the release of norepinephrine. (b) Stimulation of a particular area of the hypothalamus leads to increased release of epinephrine, whereas stimulation of another part of the hypothalamus leads to increased release of norepinephrine (19). (c) Stimulation of the sciatic nerve of the cat, or other painful stimuli, causes the secretion of epinephrine, whereas clamping of the artery causes a reflex vasoconstriction and the increased release primarily of norepinephrine. (d) In the human being, it has been reported that aggressive emotional outbursts are associated with increased urinary excretion of norepinephrine, whereas passive emotional displays are correlated with increased urinary excretion of epinephrine (17).

Hillarp and Hökfelt (26), have presented histochemical evidence for the presence of two types of endocrine cells in the adrenal medulla. They report that all the secreting cells of the medulla react with potassium dichromate whereas only 5–15% in the rat and 30% in the cat react with potassium iodate. Treatment that decreased markedly the level of epinephrine without any effect on the level of norepinephrine failed to affect those cells that formed a pigment after oxidation with potassium iodate. These data would then indicate that epinephrine and norepinephrine are formed in different cells of the medulla and may be released separately, depending on the stimulus.

Nature of Epinephrine and Norepinephrine

Epinephrine and norepinephrine are known collectively as catechol amines. Both hormones contain an asymmetric carbon and therefore each hormone can occur as two optically active isomers, the L-form (levorotatory) and the D-form (dextrorotatory). The naturally occurring isomer of the medulla is the L-form, which, in the case of epinephrine, is approximately 15 times more active than the D-isomer in the elevation of blood pressure.

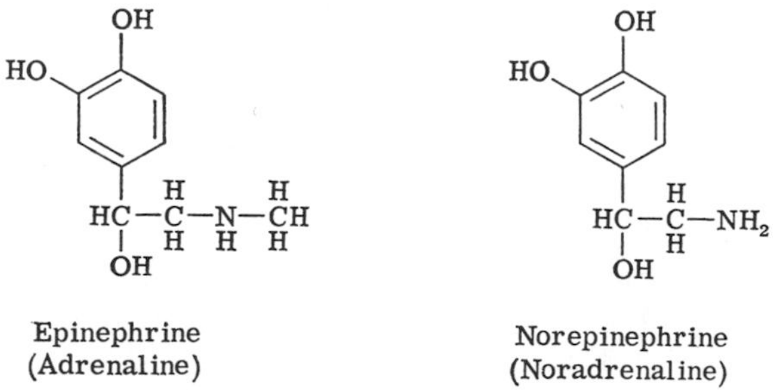

Epinephrine
(Adrenaline)

Norepinephrine
(Noradrenaline)

Fig. 6-1. Structures of epinephrine and norepinephrine.

The two hormones are very similar in structure and differ only by the presence of a methyl group. The side chain of epinephrine, containing a terminal methyl group, is a secondary amine whereas the side chain of norepinephrine, lacking a terminal methyl group, is a primary amine (Fig. 6-1). The hormones are rapidly inactivated *in vivo* or oxidized to inactive forms. As indicated above, they give distinctive color reactions with both ferric and chromium salts due to their catechol structure. Oxidation of these hormones leads to the formation of adrenochromes which condense with ethylenediamine to form fluorescent compounds. This forms the basis of a sensitive and relatively specific chemical assay for the adrenomedullary hormones.

Action of Epinephrine and Norepinephrine

Although epinephrine and norepinephrine are quite similar chemically and biologically, there are differences in their physiological actions (Table 6–1). Both epinephrine and norepinephrine influence the cardiovascular system, but to a different degree and, in some instances, in an opposite manner. Epinephrine exercises its effect on the circulatory system, essentially through its action on the heart. It increases both contractility and irritability of the heart and may lead to ventricular fibrillation. This hormone also excites the atrioventricular pacemaker in heart block and shortens the atrioventricular conduction time on prolonged stimulation. Norepinephrine has no such effect. Epinephrine and norepinephrine increase the heart rate; epinephrine is more potent in this regard. Epinephrine increases the cardiac output and the systolic blood pressure with no effect on the diastolic blood pressure. The rise in blood pressure is presumably a result of increased cardiac output. This also causes an elevated pulse pressure with only a moderate increase in mean pressure (34). Peripheral resistance is usually decreased following epinephrine, but large doses may cause peripheral vasoconstriction (23, 24). Epinephrine also effects an increase in pulmonary pressure, possibly as a result of vasoconstriction. Norepinephrine is without action or causes a slight fall in cardiac output, but it does cause, in contrast to epinephrine, a marked increase in peripheral resistance with rise in both the diastolic and systolic blood pressure. The pulse pressure is unaffected though a significant elevation of the mean pressure occurs. Norepinephrine, like its methylated analog, causes an increased pulmonary pressure (20).

The pressor amines cause vasodilation of the coronary vessels of the heart with a resulting increase in coronary blood flow. Both hormones induce constriction of the blood vessels of the skin which results in pallor. Both hormones cause constriction of the splenic vessels and con-

TABLE 6–1
PHYSIOLOGICAL ACTIVITIES OF EPINEPHRINE AND NOREPINEPHRINE[a]

Organ or system	Effect	Relative activity E:N[b]	Remarks
Blood pressure (man, cat, dog)	Increase	0.2–0.5	E, systolic mainly; N, both systolic and diastolic
Blood vessels	Constrict	1–3	—
Rabbit ear	E, dilation	—	—
Denervated limb	N, constriction	—	—
Vasoresistance (man)	E, decrease; N, increase	—	—
Coronary circulation	Dilation	1	—
Heart			
Frog, perfused	Excitation	20	—
Dog	Amplitude increased	0.3–1	—
Eye			
Iris	Dilation	15	Denervated organ more sensitive to N than E
Nictitating membrane	Excitation	710	—
Viscera			
Bronchi, histamine contraction in guinea pig	Inhibition	15–20	—
Uterus, nonpregnant (rat, cat)	Inhibition	50–150	Both E and N excite in rabbit
Intestine			
Colon, rat	Inhibition	0.2–1	—
Ileum, rabbit, guinea pig	Inhibition	1–3	—

[a] Adapted from Russell (36).
[b] E, epinephrine; N, norepinephrine; E:N, ratio of activity.

traction of the spleen. Epinephrine effects an increased blood flow through the skeletal muscle and the liver, a slight increase in blood flow through the brain, and a moderate reduction in blood flow through the

TABLE 6–2
THE EFFECT OF EPINEPHRINE AND NOREPINEPHRINE ON BLOOD FLOW[a]

Organ	Epinephrine	Norepinephrine
Liver	100% increase	No material effect
Kidney	40% decrease	20% decrease
Skeletal muscle	100% increase	No effect or slight decrease
Brain	20% decrease	Slight decrease

[a] Taken from Swann (40).

kidney (Table 6–2). Norepinephrine has no action or causes a slight decrease in blood flow through the liver and skeletal muscle and a slight decrease through the kidney and brain (43). Both amines tend to have an inconstant effect on renal dynamics. Although renal plasma flow is generally decreased, the glomerular filtration rate may be unchanged, decreased, or increased depending on the systemic blood pressure. When norepinephrine raises the systolic pressure to 170 mm Hg, the glomerular filtration rate increases along with an increased sodium excretion and diuresis. If the systolic pressure exceeds 170 mm Hg, a reduction in all three parameters occur (33). The net peripheral vascular effect of epinephrine is vasodilation whereas that of norepinephrine is vasoconstriction, although the latter does possess a limited vasodilating action.

These hormones relax the smooth muscles of the bronchi, but epinephrine is much more active than norepinephrine. Epinephrine has a marked effect on the gastrointestinal tract, causing a decrease in motility and tone of the gastric and intestinal musculature, a contraction of sphincters, and some inhibition of secretion. In the skin, epinephrine causes increased sweating and pilomotor response. Norepinephrine produces similar effects, but to a lesser degree.

Epinephrine markedly alters the blood sugar levels, causing hyperglycemia (Fig. 6-2). This action may result from dosages that are

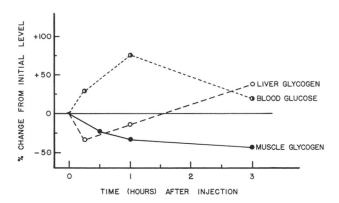

Fig. 6-2. Effect of epinephrine (0.2 mg per kilogram body weight) on the blood glucose and tissue glycogen levels of the normal rat. Data of G. T. Cori et al. (9, 10), adapted from presentation of Russell (36).

insufficient to elevate the blood pressure. Norepinephrine produces only very slight changes in blood glucose levels. The hyperglycemia produced by epinephrine is the result of three actions by the hormone. A major site of action is the liver, where the increased rate of glycogenolysis results in an outpouring of glucose into the circulation (see Chapter 13). A second site of action is the muscle, where the glucose formed from the breakdown of glycogen is converted to lactic acid in the glycolytic process. Part of the lactic acid is resynthesized to glycogen and part of it is released to the circulation and converted to glycogen or glucose in the liver (15, 46). Epinephrine may also stimulate a hyperglycemia indirectly by causing the release of ACTH from the pituitary gland. This results in an increased release of adrenal corticoids such as cortisone and hydrocortisone, hormones which are extremely potent in stimulating glycogenesis with a marked increase in liver glycogen and blood sugar levels. It is apparent that many hormones are involved in carbohydrate metabolism. These include not only epinephrine, which acts to increase blood sugar levels and counteract the hypoglycemic action of insulin, but also glucagon, which acts like epinephrine but is restricted to an action on liver glycogen only. In addition to the adrenal corticoids, thyroxine and growth hormone also influence carbohydrate metabolism. The question has been raised whether or not epinephrine may have a direct action on glucose metabolism by decreasing the rate of tissue utilization of glucose (14). This hormone reduces glucose tolerance, and the arteriovenous $(A - V)$ glucose difference is slight in the presence of the hormone.

Epinephrine is 5–10 times as active as norepinephrine in increasing oxygen consumption (24). Cold-adapted rats show a markedly greater response to the hormone than warm-adapted rats. Norepinephrine has little effect on the warm-adapted rat but possesses marked calorigenic effect in the cold-adapted animal (28). Hypercalcemia and eosinopenia usually follow the injection of epinephrine. The eosinopenic response is a result of the increased production of adrenal corticoids after release of ACTH (29, 37). Norepinephrine is only one-sixth as active as epinephrine in the eosinopenic response (29). Epinephrine has a direct effect on the central nervous system, an action which produces a feeling of restlessness, anxiety, and fatigue in the human being. Such responses are not seen with norepinephrine. In addition, epinephrine has a number of miscellaneous effects, such as concentration of pigment granules in the chromatophore, hydrolysis of neutral fat, and reduction in clotting time.

A complete description of the role of the hormones of the adrenal medulla in homeostasis also must take into account the autonomic nervous system. This system controls many of the involuntary actions of the animal organism with both an inhibitory and stimulatory effect on such organs as the heart, salivary and lacrimal glands, lungs, gastrointestinal tract, bladder. The relationship between these two systems is demonstrated by the finding that most of the postganglionic neurons of the sympathetic division of the autonomic system are adrenergic, i.e., they release norepinephrine and perhaps epinephrine. Secondly, many of the effects produced by stimulation of the sympathetic nervous system can be duplicated by the injection of epinephrine and norepinephrine. Thus the organs innervated by the autonomic nervous system are regulated in two ways: by strictly hormonal control, wherein the hormones cause the typically more widespread and longer-lasting effect, and by nervous control, of which the effect is of shorter duration and can be localized.

The present evidence indicates that norepinephrine is the neurotransmitter agent and epinephrine may not be involved at all in this phenomenon. The postganglionic neurons of the splenic nerve contain large amounts of norepinephrine, but little or no epinephrine. In addition, sectioning of the sympathetic innervation to an organ causes a complete loss of norepinephrine without affecting the level of epinephrine. It is assumed here that the neurons secreted norepinephrine, hence its disappearance after denervation; but the level of epinephrine was not affected since it was probably being secreted by the chromaffin cells in the organ, not by the neurons.

A possible role for the sympathetic-adrenomedullary system has been postulated by Cannon in his emergency theory. He suggests that the response (of flight or fright) of an organism to sudden exposure to a noxious stimulus is mediated by the sympathetic-adrenomedullary system. A sudden emergency elicits a massive response on the part of the organism permitting it to take action under such conditions, i.e., a reaction of the nature of fight, fright, or flight. Under conditions of deep emotional disturbance, the animal shows cardiac acceleration, deep respiration, inhibition of the gastrointestinal tract, sweating, pallor of the skin, increased pilomotor activity, increased blood flow through the muscles, and elevated blood sugar. All these changes are suggested as adjustments necessary to enable the organism to respond to the stimulus, possibly by running away, or by fighting. It consists then of a mobilization of the resources of the animal for prompt and rapid use. That the medullary hormones are involved in the adjustment to stressors is apparent, but the events are extremely complicated and further clarification is needed.

Assay of the Medullary Hormones

As indicated previously, any action of a hormone can be used for a bioassay if the effect can be quantified. It is obvious then that a wide variety of assays are available for epinephrine and norepinephrine (Table 6–3). Among the classical assays for epinephrine are those that measure blood pressure rise and inhibition of intestinal contractions (6).

TABLE 6–3

SENSITIVITY OF VARIOUS ASSAY METHODS TO EPINEPHRINE AND NOREPINEPHRINE[a]

Technique	Epinephrine[b] (ng)	Norepinephrine[b] (ng)
Bioassay		
Blood pressure, cat	200	100
Blood pressure, rat	50	3
Blood pressure, pithed rat	7	5
Uterus rat (2 ml bath)	0.1	15
Perfused rabbit ear	0.5	1
Intestine, rabbit	40	40
Rectal caecum, bird	2	50
Chemical assay		
Adrenochrome	10,000	10,000
Adrenolutin	20	20
Ethylenediamine	6	6

[a] Taken from data of Gaddum and Holzbauer (20).

[b] Amount required for test is stated in nanograms: 1 ng $= 10^{-6}$ mg. Amounts represent minimum sensitivity; bioassay would require 5–10 times level indicated.

The measure of blood pressure change may be carried out in a normal anesthetized animal, but a spinal cat is preferred. The brain of an etherized cat is destroyed if the cord is entered at the second cervical vertebra with a probe; the left common carotid artery is used to record blood pressure. The general procedure is to alternate administration of the unknown preparation with a standard epinephrine dose, utilizing dosages that give submaximal responses. This method is accurate to within 10%. The rat has also been used as an assay animal. Modifications of the animal preparation include treatment with antihistamines or atropine or section of vagus nerve to obtain a preparation sensitive to the amines.

A second classical assay utilizes the *in vitro* rabbit intestine. A strip of rabbit intestine (preferably from the ileum) is suspended in an oxygenated bath at 35°C. Inhibition of contraction can be obtained with 1 part of epinephrine in 230 million. Other smooth muscle responses involve rat uterus, intestine, or the caecum of the hen. In recent years, an extremely sensitive assay for epinephrine has been described which can detect a minute concentration of epinephrine in a volume of 0.1 ml saline (2). The ear of a young rabbit is denervated by excising the superior cervical ganglion and a portion of the posterior and great auricular nerves. The ear of the anesthetized animal is placed on the surface of a water bath to keep the temperature constant. The test solution is injected directly into the distal end of the central artery of the ear and observations are made on the changes in the caliber of the artery. The response can be calibrated by the injection of standard amounts of epinephrine. An older technique, involving *in vivo* or *in vitro* perfused frog heart, demonstrated the influence of epinephrine on cardiac activity.

Chemical methods have been described that have sufficient sensitivity for the determination of epinephrine and norepinephrine in the blood. In the THI (trihydroxyindole) method, the fluorescent compounds adrenolutin and noradrenolutin are formed from epinephrine and norepinephrine by the addition of an oxidizing agent and an alkali. By the use of different excitation and emission spectra of the fluorescent lutins, it has been possible to differentiate between epinephrine and norepinephrine (6, 7). The method requires about 15 ml of plasma. The bioassay techniques and the chemical assay described above give comparable results and indicate that epinephrine may or may not be detected in peripheral blood depending on whether the concentration is above or below 5×10^{-11}. The concentration of norepinephrine appears to lie between 2 and 3×10^{-10} (42). The second method also utilizes fluorimetry. This technique involves treating the catechol amines with ethylenediamine to form highly fluorescent compounds through condensation. The ethylenediamine method appears to give much higher results than the bioassay or THI methods; this may indicate that the ethylenediamine method measures other compounds in addition to epinephrine and norepinephrine.

Biogenesis, Metabolism, and Mechanism of Action

Epinephrine and norepinephrine are derived from specific amino acids obtained from the nitrogen pool of the body. Studies with C^{14}-labeled tyrosine and phenylalanine indicate that both these amino acids act as precursors in the synthesis of the catechol amines. Since labeled phenylalanine appears first and is readily converted to tyrosine, it is presumed that the same metabolic pathways hold for both amino acids.

The biosynthetic pathway for the formation of epinephrine is presented in Fig. 6-3. The first step in the synthesis is the formation of 3,4-dihydroxyphenylalanine (dopa) from the action of tyrosinase on tyrosine. This enzyme is found in a wide variety of tissues including the skin and melanocytes, although it has not been demonstrated in the adrenal medulla. However, it may be presumed to be present since both the melanocytes and the chromaffin cells arise from the neural crest. Other factors in the synthesis of epinephrine, such as dopa, dopamine,

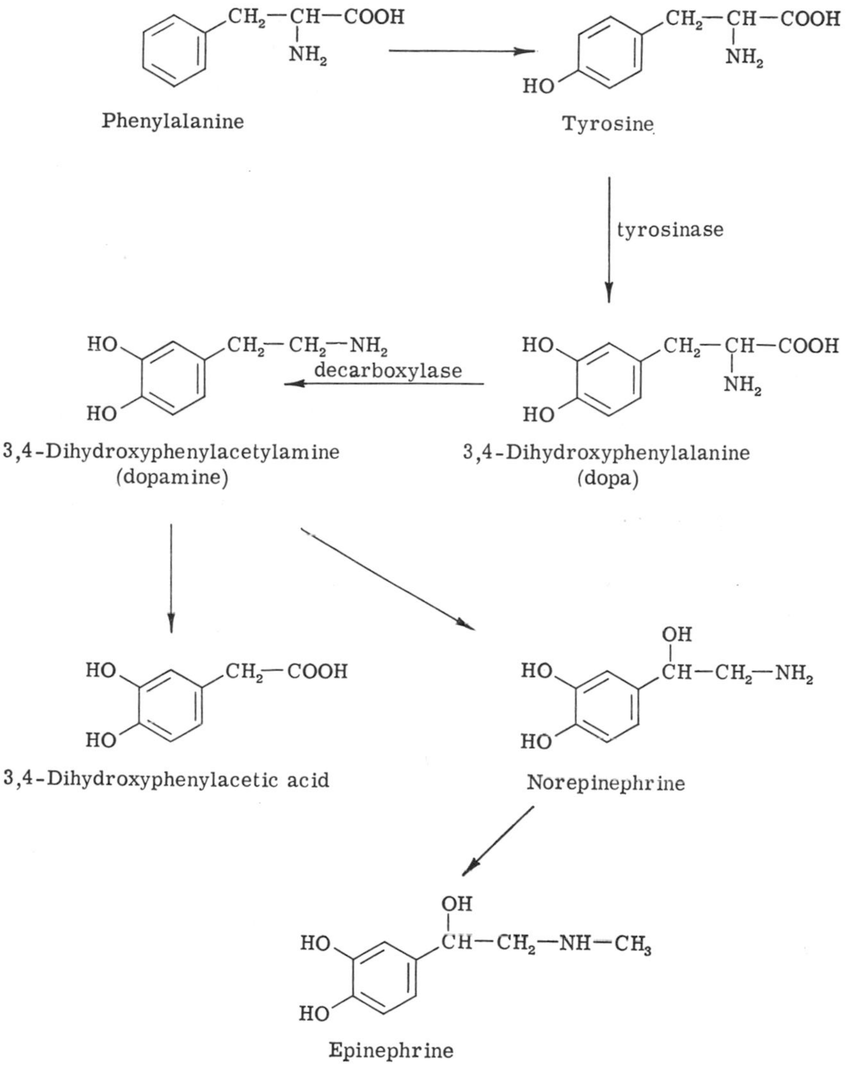

Fig. 6-3. The biosynthetic pathway for the formation of epinephrine and norepinephrine. From Blaschko (5).

and dopa decarboxylase have been found in both the adrenal medulla and the adrenergic neurons of the sympathetic system (25).

Dopa is converted to dopamine through the action of a decarboxylating enzyme (dopa decarboxylase). The dopamine is then converted either to dihydroxyphenylacetic acid through deamination and oxidation or to norepinephrine by hydroxylation. That norepinephrine is the immediate precursor of epinephrine has been demonstrated by both *in vivo* and *in vitro* studies. This final step involves the enzymatic transfer of a methyl group to norepinephrine to form epinephrine. It has been shown that the reaction can occur in a cell-free suspension of adrenal gland homogenate. This enzyme system can effect the transfer of a methyl group to norepinephrine to form epinephrine in the presence of adenosine triphosphate and methionine or S-adenosylmethionine (30). However, some evidence indicates that a small amount of methylation can occur in the absence of special methyl donors or energy-releasing compounds. It is highly likely that the adrenergic nerves of the sympathetic system produce their neurohumor by the same method as the adrenal medulla. Similar precursors have been found to be effective in biosynthetic processes. The incubation of radioactive tyrosine or radioactive dopa with homogenates of sympathetic ganglia or sympathetic nerves has resulted in the formation of radioactive dopamine and norepinephrine.

Epinephrine and norepinephrine are rapidly removed from the circulation, in a matter of minutes, through absorption by the tissues and degradation of the molecules. Very small amounts of the two hormones appear in the urine (35). The major pathways in the degradation and elimination of these hormones involve either conjugation to form a glucuronide or a sulfate or methylation to the corresponding 3-methoxy-4-hydroxy derivative (4, 22) (Fig. 6-4). Both hormones are inactivated by methylation of the *p*-hydroxyl group in the presence of an intracellular enzyme, catechol-methyl transferase, to metanephrine or normetanephrine. The methyl group is provided by methionine. This step is then followed by the conjugation of the methylated compounds to the glucuronide or sulfate, or by the oxidation of the metanephrine and normetanephrine to 3-methoxy-4-hydroxymandelic acid in the presence of amine oxidase. The amine oxidase also acts directly on the two hormones to form 3,4-dihydroxymandelic acid by oxidative deamination. The dihydroxymandelic acid is then methylated to the 3-methoxy-4-hydroxymandelic acid in the presence of a catechol-methyl transferase. In general, a much higher percentage of the hormones appear in the urine as 3-methoxy-4-hydroxymandelic acid. Following the intravenous injection of norepinephrine, approximately 30% is recovered in the form of the mandelic acid derivative whereas about 2% is in the form of the unchanged catechol amines (3).

Epinephrine produces a wide variety of effects involving carbohydrate metabolism, the activity of smooth muscle, the cardiovascular

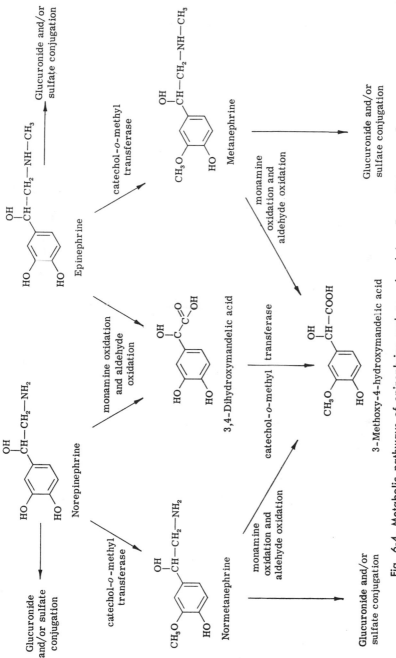

Fig. 6-4. Metabolic pathways of epinephrine and norepinephrine. From Gitlow *et al.* (22).

system, the nervous system, pigment cells, a release of ACTH, and others. It is highly unlikely that all these effects are mediated through a single mechanism. Only with regard to its action on the breakdown of glycogen in the liver and muscle is adequate information available (see Chapter 13).

Evidence has been presented to indicate that epinephrine produces its glycogenolytic effect in muscle and liver by conversion of the inactive form of phosphorylase to the active form (9, 38). This is by no means a full explanation of the mechanism of action, but it does indicate that the effect of epinephrine, like that of glucagon, is mediated through an enzyme system. In the reaction chain of glycogen to glucose 1-phosphate to glucose, the first step is a rate-limited reaction catalyzed by phosphorylase. In the presence of epinephrine, the balance between the inactive and the active phosphorylase is shifted in favor of the active form; this shift results in a marked increase in the entire reaction due to the presence of greater amounts of enzyme (speeding up the rate-limiting step of the reaction). The inactive phosphorylase enzyme is converted to the active form by an enzyme system requiring both magnesium ions and ATP. The effect of epinephrine on this system is mediated through adenosine-3′,5′-monophosphate (39) and has been demonstrated in the absence of the intact cell (18, 33). This action of epinephrine has been observed in both liver and muscle, whereas glucagon has been shown to produce this effect only in the liver.

EXPERIMENT 6–1

Adrenal Demedullation*

While complete adrenalectomy ultimately results in the death of untreated animals, the adrenal medullary tissue can be removed from experimental animals. The procedure involves removal of some adrenal cortical tissue. However, this tissue does regenerate from the capsule of the gland. The medullary cells, ectodermal in origin, do not regenerate. The demedullated animals are especially sensitive to stressors, particularly during the recovery period while the cortex regenerates. Many parameters sensitive to catechol amines are unchanged following demedullation, e.g., the catechol amine content of the heart. However, some alteration in release and excretion of catechol amines may be noted, particularly in response to adverse conditions.

Procedure and Experimental

Anesthetize a rat and prepare the animal for surgical approach as

* Cf. references (13, 16, 17, 20, 21, 26).

in adrenalectomy (Experiment 7–1). Expose the right adrenal gland and clear away the fat so the gland may be seen easily. Make a small incision through the capsule of the gland with iridectomy scissors. With curved forceps, gently press the lower surface of the gland to express and remove as much of the contents of the gland as possible. Close the incision in the skin with suture. Expose the left adrenal gland and remove this gland completely. House the animals under controlled conditions for 30 days. This period allows for regeneration of the adrenal cortex.

Subject four 150-gm rats to adrenal demedullation. After the recovery period, compare the catechol amine excretion of the operated rats with control animals. Place the operated and control rats in the cold room in metabolism cages. During the early stages of exposure collect urine samples from animals for catechol amine analysis (Experiment 6–7).

EXPERIMENT 6–2

Liver Glycogenolysis*

Epinephrine acts in a manner similar to glucagon to mobilize liver glycogen, with a resultant increase in blood sugar. Figure 6-2 illustrates the effect of epinephrine on glycogenolysis. While both glucagon and epinephrine act similarly on liver glycogenolysis, only epinephrine acts to influence muscle glycogen. Note that the early action of this catechol amine is to depress liver glycogen, but that subsequent actions lead to an increased deposition.

Procedure and Experimental

Techniques for determination of liver glycogen are outlined in Experiments 7–12 and 13–2.

Fast 4–6 young male rats, each 150 gm in weight, for 24 hours; then 4 hours prior to treatment feed each animal by stomach tube with 600 mg glucose per 100 gm body weight. After the 4-hour time lapse, inject the animals subcutaneously with 0.2 ml of solution as follows:

Controls: isotonic saline
Epinephrine: 0.02–0.06 μg/100 gm body weight
Norepinephrine: 0.02–0.08 μg/100 gm body weight

After 15 minutes, kill the animals by decapitation and determine the liver glycogen.

* Cf. references (9–11, 18, 33, 38, 46).

EXPERIMENT 6–3

Effect of Catechol Amines on Blood Sugar*

As noted in the previous experiment, the effect of epinephrine on glycogenolysis promotes hyperglycemia. In addition to the hepatic action, this agent also influences carbohydrate metabolism in muscle, where glycogenolysis results in a production of lactic acid which becomes available for hepatic glycogenesis. The action of epinephrine on the release of pituitary corticotropin results in increased glucocorticoid secretion, which causes hyperglycemia and glycogen deposition. In general, epinephrine is about four times as potent as norepinephrine in influencing carbohydrate metabolism. Epinephrine appears also to reduce glucose tolerance.

Procedure and Experimental

This experiment may be carried out by making sequential determinations of blood sugar concentrations in the rabbit or the rat (the rabbit may be preferred for class use). Each group of students is assigned 8 rats, each 150–200 gm in body weight. The animals are fasted 24 hours and then given orally 600 mg glucose per 100 gm body weight. Four hours after glucose treatment, inject the 8 animals of each group as follows:

2 Rats, control:	0.2 ml saline
2 Rats, epinephrine:	0.04 μg/100 gm in saline subcutaneously
2 Rats, norepinephrine:	0.04 μg/100 gm in saline subcutaneously
2 Rats, untreated:	Withdraw blood for glucose determination

Each group will be assigned a time interval during which blood samples are withdrawn for glucose determination (15 minutes, 30 minutes, 1, 1½, 2, and 3 hours). Blood samples may be obtained from the tail vein (Experiment 12–2) and glucose determined as in Experiment 13–2. (Experiments 6–2 and 6–3 may be combined, in that at assigned intervals animals may be killed and liver samples taken for glycogen determination and blood obtained for glucose determination.)

EXPERIMENT 6–4

Effect of Epinephrine on Corticotropin Release†

In many species, epinephrine can stimulate the release of cortico-

* Cf. references (9–11, 14, 43).
† Cf. references (17, 19, 23, 29, 37, 40).

tropin; activation of the adrenal cortex results. The emergency theory postulated by Cannon first outlined the role of the adrenal medulla in the physiological defense mechanism. Subsequent studies suggested a role of the adrenal medulla in activating corticotropin secretion. While it appears likely that epinephrine acts via the hypothalamus, the exact mechanism is in question. The response of the adrenal medulla is cited as the alarm reaction by Selye in the general adaptation syndrome (Chapter 7).

Procedure and Experimental

Obtain 4 male rats (200 gm body weight). Inject subcutaneously into each of 2 rats 0.1 ml of 1:100,000 solution of epinephrine. Two hours later determine the ascorbic acid content of the adrenal glands of control and experimental rats as described in Experiment 7–7.

EXPERIMENT 6–5

Smooth Muscle Contractions*

The adrenergic fibers to the small intestine inhibit longitudinal peristaltic contractions. *In vitro,* both norepinephrine and epinephrine can inhibit smooth muscle contractions. This experiment indicates the use of the rabbit intestine, but it should be noted that the rat intestine or uterus, and the bird caecum, have been used successfully. In several procedures, the ability of the catechol amine to depress acetylcholine stimulated contractions is recorded. If the rat uterus is used, the tissue should be obtained from an estrous animal or from a virgin female primed 24 hours previously with 50 mg diethylstilbestrol. On rat uterus, epinephrine is 100–150 times as potent as norepinephrine when assayed in minute volumes of fluid.

Procedure and Experimental

Obtain from a rabbit a strip of ileum 2–3 cm long. Suspend the strip in Tyrode solution (see Appendix A-8) and oxygenate. See Experiment 2–10 for apparatus for smooth muscle contraction. The preparation should be maintained at 35–36°C. After muscle contractions have been recorded, add epinephrine in concentrations of 0.4–0.8 μg per 100 ml of bath solution and determine the minimum dose required to cause inhibition of contractions. Use similar concentrations of norepinephrine.

To assay an unknown preparation, stimulate contractions by adding

* Cf. references (6, 16, 20, 21, 45).

10 μg acetylcholine per 1.0 ml bath fluid. One minute later, determine the depression of contractions by adding a standard dose of epinephrine (0.8–2.0 μg/100 ml). After 1 minute, again stimulate with acetylcholine and then determine the inhibitory effect of the unknown solution. Dilute the standard or unknown solutions until comparable inhibition is noted.

EXPERIMENT 6–6

Effect of Catechol Amines on Blood Pressure*

Epinephrine and norepinephrine act to increase systolic blood pressure by different mechanisms. Whereas epinephrine stimulates cardiac output, norepinephrine increases pressure through vasoconstriction and increased peripheral resistance. The blood pressure response serves as an assay to determine the strength of hormonal preparations. Both the intact rat and cat have been used as experimental animals for this determination; however, the spinal animal is preferred by some investigators since the preparation is more sensitive to catechol amines. As little as 0.005–0.05 μg of catechol amine may induce a blood pressure change in a spinal animal.

Procedure and Experimental

Anesthetize with Nembutal a rat of at least 200 gm body weight. Tie the animal to an operating board, ventral side up. Make a midline incision in the region of the neck and carefully expose the trachea, carotid arteries, and vagi. Cannulate the trachea. Loosely tie ligatures around each vagus nerve. Prepare one carotid artery for cannulation. Expose one femoral vein and insert a cannula (polyethylene tubing, PE 10) in such a manner that the tubing can be tied firmly to the leg, yet injections can be made through a syringe attached to the tubing by means of a 27-gauge needle. After cannulation of the femoral vein, inject the animal with 200 IU heparin per 100 gm body weight. Then cannulate the carotid artery (tie off the other carotid artery) and connect the cannula to a manometer, using saline as an intermediary fluid. Cut both vagi. [*Note:* In some preparations atropine is used in place of sectioning nerves.] Allow the animal to rest about 20 minutes in order for the blood pressure to stabilize.

Prepare solutions of epinephrine in concentrations of 1 μg and 0.1 μg per milliliter of saline. Each solution should contain freshly added ascorbic acid (50 μg/ml). Norepinephrine solutions may be prepared

---

* Cf. references (2, 12, 16, 20, 21, 24, 31).

in similar concentrations. All injections are to be made via the femoral cannula. The amount of fluid injected must be constant. [*Note:* It may facilitate injections to use a dual cannula connector so that the amine solution may be injected then followed by an appropriate volume of saline diluent.] All injections must be made carefully so that erratic changes in blood pressure are not produced.

Inject volumes of solution ranging from 0.02 to 0.2 ml (with each injection, add saline to bring the volume injected to a total of 0.4 ml). Determine the minimal effective doses of epinephrine and norepinephrine.

EXPERIMENT 6–7

Determination of Catechol Amines*

Of the two chemical procedures for determination of catechol amines, that involving the fluorescence analysis with trihydroxyindole (THI) appears to be the preferred method. The method has been coupled with chromatographic procedures to determine the amount of epinephrine and norepinephrine in tissue or body fluids. Other modifications also have been employed to estimate the individual or total catechol amines in urine. The method is of clinical value in screening for pheochromocytoma in which the excessive secretion of norepinephrine by tumorous chromaffin cells of the adrenal medulla may be associated with cases of hypertension.

Procedure†

Reagents

1. *Aluminum oxide,* Chromatographic grade. Suspend alumina in at least 10 volumes of water, stir, allow to settle, and decant the supernatant fluid. Repeat 3 or 4 times to remove any turbid material that may develop when alumina is suspended. Dry in an oven at 100–105°C.

2. *EDTA.* Reagent grade ethylenediaminetetracetic acid, disodium salt.

3. *Acetic acid, 0.2 N*

4. *Sodium hydroxide, 1 N NaOH*

5. *Bromothymol blue, 0.04% solution in ethanol*

6. *Potassium carbonate, 2 N K_2CO_3*

7. *Phosphate buffer, 0.2 M, pH 6.5.* Prepare solutions of 0.2 M

---

* Cf. references (7, 8, 16, 17, 22).
† Catechol amines in Urine: G. K. Turner Associates.

$NaH_2PO_4 \cdot H_2O$ and $0.2 M$ $Na_2HPO_4 \cdot 7H_2O$. Titrate one solution with the other until the pH is adjusted to 6.5. A pH meter is used to determine acidity.

8. *Sodium hydroxide, 20%.* Place 200 gm of reagent grade NaOH in the bottom of a beaker. Cover the pellets of alkali with distilled water (use caution). The heat generated will hasten the solution of NaOH. Additional distilled water is to be added to bring the solution to 1 liter volume. Allow this solution to cool before use.

9. *Hydrochloric acid, 6 N and 0.1 N HCl*

10. *Zinc sulfate, 0.25% ZnSO₄*

11. *Potassium ferricyanide, 0.25% K₃Fe(CN)₆*

12. *Ascorbic acid, 2% aqueous.* Prepare fresh solution.

13. *Sodium hydroxide: ascorbic acid.* Prepare fresh each day prior to use a 9:1 solution. Dilute 1 volume of 2% ascorbic acid with 9 volumes of 20% NaOH. *Note:* The alkali solution must be at room temperature.

14. *Stock catechol amine solution. Norepinephrine 50 μg/ml.* L-Arterenol bitartarate hydrate (9.95 mg) is dissolved in 0.1 N HCl, then diluted in a volumetric flask to 100 ml with 0.1 N HCl. This solution is stable when maintained under refrigeration.

15. *Dilute standard, norepinephrine, 0.25 μg/ml.* Dilute 0.5 ml of stock solution to 10 ml with 0.1 N HCl (added by pipette) in a volumetric flask. Dilute to 100 ml with distilled water. Keep solution under refrigeration. Prepare fresh material each week.

Note: The standard solution is used for determination of total catechol amines. In procedures which permit detection of epinephrine and norepinephrine, stock and dilute standard solutions of epinephrine are prepared to the same concentrations as indicated for norepinephrine.

Method

1. Obtain the urine sample from animals. The 24-hour urine volume is collected in HCl: 0.01 ml HCl per milliliter of urine. The urine should be maintained below a pH of 2.0.

2. Transfer an aliquot of urine (10–25 ml) to a beaker and add 1 gm alumina and 0.5 gm EDTA. Stir gently (magnetic stirrer) and add 1 N NaOH dropwise to adjust the pH to 8.5. Continue the stirring for 1–3 minutes to determine whether the pH will be maintained. Add additional NaOH if necessary to keep the pH between 8.4 and 8.5.

3. Transfer the mixture to a 50-ml centrifuge tube. Wash the beaker with distilled water and transfer to the centrifuge tube. Centrifuge the mixture. Retain the sediment and decant; discard the supernatant fluid.

4. Stir the alumina sediment with 10 ml of distilled water. Centrifuge

and discard the water. Repeat this water wash with a second volume of 10 ml distilled water.

5. Add 10 ml of 0.2 N acetic acid to the sediment and stir vigorously to elute the catechol amines. Centrifuge and transfer the supernatant fluid to a 50 ml flask. Repeat the extraction with a second 10-ml volume of 0.2 N acetic acid; add this supernatant fluid to that of the first extraction. (This extract is stable and may be held overnight or retained in the refrigerator if necessary.)

6. To develop fluorescence, transfer 2.0 ml of the sample (U) (acetic acid extract) to a test tube and add 1.0 ml distilled water. (a) For blank (B) use 2.0 ml urine sample plus 1.0 ml water; (b) for standard (S) use 2.0 ml sample plus 1.0 ml dilute norepinephrine standard.

7. Add one drop of bromothymol blue to each tube. Adjust the acidity of the solution in each tube to pH 6 by adding 2 N K_2CO_3 dropwise; shake the tubes vigorously with each addition. Add 0.5 ml of 0.2 M phosphate buffer to each tube.

8. The unknown urine extracts (U) and the standard sample (S) are treated with 0.1 ml of 0.25% $ZnSO_4$ and 0.1 ml of 0.25% potassium ferricyanide. Shake the tubes vigorously. These additions serve to oxidize the catechol amines. Time the addition of oxidizing agents so that, at 2 minutes after each addition, 1 ml of the sodium hydroxide-ascorbic acid reagent is introduced into each tube.

9. The blank (B) is treated as indicated in Step 7, then sodium hydroxide-ascorbic acid solution (1.0 ml) is added. The contents of the tube are mixed thoroughly, then 0.1 ml of potassium ferricyanide is added.

10. Samples are to be read on the fluorometer 10–20 minutes after the addition of the last reagent. For the Turner fluorometer, the instrument is balanced with the dummy cuvette provided.

11. The primary filter (excitation) should have a peak of 405 mμ, and the secondary filter should be set with a peak of 495 mμ. Read the standard samples (S) first; select the highest range at which the reading is on the scale.

12. The readings for the standard (S), blank (B), and unknown samples (U) are used to calculate total catechol amines as follows:

Readings S − U = values resulting from 0.25 μg catechol amines
Readings U − B = values resulting from catechol amines in 1/10 urine aliquot volume

or

$$\frac{U - B}{S - U} \times 0.25 \times \frac{\text{total volume urine}}{1/10 \text{ urine aliquot}} = \mu\text{g catechol amines}$$

Experimental

1. Determine the total catechol amines in the urine of normal and adrenodemedullated rats at room temperature and after subjection to stressors.

2. A 24-hour sample of urine obtained from a human being may be used for the determination of total catechol amines. See Step 1 for the amount of hydrochloric acid to be used in collection.

References

1. Abel, J. J. 1902. Method of preparing epinephrine and its compounds. *Bull. Johns Hopkins Hosp.* **13**: 29.
2. Armin, J., and Grant, R. T. 1955. Vasoconstrictor ability in the rabbit blood and plasma. *J. Physiol. (London)* **128**: 511–540.
3. Armstrong, M. D., Shaw, K. N. F., and Wall, P. E. 1956. The phenolic acids of human urine. *J. Biol. Chem.* **218**: 293–303.
4. Axelrod, J. 1959. Metabolism of epinephrine and other sympathomimetic amines. *Physiol. Rev.* **39**: 751–776.
5. Blaschko, H. 1959. Development of current concepts of catecholamine formation. *Pharmacol. Rev.* **11**: 307–316.
6. Burn, J. H. 1937. "Methods of Biological Assay." Oxford Univ. Press, London and New York.
7. Cohen, G., and Goldenberg, M. 1957. The simultaneous fluorimetric determination of adrenaline and noradrenaline in plasma. I. *J. Neurochem.* **2**: 58–70.
8. Cohen, G., and Goldenberg, M. 1957. The simultaneous fluorimetric determination of adrenaline and noradrenaline in plasma. II. *J. Neurochem.* **2**: 71–80.
9. Cori, C. F. 1940. Glycogen breakdown and synthesis in animal tissues. *Endocrinology* **26**: 285–296.
10. Cori, G. T. 1930. The mechanism of epinephrine action. VII. *Am. J. Physiol.* **94**: 557–563.
11. Cori, G. T., Cori, C. F., and Buchwald, K. W. 1930. The mechanism of epinephrine action. *J. Biol. Chem.* **86**: 375–388.
12. Crawford, T. B. B., and Outschoorn, A. S. 1951. The quantitative separation of adrenaline and noradrenaline in biological fluids and tissue extracts. *Brit. J. Pharmacol.* **6**: 8–20.
13. De Robertis, E., and vaz Ferreira, A. 1957. Submicroscopic changes of the nerve endings in the adrenal medulla after stimulation of the splanchnic nerve. *J. Biophys. Biochem. Cytol.* **3**: 611–614.
14. Dickman, S. R., Wiest, W. G., and Eik-Nes, K. 1958. Effects of epinephrine on metabolism of glucose of normal dogs. *Am. J. Physiol.* **194**: 327–332.
15. Ellis, S. A., Davis, H., and Anderson, H. L. 1955. Effects of epinephrine and related amines on contraction and glycogenolysis of the rats diaphragm. *J. Pharmacol. Exptl. Therap.* **115**: 120–125.
16. Elmadjian, F. 1962. Epinephrine and norepinephrine, *in* "Methods of Hormone Research" (R. I. Dorfman, ed.), Vol. II, pp. 371–383. Academic Press, New York.
17. Elmadjian, F., Hope, J. M., and Lamson, E. T. 1957. Excretion of epinephrine

and norepinephrine in various emotional states. *J. Clin. Endocrinol. Metab.* **17:** 608–620.

18. Fischer, E. H., Krebs, E. G. 1955. Conversion of muscle phosphorylase-b to phosphorylase-a in muscle extracts. *J. Biol. Chem.* **216:** 121–132.

19. Folkow, B., and von Euler, U. S. 1954. Selective activation of noradrenaline and adrenaline producing cells in the cat's adrenal gland by hypothalamic stimulation. *Circulation Res.* **2:** 191–195.

20. Gaddum, J. H., and Holzbauer, M. 1957. Adrenaline and noradrenaline. *Vitamins Hormones* **15:** 151–203.

21. Gaddum, J. H., and Lumbeck, F. 1949. The assay of substances from the adrenal medulla. *Brit. J. Pharmacol.* **4:** 401–408.

22. Gitlow, S. E., Ornstein, L., Mendolowitz, M., Khassis, S., and Kruk, E. 1960. A simple colorimetric test for pheochromocytoma. *Am. J. Med.* **28:** 921–926.

23. Goldenberg, J. 1951. Adrenal medullary function. *Am. J. Med.* **10:** 627–641.

24. Goldenbery, M., Pines, K. L., Baldwin, E. D. F., Green, D. G., and Roh, C. E. 1948. The hemodynamic response of men to norepinephrine and epinephrine and its relation to the problem of hypertension. *Am. J. Med.* **5:** 792–806.

25. Hagen, P., and Welch, A. D. 1956. The adrenal medulla and the biosynthesis of pressor amines. *Rec. Progr. Hormone Res.* **12:** 27–39.

26. Hillarp, N. Å., and Hökfelt, B. 1954. Cytological demonstration of noradrenaline in the suprarenal medulla under conditions of varied secretory activity. *Endocrinology* **55:** 255–260.

27. Hillarp, N. Å., Lagerstedt, S., and Nilson, P. 1953. The isolation of a granular fraction from the suprarenal medulla containing the sympathomimetic catechol amines. *Acta Physiol. Scand.* **29:** 251–263.

28. Hsieh, A. C. L., and Carlson, L. D. 1957. Role of adrenaline and noradrenaline in chemical regulation of heat production. *Am. J. Physiol.* **190:** 243–246.

29. Humphreys, R. J., and Raab, W. 1950. Response of circulating eosinophils to norepinephrine, epinephrine and emotional stress in humans. *Proc. Soc. Exptl. Biol. Med.* **74:** 302–303.

30. Kirshner, H., and McGoodnal, C. 1957. The formation of adrenaline from noradrenaline. *Biochim. Biophys. Acta* **24:** 658–659.

31. Moyer, J. H., and Handley, C. A. 1952. Norepinephrine and epinephrine effect on renal hemodynamics. *Circulation* **5:** 91–97.

32. Oliver, G., and Shafer, E. A. 1895. On the physiological action of extracts of the suprarenal capsules. *J. Physiol. (London)* **17:** 8–14.

33. Rall, T. W., Sutherland, E. W., and Wosilait, W. D. 1956. Reactivation of liver phosphorylase in slices and in extracts. *J. Biol. Chem.* **218:** 483–495.

34. Ranger, H. A., and Bradley, S. E. 1943. Systemic and renal circulatory changes following the administration of adrenine, ephedrine and paredrinol in normal man. *J. Clin. Invest.* **22:** 687–693.

35. Resnick, W., and Elmadjian, F. 1958. The metabolism of epinephrine containing isotopic carbon in man. *J. Clin. Endocrinol. Metab.* **18:** 28–35.

36. Russell, J. A. 1960. The adrenals, *in* "Medical Physiology and Biophysics" (T. C. Ruch and J. F. Fulton, eds.), Saunders, Philadelphia, Pennsylvania.

37. Schweizer, M. 1956. An explanation of some apparent anomalies in the interpretation of eosinophil levels in the guinea pig. *Endocrinology* **59:** 495–497.

38. Sutherland, E. W., and Cori, C. F. 1951. Effect of hyperglycemia-glycogenolytic factor and epinephrine on liver phosphorylase. *J. Biol. Chem.* **188:** 531–543.

39. Sutherland, E. W., and Rall, T. W. 1957. The properties of an adenine ribonu-cleotide produced with cellular particles, ATP, Mg^{++} and epinephrine or glucagon. *J. Am. Chem. Soc.* **79:** 3608.
40. Swann, H. J. C. 1958. The Hormones of the Sympathetic Nervous System and the Adrenal Medulla, *in* "Modern Trends in Endocrinology" (H. Gardiner-Hill, ed.), Chap. 12. Butterworths, London.
41. Vogt, M. 1954. The concentration of sympathin in different parts of the central nervous system under normal conditions and after administration of drugs. *J. Physiol. (London)* **123:** 451–481.
42. Vogt, M. 1960. Epinephrine and norepinephrine, *in* "Hormones in Human Plasma" (H. N. Antoniades, ed.), Chap. 56. Churchill, London.
43. von Euler, U. S. 1956. "Noradrenaline." Thomas, Springfield, Illinois.
44. Vulpian, A. 1856. Quelques réactions propres à la substance des capsules sur-rénales. *Compt. Rend. Acad. Sci.* **43:** 663.
45. West, G. B. 1950. Biological and chemical assay of adrenalin, *in* "Hormone Assay" (C. W. Emmens, ed.), pp. 91–107. Academic Press, New York.
46. Wortman, L. C., and Leonard, S. L. 1953. The effect of injections of testosterone propionate and cortisone acetate on glycogen deposition induced by epineph-rine in different skeletal muscles. *Endocrinology* **53:** 480–486.

CHAPTER 7

The Adrenal Corticoids

The hormones of the adrenal cortex are among the most potent substances available to the animal and are necessary for the maintenance of life. Total adrenalectomy invariably leads to death within several weeks if no accessory cortical tissue is present. After adrenalectomy the animal ceases to grow, loses weight, shows signs of muscular weakness and emaciation. Disturbances appear in the gastrointestinal tract, and all general metabolic processes are upset. Blood pressure and body temperature fall, hemoconcentration occurs, hypoglycemia is noted, especially after fasting, excessive sodium loss appears, and eventual failure of the kidneys occurs. Adrenalectomized animals are unable to withstand stressful conditions such as exposure to cold, toxins, trauma, etc. Changes in the environment that may have no great effect on the normal animal may be fatal in the adrenalectomized animal. Thus, one of the important physiological roles of the adrenal corticoids is in the adaptation of the organism to changes in the external environment. In addition, these hormones are concerned also with the basic metabolic processes.

Sites of Formation of the Adrenal Corticoids

The adrenal gland of the mammal is a compound structure consisting of an inner medulla that secretes epinephrine and norepinephrine and an outer cortex that secretes the adrenal corticoids. In the higher vertebrates, such as the mammals, the adrenal glands are flattened, triangular or oval structures found at the anterior poles of the kidneys. The gland is usually embedded in fat; in some species accessory adrenal tissue may also be dispersed in the same general area or along the spermatic or ovarian arteries, as in carnivores. The cortical and medullary tissue in lower vertebrates, such as amphibians, reptiles, and birds, are more variable in their relationship and tend to be interspersed, as in the bird, or to exist as separate entities, as in certain amphibians. In some of the cyclostomes and elasmobranchs, the cortical and medullary tissue are distinct and separate structures. The medullary tissue is represented by strands of chromaffin cells located along the dorsal aorta whereas the cortical cells, known as interrenal bodies, are found along the post-cardinal veins. The glands receive a rich blood supply by way of the adrenal or adrenolumbar arteries, and the secretions of the cells are released from the gland via the adrenal vein. The cortex, unlike the medulla, is devoid of nervous connections.

The cortical layer of the adrenal gland is of mesodermal origin, and the medulla is of ectodermal origin. During embryonic development the adrenal achieves its greatest relative size, wherein large numbers of nonlipoid staining cells are present in the area next to the medulla, i.e., the fetal cortex or X-zone. During late prenatal and early postnatal life, the cortex of the human being and some rodents decreases in size owing to a degeneration of the fetal zone. In postnatal life, the development of lipoid-staining cells of the zona glomerulosa and other zones of the cortex predominates.

The entire gland is surrounded by a capsule beneath which lies the first thin cortical layer, the zona glomerulosa (Fig. 7-1). This layer is

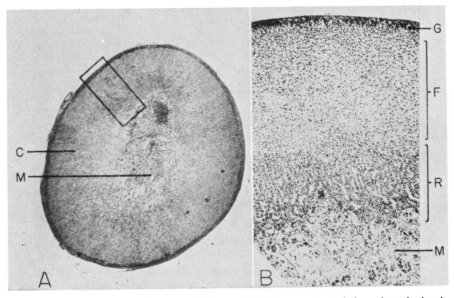

Fig. 7-1. The adrenal cortex of the rat. (A) Cross section of the adrenal gland of the rat. C, cortex; M, medulla. (B) Section from (A). G, glomerulosa; F, fasciculata, R, reticularis; M, medulla.

composed of clusters or columns of columnar cells containing lyophilic material in the cytoplasm. Beneath this area, the zona fasciculata is seen with cords of polyhedral cells in a radial array. This broad layer gradually fuses into the zona reticularis, where the cells are also in a cordlike arrangement. The cells of this layer contain lipoid droplets and pigment granules. This zone is the one that probably is derived from the X-zone, and in some animals remnants of the X-zone persist in the adult. The medullary layer of the gland is found below the zona reticularis; the border between the two layers is not clearly defined in most species.

The various zones of the adrenal cortex have been pointed out as the sites of origin of cortical steroids. However, one school of thought holds that instead of functional zonation of the cortex, the division is one related to maturation of cells. Under this hypothesis, the zona glomerulosa is considered to consist of immature cells that descend into the other zones of the cortex as they mature. Thus, the outer part of the fasciculata contains the precursors for the biosynthesis of the hormones which are synthesized in the inner fasciculata layer and released by the cells of the reticularis. Some of the information that opposes this view is found in experiments showing involution of the zona fasciculata following hypophysectomy. This involution is reversed by administration of the adrenocorticotropic hormone (ACTH, corticotropin) to the hypophysectomized animal (22). Incubation of separated zona fasciculata-zona reticularis layers with ACTH produces an increase in glucocorticoids in the incubation media. Incubation of the zona glomerulosa with ACTH has been found to be without effect on aldosterone synthesis (63). Incubation of the zona glomerulosa with steroid precursors results in the production of aldosterone whereas incubation of the fasciculata-reticularis zones with precursors gives rise to 17-hydroxycorticoids. Under these conditions incubations with both layers, fasciculata-reticularis and glomerulosa, give rise to corticosterone.

While it has been thought by some investigators that the production of aldosterone takes place in the zona glomerulosa without being influenced by ACTH (22, 63), evidence has been presented that hypothalamic and pineal factors influence the production of aldosterone (14, 46). Recent information indicates that renal angiotensin also plays a role in aldosterone production. In addition, a high rate of corticoidogenesis is accompanied by an increased production of aldosterone. As indicated by some of the studies on *in vitro* incubation of the cortical zones of the adrenal gland, corticosterone appears to be a precursor for both glucocorticoids and aldosterone. The inner layer of the zona reticularis (residual) may be the site of androgen production though evidence is insufficient to establish definitely this site of origin.

The Nature of the Adrenal Corticoids

The secretions of the adrenal cortex are steroidal in nature; they include the sex hormones progesterone, estrogens, and androgens in

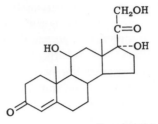

Corticosterone
Compound B

17α-Hydroxycorticosterone
Compound F, hydrocortisone

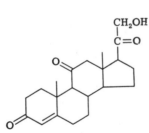

11-Dehydro-17α-hydroxycorticosterone
Cortisone, Compound E

11-Deoxy-17α-hydroxycorticosterone
Compound S

11-Dehydrocorticosterone
Compound A

11-Deoxycorticosterone,
DOC

Aldosterone

Fig. 7-2. The adrenal corticoids.

addition to the adrenocorticoids, corticosterone (compound B), 17-hydroxycorticosterone (cortisol, hydrocortisone, compound F), 17-hydroxy-11-dehydrocorticosterone (cortisone, compound E), and aldosterone (Fig. 7-2). In addition to the active steroid hormones, a number of inactive steroids have been extracted from the adrenal gland and have been identified primarily as intermediates in the biosynthesis of the adrenocorticoids. The adrenocorticoids have been classified into two categories, based on the physiological activities. The glucocorticoids, characterized by an 11-oxygen moiety (oxycorticoids), bring about an increase in deposition of liver glycogen and other responses associated with the adaptation to stress. The mineralocorticoids are usually devoid of an oxygen grouping on carbon 11; however, the potent, naturally secreted mineralocorticoid aldosterone has a hydroxyl group on carbon 11 and in addition has an aldehyde group at carbon 18, with which the internal condensation is possible. The main physiological response to the mineralocorticoids is increased retention of sodium ions by the kidney. Since the chemical structures of the glucocorticoids and mineralocorticoids are quite similar, each class of compounds possesses some physiological action of the other group.

Action of the Adrenal Corticoids

Complete removal of the adrenal cortex leads to the death of the animal within a few days to a few weeks (19, 57, 58). The operation is followed by impaired carbohydrate metabolism and a shift in the electrolyte balance with increased excretion of sodium salts and loss in water along with other signs of adrenal insufficiency (Table 7–1). The administration of adrenal cortical extract or of glucocorticoids or mineralocorticoids will maintain life in adrenalectomized animals and restore the physiological imbalances to normal in varying degrees.

While the exact role of the corticoids in physiological processes is unknown, much information has been obtained on the many actions of these compounds (Table 7–2). The glucocorticoids influence carbohydrate metabolism partly by virtue of the protein catabolic action of these steroids, which provides amino acids for conversion to carbohydrate. Since the action involves catabolism of muscle protein, administration of glucocorticoid can induce a negative nitrogen balance and a reduced growth rate (23). The loss of protein results in epidermal thinning and atrophy of muscle tissue and connective tissue cells. The conversion of amino acids to carbohydrate, coupled with the interference in utilization of sugars by glucocorticoids (see Chapter 13, glucocorticoids and hexokinase reaction), produces a hyperglycemia. In addition, this class of

TABLE 7–1

SYMPTOMS OF ADRENAL INSUFFICIENCY

1. Profound asthenia, muscle fatigue, and increased susceptibility to fatigue
2. Loss of body weight. Weight loss is at expense of body fat. In general, a weight loss occurs after the operation, but this is not invariably true as young animals often show a weight increase
3. Inability to retain sodium and chloride. Retention of potassium
4. Loss of ability to maintain body temperature
5. Severe gastrointestinal lesions
6. Hypertrophy of thymus with hemorrhage spots
7. Congestion of lungs (susceptibility to respiratory infection), liver, spleen, and pancreas
8. Diminished food intake
   a. Total anorexia as terminal symptom
   b. Rat, unlike dog or cat, will eat lettuce or some food of which it is fond until a few hours prior to death
9. Lactation and reproduction
   a. Normal litters have been born to animals fertilized before and after adrenalectomy
   b. Insufficient lactation by mother occurred
10. Marked susceptibility to stressors

TABLE 7–2

BIOLOGICAL ACTIONS OF THE GLUCOCORTICOIDS

Retardation of body growth and antagonism to growth-promoting action of growth hormone
Increase of nitrogen and potassium excretion
Production of glycosuria and hyperglycemia in rats, but not in cats
Liver glycogen deposition
Increase in body fat
Liver hypertrophy with increase of liver fat
Increase of ketone bodies in urine and blood
Decrease of plasma alkaline phosphatase
Retardation in both chondrogenesis and osteogenesis in epiphysis of tibia
Thinning of the epidermis, atrophy of sebaceous glands and of growing part of the hair
Involution of the thymus and lymph nodes with depletion and dissolution of lymphocytes
Decrease in circulating eosinophil level
Enhancement of work performance
Enhancement of resistance to nonspecific stimuli such as cold and other stressors
Inhibition of insulin effect on glycogenesis in isolated diaphragms of normal rats, but not in those of hypophysectomized animals
Inhibition of development of male accessory organs of normal rats, but not of hypophysectomized animals
Anti-inflammatory action
Decrease in gastric HCl and pepsin secretion

corticoids reduces reabsorption of glucose by the kidney. The overall result is hyperglycemia and glucosuria with increased deposition of glycogen in the liver (but not in muscle) favored by the high blood sugar level. This action of the glucocorticoids gives rise to symptoms of diabetes mellitus known as steroid diabetes in the normal animal (21) and brings about a marked exacerbation of the disease in the diabetic animal.

The glucocorticoids inhibit the conversion of carbohydrate to fat and stimulate fat mobilization from the subcutaneous tissues, actions that lead to an increased concentration of fat in both the serum and the liver. In addition, the glucocorticoids have a synergistic activity with the growth hormone in causing an increase in the accumulation of fat in the liver plus ketosis. Although the corticoids are not ketogenic, ACTH is quite active in this respect and the effect can be obtained after adrenalectomy. Thus there would appear to be some overlap in the physiological activity of ACTH and STH.

Other actions of the glucocorticoids include the feeling of euphoria following administration of the compounds and the production of steroid anesthesia following large doses of the hormones. In addition, the glucocorticoids possess some degree of mineralocorticoid activity because of the structural similarity between these two classes of steroidal hormones (Fig. 7-2, Table 7–3).

Aldosterone and deoxycorticosterone are the two potent mineralocorticoids now available with the ability to regulate electrolyte excretion. Deoxycorticosterone was first isolated from the adrenal gland and prepared synthetically, but it soon became apparent that a more active substance with regard to electrolyte regulation was still present in the amorphous fraction of the adrenal cortex. The active component of the amorphous fraction was isolated in 1952 and called electrocortin or aldostersterone (Fig. 7-2). The action of the mineralocorticoids is to promote the retention of sodium salts by the kidney (24, 59). This action appears to occur in the ascending loop of Henle and distal convoluted tubule of the nephron, where these steroids influence the exchange of potassium and sodium ions and of sodium and hydrogen ions in favor of the reabsorption of sodium.

It has now been established that only trace amounts of deoxycorticosterone exist in the adrenal gland and adrenal vein blood and that it is not a normal secretory product of the adrenal cortex. It is entirely possible that since deoxycorticosterone is a precursor in the synthesis of aldosterone, its presence in the blood is due to the escape of small amounts into the circulation. Current evidence would indicate that aldosterone is the true electrolyte-regulating hormone of the adrenal gland (60).

Recently, conclusive evidence has been presented to show the existence of 18-hydroxysteroids: 18-hydroxyprogesterone, 18-hydroxycor-

ticosterone, and 18-hydroxydeoxycorticosterone. The 18-hydroxydeoxy-
corticosterone and 18-hydroxycorticosterone are produced by the rat
adrenal gland and are present in blood. The 18-hydroxydeoxycorticos-
terone has been found to react with the Porter-Silber color reagent,
previously suggested to be specific for 17-hydroxycorticoids. The 18-
hydroxylated compounds may well be intermediates in the aldosterone
biosynthetic pathway.

Although deoxycorticosterone (DOC) and aldosterone have certain
activities in common, the two steroids also differ markedly. Aldosterone
is more like the glucocorticoids than is DOC since it has a significant
effect on carbohydrate, fat, and protein metabolism although it is much
less active than cortisone or cortisol (Table 7–3). Secondly, aldosterone

TABLE 7–3

POTENCY OF ALDOSTERONE COMPARED WITH CORTISONE IN A
GLUCOCORTICOID GROUP OF ASSAYS

Bioassay method	Potency; cortisone or cortisone acetate = 1
Eosinophil depletion test	0.25
Eosinophil depletion test	0.33–0.55
Cold survival test	1
Liver glycogen deposition test	0.33
Water load test	1

does not enhance potassium excretion to the same extent as sodium
retention; and finally, chronic treatment with aldosterone does not lead
to the diabetes insipidus-like state seen with DOC.

An antagonistic action between the glucocorticoids and mineralocorticoids is evidenced in the effect of these compounds on the inflammatory response. The glucocorticoids oppose the inflammatory reaction
and are classified as anti-inflammatory or antiphlogistic. The mineralocorticoids, on the other hand, are prophlogistic. The anti-inflammatory
action of the glucocorticoids accounts for some of the adverse effects of
hypercorticalism or of administration of the glucocorticoids, in that the
high titer of steroid may result in conditions that allow the spread of any
infection that may be present.

A. PITUITARY-ADRENAL GLAND AXIS

Studies of the relationship between the pituitary gland and adrenal
cortex elucidated the role of ACTH and its action in controlling the
release of glucocorticoids. It was shown that the administration of

adrenal cortical extracts or glucocorticoids, or the removal of the pituitary gland, brought about an involution of the adrenal gland. Subsequently, the concept of servomechanism was developed to explain the
balance that is maintained between the release of ACTH and the secretion of the glucocorticoids (17, 39, 57). In some way, the circulating
level of glucocorticoids or the metabolic products (tetrahydro derivatives) of the corticoids control the release of corticotropin. An interesting
relation has been reported on the size of the adrenal glands and the
hepatic enzymes responsible for the inactivation of the A-ring of steroids
(20, 64, 65). In female rats, which have the larger adrenal glands, the
concentration of the steroid hydrogenase in liver is higher than that in
male rats. The suggestion is implied that the increased rate of removal
of steroids in the female rat is compensated by a greater secretion of
pituitary ACTH. Additional information of the sexual dimorphism in
adrenal size and activity has resulted from both physiological and biochemical studies. Female rats have been found to survive cold stress
longer than males (68). The differences in cold stress survival, adrenal
size, and liver enzyme concentration can be abolished by castration.
Administration of androgens or estrogens to the castrated animals results
in the production of an adrenal gland characteristic of the sex of the
animal producing the particular sex hormone. Figure 7-3 depicts the sex
difference in the rate of loss of corticoids from blood.

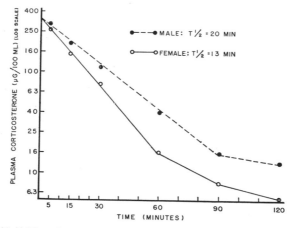

Fig. 7-3. Half-life of exogenous corticosterone in the blood of male and of
female rats. Redrawn from data of Kitay (36).

A mechanism by which ACTH induces the accelerated synthesis and
release of glucocorticoids has been suggested. While it was thought
earlier that the pituitary hormone acts on certain enzymes in the bio-

synthetic chain, current views indicate that the action may be to provide cofactors (NADPH) to stimulate a dehydrogenase enzyme in corticoid biosynthesis (5) (see also Chapter 9). Table 7–4 indicates corticosteroid secretion in normal and hypophysectomized dogs.

TABLE 7–4

ADRENALCORTICOSTEROID LEVEL IN THE ADRENAL VENOUS BLOOD OF NORMAL AND HYPOPHYSECTOMIZED DOGS[a]

Compound	Corticosteroid secretion rate (μg/kg/hr)	
	Normal dog	Hypophysectomized dog
Cortisol (compound F)	32	2.3
Corticosterone (compound B)	13	1.2
Compound S	4	0.3
Deoxycorticosterone	0.3	0.04
Aldosterone	0.3	0.14

[a] Adapted from data of G. Farrell [*Am. J. Physiol.* **182,** 269–272 (1955)].

In addition to the control of the pituitary ACTH by the glucocorticoids, much attention has been given to the role of the central nervous system in control of the anterior pituitary gland (17, 42, 46, 49, 61). Evidence indicates that factors from the hypothalamus enter the portal circulatory system and activate the anterior pituitary to release ACTH (see Chapter 9). These studies bring into focus the role of the central nervous system in the activation of the pituitary axis in response to external stimuli and to epinephrine (10, 15, 17, 33, 39, 49, 61).

B. CONCEPT OF STRESS

Hans Selye, one of the early investigators who studied the role of the adrenal cortex following exposure of animals to stressful conditions, described the general adaptation syndrome (GAS). When an animal is exposed to nonspecific noxious stimuli (stressors) such as cold, toxins, or radiations, the organism is placed in an adverse physiological state (stress). The symptoms characteristic of the stress response were found to be adrenal hypertrophy, thymus involution, and eosinopenia (55, 56, 57). The latter two reactions were found to follow administration of glucocorticoids. The GAS hypothesis states that the first reaction of the animal (alarm reaction) involves the activation of the adrenal cortex with an increased secretion of the corticoids to aid the animal in adapting to the adverse situation. Under the influence of the corticoids, the animal can adjust to the situation (state of adaptation) and survive until the defense mechanisms are exhausted (state of exhaustion) (56, 57). Much study has been undertaken to evaluate the hypothesis in regard to the development of diseases. Selye early suggested that organisms faced with long periods of resistance to stress might develop arthritic or rheumatic diseases as a result of hypercorticalism or an imbalance in corticoid secretions. Much discussion on this latter point has developed in the literature regarding stress. Many workers support the concept of "permissive action" of the corticoids in contrast to the causative role of the hormones in the development of disease. The concept of permissive action maintains that the hormones produce the proper environment for other factors to manifest their action (12, 32, 33). Many questions are yet to be answered before an accurate evaluation can be made for the role of the adrenocorticoids in the production of disorders, but no doubt exists concerning the necessity of the hormones for life and the resistance to stress.

Some of the complexities of this problem are seen in the relation of adrenal hypertrophy to function of the gland. While the glands remain enlarged for long periods during exposure to stress, the results of biological and chemical estimation of adrenal activity indicate that hypercorticalism may occur only during the first stages of exposure to stress (6, 24). In addition, the problem of preadaptation is difficult to explain, for animals exposed to a stressor, then adrenalectomized, are better able to survive a second exposure to the stressor than nonpreexposed adrenalectomized animals.

The Assay of the Adrenal Corticoids

The biological responses to stressors initially served as the end points for assay of corticoids (Table 7–5). Evaluation of the potency of the adrenal cortical extracts and of purified corticoids are based on the increased survival of adrenalectomized animals exposed to cold temperature or other stressors (8, 58, 67), and by a decrease in circulating eosinophils in normal animals (6, 68). A widely used technique for the assay of glucocorticoids is based on the increased deposition of liver glycogen (21, 51). This technique has been used to evaluate the activity of individual corticoids as well as the activity of corticoid material in blood and urine. The microscopical study of the cortex provided evidence for functional zonation of the gland (22, 63) and served to indicate possible changes in cortical activity under various conditions.

The observations of the changes in the chemical constituents of the adrenal gland following administration of ACTH, led to the development

TABLE 7–5

Tests for Increased Adrenal Activity

Animal	Test agent	End point
Young or hypophysecto-mized rat; chick	Pituitary extracts, exoge-nous ACTH, stress	Adrenal weight increase or prevention of adrenal atrophy
Rat	Pituitary extracts	Adrenal histochemistry, sudanophilic material
Rat, normal or hypophysectomized	ACTH, stress	Depletion of adrenal as-corbic acid, cholesterol
Adrenalectomized rat or mouse	Cortical extracts, corticoids	Survival in cold
Adrenalectomized rat	Cortical extracts, corticoids	Muscle work
Adrenalectomized rat	Cortical extracts, corticoids	Urinary electrolyte balance, sodium load
Rat, mouse, human being	Cortical extracts, corticoids; index of adrenal activity (stimulation)	Decrease in blood eosino-phils
Rat, mouse, bird, normal or adrenalectomized	Cortical extracts, corticoids, index of adrenal activity (stimulation)	Increase in liver glycogen
Rat	Exposure to stressors	Plasma corticosterone
Hypophysectomized rat	ACTH	Plasma corticosterone

of new tests for the study of adrenal cortical activity and ACTH. These tests are based on the depletion of adrenal cholesterol or ascorbic acid (54), and are actually indexes of adrenal stimulation by endogenous or exogenous ACTH rather than measures of corticoid release. Nevertheless, they have been used to indicate increased adrenal activity in the animals. In the rat, the decreases in glandular cholesterol or ascorbic acid are sensitive enough to serve as assay techniques for corticotropin prepara-tions and to measure the rapidity of the adrenal response to stressors. However, these changes do not occur in all species (11). Though evi-dence shows that cholesterol is a precursor for corticoids, the exact reason for the depletion of ascorbic acid is unclear. One report indicated that the ascorbic acid lost from the gland after ACTH stimulation could be accounted for by the appearance of ascorbic acid in the adrenal venous blood. Other studies, however, show that the amount of ascorbic acid in the adrenal venous blood does not account for all the material lost from the gland and that the level of corticoid in venous blood rises before the vitamin is lost from the gland (1).

Since the mineralocorticoids possess some glucocorticoid activity, aldosterone may be assayed by techniques applicable to the oxycorti-coids. Though the mineralocorticoids are less potent in this respect

(Tables 7–3 and 7–6), aldosterone has more glucocorticoid activity than DOC. However, since the prime role of the mineralocorticoids is on electrolyte balance, the assay by the effect on the sodium-potassium levels of urine is the method of choice. Table 7–6 presents the potency of various steroids in mineralocorticoid activity.

TABLE 7–6

COMPARATIVE MINERALOCORTICOID ACTIVITY OF STEROID HORMONES

Hormone	Other designation	Relative mineralocorticoid activity per unit mass
Aldosterone	Electrocortin	2500–10,000
Deoxycorticosterone	DOC	135
Deoxycorticosterone acetate	DCA, DOCA	100
Corticosterone	Compound B	14
11-Deoxy-17-hydroxycorticosterone acetate	Compound S	8
17-Hydroxycorticosterone (hydrocortisone)	Compound F	7.5
11-Dehydrocorticosterone acetate	Compound A	6.7
11-Dehydro-17-hydroxycorticosterone	Compound E	5.9
11-Dehydro-17-hydroxycorticosterone acetate	Compound EAC	5.2
Estradiol	—	3
Progesterone	—	3
Testosterone	—	1.5

One of the early methods for colorimetric determination of corticoid activity involved application of the Zimmermann technique (using dinitrobenzene) for 17-ketosteroids. Though some information can be obtained by the analysis of 17-ketosteroids in urine, the results may be influenced by the changes in the metabolism of the hormone and not truly reflect the secretion rate. Individual corticoids have been studied after separation of the steroids by paper or column chromatographic techniques. These methods permit the isolation and identification of the corticoids in blood and tissue as well as the colorimetric analysis of the materials eluted from the chromatogram. While 17-hydroxycorticoids (17-OHCS), cortisol, and cortisone have been found to be the glucocorticoids of major importance in most species, corticosterone is the principal corticoid in the rat, rabbit, mouse, and bird; aldosterone appears to be the true adrenal hormone in all species for the regulation of electrolytes (Tables 7–7 and 7–8).

A major advance in the study of blood corticoids came with the development of more sensitive techniques of colorimetric analysis. The color reagent of Porter and Silber has been coupled with methods of

TABLE 7–7

TYPE OF CORTICOIDS FOUND IN THE BLOOD OF VARIOUS SPECIES[a]

Elasmobranchii				
Ray	B			
Dogfish		F		
Eagle ray	B	F		
Actinopterygii				
Cod		F		
Carp	B	F		
Flounder		F		
Killfish		F		
Channel bass		F		
Southern kingfish		F		
Salmon	B	F	E	
Dipnoi				
Lungfish		F		
Amphibia				
Xenopus		F		
Amphiuma	B	F	E	
Reptilia				
Turtle		F		
Grass snake	B	F	E	
Aves				
Capon	B	F	E	
Mammalia				
Hamster		F		
Mouse	B			
Rat	B	—[b]	—[b]	Aldosterone[c]
Rabbit	B	—[b]		
Guinea pig		F		
Ferret	B	F		
Cat	B	F		
Dog	B	F		Aldosterone
Sheep	B	F		
Porpoise	B	F		
Monkey	B	F		
Man	B	F	E	Aldosterone

[a] Adapted from data of Dorfman (7) and Jones *et al.* (34).

[b] In mammalia, cortisol (F) is the predominant glucocorticoid secreted by the adrenal gland, except for rodents where only trace amounts of 17-hydroxycorticoids have been detected by paper chromatography.

[c] Aldosterone has been isolated from the blood of all species studied and is believed to be the circulating mineralocorticoid.

TABLE 7–8

PLASMA CORTICOID LEVELS FOUND IN THE BLOOD OF VARIOUS SPECIES[a]

Species	Ratio F:B in adrenal venous blood	Range of corticoid values in peripheral blood (μg/100 ml)	
		Cpd. F	Cpd. B
Man	10	2–28	0–10
Monkey	20	—	—
Sheep	18	—	—
Cat	8	—	—
Dog	3	—	—
Ferret	2	—	—
Rabbit	0.05	6–307	75–155
Rat	0.05	2–15[c]	8–33
Hamster	—	165[b]	—
Salmon	—	5.2	7.3

[a] Adapted from the data of Bush (4), Jones et al. (34), and McCarthy et al. (41).

[b] Values for adrenal venous blood.

[c] Based on the presence of material in blood that reacts with the Porter-Silber reagent for 17-OHCS and calculated as micrograms per 100 ml of Compound F.

chromatography and solvent partition to estimate corticoids in blood (45, 47). While these methods are mainly used for 17-OHCS, the technique can be used for corticosterone (40, 41). The corticoids also exhibit fluorescence in sulfuric acid. A very precise method has been developed for the separation of groups of corticoids by column chromatography and determination by fluorescence analysis (43). The technique of fluorescence analysis has been applied widely to the study of rat and bird blood, where corticosterone is the significant corticoid (21, 25, 26, 43).

The steroids may be present in the various tissues and fluids in the free form or conjugated with glucuronic acid, as well as in the reduced form (tetrahydrocortisol and tetrahydrocortisone). Since the corticoids are present in blood and urine in different forms, special procedures are required to determine the specific forms. Studies on the levels of the glucuronide conjugates require the hydrolysis of the esters by dilute acid or β-glucuronidase before colorimetric analysis.

Investigations of the blood corticoid levels in human beings and other animals has resulted in valuable diagnostic and scientific data. Corticoid levels are used as diagnostic tests for a number of diseases. Elevated levels of blood and urinary corticoids have been found during the early stages of stress. Studies on the rabbit and rat, animals secreting corticosterone as the principal corticoid, indicate that under certain treatments a shift in the corticoid secretion pattern may be induced, so that cortisol or a cortisol-like material is released by the adrenal gland (35, 40).

Biogenesis, Metabolism, and Mechanism of Action

Much of the information on the synthesis of adrenal corticoids has been derived from perfusion and incubation experiments in which various compounds have been exposed to the adrenal enzymes. Perfusion with cholesterol, progesterone, 17α-hydroxyprogesterone, and androgens have given rise to a presumed scheme for corticoid biosynthesis (29, 31, 35, 38). While 17-hydroxycorticosterone (compound F) is the corticoid of physiological importance in most animals, rats, mice, and rabbits secrete corticosterone (compound B) as the primary corticoid (Tables 7-7 and 7-8). Studies on the rat adrenal gland have revealed that although the gland does secrete corticosterone, the enzymes for synthesis of 17-hydroxycorticoids are present. However, in the rat, the distribution of enzymes appears to be such that oxylation of carbon-11 is favored and that this reaction reduces the hydroxylation of carbon-17, so that the former reaction precludes the latter (30). The synthetic pathways for the biogenesis of aldosterone, corticosterone, and 17-hydroxycorticosterone are presented in Fig. 7-4.

The adrenal corticoids are secreted in minute amounts and are rapidly removed from the blood stream. The half-life of most corticoids is less than 25 minutes, a duration indicative of a rapid breakdown or excretion. The major site of degradation is in the liver, where the steroids may be esterified to the glucuronide or sulfate or degraded to completely inactive forms by changes in the structure of the compound. The major metabolites now appear to be the tetrahydro derivatives in which the addition of a hydrogen into ring A results in the saturated hydroxylated derivative in place of the unsaturated ketone.

The exact mechanisms of action of the adrenal corticosteroids is still not clear, yet some information is available to indicate the activities of these hormones. Areas of the renal tubule have been shown to be influenced by aldosterone in the reabsorption of sodium ions. Several possible mechanisms have been suggested for the deposition of liver glycogen stimulated by glucocorticoids. Although the glucocorticoids stimulate renal glucose reabsorption, protein catabolism, and amino acid utilization, the significance of these latter two processes in glycogen deposition has not been established.

The suggested mechanisms of action of glucocorticoids on liver glycogen also include an influence on hepatic enzymes and on blood sugar

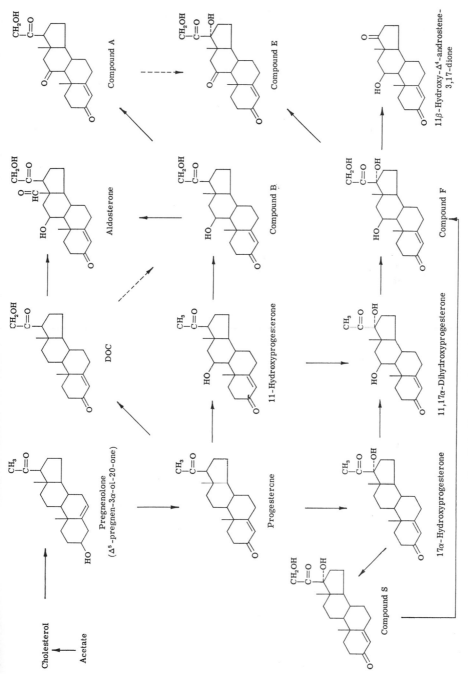

Fig. 7-4. Biosynthetic pathways for adrenal steroids.

levels (5, 12), as well as a possible reduction of extrahepatic glucose utilization. An increased blood sugar will stimulate glyconeogenesis in adrenalectomized animals. However, the effect of hydrocortisone on liver glycogen appears to be an action other than one to promote hyperglycemia (9).

Synthetic Corticoids and Anticorticoids

A number of synthetic steroids have been prepared that enhance the biological activity of the corticoids or act to antagonize these hormones. The halogenation of 17-hydroxycorticosterone (cortisol) at the 9α-position increases the glucocorticoid and mineralocorticoid potency of the molecule. A compound prepared by substituting a 2α-methyl group in addition to the 9α-fluoro group of cortisol further increases the glucocorticoid- and salt-retaining properties. The introduction of a double bond between carbons 1 and 2 (1-dehydrocortisol) markedly increases the glucocorticoid potency while the mineralocorticoid activity decreases.

Much attention is now being given to compounds that antagonize the electrocorticoids. Two such compounds are 3-(3-oxo-17β-hydroxy-4-androsten-17α-yl)propionic acid α-lactone and the 17-nor derivative of this steroid. While these compounds do not exert any action of their own on the excretion of sodium and potassium, in adrenalectomized animals they block the action of the exogenous mineralocorticoids, possibly by a competitive inhibition.

EXPERIMENT 7–1

Adrenalectomy*

In order to study the symptoms and effects of adrenalectomy, complete removal of the gland is essential. Any adrenal rests or any cortical tissue that remain following surgery may regenerate into a functioning adrenal cortex. Studies on the regeneration of the enucleated adrenal gland reveal that, like adrenalectomy, removal of the gland from its capsule is followed by a rapid disappearance of corticoids from the blood and a rise in pituitary ACTH levels (Fig. 7-5). The high levels of ACTH are maintained until the cortex regenerates and begins to secrete the various corticoids again.

Complete removal of the adrenal glands induces profound physiological changes in the animal (Table 7–1), which include a susceptibility to shock. Ether must be administered carefully and the animal watched closely, especially after one adrenal has been removed, in order to

* Cf. references (16, 18, 19, 23, 51, 56, 58).

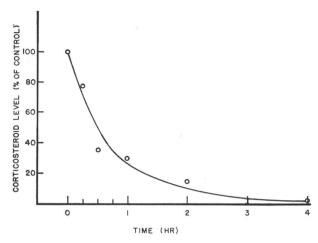

Fig. 7-5. The rate of disappearance of plasma corticosteroids following bilateral adrenalectomy. Redrawn from data of Fortier (16).

prevent death. At the conclusion of any experiment based on adrenalectomy, the animals should be examined carefully to validate the absence of adrenal tissue. While the surgical procedure is relatively simple in most experimental animals, adrenalectomy in the bird is difficult, for the glands lie close to the vena cava. Some investigators have been successful in destroying the glands by electrocautery, but even with this method the blood vessels may be damaged.

Procedure

Anesthetize a rat or mouse with ether and place the animal on an operating board, ventral side down with its nostrils exposed to an ether cone. Clip the hair from the area on both sides of the back in the region of the last rib and swab the site with Zephiran solution.

Make an incision high on the right side at an angle between the last rib and vertebral column. See Fig. 7-6, which illustrates the incision for adrenalectomy. Use care to avoid cutting the muscles around the vertebral column. Once the incision through the skin is complete, a small cut is made through the muscle layer with iridectomy scissors, and the tips of the scissors are carefully inserted through the cut and spread to widen the opening. The kidney is readily seen and the adrenal gland will be found at the anterior pole of the kidney. The perirenal fat may be grasped with forceps and carefully pulled through the opening. Grasp the fat below the adrenal gland with curved forceps and separate it from the kidney with a second pair of forceps used to tear the fat between the forceps beneath the gland and the kidney. Extreme care

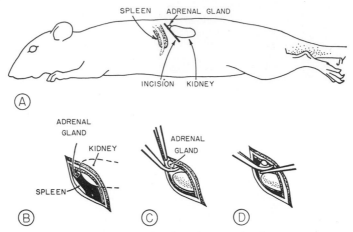

Fig. 7-6. Surgical adrenalectomy in the rat.

must be exercised to avoid grasping the adrenal gland itself since it is a fragile structure and will tear easily, leading to an incomplete adrenalectomy. The excised gland should be placed on a moistened paper towel and inspected to be sure that the entire gland has been removed. Once the gland has been removed, the incision is closed with separate sutures applied to the muscle layer and skin. The skin incision may be closed with skin clips. *Note:* At this point be sure to observe the response of the animal to the anesthetic, as it may be quite sensitive to ether.

Proceed to remove the left adrenal gland in a similar manner. However, in making the incision for the removal of the left gland, make the opening slightly more posterior and central. The spleen may have to be moved anteriorly to expose the adrenal gland (Fig. 7-6).

It is also possible to remove the adrenals with a single skin incision across the back, which can then be pulled to the right or the left side for the placing of the incisions through the muscle.

Postoperative Care and Experimental

Adrenalectomized animals should be housed individually if possible, and maintained at an even temperature, slightly higher than that normally used (80–82°F is optimal). Satisfactory maintenance requires a constant food supply, preferably a high-carbohydrate diet, and a 1% NaCl drinking solution. Review Table 7–1 for the symptoms of adrenal insufficiency. Be sure to examine the animals for adrenal rests at the termination of the experiment. This is required especially in survival studies where animals survive more than one month.

EXPERIMENT 7-2

Self-Selection of Drinking Fluids by the Adrenalectomized Rat*

One of the immediate physiological problems faced by the adrenalectomized animal is the electrolyte imbalance brought about by the loss of mineralocorticoids. As indicated in Experiment 7-1, the excessive loss of sodium can be ameliorated by the addition of sodium chloride to the diet. If adrenalectomized animals are given a choice of several drinking solutions, a preference will be given to one containing the NaCl.

Procedure and Experimental

Obtain a group of ten young male rats. Adrenalectomize five and carry out a sham adrenalectomy of the remaining five animals. Place the adrenalectomized animals in one large cage and the control rats in another. Supply to each cage the following drinking solutions in calibrated tubes: (a) tap water; (b) 1% NaCl; (c) 1% KCl. Record the daily intake of each drinking solution. *Note:* If calibrated drinking tubes are not available, use infant nursing bottles to hold the solutions. These bottles are calibrated in the metric system. If a number of student groups are undertaking this experiment, additional drinking solutions may be tested: (d) 1% NaCl and 1% glucose in the same solution; (e) 1% sodium citrate; (f) 1% glucose.

EXPERIMENT 7-3

Survival of Adrenalectomized Rats†

In the rat, the period of survival following adrenalectomy is influenced by diet, environment, genetic background, sex and age of animal; it may vary from several days to 3 or 4 weeks. A study of 5 colonies of rats revealed that 4 colonies showed a life span of 7 days with 95% mortality by 20.5 days. A fifth colony showed an average life span of 14.4 days and 50% mortality 20 days after surgery. Though the average survival of female rats was 1 day less than that for males, a high percentage of females survived indefinitely. Pseudopregnancy and pregnancy increases the survival time of female rats, and in general survival increases with age.

The diet of the adrenalectomized animal is extremely important for the maintenance of life. The addition of salt to the diet, usually in the

* Cf. references (14, 19, 23, 28, 44, 59).
† Cf. references (8, 19, 23, 67, 68).

form of a 1% NaCl drinking solution, markedly increased the life span of adrenalectomized animals. The animals are maintained and show some growth, but the treatment is only ameliorative. The salt solution simply keeps supplying the rat with sodium ions to replace those that are being lost through the renal tubules; it does not correct the improper handling of sodium by the kidney. The addition of potassium salts to the diet further increases the body level of this ion and is detrimental to the organism.

Procedure and Experimental

Obtain a group of 12 rats, preferably young mature males; adrenalectomize 10 animals; and undertake sham adrenalectomy on the remaining two, which will be used as controls. As usual, body weights of the animals are to be obtained before the start of the experiment. After the operation, treat the animals according to the accompanying tabulation.

Number of rats	Operation	Treatment
2	Sham-operated controls	None
2	Adrenalectomized controls	None
2	Adrenalectomized	1% NaCl drinking solution
2	Adrenalectomized	DCA, 1 mg per 0.1 ml suspension daily, subcutaneously
2	Adrenalectomized	2% glucose drinking solution
2	Adrenalectomized	1% KCl drinking solution

Record the body weights of all animals daily, and the time of death. After 3 weeks of treatment, kill all the animals and examine for completeness of adrenalectomy. Illustrate graphically the data for body weight changes and for mortality in the various groups of animals. Discuss the significance of sham-operated controls in studies involving adrenalectomy and endocrine experiments in general.

EXPERIMENT 7–4

Survival at Low Temperature*

Since the adrenal corticoids play a role in the ability of an organism to adapt to stress, the adrenalectomized animal shows a marked decrease in its ability to withstand exposure to stressors. One parameter used for the bioassay of corticoids has been the increased survival of adrenalectomized rats subjected to low ambient temperature. This test has been

* Cf. references (8, 58, 67, 68).

used for the assay of extracts of the adrenal cortex and the glucocorti-coids. The ability of DOC and progesterone to protect animals in cold stress also has been noted. Differences in survival of normal, castrated, and castrated sex hormone-treated adrenalectomized male and female rats is illustrative of the sex difference in adrenal cortical activity and the influence of the sex hormones on this difference.

Procedure and Experimental

Obtain a group of 16 mice; adrenalectomize 12 animals, and place them on 1% NaCl solution. The four unoperated animals will serve as controls. The adrenalectomized mice may be divided into three groups of 4 animals each as follows:

> Group 1:   Normal unoperated controls
> Group 2:   Adrenalectomized + 1% NaCl
> Group 3:   Adrenalectomized + cortisone
> Group 4:   Adrenalectomized + DCA

The injection schedule for groups 3 and 4 should follow the outline indicated in the tabulation.

Day	Time of operation	Group 3 Cortisone	Group 4 DCA
1	Afternoon	50 μg	500 μg
2	9 A.M.	50 μg	500 μg
	4 P.M.	50 μg	500 μg
3	9 A.M.	50 μg	500 μg
	10 A.M.	Expose to cold	Expose to cold

As indicated, place all animals in the cold at 10 A.M. on day 3. Animals should be housed in individual cages without bedding and be subjected to cold at 2°C. Observe the animals hourly and record the time of death of each animal. Discuss the results of the experiment in relation to the general adaptation syndrome.

If more animals are available, it is best to use 10–15 mice in each group.

EXPERIMENT 7–5

Eosinophil Depletion*

The potency of individual corticoids, and the physiological activity of the cortex have been evaluated by the decrease in blood eosinophils.

* Cf. references (6, 25–27, 48, 50, 57, 62).

The low levels of eosinophils found at night in the blood of rats and mice indicate that the adrenal cortex is most active during the time of greatest general activity. Diurnal rhythm of eosinophil levels in human beings indicates that maximum activity of the adrenal cortex occurs during the morning hours. The diurnal variation in blood corticoid level supports the evidence from eosinophil studies, since the highest plasma corticoid levels occur during the intervals of lowest leukocyte counts. A marked drop in eosinophil level has been cited as evidence for increased activity of the adrenal cortex following exposure to stressors (Fig. 7-7). In the

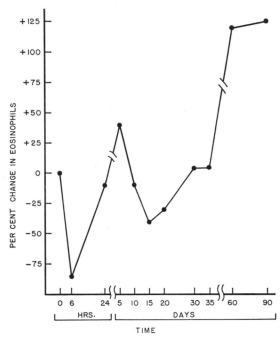

Fig. 7-7. Changes in circulating eosinophils in rats following exposure to cold stress. Adapted from data of Denison and Zarrow (6).

latter instance, the fact that eosinopenia occurred only during the first hours of cold exposure was taken to indicate that hypercorticalism is limited to the early manifestation of stress.

Procedure

Prepare the staining diluent for eosinophils by mixing the following:

>40 ml distilled water
>50 ml propylene glycol (1,2-propanediol)

10 ml of 10% aqueous phloxin B
1.0 ml of exactly 1.0% aqueous sodium carbonate

Mix the solution and filter. The diluent may be maintained at room temperature, and a fresh solution should be prepared each month.

Obtain a sample of blood from the tail vein, or orbital sinus, or by heart puncture (see Experiment 12–2). Use a leukocyte pipette and fill the pipette to the 1 mark with blood; then fill the pipette with diluent to the 11 mark.

Shake the pipette by hand for 1 minute (if a pipette shaker is used, shake for 30 seconds). Allow the pipettes to stand for 15 minutes. The diluting fluid hemolyzes all blood cells except the eosinophils, which appear shrunken and stained pink. After allowing the pipettes to stand, shake each one again for 1 minute (or 30 seconds with shaker) immediately before filling the hemacytometer. Remember to discharge the diluent from the capillary portion of the pipette before filling the counting chambers. Touch the edge of the pipette to the filling mark of the hemacytometer so as to allow just enough fluid to fill the chamber.

The eosinophils may be counted using the entire field of the hemacytometer. Count the eosinophils on both fields and average the count. Usually two (or more) pipettes are used to dilute replicate samples of blood, and the counts on the four fields of two hemacytometers are averaged. Since the entire field is counted, the calculation is:

eosinophils per cubic millimeter = average chamber count times 11.1

Experimental

Effect of Cold

Place two normal and two adrenalectomized rats in the cold (2°C). Make eosinophil counts on the experimental animals and on normal and adrenalectomized control animals every 1–2 hours. All adrenalectomized animals are to be given 1% NaCl drinking solution.

Effect of Corticoids

Treat animals according to the following schedule. Determine the eosinophil levels in all animals at 3, 6 and 18 (or 24) hours after injection. Use at least 1 normal and 1 adrenalectomized rat (maintained on 1% NaCl solution) in each group.

Group 1: Inject with 0.1 ml saline
Group 2: Inject with 50 μg cortisone
Group 3: Inject with 100 μg cortisone
Group 4: Inject with 0.1 ml epinephrine 1:1000

Group 5:   Inject with 0.1 ml epinephrine 1:10,000
Group 6:   Inject with 1–10 units corticotropin

Plot a graph showing the eosinophil changes in the treated animals as a percentage of the eosinophil levels in the control animals. Review the effect of corticoids and adrenal gland stimulants on the eosinophil level. Discuss the transient eosinopenia in cold-stressed animals in view of the general adaptation syndrome.

EXPERIMENT 7–6

Muscle Work*

The need of the adrenal corticoids in muscle work was demonstrated by Everse and de Fremery and amplified by Ingle. Like other stressors, enforced muscular contraction is poorly tolerated by adrenal insufficient animals, and early muscle fatigue is usual. Administration of the corticoids restores the muscle work ability. Both the shift in electrolyte balance and the impaired carbohydrate metabolism of adrenalectomized animals contribute to the response. Figure 7-8 illustrates the muscle contractions from a rat before and after adrenalectomy.

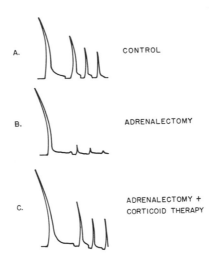

Fig. 7-8. Muscle work in the normal rat, adrenalectomized rat, and adrenalectomized rat treated with cortin. Redrawn from Everse and de Fremery (13).

Procedure

Technique for determining muscle work is as follows: A rat is

* Cf. references (13, 32, 33).

anesthetized with ether and secured to an operating board, ventral side up. Ether anesthesia is maintained by an ether cone placed over the nose of the animal. (*Note:* Be especially cautious in administering ether to adrenalectomized animals.) The animal is secured so that the only movement possible is the bending or stretching of the left hind leg from the ankle joint. Insert a small electrode in the left fossa poplitea and wrap the right hind leg with the indifferent electrode. The left hind leg is connected to a recording lever to which weights can be added so that the contractions can be recorded under different work loads. The leads to the electrodes are connected to the secondary output of a stimulator so that tetanic contractions of the calf muscles can be induced and recorded on a kymograph. Stimulate the muscle for 3 minutes, then allow a rest of 30 seconds. Thereafter stimulate the muscles three times during a 1-minute interval; then allow a half-minute rest period as follows:

> Stimulate 10 seconds
> Rest 5 seconds
> Stimulate 10 seconds
> Rest 5 seconds
> Stimulate 10 seconds
> Rest 30 seconds, then repeat

Experimental

Compare muscular fatigue in the following rats:

Normal animal
Adrenalectomized and maintained on 1% NaCl
Adrenalectomized and maintained on 50 μg cortisone given twice daily for 3 days
Adrenalectomized and maintained on 500 μg DCA given twice daily for 3 days

Account for the fatigue records obtained on the basis of the treatment of the animals used.

EXPERIMENT 7-7

Changes in Chemical Constituents of the Adrenal Gland*

The reduction in the concentration of adrenal ascorbic acid and cholesterol offers a means to assay corticotropin preparations and to test the rapidity of the adrenal response to stressors. Exposure of rats to a reduced environmental temperature induces a depletion of these glandular constituents within 1 hour, although these responses are limited to

* Cf. references (11, 25, 37, 52–54).

certain species. Although these tests indicate that the adrenal cortex is activated in as little as 1 hour after exposure to increased endogenous or exogenous ACTH, direct measurement of corticoids secreted showed that activation occurs earlier.

Determination of Ascorbic Acid

Procedure

Reagents

All reagents must be carefully prepared and should be stored in glass-stoppered bottles.

1. *2,4-Dinitrophenylhydrazine.* Dissolve 2 gm of 2,4-dinitrophenyl-hydrazine in 100 ml of 9 N sulfuric acid (analytical grade). Allow the mixture to stand overnight and then filter through Whatman no. 42 filter paper. It is preferable to use the color reagent freshly prepared, but a stock solution may be kept in a dark bottle and filtered just prior to use.

2. H_2SO_4, 85%. Add 900 ml of concentrated sulfuric acid (analytical grade) to 100 ml of distilled water. Observe the usual precaution in adding sulfuric acid to water.

3. *Thiourea.* Dissolve 10 gm of thiourea in 50 ml of absolute ethanol, then dilute to 100 ml with distilled water.

4. *Norit (acid washed).* Add 1 liter of 10% HCl to 200 gm of Norit (USP grade) in a large flask. Bring the mixture to a boil and filter with suction. Transfer the filtered residue to 1 liter of distilled water, mix well to wash the Norit, then filter with suction. Remove the filtered Norit and oven dry at 110°C.

5. *Trichloroacetic acid.* Prepare a 6% solution in distilled water. Since trichloroacetic acid is hydroscopic, many workers obtain small bottles of the material and prepare the solutions using the entire contents of the bottle. Thus, there will be no subsequent solutions of a lesser concentration due to the added water in the material.

6. *Stock ascorbic acid solution.* Accurately weigh exactly 100 mg of ascorbic acid and transfer it quantitatively to a 100-ml volumetric flask. Dilute to volume with 6% trichloroacetic acid.

7. *Standard ascorbic acid solution.* Dilute 2.0 ml of the stock ascorbic acid solution to 100 ml, quantitatively, with 6% trichloroacetic acid solution. The concentration of the standard is 20 μg/ml.

Standardization

Transfer 25.0 ml of the standard ascorbic acid solution to a 50 ml Erlenmeyer flask and add 0.5 gm of Norit. Shake vigorously for 1 minute, then filter through Whatman no. 42 filter paper. To individual test tubes add 0.0 (for reagent blank), 0.25, 0.5, 1.0, 1.5, 2.0, 2.5, and 3.0 ml of the filtrate, then dilute the contents of each tube to 4.0 ml by adding the appropriate volume of 6% trichloroacetic acid (previously shaken with Norit and filtered). Add 1 drop of thiourea solution and 1.0 ml of 2,4-dinitrophenylhydrazine reagent to each tube; mix with a small glass stirring rod and place the tubes in a boiling water bath for 10 minutes. Continue from Step 6 under Determination of Adrenal Ascorbic Acid (see below). Plot graph of optical density against actual concentration of ascorbic acid in each tube.

Determination of Adrenal Ascorbic Acid

Always run a blank sample consisting of trichloroacetic acid (Step 3) in place of the filtrate. Even though a standard curve has been obtained, it is always advisable to run at least two standard ascorbic acid preparations with each subsequent determination.

1. Weigh the adrenal gland to the nearest 0.1 ml.

2. Grind the tissue with a small volume of 6% trichloroacetic acid (2 ml) and transfer the extract to a volumetric flask (10 or 25 ml depending on dilution required for tissue). Repeat the extraction of adrenal tissue at least two more times. After the final transfer, adjust the total extract to the volume of the flask with trichloroacetic acid.

3. Filter the diluted extract into a small flask containing 0.2 gm Norit and shake for 1 minute.

4. Filter again through the same filter paper into another flask.

5. Transfer exactly 4.0 ml of the filtrate to a test tube and add one drop of the 10% thiourea solution and 1.0 ml of 2,4-dinitrophenylhydrazine color reagent.

6. Place the tube in a boiling water bath for exactly 10 minutes.

7. Remove the tube from the water bath and place in an ice bath.

8. Slowly add dropwise 5.0 ml of 85% H_2SO_4. The mixture must be stirred vigorously during the addition. In order to prevent excessive heating, the sulfuric acid must be added slowly and the tubes must be chilled in an ice bath.

9. Determine the optical density of each sample in a photometer at 515 mμ. Use the blank, prepared in the same manner as the tissue extracts, to adjust the photometer to zero optical density.

Calculations

Use dilution factor 0.23 in the following equation:

$$\text{milligrams ascorbic acid per 100 ml} = \frac{OD \times \text{factor} \times \text{dilution} \times 100}{\text{adrenal weight (mg)}}$$

Explain the derivation of the formula for calculation of results. Divide the optical density value (for each standard solution of ascorbic acid determined) by the concentration of ascorbic acid in the test tube. Plot a graph of optical density (absorbancy) vs. concentration.

Experimental

1. Distribute 8 young adult male rats into 4 groups and treat as follows:

Group 1:   Intraperitoneal injection of 0.1 ml epinephrine 1:1000
Group 2:   Inject 10 IU of ACTH
Group 3:   Expose to a temperature of 2–5°C
Group 4:   Maintain as controls

After 2 hours, quickly decapitate the animals and remove the adrenal glands; determine the adrenal ascorbic acid concentration. Tabulate the effects of the treatments on the adrenal ascorbic acid levels. *Note:* One gland from each animal may be used for Experiment 7–8, Histochemical Analysis of Adrenal Ascorbic Acid.

2. Repeat the above experiments using hypophysectomized rats.

Determination of Cholesterol

Procedure

Reagents

1. *Ferric chloride stock solution.* Dissolve 10 gm ferric chloride (reagent) in 100 ml of concentrated phosphoric acid. (The original report suggested the use of glacial acetic acid. However, other studies showed that less precipitation occurs when phosphoric acid is used, and the reagent is more stable (53).

2. *Color reagent.* Dilute 1.0 ml of the ferric chloride stock solution to 100 ml with concentrated sulfuric acid (reagent grade).

3. *Cholesterol stock solution.* Accurately weigh exactly 200 mg of cholesterol (pure, dry, ash free) and transfer it quantitatively to a 50-ml volumetric flask. Dilute to volume with glacial acetic acid to produce a solution of a concentration of 4 mg/ml.

4. *Cholesterol standard.* Transfer exactly 5.0 ml of the stock cholesterol solution to a 100-ml volumetric flask and dilute to volume with glacial acetic acid to produce a standard solution of 0.2 mg/ml.

Standardization

Transfer 0.0 (blank solution) 0.1, 0.2, 0.3, 0.4 and 0.5 ml of the standard cholesterol solutions to individual *matched* colorimeter tubes. Dilute the volume in each tube to 3.5 ml by adding the appropriate volume of glacial acetic acid. Slowly add 2.5 ml of the color reagent to each tube, allowing the solution to flow down the side of the tube and layer over the other liquid. The next critical step is to mix the two layers rapidly by swirling in a brisk circular motion. The optical density of each sample is determined in a spectrophotometer at 560 mμ after the tubes reach room temperature. The blank is used to set the instrument to zero optical density.

Plot a curve of the optical density of each sample against the actual concentration of cholesterol in each tube.

Determination of Adrenal Cholesterol

Run a sample of 3.5 ml glacial acetic acid as a blank. In subsequent determinations after standardization, always run at least two cholesterol standard solutions.

1. Weigh the adrenal gland to the nearest 0.1 mg and homogenize in a tissue grinder, using a total of 10 ml of glacial acetic acid.

2. Filter the homogenate through Munktell no. 00 paper.

3. Transfer 0.5 ml of the filtrate to a *matched* colorimeter tube.

4. Add 3.0 ml of glacial acetic acid and mix.

5. Allow 2.5 ml of the color reagent to flow slowly down the side of the tube and layer over the acetic acid.

6. Mix the two layers by swirling the tubes rapidly in a brisk circular motion. The mixing of the two layers is a critical step.

7. After the tubes have reached room temperature, obtain the optical density values in a photometer, using the blank to set the instrument to zero optical density.

Calculation

Use the equation:

$$\text{milligrams cholesterol per 100 ml} = \frac{\text{OD} \times 20 \times 100}{\text{adrenal weight (mg)}}$$

Account for each value used in the calculation formula. Compare the values obtained by calculation with values read directly from standardization curve. Divide the optical density values for cholesterol standard solutions by the actual concentration of cholesterol in the tubes.

Experimental

1. Select 10 young adult rats and distribute them into 5 groups to be treated as follows:

Group 1:   Controls
Group 2:   ACTH 10 IU
Group 3:   ACTH 40 IU
Group 4:   Epinephrine 0.1 ml 1:1000
Group 5:   Expose to 2–5°C

Four hours after the start of the treatment, kill the animals by decapitation and rapidly remove the adrenal glands. Determine the cholesterol content of the adrenal glands. Tabulate the results and account for the changes observed.

2. Repeat above experiment with hypophysectomized rats.

EXPERIMENT 7–8

Histology and Histochemistry of the Adrenal Cortex*

The changes in the zones of the cortex, as viewed microscopically, has offered evidence for the specific effects of certain treatments as in the involution of the zona fasciculata following administration of thiouracil. Alteration in the secretion of aldosterone and glucocorticoids have been correlated with changes in the size and histochemistry of the zona glomerulosa and zona fasciculata, respectively. The change in adrenal ascorbic acid, cholesterol, and other steroids may be also studied histochemically.

Procedure and Experimental

A. Histology

Examine histological preparations of the adrenal gland of the rat or rabbit. Identify the capsule, zona glomerulosa, zona fasciculata, zona reticularis, and medulla. Examine the histological preparation of a bird adrenal gland. Compare the histology of the mammalian adrenal cortex with that of the bird. Discuss the zonation of the cortex in regard to the sites of adrenal hormone production. Compare the adrenal gland of a normal rat and a rat exposed to cold 2–5°C for 1 week.

B. Histochemical Analysis of Adrenal Ascorbic Acid

Obtain adrenal glands from normal rats and from rats exposed to cold, to ACTH (10 IU), or to epinephrine (0.1 ml of 1:1000 solution) for 1 hour.

1. Remove the tissue rapidly from the animal and place immediately

* Cf. references (22, 28, 63).

in a dark vial containing silver nitrate solution (5% $AgNO_3$ solution at pH 2.0–2.5). Slit the capsule if it is present.

2. Place the vial in an incubator at 55° for 1 hour.

3. Decant the silver nitrate solution and replace with distilled water. Allow the tissue to stand in distilled water for 15 minutes.

4. Pour off the water and replace with 5% sodium thiosulfate solution (acidified). The adrenal gland should remain in the thiosulfate fixative for 30–45 minutes.

5. Proceed in the usual manner to dehydrate the tissue and embed it in paraffin for sectioning.

EXPERIMENT 7–9

Paper Chromatographic Separation of Corticoids*

The paper chromatographic separation of biological extracts containing corticoids offers a means of separating, identifying, and determining the concentration of microgram quantities of the hormones. The techniques involved require precise and careful manipulation; a number of methods are available, most of them modifications of the procedures of Bush and or Zaffaroni. The Bush method uses aqueous methanol as an immobile phase and benzene or toluene as a mobile phase. The Zaffaroni method involves paper impregnated with propylene glycol and the use of formamide as a mobile phase. In each technique a number of solvent modifications are used. Generally the Zaffaroni technique involves a longer period of chromatography but results in clearer separation of corticoids, and different chromatography solvents must be used to isolate specific steroids. The Bush method is a faster technique, which allows the separation of nearly all corticoids on one paper; the separation, however, frequently is not as clear as with the Zaffaroni method. The quantitative study of corticoids eluted from paper strips has been found to be as reliable as colorimetric techniques involving solvent partition and column chromatography. Paper chromatographic separations have been used to identify corticoids in peripheral and adrenal venous blood as well as corticoids from the adrenal gland.

Procedure

The experiment will be carried out using standard preparations of corticoids in alcohol. The chromatography of corticoids extracted from tissue or blood would be similar except that a chromatographic step to remove fatty material from the paper might be employed.

* Cf. references (2–4, 66).

Reagents

1. *Benzene or toluene.* Saturated with the 50% aqueous methanol as immobile phase.

2. *Methanol.* Prepare a 50% v/v aqueous solution of methanol. Saturate the solution with the solvent to be used as immobile phase.

3. *Filter paper.* Whatman no. 1 paper strips about 30 cm wide are satisfactory. Before steroids are applied, the paper should be washed in petroleum ether or benzene to remove lipid material on the paper. Many authorities require that for experimental work, the papers be subjected to continuous extraction with lipoid solvents for 6–24 hours before being used.

Determination

Corticoid samples. Prepare separate methanolic solutions of corticosterone, cortisone, and cortisol with concentrations of 10 micrograms per 10 microliters (10 μg/10 μl). Then prepare a mixture of the three corticoids so that 10 microliters (10 μl, 10 λ) contains 10 μg of each of the steroids. Calculate the concentrations of stock corticoid solutions and dilutions for the corticoid samples so that the use of the hormones will be conservative.

Preparation of the paper. Draw a horizontal line in pencil on the paper about 15 cm down the length of the paper (the paper should be cut so that the solvent travels with the grain of the paper). Mark, in pencil, four positions on the horizontal line for the application of samples. Be sure the application points are separated from each other and from the edge of the paper by several centimeters. In addition, during the handling of the paper, avoid touching the area in which the separation is to be achieved so that fingerprints will not interfere with the process. Mark the four spots, B, E, F, and mixture, to indicate the sample to be applied.

Use a 10 μl ultramicropipette to apply the corticoid to the paper. DO NOT apply the entire sample at one time, but apply it gradually, allowing each drop to dry before the next drop is added. Frequently chromatogram applicators employ a stream of nitrogen or air to aid in drying the paper. After all samples have been applied, the paper is placed in the chromatogram tank in the position for descending chromatography, and methanol 50% is placed in the bottom of the tank. The tank is now closed, and the paper is allowed to equilibrate with the methanol solution for 2 hours. (The preferred equilibration is an overnight process with the temperature maintained at 34°C.)

After the equilibration time, fill the solvent tray with benzene (or toluene), close the tank, and allow the separation to proceed. Usually the solvent front is allowed to attain a predetermined mark on the paper to allow a 2- to 4-hour separation. If the paper is not removed when the solvent reaches the marked point, the solvent front must be quickly marked with a pencil as the paper is removed, for the solvent evaporates rapidly. The paper is allowed to dry completely by hanging in air before attempt is made to locate the spots of corticoids. In experimental work on chromatography of steroids, exposure of paper strips to bright sunlight is avoided since ultraviolet light can induce molecular changes in the steroids.

Visualization

Visualization of the spots may be accomplished by numerous techniques. Various laboratory groups should use different means to visualize the corticoids so that the results of the various techniques can be compared. Also the chemical grouping of the steroids which react with each color reagent should be ascertained by a survey of the literature:

1. Fluorescence: Scan the paper strips with a short wavelength ultraviolet (UV) light in a dark room. *Precaution:* Recall the effect of UV radiations on tissue and note that exposure of the eyes to UV light of short wavelength should be avoided. Therefore for extended use of ultraviolet light, glasses should be worn.

2. Wet the paper with a solution of 10% NaOH in methanol, then dry it in the oven. After the alkali treatment, the fluorescence of the corticoids will be more predominant.

3. Tetrazolium reaction. Prepare a solution of 0.2% triphenyltetrazolium chloride in alcohol (store in the dark). Just prior to use, dilute two parts of the tetrazolium solution with 1 part of 10% NaOH. Wet the paper in the solution, then wash it in water. Blue tetrazolium may be used in the place of triphenyltetrazolium chloride.

4. Tollen's reagent. Prepare a solution of the following components:

> 10 ml of 0.1 N silver nitrate
> 10 drops of concentrated ammonium hydroxide
> 5 ml of 10% NaOH

Wet the paper in the mixture until dark black spots appear. Wash the paper with 1% sodium thiosulfate, then with water.

5. Review other techniques. Iodine reagent and the Zimmermann reagent are used to determine the positions of steroids separated chromatographically. With what adrenal steroids would the Zimmermann reagent be most valuable? *Note:* Paper strips moistened in water are quite delicate and will tear easily.

6. The addition of concentrated sulfuric acid to a paper strip will produce a cherry red color (seen just before the paper chars) where Reichstein's compound S is located. This corticoid frequently is not separated from corticosterone.

7. Currently many chromatographic studies are carried on using glass filter paper. With this material, the paper strips may be heated on a hot plate so that char marks will appear at the position of the corticoids.

EXPERIMENT 7–10

Determination of Plasma and Adrenal Corticosterone in the Rat*

The chemical determination of corticoids involves the extraction and purification of small quantities of materials through several partition steps. Extreme care must be taken to avoid the loss of any material or the introduction of foreign matter that might react with the color reagents. In this regard, glassware must be scrupulously clean, reagents must be purified, and colorimetric sample blanks must be considered to account for background chromogens in the biological materials extracted. The extraction procedures involve the separation of steroids from a lipoid media into an aqueous media and the partitions must be carried out with caution to avoid loss of steroid in emulsions that may form between the extraction phases. When these cautions are observed, reliable estimates of corticoid values may be obtained.

Studies on the blood and glandular corticoids reveal that the exposure of an animal to exogenous ACTH or to stressors results in a rise in the concentration of corticoids in urine, in peripheral and adrenal venous blood, and in the adrenal gland. Under conditions that induce adrenal cortical stimulation, the peripheral blood corticoid levels have been found to increase in as little as 15 minutes (Fig. 7-9). The manner in which the animal is prepared for blood withdrawal can influence the blood corticoid levels. Under ether anesthesia, the blood corticoids are higher than after Nembutal administration. The adrenal glands of rats killed with Nembutal contain higher concentrations of corticosterone than glands from decapitated animals. The time interval between Nembutal administration and withdrawal of blood influences the plasma corticosterone levels obtained. Lower corticoid levels were found in samples obtained 20 minutes after injection of Nembutal than in samples taken earlier.

While the Porter-Silber reagent (phenylhydrazine in alcohol-sulfuric

* Cf. references (21, 25, 26, 36, 40, 41, 45, 47).

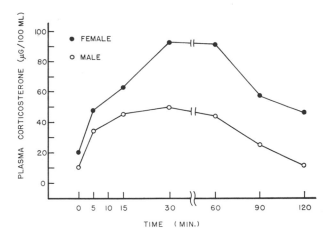

Fig. 7-9. Rise in plasma corticosterone following exposure to ether stress. Adapted from data of Kitay (36).

acid) has been considered to be specific for 17-OHCS, a number of non-17-hydroxysteroids, including 18-hydroxydeoxycorticosterone, react with this reagent. Corticosterone reacts with this reagent to produce a chromogen with an absorption maximum differing from those of the 17-OHCS. Although corticosterone can be determined with this reagent, the sulfuric acid fluorescence technique is the method of choice. In regard to the rat, paper chromatographic analysis of plasma indicates that the corticoid component is chiefly corticosterone with little or no 17-OHCS. However, several studies have indicated the presence of chromogens in rat plasma which react colorimetrically with the Porter-Silber reagent. This Porter-Silber positive material obtained from rat plasma is, in part, due to the presence of the 18-hydroxycorticoids.

Procedure

Reagents

1. *Ethanol, 33% solution (aqueous)*
2. *Ethanol, 13% solution (aqueous)*
3. *Ligroin.* 30°–60°C boiling point (petroleum ether)
4. *Sodium hydroxide, 0.1 N solution*
5. *Sulfuric acid, 30 N solution.* Prepared from analytical grade H_2SO_4.

Purification of Reagents

Ethanol. Distill from 2,4-dinitrophenylhydrazine hydrochloride.
Dichloromethane (methylene chloride, CH_2Cl_2):

1. Wash a volume of dichloromethane with an equal volume of water. Decant (or aspirate) the water layer and dry the dichloromethane over anhydrous Na_2SO_4.

2. Decolorize the dichloromethane with charcoal. Add Norit to the solvent, mix, and filter the solvent.

3. Store the solvent over NaOH flakes (reagent grade) for 24 hours.

4. Distill the dichloromethane, using a small fractionating column, and collect the fraction distilled between 40° and 41°.

Water. Water used in preparing the reagents and in the final wash of glassware must be freed from any oxidizing or reducing agents. Ordinary distilled water will not suffice. This water may be passed through a resin deionizing column, then distilled twice more. For classroom experiments, double-distilled water may be used.

Standardization

Use ultramicropipettes to transfer volumes of accurately prepared corticosterone standards (dissolved in redistilled methanol) to small test tubes. Allow the alcohol to evaporate to dryness, then add 2 ml of 30 N sulfuric acid and swirl the tubes to mix the reagent with the dried steroid. After 45 minutes, read the fluorescence of the standards against a blank in a photofluorometer. Even though a standard curve is obtained, standard samples of corticoid should be run with each determination. The samples of corticosterone, to be extracted with dichloromethane, may be prepared by dissolving the proper quantity of steroid with a minimum amount of ethanol in a volumetric flask and diluting with water. The extraction of standard amounts of corticosterone from ethanol-water is advisable in order to evaluate the extraction procedure (determine the percentage of steroid recovered).

Determination of Corticosterone in Adrenal Tissue

1. Remove the adrenal gland from the animal, clear of adhering fat and weigh on a torsion balance to the nearest 0.1 mg.

2. Homogenize the glands with 2.0 ml of 33% ethanol; then transfer the sample (with filtration) to a 5-ml volumetric flask. Dilute the homogenate to 5.0 ml with water, first using the aqueous diluent to rinse out the homogenizing tube for a quantitative transfer. Mix the solution well.

3. Remove volumes of 0.5, 0.7, 1.0, and 1.2 ml from the diluted homogenate (Step 2) and transfer to glass-stoppered centrifuge tubes. Dilute the volume in each tube to 2.0 ml by adding the appropriate volume of 13% ethanol. Carry out the following treatments on each tube.

4. Wash the extract by adding 5.0 ml of ligroin down the side of the tube. Shake vigorously and remove the ligroin by aspiration.

5. Extract the corticoids from the aqueous-alcohol solution with dichloromethane. Carefully add 5.0 ml down the side of the tube to avoid forming an emulsion. Then shake vigorously for 1 minute. Remove the aqueous layer by aspiration.

6. Wash the dichloromethane with 1.0 ml of ice cold 0.1 N NaOH. Shake the mixture for 15–30 seconds, then remove the aqueous layer. Prolonged exposure of dichloromethane extract to the alkali must be avoided.

7. Some emulsion of dichloromethane will result from the vigorous shaking during the extraction and transfer of this emulsified layer to the sulfuric acid for fluorescence must be avoided. Therefore, pipette 4.0 ml of the clear extract to a tube containing 2.0 ml H_2SO_4 and shake for 1 minute. Determine the fluorescence of the samples as described below in the section on using the fluorometer. Note the time restriction.

Determination of Corticosterone in Plasma

1. Obtain a plasma sample and transfer volumes of 0.6, 1.0, and 1.4 ml of plasma to glass-stoppered centrifuge tubes. Dilute to a volume of 2.0 ml by adding the appropriate volume of 13% ethanol.

2. Treat each tube as described above for the determination of corticosterone in the adrenal gland. Start at Step 4.

Using the Fluorometer

1. Set the activation monocrometer at 470 mμ and the fluorescence monochrometer at 525 mμ.

2. Determine the fluorescence of the standard corticosterone sample and of extracts of adrenal gland and plasma.

Note: The fluorescence of the extracts must be determined exactly 45 minutes after addition of the dichloromethane. Correct the fluorescence of the samples for any background fluorescence resulting from impurities in the extracting solvents by subtracting the value of the blank from those of the samples.

3. Prepare a calibration curve for the fluorescence of corticosterone using value of 0.02–0.12 μg corticosterone per milliliter of H_2SO_4. With each extraction, run two standard samples of corticosterone (0.05 and 0.1 μg) in ethanol in addition to the blank.

4. Use the calibration curve and separate calculations to determine the corticosterone content in the extracts of plasma and of adrenal gland

Report corticosterone content as micrograms per 100 milliliters in plasma and adrenal tissue.

Experimental

Determine the plasma and adrenal corticosterone levels in the rat or rabbit following exposure to a stressor.

Determine the plasma corticosterone levels in a hypophysectomized rat following treatment with various doses of ACTH.

EXPERIMENT 7–11

Effect of Corticoids on Carbohydrate Metabolism: Steroid Diabetes in the Bird*

In the classical studies on insulin insufficiency (Chapter 13), adrenalectomy was found to alleviate the symptoms of diabetic animals. Administration of the glucocorticoids, by virtue of actions on metabolic processes, leads to the development of a diabetic state: hyperglycemia, glucosuria, and impaired fat metabolism. This effect has been demonstrated quite dramatically in birds, where the administration of specific corticoids to chickens produced a four- to fivefold increase in blood sugar, a marked increase in water intake and excretion, and a reduction in ovulation. Of considerable interest is the observation that otherwise similar glucocorticoids do not have the same diabetogenic potency in the bird. Large amounts of corticoids induce the diabetic response whereas smaller doses bring about the deposition of liver glycogen. The effect of corticoids on liver glycogen are presented in Experiments 7–12 and 7–13.

Procedure

Adult hens will be used in this experiment. The birds are to be housed in individual cages and supplied with food and water ad libitum. Blood samples are to be withdrawn either from the wing vein or by cardiac puncture (see Experiment 12–2 for blood withdrawal techniques). Blood glucose levels are to be determined as described in Experiment 13–2. Each bird will be given daily intramuscular injections for 2 weeks. Determine the blood glucose levels at intervals of 3, 7, 10, and 14 days after initiation of treatment. For each group, plot the blood sugar level (mg/100 ml) as a function of time on treatment.

* Cf. references (12, 21, 51, 57).

Experimental

Use the following treatment schedule:

> Group 1:   Saline-Tween 80*, 0.2 ml/day
> Group 2:   Hydrocortisone, 5 mg/day
> Group 3:   Cortisone, 10 mg/day
> Group 4:   Corticosterone, 5 mg/day
> Group 5:   Deoxycorticosterone, 40 mg/day

At least 3 hens should be placed on each treatment. If a limited number of birds are available, the experiment may be limited to testing the effects of hydrocortisone and cortisone on blood glucose. Review the effects of steroids on carbohydrate metabolism of the bird.

EXPERIMENT 7–12

Effect of Corticoids on Carbohydrate Metabolism: Deposition of Liver Glycogen in the Bird†

The preceding experiment (7–11) demonstrated one situation in which the potency of cortisone was not the same as that of hydrocortisone. While it has been assumed generally that these two corticoids possess nearly the same glucocorticoid activity, this relative potency is found in mammals but not in birds.

Procedure and Experimental

Obtain a group of chicks, body weight 300–600 gm, and initiate one of the treatments described below. During the treatment, food should be removed from the cages 24 hours prior to killing the birds. At the end of the treatment period, the birds are to be decapitated and the level of liver glycogen determined. The determination of liver glycogen involves the digestion of liver, precipitation of glycogen, hydrolysis of the glycogen to glucose, and final glucose determination. Procedure for the first three steps in glycogen determination will be given here, then reference will be made to Experiment 13–2 for determination of glucose.

Use 3–5 chicks for each treatment group. Either the free corticoid or acetate derivative may be administered.

> Group 1:   Saline-Tween 80, 0.2 ml/injection
> Group 2:   Hydrocortisone, 40 μg
> Group 3:   Cortisone, 1 mg

* See Appendix A-5 for preparation of steroid vehicles.
† Cf. references (12, 21, 51, 57).

Group 4:   Corticosterone, 400 µg
Group 5:   Deoxycorticosterone, 4 mg

Note that treatments of groups 2 and 4 involve microgram quantities of steroids whereas milligram quantities are used in the other groups. The corticoids should be prepared so that the total dose is given in 4 equal intramuscular injections. Be sure to calculate the dose for each injection. The following treatment schedule may be used:

8 A.M., 1st injection
10 A.M., 2nd injection
12 noon, 3rd injection
2 P.M., 4th injection
4 P.M., decapitate animals and remove liver

The animals are to be decapitated and the liver removed quickly and frozen in a dry ice-acetone mixture. Weigh a small frozen section of the liver on a torsion balance (try to obtain a section weighing between 200 and 500 mg). Immediately transfer the liver section to 2 ml of 30% KOH in a 15 ml centrifuge tube and place it in a boiling water bath. It is important that the steps involved in removal, freezing of liver, and transfer to KOH be carried out rapidly to avoid loss of glycogen by enzymatic action. The test tube containing the liver in KOH should remain in the boiling water bath for 30 minutes. Stir gently several times during this interval.

1. After 30 minutes, remove the tube from the water bath and place in a beaker of cold water.

2. Add 2 drops of 10% $ZnSO_4$ and 4 ml of 95% ethanol. Stir the mixture and *carefully* heat to boiling in a water bath. This will precipitate the glycogen.

3. Cool the tube and centrifuge to bring down the glycogen. Discard the supernatant fluid.

4. Add 2 ml of water to the precipitate and resuspend the glycogen. Use 4 ml of 95% ethanol to reprecipitate the glycogen. Heat the tube in a water bath, then cool and centrifuge as in the previous steps, discarding the supernatant fluid.

5. Add 2.0 ml of 2.5 N sulfuric acid to each tube, and heat in a boiling water bath for 30 minutes.

6. After hydrolyzing the glycogen (Step 5) cool the tube and add 1 drop phenolphthalein solution. Then add dropwise 2.5 N NaOH solution until the *first* pink-red color is obtained. Now add a drop of 0.5 N sulfuric acid to discharge the color.

7. Dilute the preparation to 25 ml with water and mix thoroughly. Aliquots of this sample will be removed and transferred to the Folin-Wu

tube, as described in Experiment 13–2, for glucose determination. For most treatment groups, a 1.0 ml sample will suffice. However, for animals treated with hydrocortisone or corticosterone, an aliquot of the final sample may have to be diluted 1:10 and a 1.0 ml portion of this solution be transferred to the Folin-Wu tube.

EXPERIMENT 7–13

Effect of Corticoids on Liver Glycogen Deposition in the Rat or Mouse*

Early studies on the identification, extraction, and determination of potency of the glucocorticoids depended on the use of an assay involving the deposition of glycogen in the liver of the rat or mouse. The following experiment demonstrates the effect of adrenalectomy and corticoid replacement therapy on the content of liver glycogen in the mouse.

Procedure and Experimental

1. Inbred male mice (20–25 gm in weight) are placed on a high-protein diet for 2 days prior to adrenalectomy. Following adrenalectomy, the animals are maintained at 76°F and fed the high-protein diet with 0.9% NaCl substituted for drinking water. (For the first postoperative day, a 0.9% NaCl solution containing 5% glucose is recommended.)

2. Three days after adrenalectomy the mice are fasted overnight; the saline drinking solution is removed the following morning.

3. On the fourth postoperative day, a *total* of 7 subcutaneous injections are given to each mouse at the following times: 9:15 A.M., 10:00 A.M., 10:45 A.M., 11:30 A.M., 12:30 P.M., 1:30 P.M., and 2:30 P.M.

4. The accompanying tabulation describes the dosages of hormones to be injected (0.2 ml/injection volume).

Treatment	Number of mice	Total dosage administered
Control	6	—
Adrenalectomy	6	—
Adrenalectomy cortisone (Cpd B)	6	20 μg
Adrenalectomy + cortisol (17α-hydroxycorticosterone, Cpd F)	6	20 μg
Adrenalectomy + deoxycorticosterone (DOC)	6	20 μg

* Cf. references (5, 63a).

In addition, a dose response curve for cortisol may be established (5–50 μg).

5. One hour after the last injection, kill the animals by decapitation and remove the livers as rapidly as possible.

6. Determine liver glycogen content by the method described in Experiment 7–12.

References

1. Briggs, F. N., and Topel, W. 1958. The effect of ACTH on the ascorbic acid concentration of adrenal venous plasma of the rat. *Endocrinology* **62**: 24–29.
2. Bush, I. E. 1951. Paper chromatographic study of secretion of the adrenal cortex of various mammalian species. *J. Physiol. (London)* **115**: 12P.
3. Bush, I. E. 1952. Methods of paper chromatography applicable to study of steroids in mammalian blood and tissue. *Biochem. J.* **50**: 370–378.
4. Bush, I. E. 1953. Species difference in adrenal corticoid secretion. *J. Endocrinol.* **9**: 95–100.
5. Cohen, R. B. 1961. The histochemical distribution and metabolic significance of gluco-6-phosphatase activity, glycogen and lipid in the stimulated adrenal cortex. *Endocrinology* **68**: 710–715.
6. Denison, M. E., and Zarrow, M. X. 1954. Eosinophils of blood during prolonged exposure to cold and chronic administration of cortisone acetate. *Proc. Soc. Exptl. Biol. Med.* **85**: 433–437.
7. Dorfman, R. I. 1961. Comparative Biochemistry of Adrenocortical Hormones, *in* "Comparative Endocrinology" (A. Gorbman, ed.), pp. 613–623. Wiley, New York.
8. Dorfman, R. I., Ross, E., and Shipley, R. A. 1946. Studies on the "cold test" as a method for the assay of adrenal cortical steroids. *Endocrinology* **38**: 165–177.
9. Dorsey, J. L., and Munck, A. 1962. Studies on the mode of action of glucocorticoids in rats: A comparison of the effects of cortisol and glucose on the formation of liver glycogen. *Endocrinology* **71**: 605–608.
10. Egdahl, R. H. 1961. Cerebral cortical inhibition of pituitary-adrenal secretion. *Endocrinology* **68**: 574–581.
11. Elton, R. L., Zarrow, I. G., and Zarrow, M. X. 1959. Depletion of adrenal ascorbic acid and cholesterol: A comparative study. *Endocrinology* **65**: 152–155.
12. Engel, F. L., and Fredericks, J. 1957. Contribution to understanding the mechanism of permissive action of corticoids. *Proc. Soc. Exptl. Biol. Med.* **94**: 593–596.
13. Everse, J. W. R., and de Fremery, P. 1932. On a method of measuring fatigue in rats and its application for testing the suprarenal cortical hormone (Cortin). *Acta. Brev. Neerl. Physiol. Pharmacol. Microbiol.* **2**: 152.
14. Farrell, G. 1959. The physiological factors which influence the secretion of aldosterone. *Recent Progr. Hormone Res.* **15**: 275–310.
15. Farrell, G. 1959. Steroidogenic properties of extracts of beef diencephalon. *Endocrinology* **65**: 29–33.
16. Fortier, C. 1959. Pituitary ACTH and plasma free corticosteroids following bilateral adrenalectomy in the rat. *Proc. Soc. Exptl. Biol. Med.* **100**: 13–16.
17. Fortier, C., and De Groot, J. 1958. Neuroendocrine relationships. *Progr. Neurol. Psychiat.* **8**: 118–127.

18. Fortier, C., and De Groot, J. 1959. Adenohypophyseal corticotrophin and plasma free corticosteroids during regeneration of the enucleated rat adrenal gland. *Am. J. Physiol.* **196**: 589–592.

19. Gaunt, R. 1933. Adrenalectomy in the rat. *Am. J. Physiol.* **103**: 494–510.

20. Glenister, D. W., and Yates, F. E. 1961. Sex difference in the rate of disappearance of corticosterone-4-C-14 from plasma of intact rats. Further evidence for the influence of hepatic 4-steroid dehydrogenase activity on adrenocorticoid function. *Endocrinology* **68**: 747–758.

21. Greenman, D. L., and Zarrow, M. X. 1961. Steroids and carbohydrate metabolism in the domestic bird. *Proc. Soc. Exptl. Biol. Med.* **106**: 459–462.

22. Greep, R. O., and Deane, H. W. 1949. The cytology and cytochemistry of the adrenal cortex. *Ann. N. Y. Acad. Sci.* **50**: 596–615.

23. Grollman, A. 1941. Biological assay of adrenal cortical activity. *Endocrinology* **29**: 855–861.

24. Grundy, H. M., Simpson, S. A., and Tait, J. F. 1952. Isolation of a highly active mineralocorticoid from beef adrenal extract. *Nature* **169**: 795.

25. Guillemin, R. H., Clayton, G. W., Smith, J. D., and Lipscomb, H. S. 1958. Simultaneous measurements of plasma corticosterone levels and adrenal ascorbic acid levels. *Federation Proc.* **17**: 247.

26. Guillemin, R. H., Dear, W. E., and Liebelt, R. A. 1959. Nychthermal variations in plasma free corticosteroid levels in the rat. *Proc. Soc. Exptl. Biol. Med.* **101**: 394–395.

27. Halberg, F., Hamerston, O., and Bittner, J. J. 1957. Sex difference in eosinophil counts in tail blood of mature B₁ mice. *Science* **125**: 73.

28. Hartroft, P. M., and Eisenstein, A. B. 1957. Alterations in the adrenal cortex of the rat induced by sodium deficiency: correlation of histological changes with steroid hormone secretion. *Endocrinology* **60**: 641–651.

29. Hechter, O., and Pincus, G. 1954. Genesis of the adrenocortical secretion. *Physiol. Rev.* **34**: 459–496.

30. Hoffman, F. G. 1957. The *in vitro* hydroxylations of 21-carbon steroids by the rat adrenal glands. *Endocrinology* **60**: 382–389.

31. Hyano, M., Saba, N., Dorfman, R. I., and Hechter, O. 1956. Some aspects of the biogenesis of adrenal steroid hormones. *Recent Progr. Hormone Res.* **12**: 79.

32. Ingle, D. J. 1956. Some questions relating to the role of the adrenal cortex in the etiology of disease, *in* "Fifth Annual Report on Stress" (H. Selye, ed.), p. 161. MD Publications, New York.

33. Ingle, D. J. 1959. Current status of adrenocortical research. *Am. Scientist* **47**: 413–427.

34. Jones, I. C., Phillips, J. C., and Holmes, W. N. 1959. Comparative Physiology of Adrenal Cortex, *in* "Comparative Endocrinology" (A. Gorbman, ed.), pp. 582–612. Wiley, New York.

35. Kass, E. H., Hechter, O., Macchi, I. A., and Mou, T. W. 1954. Changes in patterns of corticoid in rabbits after prolonged treatment with ACTH. *Proc. Soc. Exptl. Biol. Med.* **85**: 583.

36. Kitay, J. 1961. Sex difference in adrenal cortical secretion in the rat. *Endocrinology* **68**: 818–824.

37. Knobil, E., Hayney, M. G., Wilder, E. J., and Briggs, F. N. 1954. Simplified method for determination of total adrenal cholesterol. *Proc. Soc. Exptl. Biol. Med.* **87**: 48–50.

38. Lombardo, M. E., and Hudson, H. B. 1959. The biosynthesis of adrenocortical hormone by the human adrenal gland *in vitro*. *Endocrinology* **65**: 417–425.
39. Long, C. N. H. 1956. Pituitary-adrenal relationships. *Ann. Rev. Physiol.* **18**: 409–432.
40. McCarthy, J. L., Corley, R. C., and Zarrow, M. X. 1959. Effect of goitrogens on adrenal gland of the rat. *Am. J. Physiol.* **197**: 693–698.
41. McCarthy, J. L., Corley, R. C., and Zarrow, M. X. 1960. Diurnal rhythm in plasma corticosterone and lack of diurnal rhythm in plasma compound F-like material in the rat. *Proc. Soc. Exptl. Biol. Med.* **104**: 787–789.
42. Mason, J. W. 1959. Psychological influence on pituitary-adrenal cortical system. *Recent Progr. Hormone Res.* **15**: 345–389.
43. Moncola, F., Peron, F. G., and Dorfman, R. I. 1959. The fluorometric determination of corticosterone in rat adrenal tissue and plasma: Effect of administering ACTH subcutaneously. *Endocrinology* **65**: 717–724.
44. Neher, R., and Wettstein, A. 1956. Physicochemical estimation of aldosterone in urine. *J. Clin. Invest.* **35**: 800–805.
45. Nelson, D. H., and Samuels, L. T. 1952. A method for the determination of 17-hydroxycorticosteroids in blood: 17-hydroxycorticosterone in peripheral circulation. *J. Clin. Endocrinol. Metab.* **12**: 519–526.
46. Newman, A. E., Redgate, E. S., and Farrell, G. 1958. The effect of diencephalic-mesencephalic lesions on aldosterone and hydrocortisone secretion. *Endocrinology* **63**: 723–736.
47. Peterson, R. E., Karrer, A., and Guerra, S. L. 1957. Evaluation of Silber-Porter procedure for determination of plasma hydrocortisone. *Anal. Chem.* **29**: 144–149.
48. Pilot, M. L. 1950. Use of base in fluids for counting eosinophils. *Am. J. Clin. Pathol.* **20**: 870–871.
49. Porter, J. C., and Rumsfeld, H. W. 1959. Further study of an ACTH-releasing protein from hypophyseal portal vessel plasma. *Endocrinology* **64**: 948–954.
50. Recant, L., Hume, D. H., Forshaw, P. H., and Thorn, G. W. 1950. Studies on the effect of epinephrine on the pituitary-adreno-cortical system. *J. Clin. Endocrinol. Metab.* **10**: 187–229.
51. Reineke, R. M., and Kendall, E. C. 1942. Method for bioassay of hormones of adrenal cortex which influence deposition of glycogen in liver. *Endocrinology* **31**: 573–577.
52. Roe, G. H., and Kuether, C. A. 1943. Technique for the determination of ascorbic acid in whole blood and urine through 2,4-dinitrophenylhydrazine derivative of dehydroascorbic acid. *J. Biol. Chem.* **147**: 399.
53. Rosenthal, H. L., Pfluke, M. L., and Buscaglia, S. 1960. A stable iron reagent for determination of cholesterol. *J. Lab. Clin. Med.* **50**: 318.
54. Sayers, G., Sayers, M. A., Lewis, H. L., and Long, C. N. H. 1944. Effect of adrenotropic hormone on ascorbic acid and cholesterol content of the adrenal. *Proc. Soc. Exptl. Biol. Med.* **55**: 238–239.
55. Selye, H. 1936. A syndrome produced by diverse noxious agents. *Nature* **138**: 32.
56. Selye, H. 1936. Thymus and adrenal in responses of organism to injury and intoxication. *Brit. J. Exptl. Pathol.* **17**: 234.
57. Selye, H. (ed.). 1956. "Fifth Annual Report on Stress, MD Publications, New York.

58. Selye, H., and Schenker, V. 1938. A rapid and sensitive method for bioassay for the adrenal cortical hormone. *Proc. Soc. Exptl. Biol. Med.* **39**: 518–522.

59. Simpson, S. A., and Tait, J. F. 1952. A quantitative method for the bioassay of the effect of adrenal cortical steroids on mineral metabolism. *Endocrinology* **50**: 150–161.

60. Simpson, S. A., and Tait, J. F. 1955. Recent progress in methods of isolation, chemistry and physiology of aldosterone. *Recent Progr. Hormone Res.* **11**: 183–219.

61. Slusher, M., and Hyde, J. E. 1961. Inhibition of adrenal corticosteroid release by brain stem stimulation in cats. *Endocrinology* **68**: 773–782.

62. Spiers, R. S., and Meyer, R. K. 1951. A method for assaying adrenal cortical hormones based on a decrease of circulating eosinophils of adrenalectomized mice. *Endocrinology* **48**: 316–326.

63. Stachenko, J., and Giroud, C. J. P. 1959. Functional zonation of the adrenal cortex: pathways of corticoid biogenesis. *Endocrinology* **64**: 730–743 and 743–752.

63a. Venning, E. H., Kasmin, V. E., and Bell, J. C. 1946. Biological assay of adrenal corticoids. *Endocrinology* **38**: 79–89.

64. Yates, F. E., Herbst, A. L., and Urquhart, J. 1958. Sex difference in rate of ring A reduction of 4-3-ketosteroids *in vitro* by rat liver. *Endocrinology* **63**: 887–902.

65. Yates, F. E., Leeman, S. E., Glenister, D. W., and Dallman, M. F. 1961. Interaction between plasma corticosterone concentration and adrenocorticotropin-releasing stimuli in the rat: evidence for the reset of an endocrine feedback control. *Endocrinology* **69**: 67–80.

66. Zaffaroni, A., and Burton, R. B. 1951. Identification of corticoids by paper chromatography. *J. Biol. Chem.* **193**: 749–767.

67. Zarrow, M. X. 1942. Protective action of desoxycorticosterone acetate and progesterone in adrenalectomized mice exposed to low temperatures. *Proc. Soc. Exptl. Biol. Med.* **50**: 135–138.

68. Zarrow, M. X., and Denison, M. E. 1956. Sexual difference in the survival time of rats exposed to a low ambient temperature. *Am. J. Physiol.* **186**: 216–218.

CHAPTER 8

The Thyroid Hormones

The thyroid hormone regulates growth, differentiation, and oxidative metabolism. It is intimately involved in iodine metabolism, and the enlargement of the thyroid gland in iodine-deficient animals has long served as a classical example of compensatory hypertrophy of an organ in the reestablishment of physiological balance. Though the condition of goiter was recognized by early peoples and correctly treated by administration of iodine-rich foods (seaweeds), physiological evaluation of thyroidal activity began only in the early 1800's. By the latter part of that century, Magnus-Levy and others had established the role of the thyroid gland in oxidative metabolism. Reports on the relation of iodine to goiter (39) and the isolation of thyroxine, the active principle from the gland (25), markedly advanced our knowledge of thyroid function. While the ability of the gland to concentrate iodine was recognized early, full advantage of this phenomenon could be utilized only with the advent of radioactive iodine. This plus the development of chromatographic techniques and the discovery of the antithyroidal substances has led to fuller understanding of the physiology of the thyroid gland.

Site of Formation

The thyroid gland of higher vertebrates is a bilobed structure located on the lateral surfaces of the trachea just below the larnyx. The two lobes of the gland, one on each side of the trachea, are connected by a thin isthmus which crosses the ventral tracheal surface. This characteristically well-defined location of the gland is limited to the higher vertebrates, for, in other species, the thyroidal tissue is frequently scattered and diffuse. In fishes and cyclostomes, the thyroidal tissue has been found dispersed along blood vessels and located as distant as the kidney.

An interesting comparative and evolutionary aspect of thyroid gland development has been derived from studies on primitive vertebrates (protochordates) which have no thyroid tissue (6, 7). These organisms possess an endostyle composed of longitudinal parallel folds that project into the pharyngeal cavity and are bounded with ciliated epithelial cells. The endostyle of *Amphioxus* (Cephalochordata) and some tunicates (Urochordata) has been found to accumulate radioiodine. A relationship between the endostyle of the protochordates and the thyroid gland of higher vertebrates is implied from observations on the lamprey larva. The endostyle of the larva has the ability to trap iodine and, after metamorphosis, gives rise to the thyroid gland in the adult animal. Nevertheless, though tissue homologous to the thyroid gland is present in protochordates, the physiological function of the tissue is uncertain.

The structural unit of the richly vascularized thyroid tissue is the follicle, which is composed of simple columnar or cuboidal epithelial cells resting directly on interfollicular connective tissue (Fig. 8-1). The center of the follicle contains the colloid, thyroglobulin, which is com-

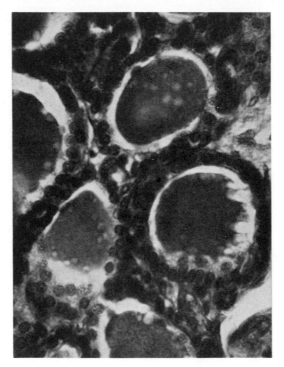

Fig. 8-1. Histology of the thyroid gland.

posed of a glycoprotein and iodinated secretions of the epithelial cells. Histological changes in the follicle are readily observed to follow modification of glandular physiology. During periods of hypoactivity in the gland, the amount of colloid in the follicle increases and the size of the epithelial cells is diminished. Conversely, cellular hypertrophy and colloid diminution occurs with the hyperthyroid state. Animals such as the ground squirrel, as well as the laboratory rat, show rhythmic seasonal changes in thyroid histology (23).

Nature of Thyroid Hormones

The isolation of thyroxine and the determination of its structure (22, 25) was followed by the identification of other iodinated compounds from the gland. Although various iodinated derivatives of the amino acid tyrosine were found (Fig. 8-2), the general consensus indicated that thyroxine was the circulating form of the hormone. Strong evidence for this view followed the report of the isolation of radioactive thyroxine from the blood of animals after the administration of I^{131} (47). However, as other iodinated compounds were investigated, the role of triiodothyronine came under intense study (18, 38). Triiodothyronine (T_3, TRIT) was found to possess more biological activity than thyroxine

TABLE 8–1

RELATIVE POTENCIES OF THYROXINE ANALOGS COMPARED WITH L-THYROXINE[a]

Compound	Animal	O_2 consumption	Growth and differentiation	TSH depression (goiter prevention)
L-Thyroxine[b]	All species	100	100	100
D-Thyroxine	Man	10–16	—	—
3,5,3'-Triiodothyronine	Man	90–140	—	280–540
	Rat	100–175	500	250–600
3,3',5'-Triiodothyronine (DL)	Rat	—	—	5
3,3'-Diiodothyronine (DL)	Rat	0–10	—	0–82
3,5-Diiodothyronine (L)	Rat	—	—	5
2',6'-Diiodothyronine (DL)	Rat, Man	0	—	0
3,5,3'-Triiodothyropropionic acid	Rat	—	—	50
	Tadpole	—	13,500–30,000	—
3,5,3',5'-Tetraiodothyropropionic acid	Rat	30–60	—	20–38
	Tadpole	—	5,000–10,000	—
3,5,3'-Tribromothyronine (DL)	Man	80–100	—	—
	Rat	—	—	17–22
	Tadpole	—	28	—

[a] From data of Pitt-Rivers and Tata (38) and Roche et al. (41).
[b] Assigned a value of 100.

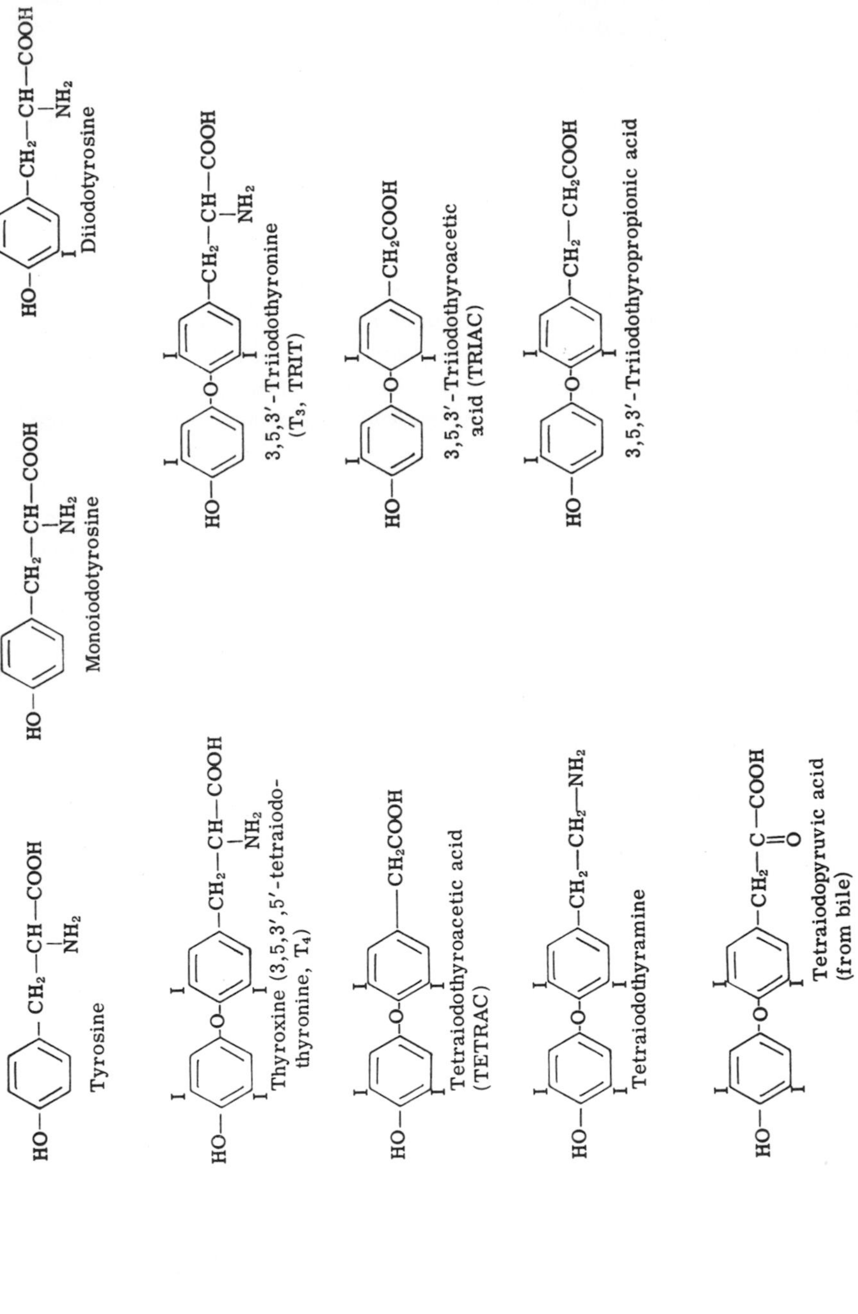

Fig. 8-2. Iodinated thyroid compounds and some thyroxine derivatives.

(T_4). Evidence for the conversion of thyroxine to triiodothyronine by various tissues supported the concept that thyroxine was converted to the triiodo form before physiological effect was exerted. While various analogs, e.g., triiodothyronine, are more effective than thyroxine in certain biological responses (Table 8–1), the tetraiodo compound is still considered to be the circulating hormone and the basis for all thyroid discussion. However, the exact nature of the active iodinated compounds found loosely bound to protein in the circulatory system is still under study.

As may be seen from the comparison of biological activities of the thyroxine analogs (Table 8–1), slight modification of the structure may result in marked changes in biological activity (4, 12, 13, 44). Such studies have led to the concept that specific analogs may be responsible for the various physiological influences of the thyroid gland (growth, metamorphosis, and metabolism). The tetraiodoacetic acid derivative (TETRAC) has been found to be more selective in stimulating oxygen consumption but has little effect on metamorphosis, whereas the tri-iodoacetic acid (TRIAC) compound is more potent than T_4 or T_3 in stimulating amphibian metamorphosis. However, these compounds have been isolated only in peripheral tissue, and their role in the circulating form of the hormone is unknown. Some of the variations in biological activity of thyroxine analogs disappear when the compounds are injected (4, 5, 16). Thus, thyroxine is considered to be the chief molecule secreted by the thyroid gland, other analogs being released to a lesser extent. The modification of thyroxine in peripheral tissue at a step prior to physiological activity is still considered to be a possibility. Table

TABLE 8–2

CONFIGURATION NECESSARY FOR THYROXINE-LIKE ACTIVITY

1. Essential molecular structure

2. Iodine must be present in the 3 and 5 positions, at least

3. The hydroxyl group must be present in position 4′
   a. Removal of the hydroxyl group or change in the position of iodine inactivates the compound (2,6-diiodotyrosine inhibits thyroxine activity)
   b. Replacement of iodine with other halogens decreases activity

4. The naturally occurring thyroid hormones are the L-isomers; although the D-forms are active, such compounds are not as potent as the L-isomers

5. The alanine side chain is not essential for activity

8–2 describes the molecular configuration necessary for thyroxine-like activity.

Action of Thyroxine

The biological activity of all thyroid preparations and compounds is typified by that of the naturally secreted thyroxine (L-thyroxine). Nearly all vertebrates have a functioning thyroid gland, but considerable variability occurs in the type of response and ability of the tissues to respond to the hormone. The three most important aspects of thyroid activity are its effects on oxidative metabolism, growth, and differentiation of tissue. In addition, the hormone has an influence on other metabolic processes including that of carbohydrates and lipid metabolism, electrolyte and water balance, nitrogen balance, and other phenomena, such as excitation and threshold to drugs.

A. METABOLISM

Investigations on the role of thyroid gland in the etiology of goiter led to the finding that the gland played a role in oxidative metabolism of all tissues. Early studies on metabolic processes with the use of direct calorimetry showed a direct relationship between basal metabolic rate and thyroid activity (9). Since metabolism and heat production can be related to the consumption of oxygen and the production of carbon dioxide, measurements of gas exchange and of excretory products can be used for indirect calorimetric studies. When the oxygen uptake of an animal is measured under standard conditions of fasting, rest, and comfortable temperature, a value for the basal metabolic rate can be obtained. Although this value does not truly represent the lowest resting metabolism, it can be used as a good index of changes in thyroidal activity.

Removal of the thyroid gland or administration of goitrogens bring about a decrease in basal metabolic rate whereas administration of thyroidal tissue or thyroxine results in an increased consumption of oxygen. Compared with the euthyroid animal, the hypothyroid organism shows a decreased food intake and reduced oxygen requirement; the converse is true in hyperthyroidism. One of the significant aspects of the metabolic process, in addition to energy production and anabolic processes, is the production of heat. Changes in the metabolic rate, reflected directly by alteration in oxygen consumption, results in a change in body heat production. Thus the thyroid gland plays an important role in the acclimatization of homoiothermic animals to a low ambient temperature. Thyroid-insufficient animals are unable to adjust to decreased environmental temperatures (30, 49) whereas normal animals show increased thyroidal activity at reduced temperatures. However, the response of the thyroid gland of the true hibernator is perplexing since the metabolic processes must decrease in order to permit the animal to subsist on body constituents during periods of hibernation at low temperature. Yet an unusual drop in environmental temperature will arouse the hibernator and stimulate thyroidal secretion.

B. METAMORPHOSIS

The process of metamorphosis, in which a larval form undergoes considerable alteration and differentiation of tissues to form the adult organism, is a complex process involving hormonal changes and modification of tissue sensitivity to hormones (see Chapter 14). The classic report of Gudernatsch (20) indicated a need for the thyroid hormone in the metamorphosis of amphibians. Immersion of tadpoles in solutions of thyroxine results in a more rapid resorption of the tail and development of adult characteristics. Pituitary deficient tadpoles, or tadpoles administered antithyroid compounds, show a delayed metamorphosis (1). Many larvae which respond to thyroxine also undergo metamorphosis in the presence of iodine. This response appears to be due to the presence of tyrosine in the tissues which can be iodinated to produce thyroxine. While dinitrophenol (DNP) is capable of producing an increased oxygen consumption, this compound has no influence on metamorphosis so that metamorphosis is not due simply to an increased rate of oxidation.

Certain salamanders show a resistance or complete inability to undergo metamorphosis. These animals, i.e., neotenous salamanders, remain in the larval state throughout life but possess the capacity for reproduction. The Mexican axolotl, for example, undergoes metamorphosis only under conditions of extreme thyroid stimulation, whereas *Necturus* is a completely neotenous salamander which fails to respond to thyroxine. Though this organism has an "active" thyroid gland in that the tissue can induce metamorphosis in tadpoles (45), the intact animal shows only slight thyroidal activity based on I^{131} uptake. Since massive doses of thyroxine have failed to bring about any metamorphic changes, this absence of response appears to indicate a lack of tissue sensitivity to the hormone.

Many authors feel that metamorphosis includes a modification of function as well as form. Higher vertebrates generally respond to thyroxine by changes in growth and metabolism, and some bony fish are also capable of responding to the hormone. Changes in the markings of the Atlantic salmon after alteration of salinity appear to be related to thyroxine (7). Metamorphic changes in eels also appear to be related to thyroxine activity.

C. GROWTH

The failure of young thyroidectomized animals to grow normally could be interpreted to be a result of reduced metabolic processes. However, studies of such animals reveal a significant influence of thyroxine on the growth and differentiation of tissue. The young hypothyroid animals are characteristically smaller (cretin, dwarfs) than euthyroid animals and show marked retardation in development of the nervous system, an effect associated with an impairment in the formation of myelin sheaths. The cretin shows marked mental retardation. Early initiation of thyroid therapy can restore normal growth and development to young hypothyroid animals (2). The growth process also requires the presence of somatotropin (see Chapter 9). Thyroxine and STH show a synergistic action on bone growth. In addition to the direct action of thyroxine on metabolic processes and its relation to growth, thyroid activity also influences other endocrine functions. Hypothyroid animals show an imbalanced pituitary function, and this hypothyroid state is accompanied by adrenal involution and gonadal atrophy. The changes in the other endocrine glands may be due to a direct result of a lack of thyroxine or an indirect effect via the pituitary gland.

D. OTHER PHYSIOLOGICAL RESPONSES

Thyroxine appears to exert a direct effect on the metabolism of carbohydrates in that the hormone increases the absorption from the intestinal tract. In addition, the hormone appears to play a role in the liver glycogen level, particularly in fishes (17). In other organisms, the depletion of liver glycogen following thyroxine administration may be a reflection of general metabolic stimulation.

The influence of thyroxine on protein metabolism and electrolyte balance is seen in the deposition of intracellular mucoprotein (leading to myxedema in the hypothyroid human being). The increased mucoprotein is accompanied by an increase in the extracellular level of salt and water. This modification in osmotic balance is reflected in the blood by a reduced volume and an increased protein content. Some of the reduction in protein anabolism seen in young animals following hypophysectomy or induced hypothyroidism can be corrected by thyroxine alone, which can adjust the nitrogen balance and restore normal tissue growth. In fishes, the activity of the thyroid hormone can be related to environmental factors influencing salt balance. Some species show

increased thyroid activity in an environment with more salt (7). Young
fish administered thyroid powder or kept in a tank with added thyroxine
show an increased growth rate over nontreated control animals (8). The
effects of thyroxine are summarized in Table 8–3.

TABLE 8–3
ACTIONS OF THYROXINE

Calorigenic
    Oxygen consumption, heat production and acclimatization to low ambient tem-
    perature (homoiotherms), oxidative phosphorylation

Growth and development (thyroxine insufficiency)
    Failure of hypothyroid organism to attain full body maturity
    Congenital hypothyroidism (cretin)—retarded ossification, reduced cerebral cortical
    maturation, decreased myelinization of nerves

Metamorphosis
    Required for metamorphosis of amphibians and some fish

Carbohydrates
    Increase in absorption from intestine, stimulation of glycogen deposition in liver

Proteins
    Myxedema, excess mucoprotein in hypothyroidism with decrease in serum protein
    Excessive hormone may induce negative nitrogen balance
    In hypophysectomized animal, may partially restore growth

Electrolytes
    Osmoregulation in fishes
    Modification of electrolyte balance in hypothyroid mammals

Lipids
    Decreases plasma cholesterol and phospholipids
    Excessive hormone results in decreased fat depots and increased ketone body
    production

Reproduction
    Gonadal atrophy and reduced fertility in hypothyroid and hyperthyroid organisms

Other endocrine effects
    Synergism with STH on bone development
    Inverse relation between adrenal and thyroid glands

    The species variation in response to thyroxine suggests variation in
tissue sensitivity to the hormone. Such changes in sensitivity are also
seen during the lifetime of the individual. The metamorphosis of tadpoles involves a complex sequence of changes in which variations in
tissue sensitivity occur during various stages of development (26). While
fish show some metamorphic and electrolytic changes following thyroxine
administration, the treatment fails to increase oxygen consumption. Sim-

ilarly, in tadpoles, thyroxine fails to stimulate increased oxygen utilization prior to metamorphosis (48). Birds and reptiles, like mammals, respond to thyroxine with an increase in oxygen consumption. However, the control of metabolism and heat production is generally more significant in homoiotherms than in poikilotherms.

Assay of Thyroxine

While histological changes in the thyroid gland serve as an excellent indicator of glandular activity, this response is really an index of thyrotropin (TSH) secretion (see Chapter 9). One of the earliest assays, a classical one, for thyroxine is the ability of the hormone to induce metamorphosis in tadpoles. This end point has been used to demonstrate thyroxine-like activity of various compounds. A second assay that has been widely utilized is based on the ability of the hormone to stimulate increased oxidative metabolism. This may be demonstrated by an increase in basal metabolic rate or by an increase in oxygen consumption or carbon dioxide release.

Since iodine is a necessary component of this hormone, the U. S. Pharmacopeia assay for thyroxine is based upon the iodine content of thyroid gland extracts. However, this assay does not provide information about the biological potency of the preparations. Circulating or blood

TABLE 8–4

NORMAL VALUES FOR PROTEIN-BOUND IODINE (PBI) IN VARIOUS ANIMALS[a]

Species	PBI (μg%) $\pm$ standard error
Man	3.5–8.0 $\pm$ 0.4
Horse	3.6 $\pm$ 0.4
Monkey	6.6 $\pm$ 0.7
Rabbit	3.3 $\pm$ 0.5
Rabbit	2.16 $\pm$ 0.34
Rat	4.5 $\pm$ 0.4
Rat	3.50 $\pm$ 0.12
Guinea pig	2.5 $\pm$ 0.5
Hamster	3.5 $\pm$ 0.4
Opossum	0.4 $\pm$ 0.2
White Leghorn chicken	1.13 $\pm$ 0.04
Pekin duck	1.14 $\pm$ 0.06
Chicken	1.16 $\pm$ 0.3
Sheep	3.7 $\pm$ 0.3
Holstein cow	4.46 $\pm$ 0.33
Guernsey cow	3.91 $\pm$ 0.22

[a] Adapted from Barker et al. (5), Katsch and Windsor (24), and Mellen and Hardy (35).

levels of thyroxine are measured by determining the amount of iodine bound to the plasma protein (5, 11). This is possible because the circulating thyroxine is loosely bound to the blood proteins. Normal ranges for levels of protein bound iodine (PBI) have been established for the human being and other animals, and this assay now serves as a diagnostic test for thyroid function (Table 8–4). Studies on the accumulation of radioiodine by the thyroid gland led to other measurements of thyroidal function. The rate of thyroidal uptake of I^{131} can be correlated with thyroxine activity. In studies with goitrogens, decreased thyroidal I^{131} levels can be observed long before thyroid hypertrophy occurs. Thyroid concentration of I^{131} serves as an invaluable medical aid because the localization of the isotope in the gland permits the rapid determination of the uptake of iodine by the thyroid. With the use of proper scanning detectors a "dot" picture of the gland which shows localized areas of the I^{131} uptake can be drawn. Such graphs serve to locate hyperactive tumorous growths of the gland. In addition, the iodine concentrating capacity of the gland can be used to "thyroidectomize" an animal. After administration of large doses of I^{131}, the radiation can destroy most of the thyroid tissue without severe damage to adjacent areas. Since the uptake and release of I^{131} by the thyroid gland can be determined by external detectors, a technique was devised to estimate the rate of thyroxine secretion in experimental animals (19). Thyroxine has the ability to bind to the globulin and albumin fractions of blood protein and is taken up by the red blood cells. One diagnostic test for thyroxine has been based on the ability of radioactive triiodothyronine to bind to the red blood cell (21). As the thyroxine level in the blood increases, the hormone occupies more of the primary binding sites (the blood proteins). Thus when the blood cells are exposed to I^{131}-T_3, more of the T_3 radioactivity appears in the red blood cells. In the hypothyroid state, the red cell uptake of T_3 is decreased.

Biosynthesis, Mode of Action, and Metabolism of the Thyroid Hormone

The activity of the thyroid gland is under the direct control of thyrotropin (TSH) from the anterior pituitary gland. In the maintenance of homeostatic balance, the thyroxine secreted acts in a servomechanism to reduce the production or release of TSH. Whether this action of thyroxine is on the pituitary gland itself or via the hypothalamus or both is still in question.

That the hypothalamus appears to play some role in the regulation of TSH release is apparent. The thyroid activity that follows injection of TSH, as indicated by increased release of radioiodine, can also be achieved by stimulation of the hypothalamus (14). Certain hypothalamic lesions either impair or inhibit TSH secretion. Such lesions may inhibit the goiter formation that normally results from administration of anti-thyroid compounds. These lesions also interfere to some degree with normal thyroid function (10).

The biosynthesis of thyroxine first requires the accumulation of iodine by the thyroid for the iodination of organic molecules. The rapidity and degree of concentration of radioiodine illustrates the ability of the gland to accumulate this necessary intermediate. Once the iodide ion has been assimilated (trapped) by the gland, the iodide must then be oxidized to free iodine (Fig. 8-3). The complete identity and mode of action of the enzymes in this energy-requiring oxidation have yet to be established. Evidence indicates that the enzyme involved in iodide oxidation acts similarly to catalase but is different in nature from that enzyme (45). In addition, an inhibitor of enzyme action appears to be present in thyroidal tissue which may act as a control on hormone synthesis.

Once free iodine is provided, the available tyrosine molecules are iodinated to mono- and diiodotyrosines (Fig. 8-3). Synthesis of the active materials is completed by the coupling of two molecules of iodinated tyrosine to form T_3 and T_4. This latter step appears to be under the influence of TSH, as is the trapping of iodide. The thyroid hormone may be secreted directly into the circulation or into the follicle where, combined with protein, it is stored as thyroglobin. A protease enzyme at the distal border of the follicular cells hydrolyzes the thyrox-ine from the protein complex and thus permits the free hormone to pass through the cell into the blood stream.

A complete understanding of the mode of action of thyroxine, in the many physiological functions of this hormone, is yet to be attained. The variation in the nature of response to the many thyroxine analogs and the influence of the route of administration complicate these studies. In many cases, thyroglobin is more active than thyroxine, especially via the oral route. Since both thyroxine and dinitrophenol (DNP) stimulate increased oxygen consumption and DNP acts to uncouple phosphate, one mode of action for thyroxine is thought to be related to the uncou-pling mechanism. This hypothesis suggests that in the chain of metabolic reactions thyroxine acts to uncouple a phosphate bond at the step just prior to a rate-limiting reaction. Thus the uncoupling action would ac-count for the increased metabolism and inefficient energy production of hyperthyroid organisms (28). While enzyme preparations from the livers of hyperthyroid animals have been found to uncouple phosphate,

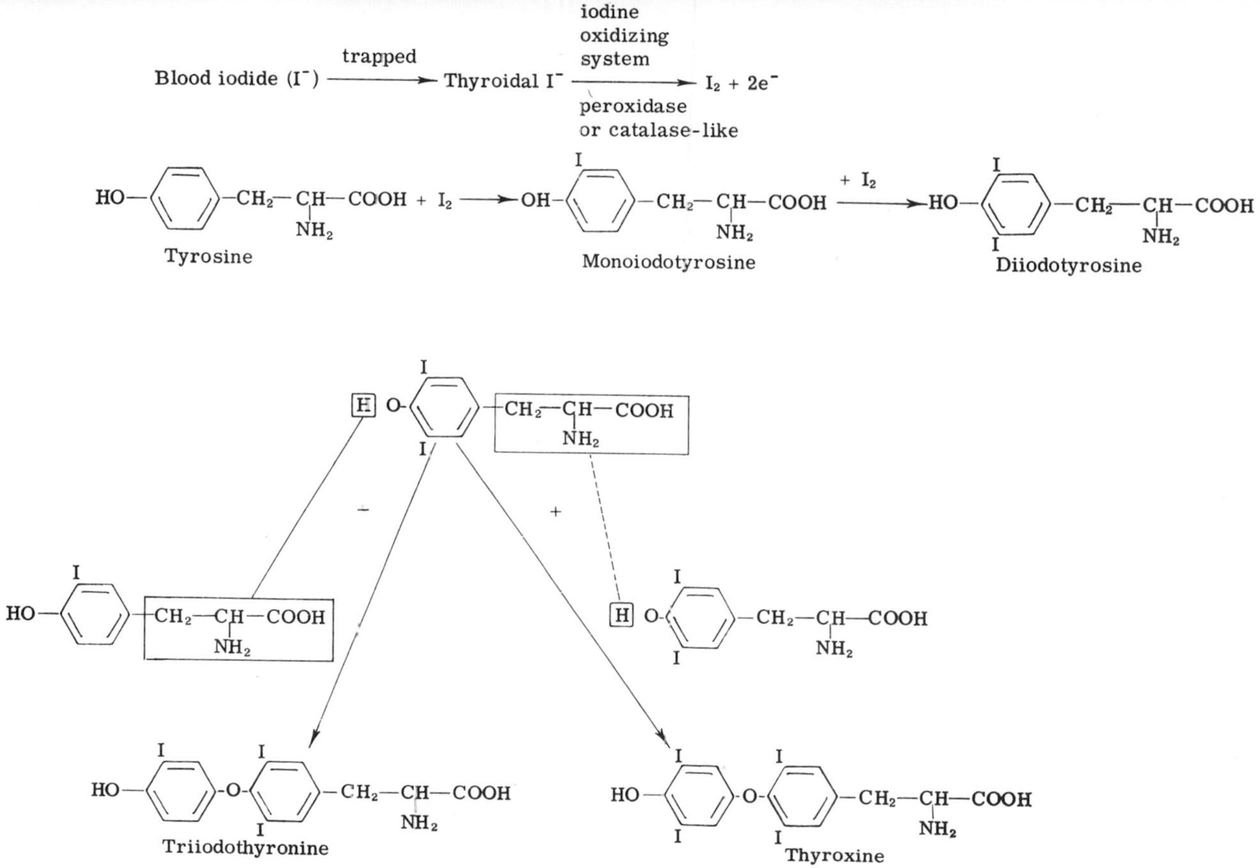

Fig. 8-3. Biosynthesis of the thyroid hormone.

the *in vitro* addition of T_4 or T_3 is without effect. A second mechanism by which thyroxine could influence metabolism and phosphorylation has been suggested by numerous investigators and involves the mitochondria (31). These organelles, which contain the enzymes for the terminal stages of oxidation (Krebs cycle and hydrogen transfer, consist of a double-layered membrane, which has been found to increase in size with thyroxine. Thus, it has been postulated that thyroxine could act to alter the permeability of the membrane and expose more metabolites to the enzymes present in the mitochondria. Other modes of action of thyroxine, to explain an observed delay in hormonal action, are related to the influences of the hormone on the activity of certain mitochondrial enzymes, particularly those involved in hydrogen transfer and protein synthesis (29). Recent studies implicate a deiodination process in the mechanism of action of thyroxine.

The rate of release and subsequent metabolism of thyroxine has been the subject of many studies. Normally some measure of iodine turnover rate can be obtained by comparing the thyroid iodine levels to that of the blood serum (T:S ratio). Thyrotropin and certain goitrogens are frequently used to flush iodine from the gland for experimental purposes. The breakdown of thyroxine releases iodine which may be recirculated to the thyroid or excreted in the kidney. The salivary glands also play a role in deiodination of the hormone. However, the importance of the liver in the metabolism of thyroxine is illustrated by the level of radio-thyroxine that appears in the bile (27). While a high level of I^{131} appears in the urine of radioiodine-treated rats, only a small fraction of this is from the presence of radioactive T_4. Significant levels of labeled CO_2 following administration of C^{14}-labeled thyroxine indicate that catabolism of the hormone in tissues may be important in the metabolism and excretion of this hormone.

Antithyroidal Agents

While lack of iodine in the diet can lead to hypothyroidism and glandular hypertrophy, numerous other agents obtained from foodstuffs or synthesized in the laboratory can lead to hypertrophy and hyperplasia of the thyroid gland (Table 8–5). Initial studies showed that rabbits fed a cabbage diet developed goiter, an indication of the presence of a goitrogen in the diet (33). The goitrogens include: analine derivatives, thiourea and thiouracil compounds, mercapto-heterocyclic and polyphenol compounds, and certain inorganic ions (Table 8–5, Fig. 8-4). The organic compounds investigated for antithyroid potential appear to require the presence of —NH—C(=S)—NH— or C_6H_4—NH— groupings for activity (3). The organic goitrogens interfere with the

TABLE 8–5

EFFECT OF VARIOUS GOITROGENS ON THE THYROID WEIGHT OF THE MALE RAT[a]

Structure	Compound	Dose (% in water)	Body weight (gm)	Thyroid weight	
				mg	(mg/ 100 gm)
—	Control	—	363	17.0	4.7
NH—C=O S=C—CH NH—CH	Thiouracil	1%	229	61.8	28.4
	+ 20 µg B_{12}	1%	329	81.8	25.0
N—C=O HS—C C NH—C—C—C—CH₃ (H₂ H₂)	Propylthiouracil	0.01%	269	146.3	54.6
		0.0005%	392	69.6	17.8
C═══C CH₃—N N C SH	Methylmercapto-imidazole (Tapazole: Lilly)	0.001%	349	31.6	9.1
		0.005	289	53.0	18.2
$KClO_4$	Perchlorate	1%	292	52.1	17.7
NH₂ ⬡ OH COOH	p-Aminosalicylic acid (PAS)	2% in feed	312	36.3	11.6
NH₂ ⬡ COOH	p-Aminobenzoic acid (PABA)	2% in feed	337	23.9	7.1
NH₂ ⬡ SO₂—N—C—NH₂ (NH)	Sulfaguanidine	2% in feed	375	60.2	16.2

[a] From McCarthy et al. (32).

iodine-oxidizing enzyme system or the iodination of tyrosine, and thus they bring about a reduction of thyroxine secretion with a resulting increase in TSH level and thyroid hypertrophy. The inorganic goitrogens inhibit the organic binding or trapping of iodine by the thyroid gland. Iodine itself may act as an antithyroid agent to reduce the organic

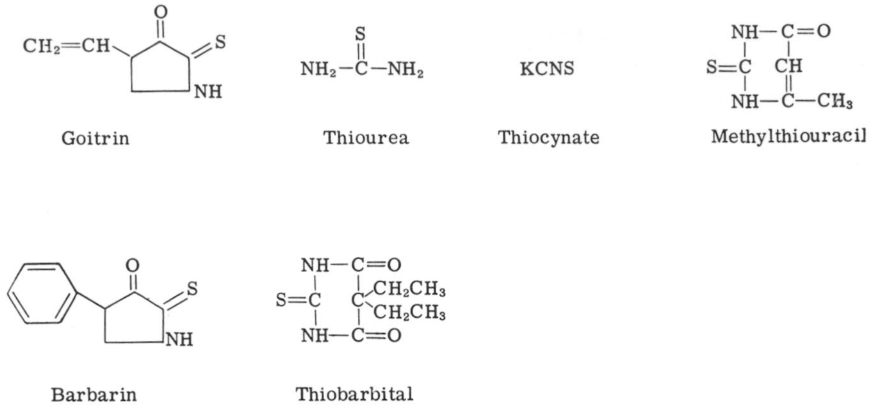

Goitrin   Thiourea   Thiocynate   Methylthiouracil

Barbarin   Thiobarbital

Fig. 8-4. Structure of other goitrogens.

accumulation of iodine. The related goitrogenic action of sodium chloride is a result of increased excretion of iodine accompanying removal of the high levels of administered chloride ion.

Studies on animals in various states of thyroid activity have revealed some other endocrine effects. Induced hyperthyroidism can bring about hypertrophy of the adrenal cortex, whereas adrenalectomy was found to result in a temporary increase in basal metabolism (34). Treatment of rats with thiouracil was shown to bring about a decrease in the absolute and relative weight of the adrenal gland, the animals showing a reduced resistance to low temperature (49). Several other goitrogens are known to bring about adrenal involution. Involution of the gonads is also a characteristic of hypothyroidism, particularly evident in young animals, where hypogonadism, decreased sex hormone secretion, and reduced fertility are evident (37). Thyroxine also stimulates spermatogenesis in hypothyroid and euthyroid animals of many species.

EXPERIMENT 8–1

Thyroidectomy in the Rat

Studies on the function of the thyroid gland frequently require complete ablation of the thyroid in order to illustrate the physiological effect of thyroxine insufficiency. The thyroidal tissue can be destroyed by radioiodine, or the synthesis of thyroxine prevented with goitrogens, but surgical removal of the gland is a relatively simple procedure. In the rodent, and other animals, surgical thyroidectomy is accompanied by a partial or complete removal of parathyroid tissue. The resulting parathor-

mone insufficiency (see Chapter 12) should be relieved by including calcium salts in the diet in the postoperative care of the animal. Surgical
removal of the thyroid gland must be carried out with care to avoid
severing the carotid arteries or recurrent laryngeal nerves, which are
lateral to the trachea.

Procedure

nembutol an

The animal is anesthetized with ether in a jar and placed on an
operating board; anesthesia is continued with an ether cone. Make a midventral incision along the neck and retract the skin, fascia, and submaxil-
lary glands to expose the sternomastoid and sternohyoid muscles (Fig.
8-5). Carefully separate the muscles along the midventral line to expose

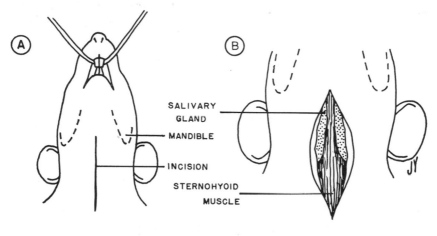

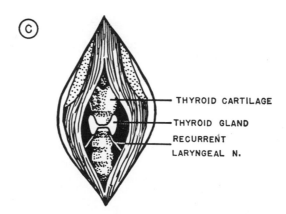

Fig. 8-5. Thyroidectomy in the rat.

the trachea and thyroid gland. If retractors are not available, bent paper clips or piano wire attached to rubber bands may be used instead. If possible, use a dissecting microscope to visualize the gland and the related vascular and neural network. Use fine forceps (watchmaker's forceps) to dissect carefully one lateral edge of the thyroid gland. Lift this edge and hold iridectomy scissors in a horizontal plane to clip the tissue between the thyroid gland and the trachea. Proceed to work under the gland, across the surface of the trachea. A delicate approach will permit the removal of both lobes of the gland and the connecting isthmus intact. When the gland has been removed, inspect the tissue and surface of the trachea for completeness of thyroidectomy. Allow the muscles to return to the normal position and close the incision in the skin with sutures. During the operation, cotton pellets may be used as sponges to reduce hemorrhage, but such pellets must be removed before the wound is closed.

Following surgery, place the animal on 1% calcium lactate drinking solution.

Experimental

These animals may now be used to study the effects of thyroidectomy on oxygen consumption, growth, and other functions.

EXPERIMENT 8–2a

Oxygen Consumption in the Rat: Effect of Thyroid and Antithyroidal Agents

The influence of the thyroid gland secretions can be measured readily by determining the rate of oxygen uptake in an animal. Since the hormone influences oxidative processes in tissues (28, 29), changes in the activity of the gland will be reflected directly by changes in the amount of oxygen utilized. Whereas thyroidectomy will remove completely the endogenous thyroxine, treatment with goitrogens will reduce thyroid activity to varying degrees, with accompanying glandular hypertrophy (Table 8–4). Conversely, the administration of thyroxine, triiodothyronine, thyroglobin, or thyrotropin (in the intact animal) will increase the metabolic rate. In this experiment, the animals will be treated with antithyroid agents and thyroxine, and the oxygen consumption of the treated animals will be compared to that of euthyroid and thyroidectomized rats.

A commercial rat respirometer is available (Phipps-Bird) which consists of a jar as the respiratory chamber, and an animal holder. If such a device is not available, a respirometer can be prepared from a large vacuum desiccator (see Experiment 8–2b).

Procedure and Experimental

Obtain 5 male rats 125–150 gm in body weight. Weigh the animals at the start of the experiment and twice weekly until termination of the experiment. Note the lengths of the various treatment periods and carry out the experiment so that all treatments will terminate on the same day. Place at least one animal on each treatment; use normal and thyroidectomized rats as controls.

Group 1:   Normal diet and drinking solution
Group 2:   Administer thiouracil 0.1% in drinking water for 3 weeks. (Thiouracil may be dissolved in distilled water by the addition of 40% NaOH dropwise to adjust the pH to 8.0 to 8.5. The solution may then be filtered through glass wool and administered to the animals as drinking solution.)
Group 3:   Administration of 1% thiouracil in ground food for 3 weeks. (Thoroughly mix the thiouracil with the ground feed.)
Group 4:   Inject subcutaneously L-thyroxine 25 μg/0.1 ml per day for 3 weeks. (Thyroxine solution may be prepared by dissolving the hormone in *a minimal* amount of 4 N NaOH and diluting to final volume with distilled water. Prolonged injection may result in irritation at the injection site.)

Determine the oxygen consumption of each animal, using either the Phipps-Bird respirometer or that described in Experiment 8–2b. Usually the respirometer chamber is flushed with oxygen, though this procedure is not necessary for routine study. (What is the percentage of oxygen in air?)

If the Phipps-Bird respirometer is used, the inside of the calibrated glass tube should be moistened with water. The animal is placed in the holder, the thermometer is attached, and the holder is placed inside the chamber. Be sure that the animal does not come in contact with a small amount of soda lime placed in the chamber. Place the gasket against the glass and close the jar with the top containing the calibrated glass tube. Allow 5 minutes for the rat to become quiet and the temperature to equilibrate. Use the index finger to apply a drop of bubble from a soap solution across the end of the glass tube so that the bubble film seals the tip of the glass. Determine the time, in seconds, required for the bubble to pass from the zero to 5-ml mark. Repeat the observation for a total of five determinations. Calculate the average time required to consume the 5-ml volume (of oxygen in air). Record the atmospheric pressure, temperature in the respirometer chamber, and time required to utilize 5 ml of oxygen in air. Calculate the liters of oxygen consumed (under conditions of standard temperature and pressure) per kilogram body weight and per square meter. Normally oxygen consumption or caloric data are reported as liters of oxygen per square meter of body surface. Examine the studies of Benedict (9) and evaluate the rationale for reporting oxygen consumption on the basis of surface area, body weight, and powers of body weight (Table 8–6). Review these factors in regard to metabolism and heat-regulating mechanisms in the dog, rabbit, rat, cow, and human being.

TABLE 8–6

BASAL HEAT PRODUCTION IN VARIOUS SPECIES: COMPARISON OF
HEAT PRODUCTION EXPRESSED ON THE BASIS OF BODY WEIGHT,
POWER OF WEIGHT, AND BODY SURFACE AREA[a]

Animal	Average adult weight	Heat production (calories) per 24 hours		
		Per kilogram	Per square meter	Per surface area (weight$^{0.73}$)
Mouse	21 gm	158	526	39.0
Rat	400 gm	82	672	41.8
Guinea pig	410 gm	85	707	43.4
Rabbit	2.6 kg	44.5	619	37.6
Cat	3.0 kg	49.8	731	44.0
Dog	14.0 kg	34.7	745	45.6
Human ♀	56 kg	22.6	790	42.7
Human ♂	65 kg	25.3	917	50.3
	Average ± standard deviation:		799 ± 38.2	46.4 ± 22.2

[a] Adapted from data of Benedict (9).

Report the oxygen consumption for the normal, thyroidectomized rats as compared to the treated groups.

Note that, in this apparatus, the animal cannot remain in the chamber indefinitely because the volume of the calibrated tube limits gas exchange. This may be demonstrated by placing an unrestrained animal in the apparatus (without soda lime). The time required for the rat to collapse may vary from $\frac{1}{2}$ to 2 hours, depending on size of the animal.

Calculations

1. Conversion of volume of oxygen at experimental pressure (P_1) and temperature (T_1, in degrees Centigrade) to volume under standard conditions (0°C, 273°K, and 760 mm mercury):

$$V_1 = \frac{(P_1)(273)}{(760)(T_1°C + 273)} \times \text{volume of oxygen consumed (5 ml or 100 ml)}$$

2. Volume of oxygen consumed per hour:

$$\frac{V_1 \times 3600}{\text{time in seconds}} \times \text{liters of } O_2/\text{hour}$$

3. Oxygen consumption per kilogram per hour:

$$\frac{\text{liters of } O_2/\text{hour}}{\text{body weight (gm)}} \times 1000 = \text{liters } O_2/\text{kg/hour}$$

4. Calculation of surface area (square meters):

$$\frac{(\text{animal weight})^{0.73} \times 10}{1000} = \text{square meters of surface area}$$

5. Oxygen consumption in liters per hour per square meter:

$$\frac{\text{liters } O_2/\text{hour (Step 2)}}{\text{surface area (Step 4)}} = \text{liters } O_2/\text{square meter/hour}$$

6. Estimate of heat production. Assuming a respiratory quotient (RQ) of 0.91, 1 liter of oxygen consumed is taken as equivalent to 4.93 calories:

$$\text{liters } O_2/\text{square meter/hour} \times 4.93 = \text{calories/square meter/hour}$$

EXPERIMENT 8–2b

Instructions for Using Respirometer (Fig. 8-6)

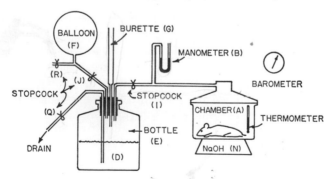

Fig. 8-6. Apparatus for determination of oxygen consumption in the rat.

Procedure

The rat is placed in chamber (A) which contains NaOH. The animal is then allowed a rest period of 5–10 minutes, after which the lid is put on in an air-tight manner. During this time, the rubber gas balloon (F) is filled with oxygen through stopcock (R). With all stopcocks closed except (J) and (Q), oxygen is allowed to run from balloon into bottle or side arm flask (E) forcing water out through (Q). Stopcocks (Q) and (J) are then closed. Seal chamber (A) and open stopcock (I). This admits oxygen into the chamber through (I). As oxygen is consumed by animal in chamber (A) the pressure is decreased as indicated by manometer (B). By adding water to (D) from the burette (G), the oxygen from (E) is displaced into (A), where it is consumed. With the system closed and the animal at rest, and more than 100 cc of oxygen in the bottle at (E), the time is checked when the manometer shows the pressure to be the same between (E), and (A) and the outside. One hundred milliliters of water is then allowed to run into (D) *gradually*, thus displacing 100 cc of oxygen toward (A). When the pressure is again equal, the time is once again checked; thus, the time required for the consumption of 100 cc of oxygen is determined. The volume of oxygen is corrected to standard conditions by correction of ambient temperature and pressure. Open the chamber (A) and close (I). The water (D) may be displaced through (Q) by filling the bottle (E) with oxygen, and the operation may be repeated without removing the animal from the chamber.

EXPERIMENT 8–3

Influence of Thyroid Function on Survival under Anoxic Conditions*

Since the thyroid secretion will influence the rate of oxygen consumption, variation in thyroid activity will modify the survival time of animals placed in a restricted oxygen environment. As in the preceding experiment, mice (or small rats) will be placed on treatments to bring about modification of glandular secretions. It has been shown that survival time in mice can be reduced from a control value of 157 ± 6.7 minutes to 87 ± 4 minutes after treatment with 0.1% thyroglobulin.

Procedure and Experimental

Obtain 9 adult male mice (or small male rats, 75 gm) and distribute them into three groups. Treat the groups as follows:

Group 1:   Normal diet for 1 week
Group 2:   Thiouracil 1%, inject 0.1 ml per day intraperitoneally for 1 week
Group 3:   L-Thyroxine 25 μg/0.1 ml per day intraperitoneally for 1 week

Place an animal in a one-half pint mason jar. Start a stop watch at the instant the top of the jar is closed securely. Determine the time

* Cf. reference (40).

until the animal takes its last breath. Record the average survival time for the three treatment groups. Relate thyroid function to time of survival.

EXPERIMENT 8-4

Metamorphosis of Tadpoles*

The influence of thyroxine on cell differentiation is easily illustrated by the classical study on metamorphosis of tadpoles. The marked alteration in metamorphosis involves a change both in form and function and is not limited to amphibians, as shown by the striking changes in certain fishes. The influence of the thyroid hormone in the metamorphic processes is easily illustrated by immersion of tadpoles in solutions containing the active principles. Such studies have revealed a marked difference in activity of thyroid analogs and have given evidence for a synergistic action between thyroxine and adrenocorticoids, inasmuch as the combined action of these hormones on protein metabolism and cell differentiation enhances the metamorphic process. The differences in potency of thyroxine analogs on metamorphosis becomes less marked when the compounds are injected into the test organisms (Table 8–7), an indica-

TABLE 8–7

COMPARISON OF POTENCY OF THYROXINE ANALYZED BY
DIFFERENT ROUTES OF ADMINISTRATION[a]

Compound	Activity compared to thyroxine		Relative activity, injection:immersion[b]
	Injection	Immersion	
Thyroxine	1.0	1.0	17
Tetraiodopropionic acid	3	21–100	1
Triiodothyronine (T_3)	17	5–20	100 (approx.)
T_3 propionic acid	7	15–300	0.4
T_3 acetic acid	7	10–24	3

[a] From data of Frieden and Westmark (16).

[b] Relative activity of each compound, as a function of route of administration, calculated from experimental studies. The effective dose obtained by injecting each compound is compared to the dose required to induce metamorphic changes by immersing tadpoles in solutions of the compounds.

cation that rates of penetration of the compounds into the organisms may be a prime factor in determining potency. It has been suggested

* Cf. references (7, 12, 15, 16, 20, 26, 46).

that the greater activity of the acetic and propionic acid derivatives of thyroxine is a result of the absence of the zwitterion effect which could reduce the rate of penetration. In any event, metamorphic changes can be influenced by immersing tadpoles in thyroxine solutions (10^{-8} to $10^{-5}\,M$) at a constant temperature for 40–120 hours. Changes in total length and width of the tail, and appearance of forelimbs, indicate resorption of juvenile tissue and the emergence of the adult organism (Fig. 8-7). The degree and rapidity of these changes is a function of the

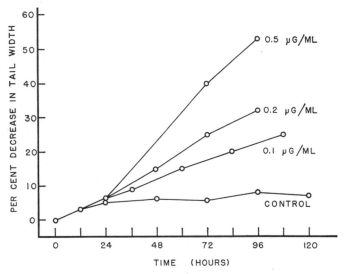

Fig. 8-7. The effect of thyroxine on metamorphosis (decrease in tail width) in the tadpole (bullfrog larvae maintained in 500 ml of solution at a temperature of 30°C). Redrawn from data of Bruice *et al.* (12).

state of development of the organism at the time of exposure and of the concentration of hormone, both of which are related to the sensitivity of the tissue.

Procedure and Experimental

Dissolve L-thyroxine in distilled water containing 6 gm NaCl per liter in the three following concentrations: 50, 100, 300 μg/liter. (*Note:* Thyroxine solutions must be adjusted to a pH of 8.0–8.5 to dissolve the hormone. Use 0.1 N alkali and 0.1 N HCl to adjust the pH; or dissolve the hormone in a minimum amount of 4 N NaOH, dilute nearly to volume, and then adjust pH.)

In addition, prepare an iodine solution by dissolving 1 gm of iodine in 5 ml of 95% ethanol; then dilute to 1000 ml with distilled water (adjust pH). Control animals are to be incubated in the NaCl solution adjusted to the pH of the thyroxine solutions.

Tadpoles of essentially the same stage of development are to be used; the organisms should show some degree of hindlimb emergence. Measure the initial length of the animals and place each animal in an *individual* wide glass dish with 500 ml of test solution (control, thyroxine, or iodine); incubate at a constant temperature. Although the temperature for satisfactory experimentation is between 20 and 25°C, the temperature selected for incubation should remain constant ($\pm 1°C$). Feed the animals small bits of spinach (5 mm³) and change the incubation fluid every 1 or 2 days. If possible, it would be preferable to aerate the solution.

Measure the length of the tadpoles every 24 hours and note the time and progress of formation of the forelimbs. The decrease in the length of the animal is essentially an index of the resorption of the tail. If *Rana catesbiana* tadpoles are used, the change in width of the tail may be noted to observe progress of metamorphosis (take measurements at the widest section of the tail). *Rana pipiens* and *R. clamitans* tadpoles may be used instead.

EXPERIMENT 8–5

Protein-Bound Iodine*

The materials secreted into the circulation by the thyroid gland rapidly become bound to the proteins in the blood. After it was found that radioactive thyroxine could be extracted from the blood following the injection of I^{131}, other studies revealed a significant relation between the amount of iodinated compounds bound to blood protein and the thyroid function. Thus, a useful test was devised to evaluate glandular function on the basis of the protein-bound iodine (PBI) level. This determination is of value in both clinical diagnosis and experimental studies of thyroid function (Table 8–4).

Procedure and Experimental

The protein-bound iodine levels will be determined for serum samples taken from rats under various states of thyroidal activity. Determine the PBI level in male rats in the following treatment groups:

Group 1:   Normal
Group 2:   Thyroidectomized for 2 weeks
Group 3:   Administered thiouracil (0.1% in drinking water) for 2 weeks

* Cf. references (5, 11, 24, 35, 47).

Group 4:   Administered 25 µg L-thyroxine per day for 1 week
Group 5:   Exposed to low ambient temperature (6–8°C) for 1 week
Group 6:   Exposed to low ambient temperature (6–8°C) for 4 hours

Reagents for PBI Determination

1. *Water.* H_2O for use in preparation of reagents and in determination of PBI is redistilled from sodium hydroxide (approximately a 2% solution of NaOH).

2. *Zinc sulfate.* 10% of the heptahydrate.

3. *Sodium hydroxide,* 0.5 N.

4. *Sodium carbonate,* 4.0 N.

5. *Sulfuric acid,* 3.5 N (98 ml of concentrated acid, specific gravity, 1.84, per liter).

6. *Hydrochloric acid,* 2.0 N (175 ml of the concentrated acid, specific gravity, 1.18, per liter).

7. *Arsenious acid.* Dissolve 3.9 gm of arsenic trioxide in 50 ml of 1 N sodium hydroxide (make sure all the arsenic trioxide is dissolved before adding the water); then add 50 ml of water, warmed to 60–80°C; finally add enough 3.5 N sulfuric acid to make 500 ml.

8. *Ceric sulfate.* Dissolve about 30 gm of ceric ammonium sulfate in a liter of 3.5 N sulfuric acid. Exactly 0.5 ml of this solution mixed with 5.5 ml of water in a colorimeter tube should give a reading of about 500 in the Klett-Summerson colorimeter (use a water "zero" with a blue no. 42 light filter). If color is too weak, add more solid ceric ammonium sulfate; if too strong, dilute with more sulfuric acid. This should be made fresh about every 2 months; a new standard curve must be determined each time it is made.

Equipment

1. *Muffle furnace* (Hoskins, type FD204).

2. *Photoelectric colorimeter* (Klett-Summerson).

3. *Water bath,* constant temperature.

4. *Hot air oven.*

Method

1. Obtain about 3 ml whole blood (see Experiment 12–2 for blood withdrawal techniques), centrifuge, save serum.

2. Add to protein-bound iodine (PBI) tubes: (a) 7 ml distilled water; (b) 1 ml serum; (c) 1 ml 10% $ZnSO_4$; (d) 1 ml 0.5 N NaOH.

3. Allow to stand for 5 minutes, centrifuge about 15 minutes, and discard supernatant.

4. Wash the remaining protein twice with 10 ml distilled water and centrifuge. The supernatant is discarded.

5. The protein is then suspended in 1 ml $4 N$ Na_2CO_3 with glass stirring rods which are rinsed with 1.0 ml distilled water before they are removed from the tubes.

6. This mixture is dried in a hot air oven at 90°C for 24–36 hours (or until dry).

7. Place tubes in a muffle furnace for 2.5 hours at 600°F.

8. Remove from furnace, cool, and to each tube add 2.5 ml $2 N$ HCl. Swirl the mixture until the white residue is dissolved. Add 10 ml distilled water and mix the contents. (If necessary, tubes may be capped and stored for up to 1 week at this point.)

9. Centrifuge the tubes for about 5 minutes and pour the supernatant into clean, dry test tubes.

10. Pipette 5-ml portions of these samples into colorimeter tubes (duplicates are prepared for every sample).

11. Add 0.5 ml arsenious acid and place the tubes in a water bath at 37°C.

12. Add 0.5 ml ceric ammonium sulfate to each tube. The colorimeter reading is made exactly 15 minutes after the addition of ceric ammonium sulfate.

13. A blue no. 42 filter is used in the colorimeter; the absorbancy is set to zero with a water blank.

14. The iodine content is determined from a standard curve previously prepared, and this value is multiplied by 250 to give the milligram of iodine per 100 ml serum.

Standard Curve for Protein-Bound Iodine

1. Stock solution which contains 100 μg iodine per milliliter is made by dissolving 130.8 mg of KI in a liter of water.

2. Place 8.48 gm of anhydrous sodium carbonate in a 250-ml Pyrex beaker and heat in a muffle furnace at 600°F for 2.5 hours. Remove and cool; add slowly 100 ml of $2 N$ HCl until all the white residue is dissolved. The volume is then brought up to 500 ml with distilled water.

3. Portions of the stock KI solution are diluted with the HCl solution prepared as above.

4. Make dilutions of the KI solution containing 0 to 1.0 μg of iodine per 5 ml of solution.

5. Dilute as follows:

> Original solution contains 100 μg/ml
> Dilute 1:10 to give 10 μg/ml
> Dilute this 1:10 to give 1 μg/ml
> Dilute this 1:10 to give 0.1 μg/ml

6. Using the solution containing 0.1 μg/ml, make dilutions of:

    a. Blank: 0 KI—0.0 μg/5 ml
    b. 1.25: 0.004 μg/ml or 0.02 μg/5 ml
    c. 2:25: 0.008 μg/ml or 0.04 μg/5 ml
    d. 3:25: 0.012 μg/ml or 0.06 μg/5 ml
    e. 4:25: 0.016 μg/ml or 0.08 μg/5 ml
    f. 5:25: 0.02 μg/ml or 0.10 μg/5 ml

12 Klett colorimeter tubes will be needed to run a duplicate of each of these samples.

7. Place 5-ml portions of each of these dilutions in the colorimeter tubes, two of each. Add 0.5 ml of arsenious acid to each tube. Place tubes in water bath at 37°C. Add 0.5 ml of ceric ammonium sulfate and read *exactly 15 minutes* later.

8. Use a blue no. 42 filter and a water blank.

9. Draw a curve for these values, plotting the micrograms of iodine against the Klett reading.

EXPERIMENT 8–6

Thyroid and Plasma Cholesterol*

The effect of thyroxine on lipid metabolism is reflected in the plasma cholesterol levels. As illustrated in Table 8–8, thyroxine and many of its analogs are capable of reducing the cholesterol level of animals on a

TABLE 8–8

EFFECTS OF VARIOUS THYROXINE DERIVATIVES ON
PLASMA CHOLESTEROL IN THE RAT[a]

Regimen	Oxygen consumption (% of normal)	Plasma cholesterol mg/100 ml)
Purina Chow	100	77
HFD + (high-fat diet, 16% casein)	100	438
HFD + thyronine	79	243
HFD + 3,5-diiodothyronine	92	190
HFD + 3,5,3′-triiodothyronine	155	251
HFD + 3,5,3′,5′-tetraiodothyronine	137	221
HFD + 3,5-diiodothyroacetic acid	95	226
HFD + 3,5,3′-triiodothyroacetic acid	153	187
HFD + 3,5,3′,5′-tetraiodothyroacetic acid	114	202
HFD + 3,5,3′-triiodothyropropionic acid	114	192
HFD + 3,5,3′,5′-tetraiodothyropropionic acid	101	251

    [a] From Ruegawer *et al.* (42).

    * Cf. reference (41).

high-fat diet. Activity of thyroid secretions are reflected by changes in the plasma cholesterol level.

Procedure and Experimental

Subject male rats to the four treatments outlined for Groups 1-4 in Experiment 8-5; obtain blood plasma and determine the cholesterol level as described in Experiment 7-7.*

EXPERIMENT 8-7

Rate of Radioiodine Uptake by the Thyroid Gland of the Rat

Information on the rate of thyroid accumulation of radioiodine provides a very sensitive and direct means of evaluating glandular activity. Since radioiodine decays with gamma emission, direct *in vivo* measurement of the thyroid I^{131} can be made provided proper detection instrumentation is used. Although a scintillation counter is more efficient for counting radioiodine, the Geiger-Müller tube may be used for this experiment.

Procedure and Experimental

Reagents

1. I^{131}. Carrier-free radioiodine (to be diluted by instructor) to provide a solution of 0.1 microcurie (μc) per 0.1 ml. The solution may have to be diluted with buffer or mild alkali in order to adjust the pH to approximate neutrality.

2. *Digesting solution.* 2 N KOH solution is to be used in digesting thyroid glands.

3. *NaI.* Solution of sodium iodide for decontamination of instruments and glassware.

Apparatus

1. *Tuberculin syringe* (1 ml), 22-gauge needle.
2. *Ether jar* for killing animals.
3. *Surgical instruments.*
4. *Torsion balance.*
5. *Test tubes* to fit well-type detector for scintillation counter.
6. *Ultramicropipettes,* 25, 50, and 100 microliters (μl; lambda, λ).
7. *Rubber gloves* for handling radioactive materials or animals treated with isotope.
8. *Laboratory monitor and survey meter.*

---

* Transfer 0.1 ml serum (or plasma) to 10 ml glacial acetic acid and continue as given on page 207, step 2.

Isotope Disposal

All glassware used for radioactive materials must be kept separate from other glassware and must be decontaminated after each use.

All animal carcasses must be stored in a deep freeze for a duration of 5–8 times the half-life of the radioactive material used (for I^{131}, 40–60 days) before disposal, unless other approved disposal means are available.

All solutions, paper, excreta, and other materials contaminated with isotope must be stored in labeled containers for a duration of 5–8 times the half-life of the isotope before disposal. *Some* liquid isotope solutions may be disposed of by pouring into the sink *provided* the sink is washed with a sufficient quantity of water (see U. S. Atomic Energy Commission regulations on isotope disposal).

Determination

A group of 10 male rats, 150–200 gm body weight, are to be injected with the isotope. Five animals are then to be housed in individual cages in a cold room (2°C) and 5 animals maintained at room temperature. One control and one cold-exposed animal are to be killed at regular intervals (e.g., 3, 6, 12, 24, and 48 hours); the thyroid glands are to be removed and the isotope activity determined. At each time interval the activity of the I^{131} standard solution is to be determined also. Remember to wear surgical gloves at all times while handling isotopes or animals treated with isotopes, *except* in the area of the counting apparatus. Do not pipette radioactive materials by mouth. To avoid ingestion of isotope, smoking or eating is not permitted in the area of isotope use. Carry out the experiment as follows:

1. Dilute the stock I^{131} solution to provide a solution of 5 μc in 0.5 ml. (*Note:* if Geiger-Müller (G-M) apparatus is to be used, prepare a 10–12 μc I^{131} solution and follow this procedure through Step 5).

2. Inject all animals with the isotope solution. An intraperitoneal injection is preferred. One operator may hold the animal ventral side up while the partner injects the solution through the skin of the abdomen held between the thumb and forefinger (similar to the subcutaneous injection technique). This technique of intraperitoneal injection avoids the danger of splattering the isotope.

3. At the time of the injection, dilute 1 ml of the isotope to 100 ml using a glass-stoppered volumetric flask (1:100); this will serve as the counting standard.

4. Control and experimental animals are to be killed at the assigned

intervals; the thyroid glands are removed, dissected free of fat, and weighed to the nearest 0.1 mg.

5. Place the glands in 3.0 ml of 2 N KOH and digest the glands completely in a water bath at 80°C.

6. *Counting by use of a well-type scintillation counter* (see Step 9 for counting by use of a G-M system): After digestion, the solution in the test tubes is adjusted to a volume of 3.0 ml (calibrated tubes facilitate this). An aliquot of the counting standard (Step 3) is diluted to 3.0 ml in a test tube. The actual volume of the aliquot of standard I^{131} used is based on the type of counting arrangement. Generally, diluting 1.0 ml to 3.0 ml may suffice. The tubes are placed in the well of the counter and counted for 5 minutes (see *Note* that follows Step 10). Calculate the counts per minute (cpm) for the thyroid glands and the counting standards, and correct for background activity by subtracting the background counts per minute from the experimental values.

7. From the counting rate of the diluted standard solution, determine the counts per minute of the volume of isotope injected into the animals. Example:

    a. Animals injected with 0.5 ml isotope

    b. Standard sample prepared by dilution 1.0 ml isotope to 100 ml

    c. Of the standard sample prepared as in (b), 2.0 ml is diluted to 3.0 ml and counted: (cpm of 2.0 ml sample $\times$ 50)/2 is the cpm of the 0.5 ml dose administered the animal.

Counting the standard sample at the same time as the thyroid glands permits calculations on the uptake of isotope without correction for rate of decay. (How is the factor 50/2 derived?)

8. Calculate from the counts per minute of the thyroid gland the percentage of injected isotope that is accumulated by the gland:

$$\frac{\text{cpm entire thyroid}}{\text{cpm 0.5 ml injected}} \times 100 = \% \text{ uptake}$$

9. *Counting by use of the Geiger-Müller system:* The glands are digested as in Step 5, and the volume is readjusted to 3.0 ml. Aliquots of the solution (25, 50, or 100 μl) are transferred into counting planchets and dried under an infrared lamp. In a similar manner, a sample of the diluted isotope standard is transferred to a planchet and dried.

10. Count the samples for 5–10 minutes (see *Note* below) and determine the counts per minute for each aliquot. Correct for background count. Determine the percentage of isotope uptake for each gland as indicated by the sample calculation:

    a. Counts per minute of 50 μl of thyroid digestion solution (1/60 thyroid gland)

b. Counts per minute of 50 μl of I^{131} standard (1:100 dilution of original isotope and 0.5 ml of original isotope solution administered)

$$\% \text{ uptake} = \frac{\text{cpm thyroid}}{\text{cpm dose (0.5 ml)}} = \frac{\text{cpm sample} \times 60}{\text{cpm standard aliquot} \times 20{,}000 \times 1/2}$$

Note: Follow the directions for operating the counter given by the instructor or instruction manual for the instrument. The adjustment of the high voltage must be carried out carefully to obtain reproducible results. In particular, the voltage on the G-M tube must not be set too high. Background counts should be obtained by operating the detector for 10–15 minutes without a sample in place. Calculate the background counts per minute; this value must be subtracted from the counts per minute of each sample. Remember the total count must be divided by the time in minutes to obtain the counts per minute.

How does placing an animal in the cold modify the rate of accumulation of I^{131}?

Review the role of the thyroid gland in acclimatization to cold and the factors that regulate the rate of thyroxine secretions. *Note:* Review the effect of anesthetics on the thyroid gland (36).

EXPERIMENT 8–8

T₃ Binding by Erythrocytes as a Diagnostic Test for Thyroid Function*

Circulating thyroxine has been shown to be bound to several proteins in blood, particularly the globulin fraction. The binding of I^{131}-labeled T_3 by the red cell has been utilized as a diagnostic test for thyroid function. Under conditions of hyperthyroidism, the increased thyroxine levels fill more of the specific binding sites of the T_4 binding proteins. Thus administration of additional I^{131}-labeled T_3 results in an increased uptake of this material by secondary binding sites as the red blood cell. Therefore, the red cell uptake is increased in hyperthyroidism and decreased in hypothyroidism. Other conditions also influence T_3 binding (Table 8–9). More recently, modifications of this technique have been devised, such as substitution of an exchange resin for red blood cells. The replacement of red blood cells by the resin offers a means of controlling the number of secondary binding sites without correcting the results for hematocrit variation.

Since the test is an *in vitro* one, it is a simple one, for only a sample of the blood of the subject need be obtained. In clinical diagnosis, this

* Cf. references (21, 43).

TABLE 8–9
SUMMARY OF FACTORS THAT AFFECT THE RED CELL UPTAKE OF T_3

Factors that decrease uptake
　　Pregnancy
　　Estrogen
　　Propylthiouracil

Factors that increase uptake
　　Anticoagulants: dicumarol, heparin
　　Nephrosis
　　Severe liver disease
　　Severe metastatic malignancy
　　Severe pulmonary insufficiency with CO^2 retention
　　Paroxysmal atrial arrhythmias

technique avoids administration of isotope to the subject and can be carried out on individuals treated with iodinated compounds. The modifications using resin in place of red cells appears to offer, in addition to a more rapid technique, a more critical diagnostic test.

Procedure

1. Withdraw 10 ml of venous blood with a sterile syringe and place in a test tube containing 0.1 ml of a 40% solution of potassium oxalate. (Citrated or heparinized blood may also be used.)

2. Dilute the I^{131}-labeled triiodothyronine (T_3) with isotonic saline to make a solution containing from 10 to 120×10^{-4} μg per 0.1 ml. (This range of concentrations may be made by diluting the T_3 as obtained from Abbott Laboratories, 100–250 times.)

3. To a 3-ml aliquot of whole blood in a 10-ml Erlenmeyer flask, add 0.1 ml of the diluted T_3. Place stopper in flask.

4. Incubate at $37°C$ in a shaker for 2 hours.

5. After the incubation period, pipette 1 ml of the blood into a counting tube and count in a well-type scintillation counter long enough to obtain the required accuracy (5–15 minutes). Correct for background.

6. Centrifuge the 1 ml of blood for 5 minutes at 3000 rpm and remove the supernatant plasma. Wash the red blood cells 5 times with tenfold volumes of isotonic saline.

7. In a similar manner count the radioactivity remaining on the red blood cells in the well scintillation counter and correct for background.

8. Determine the hematocrit.

9. Calculate the percentage of red blood cell uptake as follows:

$$\frac{\text{net counts of washed RBC} \times 100 \times 100/\text{hematocrit}}{\text{net counts of whole blood}}$$

Note that the uptake is expressed in terms of a corrected hematocrit of 100.

The T_3 cell uptake is decreased in hypothyroidism and increased in hyperthyroidism. The normal euthyroid range for the human being is 11–17% for females and 11.8–19% for males.

EXPERIMENT 8–9

Determination of the Rate of Thyroxine Secretion*

Since radioiodine is accumulated by the thyroid gland and can be detected by means of *in vivo* counting techniques, a method was devised to use this thyroidal I^{131} in estimating the rate of thyroxine secretion. The radioiodine thus accumulated by the gland is incorporated into the thyroxine production and released as radiothyroxine. The basis of the study is the use of external counting to determine the level of I^{131} before and after the administration of varying doses of exogenous thyroxine. By gradually increasing the dose of thyroxine, a level can be found that will prevent further reduction of the I^{131} in the thyroid. This dose level is taken as that equivalent to the normal endogenous secretion. While objections have been raised regarding the value of this technique, the method does offer a means of estimating the thyroxine secretion rate (TSR).

Procedure

1. Inject all animals with 2 μc of I^{131} by the intraperitoneal route.

2. Three days later, place each animal over a scintillation detector so that the thyroid region is directly over the well opening. Measure the thyroid radioactivity. In order to ensure reproducible readings, the voltage of the instrument must be adjusted properly. It would be advantageous to count a reference standard prior to each determination to ensure that reproducible results are obtained. In addition, calculations must be made to account for daily isotope decay.

3. After the thyroidal activity has been counted, all animals are to receive subcutaneous injections of thyroxine. One-half the members of each group are to be given 0.5 μg thyroxine per 100 gm body weight; the remaining members are to be given 1.0 μg of thyroxine per 100 gm body weight. Place all rats on propylthiouracil (PTU)† 0.01% in water.

The experiment is undertaken according to the following schedule:

---

* Cf. reference (19).

† Tapazole (0.004%) is preferred by many investigators.

Day 1: Inject 2 μc I^{131}
Day 4: Count thyroid areas; treat half the animals with 0.5 μg thyroxine per 100 gm body weight and the remainder with 1.0 μg thyroxine per 100 gm body weight. Start PTU treatment.
Day 5: Repeat thyroxine injections.
Day 6: Count thyroid radioactivity; increase dose of thyroxine to all animals by 1.0 μg per 100 gm body weight (1.5 and 2 μg per 100 gm body weight).
Day 7: Repeat thyroxine injections of day 6.
Day 8: Count thyroidal radioactivity; increase dose of thyroxine by an additional 1.0 μg per 100 gm body weight over dose given on day 6 (2.5–3 μg per 100 gm body weight).
Day 9: Repeat thyroxine injections of day 7.
Day 10: Count thyroid radioactivity.

When the dose of exogenous thyroxine is such that it prevents further decrease of thyroid radioactivity (other than normal decay), that dose of thyroxine is taken as the TSR. The count should be 95–100% of the previous count. Thus, if the thyroid count on day 8 is essentially that found on day 6 (after calculating decay) for animals given 2 μg of thyroxine per 100 gm body weight, then this dose of thyroxine is taken as the TSR.

Experimental

Obtain 4–8 male rats of the same weight. Maintain half the group at room temperature and place the other rats in the cold (2°C). Additional animals may be treated with thyrotropin (Chapter 9) or fed goitrogenic agents. Determine the thyroid secretion rate of these animals.

On the basis of the servomechanism involved in the control of the thyroid secretion, and the induction of compensatory hypertrophy, explain why this technique may serve to give an index of thyroxine secretion. How would the results be affected if PTU was not administered?

References

1. Allen, B. B. 1916. The results of extirpation of the anterior lobe of the hypophysis and of the thyroid of Rana pipiens larvae. *Science* **44**: 755–758.
2. Asling, C. E., Simpson, M. E., Li, C. H., and Evans, M. M. 1954. The effect of chronic administration of thyroxin to hypophysectomized rats on their skeletal growth. *Anat. Rec.* **119**: 101–114.
3. Astwood, E. B. 1955. Mechanisms of action of antithyroid compounds. The thyroid. *Brookhaven Symp. Biol.* **7**: 61–73.
4. Barker, S. B. 1956. Metabolic actions of thyroxine derivatives and analogs. *Endocrinology* **59**: 548–554.
5. Barker, S. B., Humphry, M. J., and Soley, M. H. 1951. The clinical determination of protein bound iodine. *J. Clin. Invest.* **30**: 55–62.

6. Barrington, E. J. W. 1959. Some Endocrine Aspects of Protochrodata *in* "Comparative Endocrinology" (A. Gorbman, ed.), pp. 250–267. Wiley, New York.
7. Barrington, E. J. W. 1961. Metamorphic processes in fishes and lampreys. *Am. Zoologist* **1**: 97–106.
8. Barrington, E. J. W., Barron, N., and Piggins, D. J. 1961. The influence of thyroid powder and thyroxine upon the growth of rainbow trout (*Salmo gairdnerii*). *Gen. Comp. Endocrinol.* **1**: 170–178.
9. Benedict, F. G. 1938. "Vital Energetics. A Study in Comparative Basal Metabolism." Carnegie Inst. of Washington Publ., Washington, D. C.
10. Bogdanove, E. M., and D'Angelo, S. A. 1959. The effect of hypothalamic lesions on goitrogens and pituitary TSH secretion in the propylthiouracil-treated guinea pig. *Endocrinology* **64**: 53–61.
11. Brown, H., Reingold, A. M., and Samson, M. 1953. The determination of protein-bound iodine by dry ashing. *J. Clin. Endocrinol. Metab.* **13**: 444–452.
12. Bruice, T. C., Winzler, R. H., and Kharasch, N. 1954. The thyroxine-like activity of some new thyroxine analogues in amphibia. *J. Biol. Chem.* **210**: 1–9.
13. Bruice, T. C., Kharasch, N., and Winzler, R. J. 1956. A correlation of thyroxine-like activity and chemical structure. *Arch. Biochem. Biophys.* **62**: 305–317.
14. Campbell, M. J., George R., and Harris, G. W. 1951. The acute effects of injection of TSH or electrical stimulation of the hypothalamus on thyroid activity. *J. Physiol. (London)* **148**: 5P–6P.
15. Frieden, E., and Naile, B. 1955. Biochemistry of amphibian metamorphosis. I. Enhancement of induced metamorphosis by glucocorticoids. *Science* **121**: 37–39.
16. Frieden, E., and Westmark, G. W. 1961. On the anomalous activity of thyroxin analogs in tadpoles. *Science* **133**: 1487–1489.
17. Fontaine, M. 1956. Thyroid in liver glycogen control of poikilotherms. *Compt. Rend. Soc. Biol.* **147**: 214–216.
18. Gross, J., and Pitt-Rivers, R. 1953. 3:5:3'-Triiodothyronine. *Biochem. J.* **53**: 645–652 and 652–657.
19. Grosvenor, C. E., and Turner, C. W. 1954. Effect of lactation on thyroid secretion rate in the rat. *Proc. Soc. Exptl. Biol. Med.* **99**: 517–519.
20. Gudernatsch, J. F. 1912. Feeding experiments on tadpoles. I. The influence of specific organs given as food on growth and differentiation. *Wilhelm Roux' Arch. Entwicklungsmech. Organ.* **35**: 457–483.
21. Hamolsky, M. W., Stein, M., and Freedberg, A. S. 1957. The thyroid hormone-plasma protein complex in man. II. A new *in vitro* method for study of "uptake" of labeled hormonal components by human erythrocytes. *J. Clin. Endocrinol. Metab.* **17**: 33–44.
22. Harrington, C. R., and Barger, G. 1927. Chemistry of thyroxine. III. Constitution and synthesis of thyroxine. *Biochem. J.* **21**: 169–181.
23. Hoffman, R. A., and Zarrow, M. X. 1958. A comparison of seasonal changes and the effect of cold on the thyroid gland of the male rat and ground squirrel (Clitellus tridecimlineatus). *Acta Endocrinol.* **27**: 77–84.
24. Katsch, S., and Windsor, E. 1955. Unusual value for protein-bound iodine in the serum of the oppossum. *Science* **121**: 897–898.
25. Kendall, E. C. 1915. Isolation in crystalline form of a compound containing iodine which occurs in the thyroid; its chemical nature and physiological activity. *Trans. Assoc. Am. Physicians* **30**: 402–449.

26. Kollros, J. J. 1961. Mechanisms of amphibian metamorphosis: hormones. *Am. Zoologist* **1:** 107–114.

27. Kot, P. A., and Klitgaard, H. M. 1959. Elimination of C-14 labeled thyroxine in the bile, urine and expired air of rats in latered thyroid states. *Endocrinology* **64:** 319–325.

28. Lardy, H. A., and Maley, G. F. 1954. Metabolic effects of thyroid hormones *in vitro. Recent Progr. Hormone Res.* **10:** 129–155.

29. Lardy, H., and Lee, Y. 1961. Cellular effects of thyroid hormone on different organs and species. *Am. Zoologist* **1:** 457.

30. Leblond, C. P., and Gross, J. 1943. Effect of thyroidectomy on resistance to low environmental temperature. *Endocrinology* **33:** 155–160.

31. Lehinger, A. L. 1956. Physiology of mitochondria: Relationship between mitochondria structure, oxidative phosphorylation and the action of thyroxine, *in* "Enzymes: Units of Biological Structure and Function" (O. H. Gaebler, ed.). Academic Press, New York.

32. McCarthy, J. L., Corley, R. C., and Zarrow, M. X. 1959. The effect of goitrogens on the adrenal gland of the rat. *Am. J. Physiol.* **197:** 693–698.

33. Mackenzie, C. G. 1947. Differentiations of the antithyroid action of thiouracil, thiourea and PABA from sulfonamides by iodine administration. *Endocrinology* **40:** 137–155.

34. Marine, D., and Bauman, E. J. 1921. Influence of glands of internal secretion on respiratory exchange. II. Effect of suprarenal insufficiency (by removal or freezing) in rabbits. *Am. J. Physiol.* **57:** 135–152.

35. Mellen, W. S., and Hardy, L. B., Jr. 1957. Blood protein bound iodine in the fowl. *Endocrinology* **60:** 547–551.

36. Oyama, T. 1959. Effect of diethyl ether anesthesia on thyroid function of rats. *Endocrinology* **65:** 56–63.

37. Parrott, M. W., Johnston, M. E., and Durbin, P. W. 1960. The effects of thyroid and parathyroid deficiency on the reproduction in the rat. *Endocrinology* **67:** 467–483.

38. Pitt-Rivers, R., and Tata, J. R. 1959. "The Thyroid Hormones." Pergamon Press, New York.

39. Plummer, H. S. 1923. Results of administering iodine to patients having exophthalmic goiter. *J. Am. Med. Assoc.* **80:** 1955.

40. Reisfield, D. R., and Leathem. J. H. 1950. The closed vessel technique for testing thyroid activity in mice. *Endocrinology* **46:** 122–124.

41. Roche, J., Michel, R., Wolf, W., and Etling, N. 1954. Activité biologique (antigoitrogène) de quelques nouvelles iodotyrosines et iododesaminotyrosines. *Compt. Rend. Soc. Biol.* **148:** 1738–1742.

42. Ruegawer, W. R., Alpert, M. E., and Silverman, F. R. 1960. Thyroxine analogues and cholesterol metabolism: The relative effects of various thyroxine derivatives on growth, oxygen consumption and tissue cholesterol concentration in the rat. *Endocrinology* **66:** 160–166.

43. Scholer, J. F. 1962. A simple measure of thyro-binding by plasma: A test of thyroid function. *J. Nucl. Med.* **3:** 41–46.

44. Stasilli, N. R., Kroc, R. L., and Meitzer, R. I. 1959. Antigoitrogenic and calorigenic activities of thyroxine analogues in rats. *Endocrinology* **64:** 62–82.

45. Suzuki, M., Nagashima, N., and Yamamoto, K. 1961. Studies on the mechanism of iodination by the thyroid gland: Iodine-activating enzyme and an intracellular inhibitor of iodination. *Gen. Comp. Endocrinol.* **1:** 103–116.

46. Swingle, W. W. 1922. Thyroid and amphibian metamorphosis. *J. Exptl. Zool.* **36:** 397–421.
47. Taurog, A., and Chaikoff, I. L. 1947. On the nature of plasma iodine. *J. Biol. Chem.* **171:** 439–440.
48. Warren, M. R. 1940. Thyroxin and O_2 consumption in frogs. *J. Exptl. Zool.* **83:** 127–156.
49. Zarrow, M. X., and Money, W. L. 1949. Involution of the adrenal cortex of rats treated with thiouracil. *Endocrinology* **44:** 345–358.

CHAPTER 9

Somatotropin, Corticotropin, and Thyrotropin

The tropic hormones of the anterior pituitary gland influence a variety of physiological functions related to general metabolism and the complex processes of growth and reproduction. Corticotropin (ACTH, adrenocorticotropin) and thyrotropin (TSH, thyroid stimulating hormone) exert their influence primarily by stimulation of specific target endocrine glands whereas somatotropin (STH, growth hormone) influences general somatic growth by itself and in association with other endocrine secretions. Other pituitary tropic hormones induce metabolic and bodily changes through gonadal stimulation (see Chapter 10). Advances in our understanding of the action of these hormones have stemmed from studies on their chemical structures, actions at the cellular level, and control by the hypothalamus.

Sites of Formation

The pituitary gland is noted for its inaccessibility. Located at the base of the brain, this compound gland rests in a depression of the sphenoid bone, the sella turcica. A variety of terms are applied to various areas of the pituitary gland in association with the hypothalamus (Figs. 10-1, 10-2, and 10-3). The anterior lobe is part of the area described as the adenohypophysis. The adenohypophysis differs from the neurohypophysis in that it originates from the buccal epithelium whereas the neurohypophysis is formed embryologically from the infundibulum of the brain. Unlike the neurohypophysis, the anterior lobe (pars distalis) is devoid of nervous connections with the hypothalamus. However, the hypothalamic-pituitary portal system provides a close vascular connection between the two areas (for further discussion, see Chapter 10).

The cells of the anterior lobe are classed as secretory chromophil cells and nonsecretory chromophobe cells. While the microscope appearance of the chromophil cells varies with micrological technique, these cells

263

are generally classified as acidophils and basophils. Somatotropin is believed to originate from the acidophils since changes in these cells are correlated with gigantism and dwarfism (28). Thyrotropin, like the gonadotropins, is a glycoprotein, and cells secreting such proteins react to the periodic acid-Schiff reagent (PAS positive). After thyroidectomy, typical enlarged, degranulated basophil cells appear in pituitary gland preparations (46). The basophils respond to PAS, and these cells are considered to be the source of TSH. While the source of corticotropin is still indefinite, some evidence indicates that the basophils may be the source of this protein. Alterations in the histology of basophilic cells appear after changes in adrenocortical function in some species.

Nature of the Hormones

A. SOMATOTROPIN (STH)

Much attention has been given to the structure of somatotropin in various species, and the hormone preparations from different animals show species variation both in chemical nature and in biological activity. While bovine and ovine STH appear to be branched chain peptides, STH from the higher primates (and several other species) is a straight chain. The characteristics of the various somatotropin preparations are outlined in Table 9–1. Tests of the species specificity to various STH preparations indicate that bovine somatotropin is active in rats and fish, but inactive in man, monkey, and guinea pig. The STH extracted from human or monkey pituitary glands is active in the primate and, like most preparations, is active also in the rat (Table 9–2). Immunological studies also indicate species variation in the various somatotropins (19, 25).

The STH molecule appears to have inherent lactogenic and luteotropic activity. Somatotropin promotes crop sac growth, stimulates corpora luteal cells, synergizes with ovarian hormones on mammary gland growth and with corticosteroids on the promotion of milk secretion (29). Such preparations possess some 20% of the activity of prolactin. When the extracts are treated to destroy STH activity, both the lactogenic and the luteotropic activities are lost.

B. CORTICOTROPIN (ACTH)

The tropic hormones of the adenohypophysis are known to be protein in nature, but only the corticotropins from beef, sheep, and swine have been purified sufficiently to permit determination of the sequences of amino acids in the molecule (30, 33) (Fig. 9-1). Analyses of the amino acid sequences of the corticotropins in these three species revealed that

TABLE 9-1

CHARACTERISTICS OF SOMATOTROPINS OF VARIOUS SPECIES[a]

Property	Beef	Sheep	Pig	Whale	Monkey	Man
Molecular weight	45,000	48,000	41,000	40,000	25,000	29,000
Isoelectric point	6.8	6.8	6.3	6.2	5.5	4.9
S—S bonds	4	5	3	3	4	2
N-Terminal	Phe-Thr-Ala-Ala-Phe-Ala-	Phe-Phe-	Phe-	Phe-	Phe-	Phe-Ser-Thr-
C-Terminal	---Leu-Ala-Phe-Phe	-Ala-Leu-Phe	-(Leu-Ala-Phe)-Phe	-Leu-Ala-Phe	-(Ala-Gly-)-Phe	-Leu-Phe

[a] From Li (31).

TABLE 9–2

BIOLOGICAL RESPONSES[a] OF DIFFERENT ANIMALS
TO GROWTH HORMONES FROM VARIOUS SPECIES[b]

Experimental animal	Pituitary growth hormone							
	Ox	Sheep	Human	Monkey	Pig	Whale	Horse	Fish
Human being	−	−	+	+	?	?		
Monkey	−		+	+	−			
Sheep	+							
Goat	+							
Ox	+							
Rat	+	+	+	+	+	+	+	−
Moose	+		+	+				
Guinea pig	−		−	−	−			
Dog	+		+	+	+			
Cat	+							
Tadpole	+							
Fish	+							+

[a] Responses: −, no response; +, a definite response; ?, response doubtful or not yet established.

[b] From Papkoff and Li (44).

the first 24 amino acid residues are identical and that there are only minor differences in the order of the remaining amino acids. A synthetic peptide has been prepared in which the first 23 amino acids are identical to those found in the natural corticotropins (26). For this synthetic material nearly full ACTH activity has been found in all parameters tested, lesser activity being found in the synthetic peptides of 17 and 19 amino acid residues (32, 47). In the sequence of the first 13 amino acids of the corticotropins, some residues are identical with those found in the melanocyte stimulating hormone (Chapter 11), and this accounts for the chromatophorotropic activity inherent in these hormones.

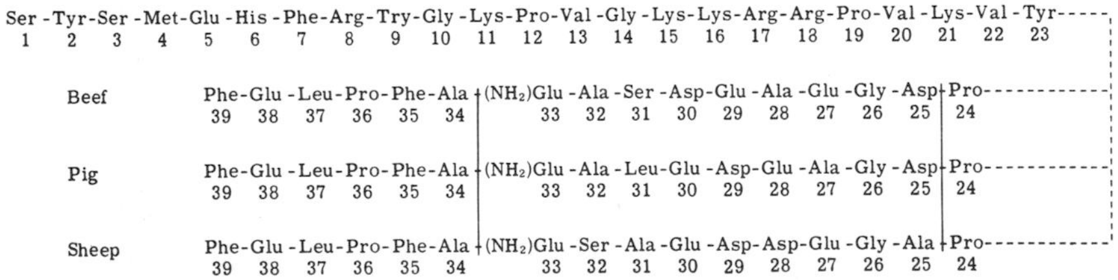

```
Ser -Tyr-Ser -Met-Glu -His -Phe-Arg-Try-Gly -Lys-Pro-Val -Gly -Lys-Lys-Arg-Arg-Pro-Val -Lys-Val -Tyr----
 1    2    3    4    5    6    7    8    9   10   11   12   13   14   15   16   17   18   19   20   21   22   23

    Beef        Phe-Glu -Leu-Pro-Phe-Ala ⊣(NH₂)Glu -Ala -Ser -Asp-Glu -Ala -Glu -Gly -Asp⊢Pro-----------
                 39   38   37   36   35   34        33   32   31   30   29   28   27   26   25  24

    Pig         Phe-Glu -Leu-Pro-Phe-Ala ⊣(NH₂)Glu -Ala -Leu-Glu -Asp-Glu -Ala -Gly -Asp⊢Pro-----------
                 39   38   37   36   35   34        33   32   31   30   29   28   27   26   25  24

    Sheep       Phe-Glu -Leu-Pro-Phe-Ala ⊣(NH₂)Glu -Ser -Ala -Glu -Asp-Asp-Glu -Gly -Ala ⊢Pro-----------
                 39   38   37   36   35   34        33   32   31   30   29   28   27   26   25  24
```

Fig. 9-1. Structures of various corticotropins. Fractions 1–17, 1–19, 1–23 are synthetic α-corticotropins; 1–13 fraction includes MSH potency; residues 25 through 33 indicate species variations in molecules. Adopted from Li (31).

C. Thyrotropin (TSH)

Efforts to determine the nature of thyrotropin have made little progress because of the difficulty of purifying the hormone. Extraction procedures involving chromatography on ion exchange resins have led to a heterogeneous preparation with as many as four components (40). As some fractions of thyrotropin were found to be more potent in producing exophthalmos than others, the existence of a separate exophthalmos-producing substance (EPS) has been suggested. In addition, studies on Graves' disease indicate that TSH alone may be insufficient to produce the changes in the orbit and perhaps an abnormal thyrotropin molecule is involved (1, 2, 11, 12, 40).

Purified TSH has been found to be unstable; thus it has been thought that, *in vivo*, TSH becomes a free, labile molecule when separated from a protein carrier (40). Variation in the type of TSH-protein complexes in blood could be of physiological importance, in that the time relationships in response to thyrotropin may be a function of the type of TSH-carrier complex. The various TSH preparations have shown luteinizing (LH) activity as well as exophthalmos activity. Since preparations of LH also show some thyrotropic activity, both hormones may have some amino acid sequences in common (40).

Action of STH, ACTH, and TSH

A. Somatotropin

The biological activity of somatotropin is evidenced by the complex series of changes which bring about an increase in body size. This biological event, termed growth, consists of marked changes in a number of parameters which include modification in metabolism and changes in size and activity of cells (56). Administration of somatotropin brings about a positive nitrogen balance, an increase in level of certain enzymes, an increase in skeletal size and changes in carbohydrate metabolism as well as other metabolic events (Table 9–3). The STH treatment may readily induce an increase in blood sugar and a metasomatotropic diabetes (9). Since the level of blood sugar may control insulin release, some investigators contend that the action of STH on carbohydrate metabolism is to bring about an increased insulin demand. The accelerated deposition of body protein following STH treatment is accompanied by a decrease in fat stores. Some evidence indicates that this hormone can accelerate the transport of amino acids across cell barriers. The decrease in fat synthesis following STH administration is associated

TABLE 9–3

METABOLIC ACTIONS OF STH, ACTH, AND TSH USED IN THE
ASSAY OF THE HORMONES[a]

Somatotropin

Growth	Body weight in intact or hypophysectomized rat or dwarf mouse	
	Organ weight increase: thymus, liver	
	Tail length in rat	
	Width of tibial epiphysis	
Metabolism	Nitrogen:	Nitrogen balance, N^{15} retention, decrease in plasma amino nitrogen and blood urea, tissue enzymes
	Phosphorus:	Increase in plasma phosphate
		Increase in phosphatase, plasma or tibia
	Sulfur:	Uptake by muscle protein (S^{35})
	Carbohydrate:	Muscle or cardiac glycogen maintenance in fasted animal or increase in normal rat, respiratory quotient depression, diabetogenic action

Corticotropin

Corticoidogenesis	*In vitro* steroidogenesis by rat adrenal gland
	In vivo changes in plasma and adrenal corticoids (rat or guinea pig)
Adrenal chemical constituents	Decrease in adrenal ascorbic acid or cholesterol, change in adrenal venous plasma ascorbic acid
Gland weight	Involution of thymus, increase in adrenal weight
Survival time	Endotoxin-treated or cold-exposed animals
Eosinophils	Depression in rats
Carbohydrate	Increased liver glycogen

Thyrotropin

Thyroid weight	*In vivo* bird, *in vitro* tissue slice
I^{131} uptake	Increase uptake in immature rat, mouse, guinea pig, chick, tadpole
	Increase uptake in hypophysectomized animal or *in vitro*
Thyroid I^{131} release	Intact rat, mouse, chick
P^{32} uptake	Thyroid of chick, guinea pig or rat tissue slice

[a] Adapted in part from Papkoff and Li (44).

with the effects of the hormone on induction of hepatic mobilization of fat, increase in ketogenesis, and reduction of the respiratory quotient (RQ). Somatotropin may also enhance the utilization of fatty acid carbon skeletons for protein synthesis, with indications that the stimulation of ketone body formation is associated with a depression in fatty acid synthesis (29). The effect of STH in inducing weight increase in the rat is readily demonstrated (Fig. 9-2). The adult rat, after attaining a

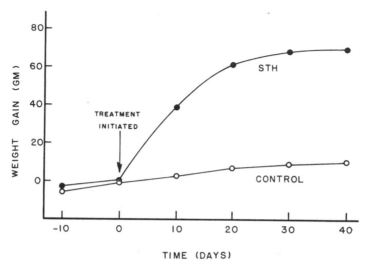

Fig. 9-2. Weight gain in adult female rats following daily injections of somato-tropin extracts of rat pituitary glands (treatment: extract of 25 mg pituitary gland, wet weight, per rat per day). Redrawn from Emerson (14).

weight plateau, will show an additional increase in size with administration of STH. Though maintained growth has been induced in somato-tropin-treated female rats, other STH-treated rats and mice appear to become refractory to a given level of growth hormone preparation (14, 27, 36). In such animals, further weight gain may be obtained only if the dose of hormone is increased. The effect is observed in the absence of demonstrable antibodies to the hormone (15).

B. CORTICOTROPIN

Corticotropin acts on the adrenal cortex to stimulate the production and release of the oxycorticoids (glucocorticoids) primarily. Administration of ACTH is followed by a rapid rise in the concentrations of corti-costeroids in peripheral blood as well as an increased level of hormones in adrenal venous blood (23) (see Chapter 7). *In vivo*, steroidogenesis may be achieved by incubation of adrenal cortical tissue with cortico-tropin (20, 52). In such studies, the primary corticosteroids stimulated are the oxycorticoids, though some increase in mineralocorticoid production has been observed. Thus, the principal effect of corticotropin is to stimulate corticosteroidogenesis, an action which can be demonstrated *in vivo* and *in vitro*. Other signs of ACTH activity are an increased adrenal weight following hormone treatment and a decrease in adrenal cholesterol and ascorbic acid that occurs in some species (13, 53, 54). The increased corticosteroid level following corticotropin treatment also brings about involution of the thymus gland and eosinopenia. Though the *in vitro* incubation of ACTH with adrenal tissue does increase the production of aldosterone, other factors appear to be involved in the control of mineralocorticoid release, as pineal glomerulotropin or renal angiotensin (43).

The ability of corticotropin to increase the survival of hypophysectomized-stressed animals, and the reaction of the pituitary-adrenal axis in stressed animals has suggested that ACTH secretion may be under neural control. Because a variety of nonspecific agents (stressors) induce ACTH release, a neurogenic factor was postulated as one possible control of ACTH release. Potent factors capable of bringing about release of ACTH have been isolated from the hypothalamus. Currently, further purification and identification of these corticotropin-releasing factors (CRF) are underway (24). Additional evidence for the hypothalamic involvement in the control of the pituitary-adrenal axis comes from studies on injection of micro amounts of corticosteroids into the hypothalamus (10). Such treatment appears to suppress corticotropin release.

Investigation of the metabolic effects of corticotropin reveal that ACTH may have actions (in addition to chromatophorotropic activity) independent of the adrenal gland. The ability of ACTH to antagonize the action of somatotropin on the tibia, and the influence of the hormone on promoting ketosis (16) represent additional and extraadrenal biological activities inherent in this protein molecule. The synthetic ACTH polypeptides, containing the first 17, 19, and 23 amino acid residues also show ketogenic and MSH activities (26, 32).

C. THYROTROPIN

The administration of thyrotropin is followed by the anatomical and physiological signs of thyroid stimulation. In addition to cellular hypertrophy (*in vivo* and *in vitro*), TSH administration is followed by increased oxygen consumption and release of stored thyroid I^{131}, the result of a promotion of thyroid hormone release (Fig. 9-3). Furthermore, the thyrotropic stimulation of increased uptake of I^{131} by the thyroid gland is evidence which suggests that the tropic factor stimulates thyroid hormone synthesis. The normal effects of the thyroid hormone, exerted on growth and metamorphic processes, can be reversed by

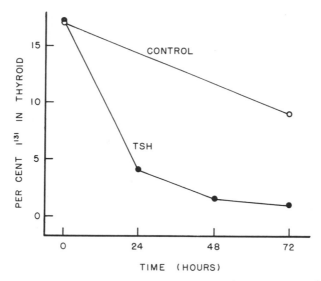

Fig. 9-3. Effect of thyrotropin on the release of previously accumulated I^{131} from the thyroid gland of the chick. Redrawn from Rawson (47).

hypophysectomy and restored by TSH administration in such animals as hypoprivic tadpoles. The exophthalmia following TSH treatment appears to be a direct effect on the eye and a separate response which can be produced experimentally (1, 2, 11). However, evidence for a separate exophthalmic factor exists. A number of studies involving hypothalamic lesions have been undertaken to elucidate the degree of hypothalamic control of thyrotropin release (6). Hypothalamic lesions appear to be capable of reducing TSH release, whereas electrical stimulation of the hypothalamus increases thyrotropin release. In contrast to ACTH and TSH, somatotropin appears to be free from hypothalamic control (21).

Assay of Somatotropin, Corticotropin, and Thyrotropin

A. SOMATOTROPIN

The first assay for somatotropin involved the increase in weight of "plateaued" rats, i.e. adult animals having reached the stage of slowest rate of weight increase, a stage that occurs at approximately 6 months of age (18, 39). This method was soon modified to utilize the hypophysectomized rat, and thereby endogenous STH was eliminated and a more sensitive and precise animal preparation was available (27, 39). In addition, immature rats could now be used since the growth rate is markedly depressed following hypophysectomy. Nevertheless, the assay suffered from the need for using many animals to obtain significant results, as well as a requirement for a long injection period. In addition, prolonged treatment caused a refractory state to develop in some of the animals (14, 15, 27, 36). Various observations on the effect of somatotropin on bone quickly led to the use of the response of the epiphyseal cartilage plate of the tibia as an STH assay (18, 38, 44). Both the hypophysectomized rat and mouse have been used as assay animals for the tibia test. The tibia test provides a much greater sensitivity for somatotropin assay than methods involving weight gain of plateaued or hypophysectomized rats (total dose of 5 μg for the tibia test versus 10 or 50 μg per day for the growth test).

Among the many assays suggested for STH is the determination of S^{35} incorporated into the chondroitin sulfate of the cartilage (41), the decrease in blood urea, and the increase in plasma fatty acids. Immunological assays utilizing the precipitin reaction, and other serological tests with STH antisera have been made (33). The immunological reactions are being used as an aid in studying the specificity of hormones from various species (19). The presence of other hormones may influence markedly the biological assays of somatotropin. Corticotropin may antagonize some of the growth response to STH while other factors synergize with somatotropin. Thyroxine (or TSH) alone may increase the tibial cartilage width whereas ACTH appears to decrease the cartilage plate width (38).

B. CORTICOTROPIN

The assays for corticotropin have employed both the physiological and chemical changes related to stimulation of the adrenal gland by ACTH. Some of these parameters involve direct evaluation of corticosteroid levels while other methods are indirect and relate to the physiological responses resulting from the increased adrenal secretions. Adrenal hypertrophy and thymus involution following ACTH administration are responses suitable for the assay of corticotropin. Like thymic involution (8), eosinopenia, as a result of increased adrenal activity, serves as an assay for ACTH in hypophysectomized rats (55). Among the most useful and specific assays for ACTH are those based on the depletion of the adrenal ascorbic acid and cholesterol. Though these changes are limited to certain species, the responses appear specific for corticotropin and are quite precise. These methods, and particularly those involving ascorbic acid depletion, are widely used to establish levels of ACTH in various tissues and the response of animals to stimuli inducing corticotropin release (23).

More significant and valuable methods of detecting corticotropin activity were devised once chemical methods of determining adrenal corticosteroids in blood and tissue became available. The increase in plasma corticosterone in the rat has been related to corticotropin activity (23). Similarly, a useful assay for corticotropin has been based on corticosteroid production by slices of adrenal gland (20, 52).

Many modifications of the *in vivo* and *in vitro* techniques for corticosteroid analysis have been employed (e.g., variations in route of corticotropin administration, prior treatment of the animal, type of animal and method of corticoid extraction); in general, however, the assays of corticotropin based on the determination of adrenal corticosteroidogenesis appear to be the most direct measure of ACTH.

C. THYROTROPIN

The early methods for thyrotropin assay involved a measure of the increase in thyroidal weight or cell height as a function of TSH (5, 11, 48, 49). More sensitive techniques became available following studies on the uptake and release of radioiodine by the target gland (Table 9–4). TSH can now be assayed by the increased thyroid accumulation of I^{131} in the normal rat, guinea pig, and day-old chick (42, 50). Such methods involve a 1-3-day treatment with thyrotropin, followed by isotope administration and determination of thyroid I^{131} 1–24 hours later. Hypophysectomized rats have been employed to reduce endogenous thyroid stimulation. Since thyrotropin also influences the release of thyroxine as well as the synthetic process, assays have been based on the rate of release of previously trapped I^{131} by the thyroid gland. Again, chicks, mice, rats, and guinea pigs served as the experimental animals (4, 37). The release of accumulated radioiodine by the thyroid gland of normal animals has been used to determine thyroid secretion rate and thyrotropin release. Exogenous thyroxine is administered to isotope-treated, goitrogen-fed animals (to prevent recycling of I^{131} to the thyroid gland) to block the thyroid release of I^{131}. Administration of thyrotropin, then, can restore the release of thyroid I^{131}, previously blocked by thyroxine (45). Other isotope methods have been employed to estimate thyrotropin activity. The uptake of radiophosphate by the thyroid gland of hypophysectomized rats has been shown to be related to the dose of thyrotropin (7, 22). Generally, the techniques involving the use of I^{131} appear to be preferable. However, a combination of most of these methods was used to establish the international thyrotropin standard (42). Tables 9–4 and 9–5 summarize the sensitivities of some assay methods for these hormones (3).

TABLE 9–4

SOME BIOASSAY METHODS FOR STH, ACTH, AND TSH[a]

End point	Animal	Treatment		
		Injections[b]	Time	Dose range
Somatotropin				
Body weight	Rat ♀ 250 gm	10–14 daily, ip or sc injection	10–14 days	0.5–10 U
Body weight	Rat, immature hypophysectomized	10–14 daily, ip or sc injection	10–14 days	0.05–1.0 U
Tibial width	Rat, immature hypophysectomized	4 daily, ip or sc injection	4 days	0.005–0.1 U
Corticotropin				
Adrenal ascorbic acid depletion	Rat, hypophysectomized	1 iv (1 sc)	1 hour (3 hours)	0.2–10 mμ
Corticosteroid production	*In vitro*	1	2 hours	2–50 mμ
Thyrotropin				
Thyroid I[131] depletion	Day-old chick	1 sc	1–2 days	1–10 mμ
Thyroid I[127] depletion	Day-old chick	3	3 days	2–10 mμ
I[131] release	Mouse	1 iv	2 hours	0.1–1 mμ
Weight thyroid slice	*In vitro*, bovine thyroid	—	1 day	0.05–0.5 mμ
Thyroid I[131] uptake	Rat, mouse, or chick	2 sc	1 day	10–100 mμ
Thyroid P[32] uptake	Chick	1 iv	6 hours	0.5–5 mμ

[a] From Bates (3).
[b] Route: ip, intraperitoneal; iv, intravenous; sc, subcutaneous.

Biogenesis, Metabolism, and Mechanism of Action

Little is known of the biosynthesis of the pituitary protein hormones. In view of the techniques involved in extraction, considerable thought has been given to the relationship between the nature of the isolated protein hormones and the nature of the molecules secreted and acting *in vivo*. However, evidence from a study on extraction of hypothalamic factors suggests, as one possibility, that ACTH and MSH may have

TABLE 9–5
A Comparison of the Sensitivities of Various Tests for TSH[a]

Animal	End point	Sensitivity based on guinea pig thyroid test as 1
Guinea pig	Histology of thyroid	1
Guinea pig	Thyroid gland weight	4–10
Guinea pig	Cell height of thyroid	<1
Hypophysectomized rat	Respiration	>1
Chick	Thyroid weight	<1
Chick	Thyroid iodine loss	0.1
Chick	Cell height of thyroid	0.25
Tadpole	Metamorphosis	0.01
Guinea pig	Cytological changes in thyroid	0.001

[a] From A. Albert, *Ann. N. Y. Acad. Sci.* **50**: 466–490 (1950).

common precursors in the hypothalamus (24). The metabolic fate of the active proteins is uncertain. Though attempts have been made to assay STH, ACTH, and TSH in body fluids, information on metabolic changes is unavailable. The many points of action of these protein hormones suggest that various mechanisms are involved. This appears especially true for somatotropin. The full significance of STH in stimulating amino acid transport, modification of lipogenesis, and other metabolic parameters is yet to be revealed. TSH appears to act primarily on its target gland (3), involving the trapping of iodide and the synthesis and release of thyroid hormone. However, the precise role of TSH at the cellular level is unknown. The dichotomy between the pituitary secretions of thyrotropic factors in the normal animal and that in Graves' disease, wherein the latter condition may be associated with exophthalmia, is yet to be completely resolved. In the case of Graves' disease, TSH alone appears to be unable to account for the exophthalmos and another factor, or a modified TSH, seems to be involved. While several investigators have reported isolation of a separate exophthalmos-producing substance, others contend that thyrotropic and exophthalmic activities may be contained within the same molecule (40).

For the action of corticotropin, some insight into the mechanism of action appears evident. Histological changes appear in the mitochondria of the adrenal gland following hypophysectomy. These changes seem to be related to the levels of ACTH and to the increase in time for corticotropin action as a function of time after surgery (51). Moreover, the inactivity of the hormone in cell-free extracts and other *in vitro* studies implicate the corticotropin hormone in mitochondrial enzymatic activities related to steroidogenesis. Corticotropin appears to act in conjunction with 3′,5′-adenine monophosphate to provide nicotinamide adenine dinucleotide phosphate (NADP; old terminology, TPN) for a rate-limiting dehydrogenase enzyme in the corticoid biosynthetic pathway (25).

All three of these hormonal factors appear to be antigenic. Comparative studies between these hormones and the antibodies produced to them have provided data of both a qualitative and quantitative nature (19, 35, 44).

EXPERIMENT 9–1

Growth Stimulation in Mice or Rats*

Stimulation of growth in the adult rat was an early test for the action of somatotropin. Modifications and improvements of the test included the use of hypophysectomized rats and mice. Although continuous administration of somatotropin to plateaued rats failed to induce continued growth and the animals "plateaued" at a higher level, weight gain could be induced again by administration of a higher dose of growth hormone. In some cases the refractory response is unexplained, as antibodies to somatotropin were absent in the blood of the treated rats. Among hormonal factors that modify the response, ACTH and TSH are particularly significant.

Growth hormone is not readily available for laboratory use, and investigators employ procedures for extracting a crude growth promoting preparation from pituitary glands (see Experiment 9–2). Although the experiment indicates the use of plateaued female rats, or littermate mice, the animals of choice are hypophysectomized rats (immature) or mice (35 day). The procedure for hypophysectomy is described in Experiments 10–1 and 10–2. The growth response is depicted in Fig. 9–2.

Procedure and Experimental

Each group is to use 4 adult female rats, approximately 250 gm body weight. The animals should show an average weight gain of less than 0.5 gm per day.

Inject each animal daily with the assigned dosage of somatotropin preparation using the subcutaneous route of administration. If a commercial preparation is available, it is dissolved in mammalian saline, adjusted to pH 9–10. Record body weight, every 1–3 days for 2 weeks. The dose range for treatment should be 50–150 µg bovine somatotropin

---

* Cf. references (14, 15, 17, 27, 36, 39).

per day, or extract equivalent to 10–100 mg pituitary per day. Control animals are injected with the alkaline saline solution.

Plot the growth curves for each group of animals and also plot the dose-response curve.

EXPERIMENT 9-2

Preparation of a Pituitary Growth Hormone Extract*

The extraction of the various hormonal factors from the pituitary gland is usually coupled with techniques involving chromatography to purify the hormones. Though complex procedures are required to obtain such purified protein factors, some extracts of the pituitary gland provide usable hormonal preparations. However, such unpurified materials may contain other hormonal factors that can influence the biological response by which the preparation is being tested.

Procedure and Experimental

While this method may be applied to the pituitary glands from a variety of species, for many laboratories the most readily available glands are from laboratory animals. Glands from rats used in other experiments may be removed, weighed, frozen, and saved until sufficient tissue is available for extraction (10–25 glands). *Note:* Be sure to record the total original wet weight of the tissue.

1. The removed glands are quick frozen (in dry ice) and stored in the deep freeze until extraction is undertaken. Remove the glands from the freezer and crush the glands to a powder while they are still in the frozen state.

2. Subject the powder to alternate slow freezing and thawing 3 or 4 times to induce cellular disruption. Add to the powder, 9 volumes 0.1 M Na_2CO_3 (a 1:9 dilution of powdered gland); subject the material to a temperature of 0°C for 6 hours and stir (gently, to avoid the production of foam).

3. Upon completion of the gentle stirring, carefully adjust the extract to a pH of 10.0. Determine the final volume of the extract and, if necessary, dilute with water (pH 10.0) to produce the volume that contains the desired weight of pituitary gland per milliliter (or 0.1 ml).

4. Calculate, then add, the amount of sodium chloride that will be required to produce an isotonic solution. Filter the solution through filter paper; then place volumes of extract in vials and quick freeze.

* Cf. references (14, 15, 33).

5. Each vial should contain the volume of extract necessary for injection each day. Thus, vials may be removed from the cold and thawed on the day of use.

EXPERIMENT 9–3

Response of the Tibia to Somatotropin*

Following the observations by numerous investigators of the response of cartilage to the growth promoting extracts of the pituitary gland, additional studies suggested that the response of the epiphyseal cartilage plate would be a sensitive and suitable assay for somatotropin. Significantly, while marked species variation is noted in the structure of somatotropin and in the interspecies response to a given somatotropin, the rat responds to the STH from nearly all species thus far tested (Table 9–2). Besides somatotropin, a variety of hormones and other agents modify the epiphyseal cartilage growth. Increased cartilage width has been observed following administration of estrogen, antibiotics, and thyroxine. The assay is carried out on hypophysectomized rats or mice.

TABLE 9–6
ESTIMATE OF THE RELATIVE GROWTH HORMONE CONTENT IN PITUITARY
GLANDS OF INTACT AND THYROIDECTOMIZED, STRESSED RATS[a]

Animal treatment	Recipients	
	Number of animals[b]	Tibial epiphyseal width (μ)
Control	16	203 ± 8
50 mg STH	13	260 ± 10
100 mg STH	17	317 ± 6
200 mg STH	12	393 ± 12
Intact animals[c]	19	320 ± 15
Intact and stress[d]	8	380 ± 13
Thyroidectomized 14 days	9	300 ± 18
Thyroidectomized 14 days and stress	9	368 ± 18
Thyroidectomized 100 days	7	214 ± 7
Thyroidectomized 100 days and stress	8	207 ± 15

[a] From Knigge (28).
[b] Hypophysectomized rats, 22–25 days old.
[c] Pituitary gland preparations from treated rats.
[d] Stress induced by exposure to 70°C water for 5 seconds, 12 hours prior to death.

* Cf. references (18, 28, 38, 44).

Li and co-workers found that the route of hormone administration and vehicle appeared to have little influence on the degree of the response; however, twice daily injections were more effective in eliciting a response than single injections. Table 9–6 illustrates results obtained using the tibia test to assay STH and to estimate pituitary hormone levels.

Procedure and Experimental

Hypophysectomize 8–12 female rats (28 days of age) (see Experiments 10–1 and 10–2) and begin the assay 2 weeks after surgery. (Note growth rate during the interval.) One group of rats is to be injected twice daily with a control saline solution pH 10.0 (0.2–0.5 ml intraperitoneally). The remaining two groups of animals should be administered differing doses of the STH preparation (e.g., 2.5 mg and 5 mg of rat or bovine pituitary extract per animal per day). The injections are administered for 4 days; on the fifth day the animals are killed and the tibias are removed and dissected free of adhering tissue. The bones are split sagittally from the proximal end and then washed in water for 10 minutes. After washing, they are placed in acetone for 5–60 minutes, washed in water for 3 minutes, then stained by being placed in 2% silver nitrate for 2 minutes. After staining, the bones are rinsed in water. While tissues are immersed in water, they are to be exposed to a bright light to turn calcified tissue a brown color. The materials then are examined microscopically under low power with an ocular micrometer. On each bone, 10 measurements are made of the epiphyseal width (the unstained portion of the tissue).

In the normal assay procedure, three doses of a standard STH preparation are administered to test animals, and the unknown preparation is given to three other groups of rats.

EXPERIMENT 9–4

Effect of Corticotropin (ACTH) on Adrenal Weight of the Bird*

One of the earlier indexes of adrenal stimulation was that of glandular hypertrophy found in animals exposed to stressing agents (Chapter 7). Subsequent investigations showed that the adrenal gland was under pituitary-hypothalamic control and that ACTH treatment would bring about the adrenal hypertrophy. The response to corticotropin is more dramatic in the hypophysectomized rat than in the normal animal. However, normal rats will show the adrenal enlargement after 6–24 hours of

* Cf. references (8, 13, 57).

exposure to a cold temperature or after treatment with formaldehyde or epinephrine.

For some time, it appeared that the domestic bird was unresponsive to mammalian ACTH, as treatment with the hormone failed to bring about an increase in adrenal weight or to induce cholesterol depletion. However, studies in which the corticotropin was administered in a beeswax-oil vehicle showed that ACTH treatment was followed by adrenal hypertrophy. Moreover, this study pointed out again the importance of the vehicle and route of administration of the hormonal agent.

Procedure

1. Preparation of beeswax-oil vehicle: The vehicle is prepared by dissolving beeswax in peanut oil so that the concentration of beeswax is 5% [H. M. Bruce and A. S. Parkes, *Lancet* **262**: 71–72 (1952)]. This mixture has to be heated to 50°C to liquefy the material.

2. Beeswax-oil suspension of ACTH: The assigned dose of ACTH (1–10 IU/0.4 ml per bird per day) must be suspended in the vehicle by grinding. From the potency of the ACTH preparation (IU/mg), it will be necessary to calculate the amount of hormone (weight in milligrams) required to treat 4 birds with the assigned dose for 7 days. Prepare the amount required, plus an extra 10–20% to allow for loss of material during transfers and injections. Place the weighed amount of corticotropin preparation powder in a mortar and grind with one-third the volume of beeswax-oil mixture (50°C). Transfer the suspension to a small bottle. Successively add the two remaining one-third volumes of vehicle to the mortar, grind, and transfer to the bottle. *Note:* The beeswax-oil mixture will have to be at a temperature of 50°C in order to liquefy the vehicle. Thus the ACTH-suspension and the syringe will have to be heated in an oven to 50°C prior to the injections.

3. Saline preparation: Dissolve the assigned dose of ACTH (as given in Step 2) in saline so that each animal will receive a 0.4 ml volume daily.

Experimental

Obtain 12 cockerels about 15 days of age, assign 3 birds to each of 4 groups, and treat as follows:

Group 1: Inject with saline alone (0.4 ml/day)
Group 2: Inject with assigned dose of ACTH in saline (0.4 ml/day)
Group 3: Inject with beeswax-oil vehicle alone (0.4 ml/day)
Group 4: Inject with assigned dose of ACTH in beeswax-oil vehicle (0.4 ml/day)

All injections should be made intraperitoneally daily for 7 days. On day 8, all animals are killed and the adrenal glands removed. Free the glands from adhering tissue and weigh on a torsion balance to the nearest 0.1 mg. Calculate the weight of the glands per 100 gm body weight of animal (relative adrenal weight, mg/100 gm).

Compare the effects of various doses of ACTH in the two vehicles on the adrenal gland weights. Plot the per cent increase in relative gland weight (mg/100 gm) as a function of dose of ACTH. Review the effects of vehicles and routes of administration on responses to androgens and estrogens.

EXPERIMENT 9–4a

Effect of ACTH on the Adrenal Weight of the Rat

Procedure and Experimental

Six male rats and 4–6 hypophysectomized rats (1–2 weeks postoperative) are used in this experiment; each animal should weigh approximately 200 gm. (*Note:* See Experiments 10–1 and 10–2 for hypophysectomy; if hypophysectomized animals cannot be used, perform the experiment using intact animals.) An assigned dose of ACTH (1–20 IU/0.1 ml per rat per day) is dissolved in saline. Three of the normal rats and half the number of hypophysectomized rats receive daily injections of saline as controls. Three normal rats and the remaining hypophysectomized animals are given the ACTH preparation in saline. All injections are given daily, by the subcutaneous route, for 7 days. In addition, 2 intact rats may be given daily intraperitoneal injections of epinephrine (0.1 ml of 1:1000) and 2 other rats may be injected with 0.1 ml of 1.0% formaldehyde to stimulate endogenous ACTH release. On day 8, kill all animals and remove the adrenal glands. Clean the glands of adhering tissue and weigh on a torsion balance. Calculate the relative weight (mg/100 gm) for each gland. Hypophysectomized animals must be examined for the completeness of the operation.

EXPERIMENT 9–5

Effect of Corticotropin on Adrenal Ascorbic Acid and Cholesterol Levels*

Although the effect of corticotropin on the size of the adrenal gland does serve as an index of adrenal stimulation, more sensitive parameters for the detection and assay of the hormone, are based on the observa-

* Cf. references (13, 23, 26, 53, 54).

tion that ACTH induces depletion of the adrenal cholesterol and ascorbic acid in certain species. Though these responses occur only in a limited number of species, and the significance of the responses is uncertain, the changes observed do serve as a satisfactory assay for the hormone. Since exposure to stressors may modify the responses, the animals should be maintained under controlled conditions. If possible, house the experimental animals in the laboratory prior to this experiment.

Procedure and Experimental

While the assay of corticotropin is usually carried out on hypophysectomized rats, the response of the adrenal components may be observed in intact animals. However, the release of endogenous ACTH would tend to invalidate the use of nonhypophysectomized rats. If nonhypophysectomized rats are used, it is essential that they not be excited.

Adrenal Ascorbic Acid

Each group should comprise 6 rats; 3 animals are to receive the saline control solution while the other animals are to be injected with assigned doses of corticotropin (1–10 mU). Administer all solutions by intravenous injection into the tail vein. Then return the animals to their cages.

One hour after injection, kill all animals by decapitation, remove the adrenal glands, and *weigh* the tissues. The adrenal glands from each animal are to be placed in trichloroacetic acid, and the ascorbic acid is to be determined as described in Experiment 7–7.

Adrenal Cholesterol

As above, each group should contain 4–6 young rats. Maintain 2 or 3 animals as saline-injected controls. The remaining animals are injected intravenously with the assigned dose of corticotropin (1–50 mU). Kill all animals 3 hours after the injection of hormone. Remove the adrenal glands and clean off adhering tissue. Weigh the glands, then proceed to determine the cholesterol content of the adrenal glands from each rat as described in Experiment 7–7. Record the results for all groups for the decrease in adrenal cholesterol with dose of corticotropin.

EXPERIMENT 9–6

In Vitro Steroidogenesis with ACTH*

The investigation of the action of ACTH on adrenal morphology, histology, and chemical composition was followed by studies on the

* Cf. references (20, 25, 32, 34, 52).

levels of adrenal corticosteroids in peripheral and adrenal venous blood after corticotropin administration. Incubation of adrenal tissue with corticotropin showed that the hormone could stimulate corticosteroido-genesis *in vitro*. Moreover, this *in vitro* technique provides an accurate assay method for corticotropin. Other *in vitro* studies have provided information of the possible mechanism of ACTH action in conjunction with 3′,5′-adenosine monophosphate and the nicotinamide adenine dinu-cleotide phosphate (NADP) coenzyme, to stimulate a rate-limiting dehy-drogenase enzyme in the corticoid biosynthetic pathway. In the *in vitro* studies, the presence of calcium ions has been shown to be a prerequi-site for the action of corticotropin. Preincubation of the adrenal glands provides a better substrate, and studies of significance of preincubation indicate that ACTH stimulates corticosteroid synthesis as well as release. With incubation, free corticotropin disappears from the *in vitro* system.

Procedure

Reagents

1. *Krebs-Ringer bicarbonate solution.* Prepare a modified solution (0.025 M bicarbonate) (see W. W. Umbreit, R. H. Burris, and J. F. Stauffer, "Manometric Techniques and Tissue Metabolism." Burgess, Minneapolis, Minnesota, 1949). Add to the Krebs-Ringer bicarbonate, glucose (200 mg/100 ml) and adjust the calcium ion concentration to 0.5 to 1.0 mM (KRBG solution; see Appendix A–8).

2. *Dichloromethane* (methylene chloride). Purify dichloromethane as described in Experiment 7–10.

3. *Oxygen gas,* 95% O_2–5% CO_2.

Apparatus

1. *Beckman DU spectrophotometer,* or similar instrument, with provi-sion for cooling lamp housing or cell compartment (cooling spacers).

2. *Microcuvettes,* quartz, for spectrophotometer (Pyrocell Co., New York).

3. *Incubation apparatus:* metabolic incubator (Dubnoff shaker) or Warburg apparatus.

4. *Micro or semimicro centrifuge tubes,* 2–5 ml, glass stoppered.

Incubation Procedure

1. Equilibrate the KRBG solution with the gas mixture, then pipette 1.5 ml into the 10-ml beakers used as incubation flasks for Dubnoff incu-bator (or Warburg semimicro flasks).

2. Decapitate the animals and rapidly remove the adrenal glands.

Free the glands from adhering tissue and weigh on a balance to the nearest 0.05 mg (a microtorsion balance or equivalent must be used in place of the usual torsion balance). Place the pair of adrenals in a covered petri dish containing the KRBG medium and place the dish on crushed ice. (The plates may be placed on ice contained in a desiccator or similar device to maintain a humid, cold environment.) A piece of filter paper may be marked, with pencil, into eight sectors and moistened with the KRBG solution. The glands from each animal must be kept together.

3. Use iridectomy scissors to divide each gland into quarters (eight quarters from each pair of adrenal glands). Place one quarter in each of eight sectors of a marked piece of filter paper in a petri dish. Moisten the paper with KRBG solution, cover the dish, and place over crushed ice in a desiccator.

4. Repeat Steps 2 and 3 until the adrenal glands of each treatment group are quartered and divided among the eight sections. Then weigh the adrenal quarters in each section and transfer to the incubation flasks from Step 1 (make sure the flasks are numbered and the adrenal weights are recorded with the appropriate flask number).

5. Flush the Dubnoff incubator unit (or Warburg apparatus) with the O_2–CO_2 gas mixture for 1 hour. The temperature is maintained at 38°C.

6. During the incubation period, prepare the ACTH solutions. Normally two levels of standard corticotropin (low concentrations, S_1; high concentration, S_2), with two levels of unknown (low concentration, U_1, high concentration, U_2) are used. Duplicate samples of S_1, S_2, U_1, and U_2 are used. However, the amount (volume) of hormone added to each flask is adjusted to the adrenal weight in order to keep a constant weight-volume ratio (e.g., add 100 μl of solution for each 30 mg adrenal weight). In addition the volume of hormone added must be constant irrespective of dose. Therefore, dissolve weighed samples of hormone in 0.025 N acetic acid so that the final concentrations will be in the range of 500–1000 milliunits per milliliter (mU/ml). Dilute aliquots of the samples (standard and unknown) with saline so that concentrations of 10–50 mU/100 μl (0.1 ml) may be attained. *Note:* Concentrations of S_1, S_2, U_1, and U_2 should be contained within the same volume (i.e., 100 μl); the volume of solution added to each flask is to be adjusted to the weight of the adrenal gland (see above).

7. After the preincubation period (Step 5), aspirate as much of the medium as possible from the incubation flasks. Replace with 1.4 ml of KRBG solution.

8. Add the corticotropin preparations to the test flasks (randomly

select flasks to receive the various preparations; each sample should be run in duplicate).

9. Incubate flasks with shaking, at 38°C in the presence of the O_2–CO_2 gas mixture. The duration of this final incubation is 2 hours.

10. Add to each glass-stoppered centrifuge tube (one tube for each flask), 1.0 ml of purified dichloromethane. At the end of the incubation, transfer 1.0 ml of the medium from each flask to a corresponding centrifuge tube.

11. Shake the tubes vigorously for 30 seconds and centrifuge at 2500–3000 rpm for 5–10 minutes to separate the emulsion formed by the vigorous shaking. Repeat centrifugation, if necessary, to separate the upper aqueous and lower dichloromethane phases.

12. Transfer the dichloromethane phase to a quartz microcuvette and obtain spectrophotometer readings at 230, 240, 250, 255, and 260 mμ. (*Note:* The lamp housing or cuvette chamber must be cooled since dichloromethane has a low boiling point and may evaporate from the cuvettes.) Read the samples against a control (1.0 ml of dichloromethane shaken with 1.0 ml of KRBG solution as in Step 11). A fine glass pipette or syringe and needle may be used to transfer the solvent. However, as the solvent has a low vapor pressure, care must be taken to avoid loss of the solvent from the pipette or syringe.

13. The optical density values (OD) are used to evaluate the responses to corticotropin. *Note:* The 1:10 dilution of the corticotropin is taken into account.

$$\frac{OD_{240} - OD_{255}}{\text{mg adrenal weight}} \times 10$$

14. See Saffran and Schally (52) for analyses of data to evaluate the potency of unknown corticotropin samples.

Experimental

Carry out the experiment on corticosteroidogenesis by assaying "unknown" corticotropin preparations (provided by instructor) against a standard corticotropin preparation. See Step 6 regarding the dilution of samples. Use eight male rats (maximum body weight 200 gm with all animals within a weight range of 10–15 gm. Follow the steps outlined in the procedure.

As an alternate to the assay of corticotropin, corticosteroidogenesis may be evaluated by comparing steroid production of adrenal glands incubated with and without ACTH. Prepare the adrenal glands from eight male rats as described above. Prepare 2 or 3 samples of standard corticotropin (1–10 mU/100 μl). Run all samples in duplicate. Determine the corticosteroidogenesis in the adrenal glands as a function of dosage of ACTH.

Microliter quantities of corticosterone (0.1–10 mg in alcohol) may be transferred to test tubes and evaporated to dryness. Add 1.0 ml of dichloromethane to each tube (as in Steps 10 and 11) and obtain the optical density values. *Note:* Steroids show an absorption maximum at 240 mμ. These data will not provide a quantitative basis for the steroid production by the *in vitro* adrenal glands, but they will illustrate the order of magnitude of steroids produced.

EXPERIMENT 9–7

Thyrotropin and the Thyroid Gland Weight of the Chick*

Isotopic techniques have largely replaced the use of gland weight as an assay end point for thyrotropin. However, thyroid hypertrophy following TSH administration demonstrates target organ change in response to administration of tropic hormone. The histological results of this stimulation are outlined in Experiment 9–8. It will be noted that the level of TSH required to induce gross morphological changes is greater than the dose necessary to induce histological modifications (Table 9–5).

Procedure and Experimental

This experiment is to be undertaken using day-old chicks. Four birds, used as controls, are injected with saline, and 4 birds are injected with a saline-TSH preparation. Each bird should be given a single subcutaneous injection daily for 4 days. On the fifth day, the animals are killed and the thyroid glands dissected free and weighed. The relative weights of the glands (mg/100 gm) are determined and recorded. Thyrotropin should be dissolved so that the total dose (0.2–1 unit TSH per bird) is given during the 4-day injection period.

EXPERIMENT 9–8

Direct Measurement of Thyroid Epithelial Height as an Index of Thyrotropic Action†

The influence of the thyrotropic hormone on the increase in size of the target gland is reflected directly in the increased height of the cellular

* Cf. references (5, 11, 47–49).
† Cf. references (47–49).

epithelium of the gland. The administration of thyrotropic preparations to immature guinea pigs or day-old birds provides an assay method for TSH based on direct measurement of the cell height (Table 9–7). Treatment usually involves a 3–5 day series of subcutaneous injections.

TABLE 9–7

RESPONSE OF ACINAR CELL HEIGHT OF THE BIRD TO
INCREASING DOSAGE OF THYROTROPIN[a]

Treatment	Number of animals	Cell height (μ)	Average standard deviation
Control	8	2.46	0.45
1/8 Unit[b]	8	3.03	0.49
1/4 Unit	10	3.62	0.52
1/2 Unit	8	3.88	0.70
1 Unit	9	4.18	0.53

[a] From Rawson and Salter (48).
[b] Junkmann-Schöller units.

Procedure and Experimental

Four young female guinea pigs (each weighing 180–250 gm) per group are used. Administer the assigned dose (or doses) of thyrotropin (0.05–1 unit total dose) to the three test animals for 3 days. The fourth guinea pig is retained as control and given the injection vehicle by the subcutaneous route. On day 4, all animals are killed; the section of trachea containing the thyroid gland is removed and fixed in formaldehyde (10%). The tissue is embedded in paraffin and mounted for sectioning. The paraffin block containing the tissue is mounted so that the long axis of the gland is at right angles to the slide. The tissue sections are stained with hematoxylin and eosin. Examine the slides microscopically, using the oil immersion objective and an ocular micrometer. Determine the cell height of 200 successive distinct acini (cell limits must be clearly defined). Record the average cell height as a function of hormone administration.

EXPERIMENT 9–9

Experimental Exophthalmos in Fish*

Exophthalmia has been associated with excessive pituitary activity in the hyperthyroid state, but the condition does not always accompany

* Cf. references (1, 2, 11, 12).

increased thyrotropin release and may require a substance in addition to TSH. The experimental production of exophthalmia, using various pituitary gland preparations, in the Atlantic minnow (*Fundulus*) and goldfish led to suggestions that a separate exophthalmos-producing factor may be required to induce the orbital change. Although preparations of thyrotropin usually induce the response, variations in results have been observed.

Procedure and Experimental

Goldfish about 10 cm in body length are to be used in this experiment (if available, *Fundulus* is the preferred animal). The animals are placed in bowls of water; colored thread may be passed through the lower lip to serve as a marker. Calipers are used to measure the intercorneal distance of each fish. For each test group, two or three animals should be used as controls, and an equal number to test the assigned dose of thyrotropin (0.1–1 mg/day). Injections are made daily for 3–5 days; the intercorneal distances are to be measured at 24-hour intervals. The injections are made by passing the syringe needle into the anal vent and then through the gut wall into the intracoelomic cavity. This technique of injection is used to avoid leakage of the injected material. Record the percentage of orbital change (increase in interorbital distance as a function of time of treatment and as a function of dosage of hormone).

EXPERIMENT 9–10

Thyroid Depletion of Radioiodine*

The accumulation and release of I^{131} by the thyroid gland provides a sensitive method for evaluating gland function. Radioiodine is used to detect the presence of thyroxine in blood (see Chapter 8). The depletion of I^{131} has served as a bioassay method for thyrotropin as the hormone brings about a rapid loss of isotope from the gland. The techniques involve measurement of depletion of thyroid I^{131} in day-old chicks, or of increase in blood I^{131} in mice (15 gm) pretreated with radioiodine then treated with TSH.

Procedure and Experimental

Prepare a solution to contain a mixture 8 μg *l*-thyroxine and 1 mg propylthiouracil per 0.2 ml. Inject into each of five 1-day-old chicks 2 μc I^{131} (retain a sample of I^{131} for reference). On the next day (day 2),

* Cf. references (3, 4, 37, 47).

hold the animals over the well of a scintillation counter and count the thyroid area for 2 minutes (see Experiment 8–7). Use only those birds showing more than a 15% uptake of isotope. Inject 3 birds with the assigned dose of thyrotropin (0.5–10 mU) followed by 0.2 ml of the PTU-thyroxine solution. (The PTU prevents the recycling of I^{131} to the thyroid gland, and thyroxine inhibits endogenous TSH-release.) On the third day, 24 hours after TSH administration, count the thyroid area of each animal. Repeat the injections of the TSH solution and that of the blocking agents. Count the thyroid area again on day 4. Record thyroid depletion as a function of time (i.e., day 2 to day 3 and day 3 to day 4). Plot the decrease in thyroid I^{131} (corrected for radioactive decay) as a function of time (Fig. 9-3) and dose of thyrotropin.

References

1. Adams, D. D., and Purves, H. D. 1957. The role of thyrotropin in hyper-thyroidism and exophthalmos. *Metab. Clin. Exptl.* **6**: 26–35.
2. Albert, A. 1945. The experimental production of exophthalmos in *Fundulus* by means of anterior pituitary extracts. *Endocrinology* **37**: 389–406.
3. Bates, R. W. 1962. Some practical bioassay methods for hormones of the adeno-hypophysis. *Acta Unio Intern. Contra Cancerum* **18**: 280–292.
4. Bates, R. W., and Cornfield, J. 1957. An improved assay method for thyrotropin using depletion of I-131 from the thyroid of day old chicks. *Endocrinology* **60**: 225–238.
5. Bergman, A. J., and Turner, C. W. 1939. A comparison of the guinea pig and chick thyroid in the assay of thyrotropic hormone. *Endocrinology* **24**: 656–664.
6. Bogdanove, E. M., and D'Angelo, S. A. 1959. The effects of hypothalamic lesions on goitrogenesis and pituitary TSH secretion in the propylthiouracil-treated guinea pig. *Endocrinology* **64**: 53–61.
7. Borell, U., and Holmgren, H. 1949. Determination of thyrotropin by means of radioactive phosphorus. *Acta Endocrinol.* **3**: 331–341.
8. Bruce, H. M., and Parkes, A. S. 1952. Assay of adrenocorticotropic hormone (ACTH) on the thymus of the nestling rat. *Lancet* **262**: 790–793.
9. Campbell, J. 1955. Diabetogenic actions of growth hormone, in "Hypophyseal Growth Hormone, Nature and Action" (R. W. Smith, O. H. Gaebler, and C. N. H. Long, eds.), pp. 270–285. McGraw-Hill, New York.
10. Davidson, J. M., and Feldman, S. 1962. Adrenocorticotropin secretion inhibited by implantation of hydrocortisone in the hypothalamus. *Science* **137**: 125–126.
11. Dobyns, B. M., and Steelman, S. L. 1953. The thyroid stimulating hormone of the anterior pituitary as distinct from the exophthalmos producing substance. *Endocrinology* **52**: 705–711.
12. Dobyns, B. M., Wright, A., and Saunders, M. A. 1962. A question of the exophthalmos-producing quality of T3. *Endocrinology* **70**: 864–866.
13. Elton, R. L., Zarrow, I. G., and Zarrow, M. X. 1959. Depletion of adrenal ascorbic acid and cholesterol: a comparative study. *Endocrinology* **65**: 152–157.
14. Emerson, J. D. 1955. Development of resistance to growth promoting action of anterior pituitary growth hormones. *Am. J. Physiol.* **181**: 390–394.

15. Emerson, J. D., and Emerson, G. M. 1960. Failure to demonstrate antihormonal antibodies in rats after maximal response to daily administration of growth hormone. *Proc. Soc. Exptl. Biol. Med.* **105**: 102–103.
16. Engel, F. L., and Engel, M. G. 1958. The ketogenic activity of corticotropin, a presumed extra-adrenal action. *Endocrinology* **62**: 150–158.
17. Evans, H. M., and Simpson, M. E. 1931. Hormones of the anterior hypophysis. *Am. J. Physiol.* **98**: 511–546.
18. Evans, H. M., Simpson, M. E., Mark, W., and Kibrick, E. 1943. Bioassay of the pituitary growth hormone. Width of the proximal epiphyseal cartilage of the tibia in hypophysectomized rats. *Endocrinology* **32**: 13–16.
19. Fishman, J., McGarry, E. E., and Beck, J. C. 1959. Studies using anterior pituitary hormones as antigens. *Proc. Soc. Exptl. Biol. Med.* **102**: 446–447.
20. Fortier, C. 1959. Relative production of fluorescent and UV-absorbing steroids by incubated rat adrenal glands. *Can. J. Biochem. Physiol.* **37**: 571–574.
21. Fortier, C., and de Groot, J. 1958. Neuroendocrine relationships. *Progr. Neurol. Psychiat.* **8**: 118–129.
22. Greenspan, J., Kriss, R., Moses, L. E., and Lew, W. 1956. An improved bioassay method for thyrotropic hormone using thyroid uptake of radiophosphorus. *Endocrinology* **58**: 767–776.
23. Guillemin, R. H., Clayton, G. W., Smith, J. D., and Lipscomb, H. S. 1958. Simultaneous measurements of plasma corticosterone levels and adrenal ascorbic acid concentrations. *Federation Proc.* **17**: 247.
24. Guillemin, R., Schally, A. V., Lipscomb, H. S., Anderson, R. N., and Long, J. M. 1962. On the presence in hog hypothalamus of B-corticotropin releasing factor, A- and B-melanocyte stimulating hormone, adrenocorticotropin lysine, vasopressin and oxytocin. *Endocrinology* **70**: 471–477.
25. Hilf, R., Breuer, C., and Borman, A. 1961. Adrenal adenine nucleotide-metabolizing enzymes: Alterations induced by ACTH treatment. *Arch. Biochem. Biophys.* **94**: 319–327.
26. Hoffman, K., Yajima, H., Yanaihara, N., Liu, T-Y., and Lande, S. 1961. Polypeptides. XVIII. The synthesis of a tricosapeptide possessing essentially the full biological activity of natural adrenocorticotropin (ACTH). *J. Am. Chem. Soc.* **83**: 487–489.
27. Kibrick, E. A., Becks, H., Marx, W., and Evans, H. 1941. The effect of different dose levels of growth hormones on young hypophysectomized female rats. *Growth* **5**: 437–447.
28. Knigge, K. M. 1958. Cytology and growth hormone content of rat pituitary gland following thyroidectomy and stress. *Anat. Record* **130**: 543–551.
29. Knobil, E. 1961. The pituitary growth hormone, *in* "Growth in Living Systems" (M. X. Zarrow, ed.), pp. 353–381. Basic Books, New York.
30. Levy, A. L., Geschwind, I. I., and Li, C. H. 1955. Corticotropin (ACTH) II. Amino acid composition of A-corticotropin. *J. Biol. Chem.* **213**: 187–196.
31. Li, C. H. 1961. Some recent knowledge of comparative endocrinology of anterior pituitary adrenocorticotropic, gonadotropic and growth hormones. *Gen. Comp. Endocrinol., Suppl.* **1**: 8–11.
32. Li, C. H. 1962. Synthesis and biological properties of ACTH peptides. *Recent Progr. Hormone Res.* **18**: 1–32.
33. Li, C. H., Geschwind, I. I., Dixon, J. S., Levy, A., and Harris, J. 1955. Corticotropin (ACTH) I. Isolation of A-corticotropin from sheep pituitary glands. *J. Biol. Chem.* **213**: 171–185.

34. Li, C. H., Meienhofer, J., Schnabel, E., Chung, D., Lo, T-B., Ramachandran, J. 1960. The synthesis of a nonadecapeptide possessing adrenocorticotropic and melanotropic properties. *J. Am. Chem. Soc.* **82:** 5760–5762.

35. Li, C. H., Moudgal, N. R., and Papkoff, H. 1960. Immunological investigations of human pituitary growth hormone. *J. Biol. Chem.* **235:** 1038–1042.

36. Lostroh, A. J., and Li, C. H. 1958. Effect of growth hormone and thyroxine on body weight of hypophysectomized C3H mice. *Endocrinology* **62:** 484–492.

37. McKenzie, J. M. 1958. The bioassay of thyrotropin in serum. *Endocrinology '62:* 372–382.

38. Marx, W., Simpson, M. E., and Evans, H. M. 1940. Bioassay of growth hormone of the anterior pituitary. *Endocrinology* **30:** 1–10.

39. Marx, W., Simpson, M. E., and Evans, H. M. 1944. Specificity of the epiphyseal cartilage plate for the pituitary growth hormone. *Proc. Soc. Exptl. Biol. Med.* **55:** 250–252.

40. Morris, C. J. O. R. 1962. The chemistry of thyrotropin. *Proc. Roy. Soc. Med.* **55:** 10–12.

41. Murphy, W. R., Daughaday, W. H., and Hartnett, C. H. 1956. The effect of hypophysectomy and growth hormone on the incorporation of labeled sulfate into tibial epiphyseal and nasal cartilage of the rat. *J. Lab. Clin. Med.* **47:** 715–722.

42. Mussett, M. V., and Perry, W. L. M. 1955. The international standard for thyrotrophin. *Bull. World. Health. Organ.* **13:** 917–929.

43. Page, I. H., and Bumpus, F. M. 1962. Angiotensin—a renal hormone. *Recent Progr. Hormone Res.* **18:** 167–177.

44. Papkoff, H., and Li, C. H. 1962. Hypophyseal growth hormones, *in* "Methods in Hormone Research" (R. Dorfman, ed.), Vol. II, pp. 671–704. Academic Press, New York.

45. Premachandra, B. N., and Turner, C. W. 1960. Thyrotropic hormone secretion rate (TSH) in the fowl. *Poultry Sci.* **39:** 1286.

46. Purves, H. D., and Griesbach, W. E. 1956. Changes in the basophil cells of the rat pituitary after thyroidectomy. *J. Endocrinol.* **13:** 365–375.

47. Rawson, R. W. 1950. Physiological reactions of the thyroid stimulating hormone. *Ann. N. Y. Acad. Sci.* **50:** 491–507.

48. Rawson, R. W., and Salter, W. T. 1940. Microhistometric assay of thyrotropic hormone in day old chicks. *Endocrinology* **27:** 155–157.

49. Rawson, R. W., and Starr, P. 1938. Direct measurements of thyroid epithelium. *Arch. Internal. Med.* **61:** 726–738.

50. Reiss, J. M., and Wyatt, A. F. 1956. The bioassay of thyrotropic hormone in new born rats. *J. Endocrinol.* **13:** 412–416.

51. Sabatini, D. D., De Robertis, E. D. P., and Bleichman, H. B. 1962. Submicroscopic studies of the pituitary action of the adrenocortex of the rat. *Endocrinology* **70:** 390–406.

52. Saffran, M., and Schally, A. V. 1955. *In vitro* bioassay of corticotropin: modification and statistical treatment. *Endocrinology* **56:** 523–532.

53. Sayers, G., Sayers, M. A., Liang, T. Y., and Long, C. N. H. 1946. The effect of pituitary adrenotropic hormone on cholesterol and ascorbic acid content of the adrenal of the rat and guinea pig. *Endocrinology* **38:** 1–18.

54. Sayers, M. A., Sayers, G., and Woodbury, L. W. 1948. Assay of adrenocorticotropic hormone by the adrenal ascorbic acid depletion method. *Endocrinology* **42:** 379–393.

55. Spiers, R. S. 1953. Assay of ACTH activity based on the eosinopenic response in normal and hypophysectomized mice. *Endocrinology* **52**: 300–310.
56. Weiss, P. 1955. What is growth? *In* "Hypophyseal Growth Hormone, Nature and Action" (R. W. Smith, O. H. Gaebler, and C. N. H. Long, eds.), pp. 3–16. McGraw-Hill, New York.
57. Zarrow, M. X., Greenman, D. L., Kollias, J., and Dalrymple, D. 1962. The pituitary-adrenal axis in the bird. *Gen. Comp. Endocrinol.* **2**: 177–180.

CHAPTER 10

The Gonadotropins

The gonadotropins, with the exception of prolactin, act only on the gonads to stimulate gametogenesis and synthesis of the gonadal hormones. These hormones, secreted by the anterior pituitary gland, regulate reproductive function and activity. However, it has become increasingly evident that the central nervous system as well as the pituitary gland are intimately related in reproductive function. External stimuli such as light, temperature, sound, odor, and touch affect, directly or indirectly, reproductive processes from ovulation and mating to nest building and maternal behavior. Internal stimuli such as the circulating levels of gonadal hormones reflect back through the nervous system to affect behavior and hypophyseal function. Many of these stimuli impinge on the hypothalamus, and the responses to these stimuli are often mediated by changes in the secretion rates of the tropic hormones of the anterior pituitary gland, including the gonadotropins.

Site of Formation

Two sites of production of gonadotropins are the anterior pituitary gland and the placenta.

A. The Anterior Pituitary Gland

The anterior lobe of the hypophysis is derived embryologically from buccal ectoderm and lies with the other components of this gland in the sella turcica of the sphenoid bone, under the median eminence of the brain. It is functionally connected with the hypothalamus only by a portal system of blood vessels. Histologically, three major cell types are observable under the usual staining procedures; chromophobes, acidophils, and basophils (Fig. 10-1).

The chromophobes are thought to be nonfunctional reserve cells that become chromogenic when the cells become active. The basophilic staining cells are the secretory source of the gonadotropins, i.e., the follicle stimulating hormone (FSH, FRH) and luteinizing hormone (interstitial

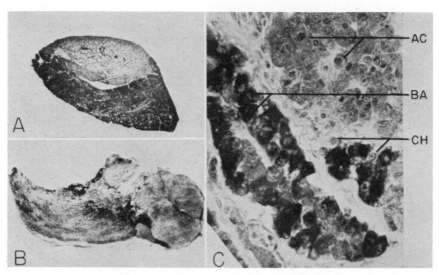

Fig. 10-1. (A) Sagittal section through the pituitary gland of the rat. Pars distalis (dark staining tissue) below; pars nervosa above. (B) Sagittal section through the pituitary gland of the human being. Pars distalis, left; pars nervosa, right. In both (A) and (B), "anterior" is toward the left. (C) Section through the pars distalis of the hypophysis of the human being (from 200×). *AC*, acidophils; *BA*, basophils; *CH*, chromophobes.

cell stimulating hormone, LH, ICSH). The acidophilic staining cells secrete luteotropic hormone (LTH; prolactin or lactogenic hormone). Histological evidence suggests that the location of chromophil cells within the pituitary gland may be specific for the type of gonadotropin secreted.

The major blood supply of the anterior pituitary gland is through branches of the internal carotid artery and circle of Willis. A systemic system supplies the pituitary gland directly via the superior hypophyseal arteries (branches of the internal carotid and circle of Willis). A portal system, also derived from these arteries ramifies first in the median eminence of the brain as a primary plexus of capillary tufts or loops which then form a series of portal vessels. These vessels travel down along the pituitary stalk to break up and supply the sinusoids within the substance of the anterior pituitary gland. Thus, an intimate vascular link exists between the hypothalamus and the anterior pituitary gland (Fig. 10-2). No nerve tracts between the hypothalamus and the adeno-hypophysis have been found.

Transection of the pituitary stalk, with measures taken to prevent regeneration of its vascular supply from the median eminence, effectively destroys the normal function of the anterior pituitary gland, even though the systemic blood supply is adequate. However, if the portal vessels are allowed to regenerate, the adenohypophysis becomes functional despite the transection (53). Thus, the vascular link between the hypothalamus and the anterior lobe appears to be necessary for the normal functioning of the gland. Figures 10-2 and 10-3 diagrammatically

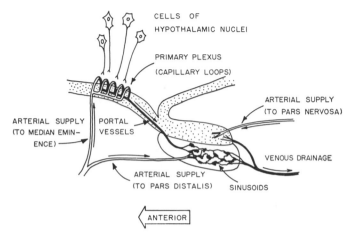

Fig. 10-2. Schematic representation of the vascular supply of the hypophysis.

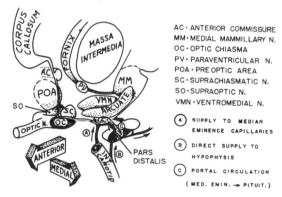

Fig. 10-3. Schematic representation of the relationship of the pituitary gland to the hypothalamus.

illustrate the relation of the anterior pituitary gland to its vascular supply and the hypothalamus.

B. The Placenta

The placenta of several mammals has been shown to be a source of gonadotropins. In the pregnant human being, the Langhans cells of the placenta (the cytotrophoblast), which line the chorionic villi, secrete a gonadotropin which has activity similar to that of luteinizing hormone. This hormone is called chorionic gonadotropin (HCG, CGH; anterior pituitary-like substance, APL); because it is excreted in the urine during pregnancy, it has also been termed "pregnancy urine" hormone (PU).

The serum of pregnant mares has been found to contain a gonadotropin which is predominantly FSH-like in action. This hormone, pregnant mare serum gonadotropin (PMS), is thought to originate from cells in the endometrial cups of the pregnant animal (16).

The placenta of the rat and guinea pig is reported to produce a gonadotropic hormone that is essentially luteotropic in action and may be identical to prolactin in these species (7, 19).

Nature of the Gonadotropins

All the gonadotropins are proteins. Although the chemical structures of these hormones are not presently known, all with the exception of prolactin are glycoproteins containing a hexose and hexoseamine moiety. Table 10–1 lists some of the properties of the gonadotropins and the relative degree of purification at the present time.

TABLE 10–1

The Gonadotropic Hormones

Hormone	Source	Approx. mol. wt.	Isoelectric point	Carbohydrate necessary for activity	Usual contaminating gonadotropins after purification
FSH	Ovine, porcine	29,000	4.5	Yes	LH
LH	Ovine, porcine	28,000–30,000	4.6 7.45	Somewhat Somewhat	(FSH) (FSH)
LTH	Bovine, ovine	32,000	5.7	—	None
HCG	Human	100,000	3.2	Yes	None
PMS	Equine	30,000	2.6	Yes	None

Because of the protein nature of these hormones, they are subject to inactivation by heat, by changes in pH, or by treatment with proteolytic enzymes. The gonadotropins are not very stable in solution, and PMS is liable to loss of activity even in the dry state. Although the activity of the gonadotropins are usually not considered species specific, there is a wide variation in potency, dependent upon the animals in which they are used. These hormones are capable of producing antibodies, and the immunological response is a means of testing the chemical similarity of extracts obtained from different species. Animals injected for prolonged periods with gonadotropins obtained from a different species develop antihormones to the injected material. Although these animals become refractory to further treatment with the original preparations, they may respond to gonadotropins obtained from another source. Thus, the antibodies or antihormones that appear may be species specific, but the hormones themselves are not.

Action of the Gonadotropins

Because of the difficulty of preparing pure hormones, descriptions of the physiological activities of the gonadotropins are necessarily complicated by the interference of contaminating substances, namely other gonadotropins that can augment or inhibit the responses observed. This difficulty is carried over in the assays for the gonadotropins and in the inability to develop international standards based on absolute parameters of dose-response relationships.

A. THE FEMALE MAMMAL: FOLLICULAR GROWTH AND OVULATION

Growth and development of the follicles of the ovary is a result of the action of FSH. The primary ovarian follicle consists of an oocyte surrounded by a layer or two of small granulosa cells. The follicle grows to a point where six or seven layers of granulosa cells surround the oocyte. FSH promotes further growth by an increase in size and number of these cells and of the surrounding theca cells. This is followed by increased secretory activity on the part of the granulosa cells resulting in the formation of an antrum, i.e., a central space filled with a fluid, the liquor folliculi. The follicle is now almost mature and is known as a vesicular follicle.

The luteinizing hormone aids in the final development of the mature follicle. This hormone facilitates the production of estrogen by the FSH-primed follicle; it also induces a final surge in the growth of the follicle prior to ovulation. Further release of LH by the hypophysis results in rupture of the follicle, release of the ovum, and transformation of the follicular remains into a corpus luteum (48). LH by itself has some effect on the ovary, as evidenced by experiments in hypophysectomized animals. Under microscopic examination, stimulation of ovarian interstitial tissue is observed following treatment with LH alone (86).

The release of estrogen by the ovary during the growth phase of the follicles is thought to regulate pituitary secretions in favor of LH. FSH and LH are both necessary for estrogen secretion, but the estrogenic hormone has been shown to both suppress the release of FSH and facilitate the release of LH (43). Recent experiments have also implicated the progestogens in a similar fashion. These hormones, known to be present in small amounts prior to ovulation in several mammals (rat, guinea pig, rabbit, mouse, monkey, human being, and others), facilitate ovulation (29, 31, 49, 58, 77). Both classes of steroids presumably elicit their gonadotropic regulating effects through an action on the hypothalamus (perhaps in a fashion similar to the manner in which they evoke sexual receptivity or estrus).

In the laboratory rat, a mammal which is a spontaneous ovulator, LH is released normally in a cyclic fashion. The cyclicity of LH release has been shown to be somewhat dependent upon the diurnal rhythm of illumination (28). Under conditions of 14 hours of daylight and 10 hours of darkness, LH release usually occurs 9–11 hours after the onset of the light period during the day of proestrus. Ovulation occurs during the dark period, 10–12 hours later. If the animal is under barbiturate anesthesia during the 2-hour critical period of the light phase, LH release may be inhibited and ovulation is then delayed for 24 hours.

In mammals which are induced ovulators, such as the rabbit, cat, and ferret, stimulation of the cervix during estrus, e.g., coitus, will result in LH release and ovulation. In the rabbit, LH release occurs within minutes after mating and ovulation may be observed 10–11 hours later.

Thus, in both induced and spontaneous ovulators, LH release may in a large measure be neurally controlled. The yearly cyclicity of some seasonal breeders may be related to the effects of light and temperature on gonadotropin release. Hastening of the onset of the breeding season in some sheep can be obtained by lowering the environmental temperature and decreasing the length of daylight. Conversely, lengthening the time of illumination (as might be observed during the spring) causes the regression of reproductive activity in these animals. Presumably the action of light, temperature, touch, and other stimuli is mediated through the hypothalamus to affect the rates of secretion of FSH and LH.

B. THE FEMALE MAMMAL: ACTIVATION AND MAINTENANCE OF THE CORPUS LUTEUM

As stated above, after ovulation, LH promotes the luteinization of the remaining theca and granulosa cells of the ovulated follicle. In some mammals (shrew) luteinization may occur prior to ovulation; in others (rat, mouse) the administration of LH can cause luteinization of unovulated follicles. Ovulation, therefore, is not a requisite for luteinization.

The activation of the corpus luteum to a functional state is generally accepted as one of the principal effects of luteotropin (prolactin, LTH,

LGH) (24). In animals in which ovulation has not occurred, or in immature or long-term hypophysectomized animals, injection of LTH has no effect on the ovary. However, under suitable conditions LTH promotes the secretion of progestogen by the corpus luteum. In the rat, LTH must act within a day or two after ovulation, an indication that the luteal elements in this species are responsive to the hormone only transiently. However, LTH must evidently be present for the continuous release of progesterone by the corpus luteum, since luteal regression and cessation of progesterone release occurs after hypophysectomy, but not with LTH treatment.

The release of luteotropin by the pituitary gland varies among the mammals. In those animals with "built-in" luteal phases (e.g., sheep, pig, guinea pig, human being) a luteotropic substance is probably released from the hypophysis in conjunction with LH, or shortly thereafter. In the rat, mouse, hamster, and other mammals which ovulate spontaneously but do not exhibit the luteal phase of the cycle, stimulation of the cervix by mating elicits the release of LTH by the hypophysis. The injection of reserpine or chlorpromazine into rats in estrus also elicits the release of LTH, as evidenced by the initiation of pseudopregnancy (8). If the pituitary gland of the rat is removed from beneath the median eminence and transplanted beneath the kidney capsule, the transplant will secrete luteotropin for an indefinite period (26, 68). These experiments provide strong evidence for neural control over LTH secretion and suggestive evidence for a neural block of LTH release during normal cyclic activity in this animal. In animals, such as the rabbit and cat, which ovulate only after coitus, a luteotropic substance is released, probably as a result of the stimulation of the uterine cervix. It has been suggested that the estrogen secreted by the ovary is luteotropic, for functional corpora lutea normally form after ovulation. In the rabbit, however, the corpora lutea require the presence of the hypophysis for a continued functional existence (88).

The relationship between luteotropin secretion and gonadal secretion has not been well defined. Estrogen has been shown to be luteotropic in rabbits, as indicated above, and in rats, promoting the activity of corpora lutea. However, this action requires the presence of the hypophysis, indicating either a direct action on the ovary to sensitize it to the pituitary secretions or on the hypothalamohypophyseal complex to either inhibit luteolytic mechanisms or facilitate LTH release.

Progestogen is thought to depress the secretion of LTH by the pituitary in the pig and the guinea pig, as evidenced by the decrease in the size of the corpora lutea in these animals after treatment with the luteal hormone (3, 79). However, in the rat (79), progesterone has no effect on luteal size and has, in fact, been suggested as a luteotropic substance acting in a manner similar to that postulated for estrogen (76). The action of progestogen on the follicle-stimulating and ovulating hormones of the hypophysis is a well known phenomenon, however. A suppression of FSH-LH activity (ovulation) is observed during the luteal phase of the cycle, during pseudopregnancy and pregnancy, and in animals treated continuously with progestogens.

Thus, in the absence of a proved feedback mechanism for luteal-luteotropin interaction, various mechanisms have been suggested to explain the recurrence of cyclic activity. The uterus has been implicated in some of these systems for several reasons: in the rat, hamster, guinea pig, sheep, and other animals, hysterectomy prolongs the luteal (or pseudopregnancy) phase of the cycle; the implantation of beads in the uterus of sheep (67) or the induction of deciduomata in rats alters the length of the luteal phase. Also, extracts of uteri of sheep, rats, guinea pigs, and cows are capable of modifying the length of pseudopregnancy, depending upon the stage of the cycle from which the extract is taken and when it is administered. The suggestion from these experiments is that the progestational uterus (nondeciduomatous and nongravid) may be luteolytic. The presence of a deciduoma, pregnancy, or hysterectomy removes the luteolytic mechanism and prolongs the cycle. If distention of the uterus is a factor (67), then neural mechanisms may also be involved. The luteolytic action of the uterus may be the result of a direct action on the corpus luteum or on the pituitary gland to inhibit LTH release.

Other hypotheses involve the concepts of a "fixed life-span" of the corpus luteum, or a "breakthrough" in secretion of FSH-LH by the pituitary gland, since combinations of these hormones are known to be luteolytic (48). The fixed life-span hypothesis may be questioned by results obtained from experiments described below.

The study of LTH has been further complicated by the fact that, in some mammals, lactation prolongs the life-span of the corpus luteum. It has been demonstrated that the stimulus-response relationship in the lactating animal is of a pattern similar to that elicited by coitus or cervical stimulation and LTH release in some species, and the same as that which results in the release of oxytocin by the posterior lobe of the pituitary gland (Chapter 11) during lactation. It has been suggested that oxytocin may be part of the system which causes the release of prolactin by the pituitary gland (11). In the rat, mouse, and sheep (65) prolactin (lactogenic hormone) is luteotropic. In the rat and mouse these two hormones are thought to be identical. In the rabbit, guinea pig, human being, and cow, prolactin is not luteotropic. However, in human beings, persistent lactation after stalk transection or prolonged treatment with tranquilizers is evidence of secretion of prolactin and suppression of FSH-LH activity (57). These phenomena indicate the similarity in physiological response between LTH and prolactin. In the rat, continuous LTH (prolactin) secretion can be obtained either by transplantation of the pituitary gland to a site distant from the median eminence or by continuously providing a nursing mother with suckling pups. In both cases, corpora lutea can be maintained for prolonged, probably indefinite periods, thus providing evidence against the theory of a fixed life-span of the corpus luteum (29).

C. The Female Mammal: Gestation

Human chorionic gonadotropin (HCG) is secreted by the placenta of the human female (5) and is LH-like in action, as evidenced by its ability to induce ovulation in FSH-primed immature rodents and in estrous rabbits. The hormone is also luteotropic (but not lactogenic) because of its ability to delay the onset of menstruation in primates when given simultaneously with prolactin (36) and to elicit a pseudo-pregnancy in rodents. HCG has little effect on follicular growth. This hormone is secreted in copious amounts during the first trimester of pregnancy in the human being. Residual amounts of the hormone are easily detectable thereafter. Shortly before delivery a second, smaller, peak of HCG secretion is observed.

The gonadotropin obtained from the placenta of the pregnant mare (PMS) (16) is extremely active in promoting growth of the follicles (with slight luteinization), indicating an activity similar to that of FSH. This hormone appears also during the first third of gestation, but it is not observed during the latter part of pregnancy in the mare. The placenta of the rat and guinea pig produce a gonadotropin which for all practical purposes is luteotropin (7). In the rat, this substance is similar to prolactin.

D. The Female Mammal: Lactation

Prolactin, or lactogenic hormone, is usually considered to be a gonadotropin, although, as its name implies, it is intimately concerned with the function of the mammary gland. It has been noted above that in some mammals prolactin and luteotropin may be identical. In others this may not be true. In any case, preparations of luteotropic hormone have prolactin activity by definition, since the potency of LTH may be measured on the crop sacs of pigeons, an assay for prolactin. It is possible, however, that future work may show that not all luteotropins possess the ability to stimulate the crop sac and the mammary gland.

The action of prolactin is readily observed in the mammary gland primed with estrogen and progestogen. This action is primarily the formation and secretion of milk (18, 60, 61). For complete growth, differentiation, and secretory activity however, many other hormones are also necessary. Among these are the adrenal steroids, thyroid hormone, parathormone, growth hormone, insulin, and the ovarian steroids. Milk secretion can be inhibited by treatment with estrogen and progestogen (63, 64). It is thought by some that the presence of the ovarian steroid hormones during pregnancy promotes the growth and differentiation of the mammary gland but does not allow full secretory activity. After parturition, when the levels of the sex steroids are markedly reduced, milk secretion reaches maximum activity. The inhibiting effect of estrogen and progestogen on milk secretion by the mammary gland in response to prolactin can be overcome by treatment with greater dosages of the lactogenic hormone (64). There is no evidence that the ovarian steroids are required to maintain lactation once it is initiated. However, prolactin is essential as well as the growth hormone, since lactation is terminated after hypophysectomy.

As might be expected, variations occur throughout the mammals in the facility with which lactation can be induced and maintained. At one end of the spectrum is the domestic cow, which in some instances can be provoked to secrete and release milk merely by manipulation of the nipples of the udder, and will continue to lactate during ovulation, mating, and gestation, irrespective of variation in endocrinology or season. At the other end of the scale is the human being, who has come to rely on the domestic cow for his milk supply.

E. THE MALE MAMMAL

In the male, FSH causes an increase in testicular weight, a reflection of its growth promoting action on the seminiferous tubules (47, 87). The hormone also has a gametogenic action in males, most easily observed in immature or hypophysectomized animals. LH (ICSH) stimulates the production of androgenic hormones by the interstitial cells of the testis (45). Administered immediately after hypophysectomy in the adult, LH is capable of maintaining the full reproductive activity of the male because of its effect on androgen secretion (44). After long-term hypophysectomy, preliminary priming with FSH is usually necessary to elicit the same response. The two gonadotropic hormones potentiate each other in their effects on the male in a fashion similar to that observed in the female.

Androgen, administered in small doses to normal males, usually causes testicular atrophy as a result of the effect of the steroid on suppression of gonadotropin release by the hypophysis. However, at a higher dose level, or in freshly hypophysectomized animals, treatment with androgen can maintain normal reproductive function. PMS has both FSH and LH effects in the male and HCG has LH-like activity. The action of LTH in the male is unknown. The hormone may potentiate the effect of androgens on the accessory sex tissues of some male mammals.

The effect of light and temperature on gonadotropic secretion has been evidenced in male as well as female seasonal breeders. Regression of testicular function and all the secondary sex characters supported by androgens occurs at the end of the breeding season in some mammals (e.g., ground squirrel, weasel, shrew) to return again at the onset of the next season. In many instances, treatment with hypophyseal gonadotropins can effect a recrudescence of testicular function. Evidence is also being accumulated to suggest a 3–4-day cyclic variation in male gonadal activity (rabbit) similar in some respects to that observed in the female (21).

F. THE BIRD

FSH and PMS are follicle stimulating in the domestic hen; however, multiple stimulation of ova is often observed after treatment with mammalian gonadotropins, and the normal hierarchy of follicular size is lost (69). LH and HCG induce ovulation in the bird as in the mammal. Ovulation occurs 10–12 hours after the administration of LH in the hen, but multiple ovulations are usually observed (70). In general, avian gonadotropins are more effective in birds than are hormones of mammalian origin.

Estrogen administered to intact birds tends to delay LH release and ovulation (34). Progesterone, as in mammals, can facilitate or inhibit ovulation in the bird, depending on the time of administration (34). These effects are a result of the action of the steroids on the hypothalamus. LTH (prolactin) induces broodiness or nest building in some birds and causes growth of the crop sac in pigeons (14, 74) (Fig. 10-11).

Some of the most interesting relationships between environment and reproductive function have been observed in birds (78, 92, 96). Environmental factors such as light and temperature (presumably through their effects on the hypothalamus and its subsequent action on the release of gonadotropins by the hypophysis) regulate the timing of migratory

flights, reproductive behavior (such as singing, territoriality, nest building), and nuptial plumage. On a short-term basis, the diurnal photoperiod controls the ovulation and oviposition in domestic birds in a
fashion analogous to (but more complex than) that of the estrous cycle
and ovulation in mammals (9, 35, 66).

G. OTHER FORMS

The response of other nonmammalian forms to pituitary extracts or
purified gonadotropins has also been noted. The end points usually observed are those of spermiation, ovulation, and oviposition. Of major
interest is the response of many amphibians to some of the mammalian
gonadotropins. FSH and LH are active in causing ovulation and spermiation. The action of HCG on the amphibian gonad has become the basis
for several diagnostic tests for pregnancy. These assays utilize the
female toad *Xenopus laevis,* the male toad *Bufo arenarum,* and the male
frog *Rana pipiens* (Table 10–3).

Assay of the Gonadotropins

A. FSH

The physiological end points used for assay of FSH activity are
measures of increase in weight or follicle size of the ovaries of immature
or hypophysectomized rats and mice (23, 25) and increase in weight of
the testis of hypophysectomized rats (46, 85). Secondary or indirect
responses, such as the increase in uterine weight of immature mice, have
also been used.

In the purification of FSH, some residual LH activity is usually
present (either as an integral part of the FSH molecule or as a separate
contaminant). The presence of small, but variable amounts of LH contamination causes variation in the assay for FSH, and for this reason it is
difficult to compare the potencies of hormones purified by different
methods or in different laboratories. However, assays for FSH have
been devised which negate the contaminating effect of LH. In these
assays, injections of substantial amounts of HCG are used to saturate
the animal with LH-like activity (Fig. 10-8). No effect is observed when
FSH is absent, but when the test substance is administered, two advantages are noted: variation in LH contamination of the test substance
is minimized, and the HCG augments the response obtained with the
preparation. These assays, which utilize changes in ovarian weight of
immature rats or mice, are much more sensitive than the nonaugmenta-
tive assays using the same parameters (15, 89) (Table 10–2).

Because FSH is not available as a pure hormone, complete standardization is not possible. Arbitrary reference standards are therefore used, and the results of assays are usually expressed in terms of "rat units" (RU) or "mouse units" (MU). Assays may be quantal or graded. The quantal assay involves determining the dose of hormone which causes a specified percentage (usually 50 or 67%) of the animals to respond. This is usually defined as the animal unit. The graded assay measures a graded response (such as ovarian weight), and a specified point on the dose-response curve (perhaps 3 or 4 times the control value) may be defined as an animal unit. Comparison of various preparations with each other or with an arbitrary reference standard thus can be made on the basis of the amount of preparation necessary to give equivalent responses. A reference standard must be run simultaneously when results from different laboratories are to be compared.

Assays for PMS use similar end points to those for FSH. However, since PMS has been purified rather well, an international standard has been established with 1 International Unit (IU) equivalent to 0.25 mg of the international standard preparation.

B. LH

The assays for LH are varied. Some of the responses are provided by pretreating animals with FSH or PMS. Thus, increase in ovarian weight, ovulation, luteinization, and interstitial cell repair (female) all have been used as assay parameters. The ability of LH to cause androgen secretion by the testis is the basis for assays of LH by measuring the resulting increase in weight of the ventral prostate gland or seminal vesicles in the immature or hypophysectomized male rat. This is an indirect but sensitive measure of LH action on the testis (47). FSH does not interfere with this response, but LTH may.

The ability of LH to cause coloration of feathers of the weaver finch has provided the basis for a very sensitive assay for LH (83, 95). PMS and HCG, both possessing some inherent LH activity, are active in this test. Contaminating LH, present in FSH samples, is also active. Nonluteinizing gonadotropins do not interfere with the response.

Recently an assay has been developed for LH which measures the ability of this hormone to deplete the ascorbic acid content of corpora lutea of pseudopregnant rats (72, 73). Immature rats are most sensitive, and these are made pseudopregnant by a priming procedure involving treatment with PMS followed by administration of HCG. About 1 week after HCG treatment, the ascorbic acid content of the ovaries is determined before and after treatment with the test substance. LH content of the test sample is related to the per cent depletion of ascorbic acid and compared with an arbitrary reference standard (Fig. 10-10).

As with the assays for FSH, tests for LH activity may be quantal or graded. Arbitrary standards are used, and the results of assays, compared with the standards, may be expressed as rat units, mouse units, weaver finch units (WFU), etc., or in terms of the equivalent dose of standard necessary to elicit the same response. Secondary response assays are sometimes expressed in terms of doses of estrogen (or androgen) necessary to elicit equivalent responses. Several assays for LH are compared in Table 10–2.

TABLE 10–2

COMPARISON OF SEVERAL ASSAYS FOR FSH AND LH

Hormone standard	Assay	Approx. minimal effective dose (μg)	Approx. relative sensitivity
FSH[a] (NIH-FSH-S1)	Ovarian histology (follicular growth)	75	1.0
	Ovarian weight (augmentation, 20 IU HCG)	50–100	1.5–0.75
	Ovarian weight	250	0.3
LH[b] (Armour LH-227-80)	Ascorbic acid depletion ovary	0.075	1.0
	Hyperemia of ovary	0.6	0.125
	Ventral prostate	2.5	0.03
	Interstitial cell repair	3.0	0.025
	Weaver finch reaction	5.0	0.015

[a] From National Institutes of Health (NIH) Endocrinology Study Section specification sheet for FSH-S1 (1961).

[b] Data taken from Parlow (73).

HCG, as stated previously, has action similar to LH. Thus, some of the assays that are useful for LH determination yield positive results with HCG. However, the ability of this hormone to cause ovulation (oviposition) or sperm release in a number of amphibians has provided a useful method for both the assay and clinical determination of the presence of HCG. The early diagnosis of pregnancy in the human being is based upon the ability of urinary concentrations of HCG to effect ova or sperm release in various frogs, ovulation in the rabbit, hyperemia of the ovary of immature rats, and other phenomena indicative of the action of LH. The international unit of HCG is equivalent to 0.1 mg of the standard preparation. Table 10–3 depicts several of the diagnostic tests for pregnancy based upon the presence of HCG in urine.

TABLE 10–3

DIAGNOSTIC TESTS FOR PREGNANCY BASED UPON
THE PRESENCE OF HCG IN URINE

Animal	Sex	End point	Approx. minimal effective dose (IU)	Effectiveness (%)	Reference
Immature mouse	F	Corpora hemorrhagica	1	98	(5)
Isolated rabbit	F	Corpora hemorrhagica	5	98.5	(38)
Xenopus laevis	F	Oviposition	1	98.5	(10, 84)
Bufo arenarum	M	Sperm release	2	98–100	(39)
Rana pipiens	M	Sperm release	2	85–99	(94)
Immature rat	F	Hyperemia of ovary	0.4	99	(33)
—	—	Inhibition of hemagglutination	—	99.8	(93a)

C. PROLACTIN (LTH)

Several assays for prolactin have been devised (6, 17, 50). Probably the most sensitive are those involving growth of the crop sac of pigeons (62, 74) (Fig. 10-11). In suitably primed rats, prolactin causes the formation of functional corpora lutea. The assay of prolactin using this parameter involves making an estimate of potency based upon the development of a deciduoma, maintenance of pregnancy, implantation, or inhibition of estrous cycles, all phenomena dependent upon the secretion of progestogens from the corpora lutea. These assays are therefore indirect measures of luteotropic action. Prolactin has a direct effect on the mammary gland, and this action is the basis for several assays using the rabbit or guinea pig.

LTH has been prepared in rather pure form. The international unit is equivalent to 0.1 mg of the standard preparation.

Biogenesis, Metabolism, and Mechanism of Action

Because of the difficulties involved in the chemical separation of FSH and LH, it has been thought by some that the two activities may reside on a single large mother protein and that variations in the rate of release of this large molecule or "gonadotropic complex" account for the changes in physiological action. Others, and this includes the majority of investigators, believe that the two activities are represented by two separate and distinct molecules. Cytological evidence for the presence of two types of basophilic cells for the production of FSH and LH is added proof for the latter concept.

Control of the release of the gonadotropic hormones is thought to be through the hypothalamus (30, 54, 80). In the cat and rabbit, stimulation of the basal tuberal area results in ovulation. Lesions in this area prevent ovulation induced by copulation. In the rat, ovulation can be induced by stimulation of the preoptic area of the hypothalamus at appropriate times of the cycle. Normal animals, under barbiturate anesthesia, do not ovulate unless so stimulated. The action of progesterone and estrogen on the release or inhibition of gonadotropin is thought also to be mediated through the anterior hypothalamus in the rat.

Olfaction and light affect hypophyseal function through a presumable action on the hypothalamus. As has been mentioned earlier, LH release seems to be controlled by the length of the photoperiod in many birds and mammals. Continuous illumination causes persistent estrus in some strains of rats, a condition which can be periodically interrupted by injection of progesterone. Presumably the progesterone acts by facilitating LH release and ovulation.

Recently, it was shown that olfaction may have an effect on gonadotropin release (71). In some strains of mice, the presence of strange males (of the same or another strain) prevents the release of LTH necessary for luteal function and implantation after mating. The olfactory system has been implicated in the block of LTH release, and the inhibition may be overcome by destroying the olfactory bulbs of the females or by injections of LTH.

Little is known concerning the metabolism and mechanisms of action of the gonadotropins. Both FSH and LH are excreted in urine as active hormones, as is HCG and prolactin. PMS does not pass the renal barrier readily, and for this reason injections of this hormone may remain in circulation for prolonged periods and may be recovered easily from the blood.

EXPERIMENT 10–1

Hypophysectomy, Parapharyngeal Approach

Removal of the pituitary gland affects every phase of activity in mammals. Significant changes occur in general metabolism, water and electrolyte balance, and reproduction, to mention a few. The technique of hypophysectomy is therefore useful in the study of the physiology of animals. In this experiment and in the succeeding one, two methods of hypophysectomy of the rat are presented. It is hoped that the student will learn to master at least one of these techniques, difficult as they may seem at first.

Procedure

Rats weighing 100–180 gm are most easily handled. Anesthetize the animal with ether (or Nembutal) and place it on its back with the feet tied down securely to prevent movement. Anchor the head by placing a rubber band around the incisors and tacking the ends down to the operating board. Clean the neck with Zephiran. A small longitudinal

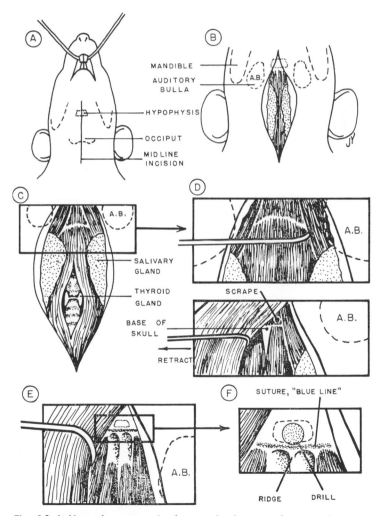

Fig. 10-4. Hypophysectomy in the rat via the parapharyngeal route.

incision is made in the neck at the level of the thyroid gland and up toward the symphysis of the mandible (Fig. 10-4A). The salivary glands are carefully separated to each side, the tracheal muscles are separated, and the trachea is exposed as for thyroidectomy (Fig. 10-4C). Insert a large-bore (18-gauge) slightly blunted syringe needle into the trachea to facilitate respiration. If ether anesthesia is used, transfer the ether cone from the animal's nose to the other end of the needle. Retract the trachea, esophagus, and tracheal muscles to one side, exposing the base of the skull (Fig. 10-4D).

Place retractors (easily made with rubber bands and paper clips) in strategic positions around the area to keep it well exposed. Carefully clean the surface of the skull by blunt dissection, working in an anterior direction until the landmarks seen in Fig. 10-4E and F are observed.

Drill carefully between these landmarks with a dental drill until the skull is perforated. (Be certain that the drill hole is centered as precisely as possible; otherwise profuse bleeding, resulting in death, will occur.) The pituitary gland should be seen directly under the point of entry. The hole may fill with blood, but this can be aspirated away. Remove the gland by strong suction. (A fine pipette attached to the vacuum line of a water aspirator will do.) Remove all retractors, aspirate the tracheal cannula gently, but briefly, remove the cannula and close the skin incision with wound clips. Hypophysectomized rats are best kept in a warm environment (25–27°C) in individual cages. It may be necessary to feed ground food for a while or milk and bread. A 10% glucose solution for drinking water is also of value in the early postoperative care of the animal.

Practice the operative procedure first on freshly killed animals to obtain familiarity with the technique. Remove the brain afterward and determine whether any pituitary fragments were left *in situ*.

EXPERIMENT 10–2

Hypophysectomy, Intra-aural Method

The following method of hypophysectomy (90) in the rat has several advantages in that it is rapid, simple, and involves only minor surgical procedure. The disadvantages are that the operation is performed completely by touch, the size of the animal is an important factor in the success of the operation, and careful inspection of the removed tissue after the operation and of the animal after completion of the experiment should be done (as always) since it may be difficult to remove the entire gland in one piece. The procedure should be practiced on dead animals first to obtain sufficient dexterity and familiarity with the method.

Procedure

Rats (100–120 gm) are anesthetized with Nembutal by intraperitoneal injection. A 5.0-ml syringe is fitted with a 16-gauge needle (BD T 462 LNR) and filled with 1.0 or 2.0 ml of saline. When the rat is under deep anesthesia, grasp it with the left hand and hold the syringe with the right hand. Hold the rat's head firmly without pressing the trachea. The injection needle, held bevel down, is inserted in the external auricular opening and pushed carefully through the canal without any resistance or friction (Fig. 10-5).

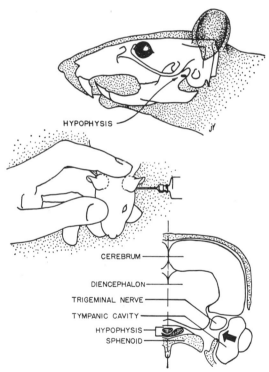

Fig. 10-5. Hypophysectomy in the rat via the intra-aural approach. Adapted and modified from Tanaka (90).

Puncture the eardrum (a short "snap" is felt) and turn the needle to point slightly forward and down toward the forward base of the other ear. Run the needle against the hard bone wall and break through the bony wall at a small channel felt by pointing the end of the needle slightly upward. At that moment, a slight resistance is felt, different from that observed during perforation of the bony wall.

Push the needle slightly, feeling its bevel contacting with the dorsal wall of the sphenoid bone; the end of the needle enters the diaphragma sella and is situated just over the rat's pituitary gland without damaging the trigeminal nerve. Drawing gently on the syringe plunger without changing the position of the needle, the hypophysis is removed and sucked into the syringe.

After removing the syringe from the rat, examine the contents to determine whether or not the hypophysis is present. The gland can be pushed out onto a watch glass and can be easily distinguished from other brain tissues by its slight pink color. However, it is more accurate to examine the tissue under a drop of glycerin through the microscope.

Hypophysectomized rats are maintained, in a quiet room adjusted to about 25°C, with a good supply of drinking water and a suitable diet (see Experiment 10–1).

The above method can be carried out quickly, giving a minimum of operating shock to the animal. Once skilled in this method, the operator can hypophysectomize about one hundred rats within an hour.

Body weight	Syringe needle size
25–40 gm	21 gauge
40–80 gm	18 gauge
>180 gm	16 gauge

EXPERIMENT 10–3

Hypophysectomy of the Chicken

The surgical approach for hypophysectomy in the chicken is similar to the parapharyngeal method used in the rat, except that entrance into the sella turcica is effected through the roof of the mouth.

Procedure

White Leghorn cockerels weighing between 300 and 1400 gm may be used. Pretreat each bird with an intramuscular injection of 1.25 mg morphine sulfate per 100 gm body weight. About 15 minutes later, inject intravenously about 3 mg Nembutal per 100 gm body weight. Most of the Nembutal may be administered rapidly. However, after the bird becomes limp, the anesthetic should be injected slowly while pain responses are checked frequently by pinching the comb, as the chicken is very readily overanesthetized with Nembutal. After the initial intravenous injection of Nembutal, further injections which may be required are given intraperitoneally. As individual birds may vary widely in their response to the barbiturate, the dosage of Nembutal suggested above is only approximate.

Place the bird on its back and make a longitudinal incision (about 2 cm) through the skin between the wattles, starting about 1.5 cm behind their anterior margin (Fig. 10-6A, incision 1).

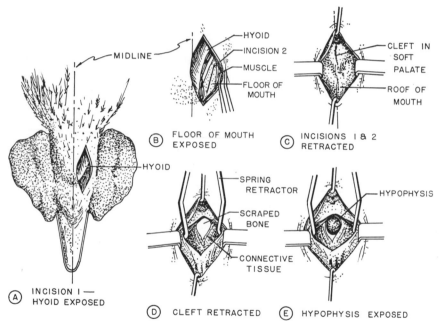

Fig. 10-6. Hypophysectomy of the chicken. (Courtesy of D. L. Greenman.)

By separating the muscles at the right of the hyoid apparatus, an avascular strip of tissue, free of muscle, may be seen. This is the floor of the mouth. Make a 2-cm incision in an anterior-posterior direction in this area (Fig. 10-6B, incision 2).

Retract simultaneously incisions 1 and 2 to reveal the roof of the mouth, which contains a cleft in the soft palate. Retract also the anterior and posterior margins of these incisions (Fig. 10-6C).

Deepen the posterior portion of the cleft by sharp dissection, and separate the two sides of the cleft with a spring retractor (Fig. 10-6D).

Clear the underlying rostrum of connective tissue, to reveal bone, with a slight depression in the midline close to the crest of the basitemporal bone (Fig. 10-6D). While not essential, a binocular dissecting microscope is useful for the subsequent steps in the procedure.

Drill an oval hole (3 mm by 5 mm) in the depression noted in the posterior rostrum. The posterior margin of the hole should extend to the base of the crest of the basitemporal bone (Fig. 10-6E). The posterior part of the anterior pituitary gland may be seen when the hole is about 3 mm deep. Since the hypophysis lies at an angle to the horizontal plane, the anterior part of the drill hole must be deepened further in order to expose the remainder of the gland.

Remove the last plate of bone with a fine, hooked dissecting needle, and clean the area to expose the whole lobe of the anterior pituitary gland (Fig. 10-6E). The sheet of connective tissue covering the pituitary gland must be torn down the midline and moved to one side. Remove the gland by aspiration with a cannula connected to a water aspirator. At the time of removal, a spurt of blood frequently occurs, but this usually subsides enough to allow exploration of the area to determine completeness of the operation.

The cavity is then filled with Gelfoam, a suture is taken in the floor of the mouth, and the skin is brought together with a wound clip. Hypophysectomized birds should be caged individually. The room must be kept at a constant temperature above 70°F and should be under *continuous* illumination, so that the birds may feed at will.

EXPERIMENT 10–4

Transplantation of the Hypophysis*

Transplantation of grafts of the anterior pituitary gland to a site distant from the median eminence in the rat results in the continuous secretion of prolactin. Under these conditions rats may become pseudopregnant, exhibiting continuous secretion of LTH and a prolonged functioning of the corpus luteum. The operation can be performed using a pituitary gland from a freshly killed donor animal or from the rat to be operated on. The former operation is usually simpler, but the tissue must be replenished every 10–20 days or so, as the graft does not "take" permanently.

Procedure

The hypophysis may be easily inserted beneath the capsule of the

* Cf. references (26, 27).

kidney while the animal is under ether anesthesia. The incision to be made in the skin is slightly posterior to that used for adrenalectomy. A sharp forceps is used to puncture the capsule and to spread a pocket between the capsule and the kidney tissue proper. The graft is inserted deep into the pocket.

Experimental

Perform the operation on intact rats using glands from donor rats. Follow vaginal smears pre- and postoperatively. Select several rats and traumatize the uteri by mechanical means (Experiment 3–2) to elicit decidual responses. Perform the traumatization on days 4, 6, and 8 of the induced pseudopregnancy. For control animals, use intact pseudopregnant rats which do not contain transplants.

EXPERIMENT 10–5

Parabiosis in Rats

Parabiotic union has proved a useful method in investigation of pituitary-gonadal relationships (51, 56, 81). In unions in which one animal is hypophysectomized and the other ovariectomized, the effects of increased pituitary secretions can be observed in the gonads and reproductive tract of the hypophysectomized mate. Because the steroid hormones are rapidly inactivated by liver and other tissues, the feedback mechanism does not operate effectively since effective amounts of steroid hormones are not available to the ovariectomized partner.

The following method of parabiosis is relatively successful if young littermates of similar weight are used. The sex of the parabionts will of course depend upon which parameters are of interest. Males may be united with females.

Procedure

Two animals, preferably littermates of similar weights, between 30 and 60 days of age usually give the best results in terms of compatibility and survival. The hair is clipped from the opposite side of each animal, so that a bare section of skin extending longitudinally from behind the ear to the tail, and ventrally from the spinal cord around to the midventral line, is exposed. The hair on the lateral surfaces of the upper fore- and hindlimbs is also removed. Wash the exposed area with 1:1000 benzalkonium chloride (Zephiran).

One animal is placed under ether anesthesia, and a single incision is made from a point about 1.0 cm behind the ear in a posterior direction

(1.0 cm lateral to the middorsal line) to a point on the lateral surface of the hind leg at the level of the posterior margin of the ischium. The incision is now continued in an anterior direction over the anterior portion of the upper hindlimb, along the ventrolateral margin of the abdomen and thorax, and finally toward the ear to meet and complete an elipse of excised skin. The skin section is carefully reflected (leaving as much fat as possible adhering to the animal) and removed. A sterile gauze pad, moistened with physiological saline, is used to cover the exposed wound while the opposite side of the second animal is similarly prepared. Care must be taken to ensure an approximately equal size of the exposed areas of both animals. (This section of skin is removed so that a tighter joining can be effected, thus limiting the twisting of animals and stretching of skin which may ensue postoperatively.)

When both animals have been suitably prepared, a longitudinal incision on the lateral surface of the abdominal cavity is made (Fig. 10-7A), and interrupted sutures are taken simultaneously through all four flaps of muscle, thus joining the animals. Although some experi-

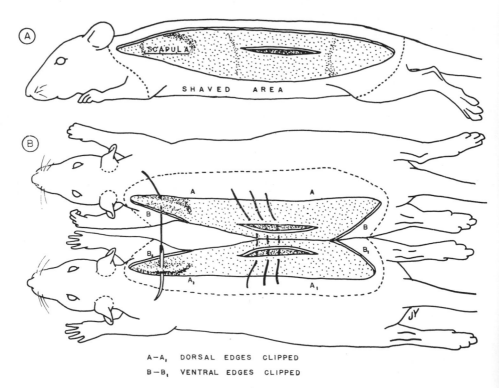

A—A, DORSAL EDGES CLIPPED

B—B, VENTRAL EDGES CLIPPED

Fig. 10-7. Parabiosis in the rat.

ments may necessitate leaving the abdominal cavities of both animals open to each other, it is usually more practical to suture the muscle flaps so that no herniation of intestine can occur from one animal into the next (Fig. 10-7B).

Medial edges of the adjoining scapulae should be anchored to each other by two or three sutures (Fig. 10-7B). These sutures will loosen after several days, but need not be retaken since their main purpose is to facilitate healing of the areas by limiting movement of the animals.

Wound clips (11 mm) are laid out on a paper towel to facilitate handling. One suture is taken behind the ear to oppose the dorsal edges of each skin flap evenly. Wound clips are fastened into the skin edges along the dorsal surface about 1 inch apart, taking care that the incision is clipped evenly with the undersurfaces in apposition along its length. Turn the animals over on their backs and proceed in a similar fashion on the ventral surface. Fill in with wound clips so that they are spaced about 8 mm apart. Care should be taken that the anterior and posterior ends of the incision are well closed. Reinforcement of these areas with sutures is recommended. One or two sutures should be taken to join the adjacent ears of the animals to each other. This operation aids in limiting movement during the postoperative period. Clips may be removed after 10–14 days.

The critical period for the parabiont is during the first 2 weeks postoperatively. During this time, parabiosis intoxication can occur, killing both animals. Use of young littermates and maintenance of semisterile technique during the operation tends to minimize this reaction. Successful parabionts can maintain life for periods as long as the life span of single animals.

Experimental

1. Determine the vaginal cycles of each of a pair of parabionts. Do they coincide?

2. Stimulate the cervix of one partner and observe any changes in cycle length in both partners. What happens?

3. Inject into one of a pair of parabionts 1.0 μg estradiol for 7 days. What is the effect of the estrogen on the vaginal smears of both animals? Autopsy; weigh ovaries and uteri of both animals.

4. Inject into one of a pair of parabionts 50 IU PMS. Observe vaginal smears. Autopsy both animals 3 days later and weigh ovaries and uteri. Compare with noninjected controls and with animals treated with estrogen.

5. Establish several parabiotic unions between normal and castrated

littermates. Inject varying doses of estrogen or androgen for 1 week into the castrate parabiont of each pair. Weigh the gonads and reproductive tract of the normal parabiont.

EXPERIMENT 10–6

The Production of Electrolytic Lesions in the Hypothalamus*

The hypothalamus and related areas have been demonstrated to be of importance in the control of hypophyseal function. In the rat, several areas have been broadly outlined with respect to control of gonadotropin secretion. Some of these areas are still vaguely defined, and it is impossible as yet to make generalizations concerning specific functions of each of the nuclei. Table 10–4 lists some of the areas in the rat hypothalamus and temporal lobe and the effects observed after stimulation or destruction.

TABLE 10–4
AREAS IN THE CENTRAL NERVOUS SYSTEM THAT AFFECT REPRODUCTIVE ACTIVITY IN THE RAT

Area	Lesion	E.S.[a]	Response	Reference
Amygdala	X	—	Precocious puberty	(22, 41)
Arcuate nucleus, hypothalamus	X	—	Precocious puberty	(41)
Preoptic area, hypothalamus	—	X	Ovulation (LH release)	(30)
Preoptic area, hypothalamus	X	—	Inability to ovulate in response to progesterone	(49, 91)
Paraventricular nucleus, hypothalamus	X	—	Prevent atrophy of gonads as a result of steroid treatment	(32)
Anterior hypothalamus	X	—	Precocious puberty	(22)
Anterior hypothalamus	X	—	Constant estrus	(49)

[a] Electrical stimulation.

Procedure

A. Procedure for Preparing Lesioning Electrodes

Materials

1. *Insect pins,* stainless steel, No. E-80, Size 1, Clay-Adams Co., New York

* Cf. references (12, 20).

2. *Insulator,* Epoxyville Electrode Insulator-60Dl-M, Epoxylite Corp., 10820 E. Central, El Monte, California

3. *Oven,* 350°C

4. *Wire*

5. *Male plug,* to fit stimulator

Method

1. Clip off head of several (½ dozen) insect pins and press the pins onto a strip of adhesive tape, leaving as much of each pin as possible extending from the side of the tape. The pins should be evenly spaced on the tape.

2. Attach the tape to the wall of a 50-ml beaker (at base) by rolling the beaker over the tape so that the pins extend below the base, points down.

3. The insulator is poured into a test tube, and the exposed pins are dipped in the insulator individually. As each electrode is withdrawn from the liquid insulator (epoxylite), keep it in contact with the inner wall of the test tube. This helps to eliminate bubbles.

4. After all electrodes are dipped, bake them at 350°C for 30 minutes. Cool for 5 minutes before applying the next coat of insulator. A total of four coats of insulator are required.

5. Cut off the tapered tip of the electrode, and scrape between 0.3 and 0.5 mm of insulation from the electrode. The size of the lesion is a function of the exposed area as well as current and duration of application.

6. Solder the wire to the other end of the electrode, and the male plug to the other end of the wire.

B. Procedure for Lesioning Rats Using the De Groot Atlas (20)

1. Become familiar with the principles involved in the use of the stereotaxic instrument. What is the zero vertical plane? What is the zero horizontal plane? See Fig. 1 of the Atlas.

2. "Zero" the electrode *tip* on both of these planes and record the positions for each plane. (Be certain that the *electrode* is aligned in the vertical plane with respect to the stereotaxic instrument.)

3. Calculate the position to which the electrode must be moved in order to reach the deep brain structures desired (consult atlas). This position is a point (distant from the "zero" coordinates) described by 3 coordinates: distance from "zero" in an anterior-posterior line; distance laterally from the midline; and distance from "zero" in depth. In young animals (150–200 gm) an external point on the surface of the skull may be used as a convenient "zero" point. This point is the junction of the

frontal and parietal bones, the bregma. If this is done, the position to be lesioned is calibrated in terms of distance from bregma, using the Atlas.

4. Prepare the rat (180–240 gm) for the stereotaxic instrument in the following manner: Anesthetize with ether or Nembutal. Insert the ear bars after making a small incision through the cartilage so that the bars rest securely against the bone of the external auditory meatus. Anchor the incisors with the incisor bar and test the preparation to ensure its rigidity.

5. Clip the hair from the surface of the skull. Wash the skin with Zephiran, and make a midline incision in the skin with a scalpel. Scrape the surface of the skull with a scalpel to remove connective tissue.

6. Place the electrode over the calculated area where the lesion is to be made. Place a dot with a soft lead pencil at this position on the skull. Do likewise for the same region on the other side of the midline.

7. Using a dental drill, make a small hole in the skull for each of the bilateral positions. (If these areas are close to the midline, the holes may be connected across the midline.) The holes should be larger than the electrode and additional drilling may be needed to admit the electrode without deflecting it. Pick off the bone chips and prick the dura so that the electrode is not deflected as it enters.

8. Position the electrode and lower it to the designated depth.

9. An indifferent electrode (a brass rod several millimeters in diameter) is moistened with saline and inserted in the anus. This electrode should be connected to the ground terminal on the lesioning instrument.

10. The instrument should be turned on and warmed up before the lesioning electrode is plugged into the terminal. Be certain that the *current is off*.

11. Turn up the rheostat to 1 milliampere of current, then time it at this level for 10 seconds. (Time varies with the size of the lesion desired.) During this period the voltage reading should not be high. If it is, there is probably a short circuit in the system.

12. Elevate the electrode until it is above the skull; repeat the procedure for the other side.

13. Remove the electrode and close the incision with wound clips. Place the animal in a warm environment (under an incandescent lamp) until it has regained consciousness.

C. Procedure for Determining the Location and Extent of the Lesion

In order to determine the placement and extent of the lesions, serial sections of the brain *must* be made at the termination of the experiment. (The data collected from the experiment are obviously not valid if the location of the lesion is not confirmed by histological sections.)

The brain is carefully removed from the skull and fixed in 10% formalin for several days. A needle is run through the entire brain in an anterior-posterior direction on one side and left in during the fixing procedure. (The resulting hole will identify the "left-right" relationship during sectioning in case any single section is reversed.)

After fixing, the brain *must* be trimmed so that the serial sections will be oriented correctly for comparison with the atlas. To do this, place the brain on its right side so that it is oriented exactly as in Fig. 1 of the atlas. Slice off the frontal lobes in such a manner that the cut is parallel to the zero vertical plane. Remove the cerebellar portion, posterior part of the cerebrum, and medulla by a similar cut (parallel to the zero vertical plane). The section that is left should contain the major portion of the cerebrum, all the thalamus and hypothalamus, and, under ideal conditions, the hypophysis.

The tissue is now prepared for celloidin embedding or for frozen sectioning. Sections may be cut about 60 μ thick. Stain with thionine using the method of Windle *et al.* [W. F. Windle, R. Rhines, and J. Rankin, *Stain Technol.* 18: 77–86 (1943)] or any modification of it.

Experimental

Produce lesions in selected areas of the hypothalamus of the rat and note any effects on reproductive function. Note location and extent of lesions.

The Extraction of Human Pituitary Gonadotropins from Urine—Kaolin Adsorption Method*

The following method or some modification is commonly used to extract gonadotropins from human urine. The final product is relatively impure and contains predominantly FSH activity with some LH. The extraction may be performed with the aid of a high-pressure mechanical "speed-filter" or by substituting a Büchner funnel under vacuum for the filtration in Step 3. The use of urine from postmenopausal women will give better yields than that from other subjects owing to the presence of increased amounts of FSH.

Procedure

1. Adjust a 24-hour or a 48-hour specimen of urine to pH 4.5 with glacial acetic acid (by pH meter).

2. Add 20 gm kaolin (Oxford-English Tamms Industries, Chicago, Illinois) and stir briskly for 5 seconds.

* Cf. references (1, 2, 13).

3. Pour urine into the chamber of the self-regulating pressure apparatus and filter it. Discard the filtrate, or save for determination of estrogen, 17-ketosteroids, and corticosteroids if desired.

4. Filter 2 liters of tap water containing 1 ml of glacial acetic acid through the kaolin bed of the pressure chamber and discard the wash.

5. Add 100 ml of 2.0 N NH$_4$OH to the pressure chamber, filter, collect eluate; pour into chamber again, filter, and collect again. Add 50 ml of distilled water to chamber, filter and add to the main eluate.

6. Adjust eluate (approximately 150 ml) to pH 5.5 with glacial acetic acid. About 9 ml of acid is required.

7. Add 2 volumes of acetone, stir, and let stand in the refrigerator for 30 minutes.

8. Centrifuge; discard the supernatant acetone.

9. Air-dry. Keep protected from humidity until time of assay.

EXPERIMENT 10–8

The Extraction of Human Pituitary Gonadotropins from Urine—Alcohol Precipitation Method*

Procedure

1. Collect a fresh 24-hour sample of urine in a bottle containing 10 ml of glacial acetic acid.

2. Add more acetic acid, if necessary, to bring the pH of the urine to approximately 5.

3. Filter and add NaCl to make a 1% concentration.

4. Precipitate with 5 volumes of 95% ethyl alcohol (EtOH).

5. Refrigerate overnight or until the supernatant fluid is clear.

6. Siphon off the supernatant and collect the precipitate in centrifuge tubes. Centrifuge at the final stage to separate all the precipitate from the supernatant fluid.

7. Wash the precipitate with 50–60 ml of ether, breaking up the precipitate carefully.

8. Centrifuge, discard the ether, and dry the precipitate in a desiccator.

9. Extract the precipitate three times with 25–30 ml of distilled water. After thoroughly breaking up the precipitate, allow each extraction to stand for 30–40 minutes. Centrifuge. Save each extract.

10. Pool the three extractions and dialyze against running tap water for 4–6 hours.

* Cf. reference (55).

11. Reprecipitate the dialyzate with 5 volumes of 95% EtOH after adding 0.1–0.2 gm of NaCl.

12. Refrigerate overnight.

13. Siphon off most of the supernatant and collect the precipitate in a 50-ml centrifuge tube.

14. Wash the precipitate with 20 ml of ether and dry overnight in a vacuum desiccator. This precipitate is stable and can be stored at room temperature.

EXPERIMENT 10–9

The Assay of FSH by Increase in Uterine Weight of the Mouse

Materials prepared by the methods of Experiments 10–7 and 10–8 may be assayed by this procedure (59). The assay is based upon the secretion of estrogen by the gonadotropin-stimulated ovaries of immature mice. Since the mice used in the assay are not hypophysectomized, there is a possible LH source from both the pituitary gland and from the extract to synergize with the FSH.

Procedure

If pooled urinary or pituitary extracts are used, the material can be weighed and dissolved in distilled water so that each animal will receive a total volume of 1.2 ml in six injections. Varying dilutions of the extract are prepared in order to establish a dose-response curve.

If 24-hour urinary extracts are used and it is desired to obtain the gonadotropin level in each 24-hour sample, the 24-hour extract is dissolved in 6 ml of distilled water and dilutions are prepared as shown in the tabulation.

Proportion of 24-hour sample to each mouse		To prepare from 6 ml extract, add the following combinations:		Total volume (ml)	Volume to be used (ml)	Number of mice	Number of injections per mouse	Volume per injection (ml)
Per cent	ml extract	Extract (ml)	+Distilled water (ml)					
20.	1.2	1.5	—	1.5	1.2	1	6	0.2
10.	0.6	2.0	2.0	4.0	3.6	3	6	0.2
5.	0.3	1.0	3.0	4.0	3.6	3	6	0.2
2.5	0.15	0.5	3.5	4.0	3.6	3	6	0.2
1.25	0.075	0.4	6.0	6.4	3.6	3	6	0.2
0.625	0.00375	0.2	6.2	6.4	3.6	3	6	0.2

1. Female mice, 21 days of age (weighing 6–8 gm), are used.

2. Each mouse receives 0.2 ml subcutaneously according to the following schedule:

Day	Hour	Injection no.
1	4 PM	1
2	9 AM	2
2	4 PM	3
3	9 AM	4
3	4 PM	5
4	9 AM	6
5	9 AM	Kill

3. A total of six injections is given to each mouse; 24 hours after the last treatment, all animals are killed.

4. The uteri are dissected out, rapidly freed of extraneous tissue, split down the center to remove intrauterine water, if present, blotted gently on bibulous paper, and weighed on a torsion balance to the nearest 0.1 mg.

5. Regression curves are prepared for each sample of urine, and the unitage is obtained from these curves. One mouse uterine unit (MU) may be defined as the amount of gonadotropin that will produce a doubling in the weight of the uterus as compared with control animals. Standard curves may also be prepared using either an arbitrary gonadotropin standard or graded dosages of estrone. The results are then expressed in terms of equivalents of standard. This procedure must be done if the results are to be compared with those of other laboratories.

EXPERIMENT 10–10

The Assay of FSH by HCG Augmentation*

The use of chorionic gonadotropin to augment the responses observed with FSH results in an assay with increased sensitivity (two- to tenfold) and a decrease in variation due to LH contamination. Either immature mice or rats may be used. Ovarian weight is the parameter measured in this experiment (Fig. 10-8).

Procedure

1. Female rats 21–22 days of age are used. [The immature mouse may be used also (15).]

* Cf. references (15, 89).

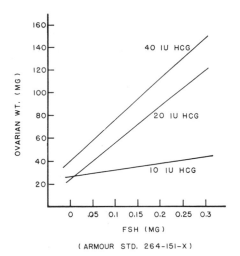

Fig. 10-8. Regression lines for the augmentation assay of FSH using HCG as the synergist. The end point is the weight of the ovary of the immature rat. Taken from Steelman and Pohley (89).

2. FSH material to be tested is mixed with HCG; the resulting mixture is injected three times daily for 3 days in a volume of 0.5 ml per injection (total of 9 injections, total volume 4.5 ml per rat).

3. Injection dose of HCG: 20 IU total (20 IU/4.5 ml).

4. Animals are killed 72 hours after the first injection; the ovaries are removed and weighed to the nearest 0.1 mg.

5. A FSH preparation of known potency should be run for comparison purposes.

Experimental

Assay several preparations of FSH with and without the synergist.

Assay an extract of the pituitary gland with and without the synergist.

EXPERIMENT 10–11

The Assay of LH by Increase in Weight of the Ventral Prostate Gland of the Rat

Best results are usually obtained with this assay (47) when hypophysectomized, immature rats are used. However, intact immature rats may also be used.

Procedure

Male rats are hypophysectomized at 21–22 days of age. Two days postoperatively, graded doses of the test material are injected subcutaneously, once a day for 4 days. Twenty-four hours after the last injection, the animals are killed and the ventral lobe of the prostate gland is removed and weighed on a torsion balance.

At least 3 points should be run, using 6 animals per point. A standard is run simultaneously; the unknown is compared to the standard in terms of equivalent amounts of material necessary to produce the same response (for instance, 100% increase in weight). Androgen may also be used as a standard.

Experimental

Assay an LH preparation obtained from the pituitary gland.

EXPERIMENT 10–12

Superovulation with LH or HCG

The present experiment demonstrates the ease with which ovulation can be induced in immature rats (97, 98). Both the "per cent animals ovulating" and the "number of ova released" may be plotted against the dosage of ovulating hormone. The response has been suggested as a bioassay for LH or HCG (Fig. 10-9).

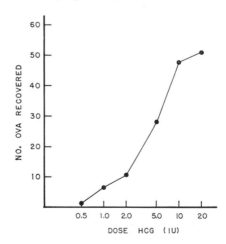

Fig. 10-9. Superovulation in the immature rat treated with PMS followed by HCG. Adapted from Zarrow *et al.* (97).

Procedure

1. All hormones are prepared in an aqueous medium: either physiological saline solution or phosphate buffer, pH 8.

2. Immature female rats (23 days of age) are injected with a priming dose (either subcutaneous or intramuscular) of 30 IU of PMS followed by an injection of the ovulating substance (pituitary extract, LH, or HCG) 56 hours later.

3. Animals are killed 18–24 hours after the final injection. The oviducts are removed and examined under a dissecting microscope at a magnification of 40 times. Ovulation is easily noted by the presence of an enlarged translucent segment of the tube, through which the ova can be seen.

4. This segment is punctured and the entire mass of ova and cumulus cells is expelled.

5. The egg mass is treated with hyaluronidase or spread out with dissecting needles, and the ova are counted.

6. The animal is ten to fifteen times more sensitive to the ovulating substances injected by the intravenous route than by the subcutaneous route.

Experimental

Establish a dose-response curve for LH and HCG.

EXPERIMENT 10–13

Assay of LH by Depletion of Ascorbic Acid of the Ovary

The measure of LH activity by ascorbic acid depletion (42, 72, 73, 82) is a precise assay that is not influenced by FSH, LTH, ACTH, or other pituitary tropic hormones. The assay is based upon the depletion of ascorbic acid from the corpora lutea of immature pseudopregnant rats. Mature animals do not respond well. Pseudopregnancy is induced by injection of PMS followed by HCG. The assay can measure LH activity of LH, HCG, PMS, and FSH extracts and thus does not distinguish between these hormones qualitatively. Usually the test is run with two dose levels of unknown (with a fourfold or fivefold interval between dosages) and two dose levels of a reference standard (Fig. 10-10). Five or six rats per point should be used. However, several extra animals should be prepared for convenience, in case of losses during the preparatory procedure.

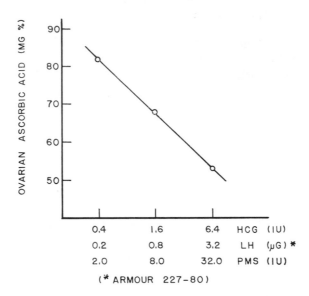

Fig. 10-10. Assay of LH by the ascorbic acid depletion technique. Taken from Parlow (73).

Procedure

Animal Preparation

Immature female rats (25–26 days of age) are injected subcutaneously with PMS (50–75 IU) followed 56–65 hours later with HCG (25–75 IU subcutaneously). The rats are used 5–9 days after the injection of HCG (7 days yields optimum results). At this time, 1.0 ml of the material to be tested (or saline for control animals) is injected intravenously (tail vein or saphenous vein). Two to four hours later the ovaries are rapidly removed, cleaned of fat, and weighed on a torsion balance. The time of ovariectomy must be kept standard. Ascorbic acid content of the ovaries is determined by the method of Mindlin and Butler [*J. Biol. Chem.* **122:** 673–686 (1938)].

In order to determine LH content of the material being tested, two standard curves must be established: (a) the relationship between optical density of the indicator and the concentration of known amounts of ascorbic acid and (b) the relationship between the dose of a standard LH preparation and percentage of depletion of ascorbic acid of the ovary.

Materials to be Tested for LH Activity

1. *Standard LH solutions.* Concentrations of 0.4 and 2.0 μg LH per

milliliter Ringer solution are prepared. These are the dosages to be injected intravenously (see Animal Preparation).

2. *Pituitary extracts.* Either fresh or quick-frozen pituitary glands may be used. The gland is removed from the experimental animal, the pars distalis is dissected free, weighed on a torsion balance and assayed fresh, or quick frozen by touching the gland to the side of a test tube immersed in a dry ice-acetone bath. The frozen gland may be stored in a deep freeze until the time of assay. At the time of assay, the gland is homogenized with a glass stirring rod, and 2.0 ml saline is added and mixed. The material is centrifuged, the supernatant is collected, and dilutions are made for assay. A fivefold variation in concentration of pituitary extract is prepared for injection intravenously (see Animal Preparation). (For example, 0.02 and 0.1 of a pituitary gland per milliliter saline may be injected into the assay animals.)

3. *Controls.* Physiological saline or Ringer's solution (1.0 ml) is injected intravenously into control assay animals (see Animal Preparation).

Method of Assay

1. Preparation of ovaries. Homogenize each ovary (obtained as described in Animal Preparation) in 5 ml of 2.5% metaphosphoric acid (MPA). Add 5.0 ml of MPA and mix. Keep solutions on ice. Filter (Whatman no. 40 paper) into test tubes in an ice bath. Store clear homogenates in refrigerator until time of analysis. These are the test solutions.

2. Colorimetric analysis. Add 2.5 ml of the indophenol-acetate solution to 2.5 ml of the test solutions (ovarian extracts, ascorbic acid standards) and mix. Colorimetric analysis is performed with readings of optical density at 515 mμ. (Reagent blank: 2.5 ml indophenol-acetate solution and 2.5 ml of 2.5% MPA.) Results may be expressed as milligrams per 100 gm ovarian ascorbic acid, as per cent ascorbic acid depletion, or in terms of the standard LH preparation.

Preparation of Extracts and Standards for Assay

1. *Ovarian extracts.* It may be necessary to dilute these to give reliable readings. To do this, remove a small sample obtained from Step 1 of Method of Assay (note the volume) and make the dilution with MPA to 2.5 ml. This may now be analyzed as in Step 2 of Method of Assay.

2. *Ascorbic acid standards.* The ascorbic acid standards will contain 1.0, 2.0, and 3.0 μg acid per 1.0 ml solution. These are prepared as follows: A stock solution is prepared by dissolving 10 mg USP ascorbic acid in 2.5% MPA and diluting to 100 ml with 2.5% MPA. Store this in the deep freeze in a number of small vials. Dilute 0.5, 1.0, and 1.5 ml of

the stock to 25 ml by adding 2.5% MPA. The resulting solutions contain 2.0, 4.0, and 6.0 μg ascorbic acid per milliliter of solution. When mixed with the indophenol-acetate as in Step 2 (Method of Assay), the solutions will contain 1.0, 2.0, and 3.0 μg ascorbic acid per milliliter of solution.

Reagents for Assay

1. *Metaphosphoric acid (MPA)*. Freshly prepare for each assay and refrigerate. Concentration, 25 gm MPA in 500 ml distilled water. Dilute to 2.5% for use (1 part MPA, 1 part distilled water).

2. *Indophenol-acetate solution*. Equal volumes of the following two solutions are mixed and used for the assay:

    (a) *Indicator solution*. Dissolve in water at 85–95°C, 10 mg of 2,6-dichlorobenzene-1-indophenol. Filter and dilute to 250 ml. Freshly prepare and refrigerate for each assay.

    (b) *Sodium acetate*. Add 11.325 gm sodium acetate to 250 ml distilled water. Adjust the pH to 7.0 ± 0.2 by addition of 0.6 ml of 6% acetic acid. Prepare freshly and refrigerate for each assay.

Experimental

Determine the LH content of the pituitary glands from immature rats and from mature female rats during (a) proestrus and (b) estrus.

EXPERIMENT 10–14

The Assay of HCG by Vaginal Cornification

This assay (52) is based upon the ability of HCG to cause the secretion of estrogen by follicles of the immature rat ovary. The assay may be standardized against estrogen or against a standard HCG of known purity.

Procedure

1. Immature female rats 3–4 weeks old are used. The concentrations of HCG are made up in increasing steps of 50% difference. A minimum of three concentrations must be used. Thus, three groups of 6 rats each are used in the assay.

2. The selected amount of material is dissolved in distilled water and injected in 6 subcutaneous injections of 0.1 ml each per rat. Thus, a minimum of 3.6 ml of solution is required per group. When 50% or more

of the animals in any group give a positive reaction, that group is declared "positive."

3. Standardization is complete only when 33% of animals at one dose level give positive reactions and the next lower dose level results in 0% positive reactions. Dosage range is from about 0.25 to 1.0 IU HCG.

4. Smears are stained and read as in the estrogen assay (Experiments 2–1 and 2–4). The schedule for injections and smears follows:

Injections:	Day 1	1:00 PM	0.1 ml
		4:30 PM	0.1 ml
	Day 2	9:00 AM	0.1 ml
		1:00 PM	0.1 ml
		4:30 PM	0.1 ml
	Day 3	9:00 AM	0.1 ml
Smears:	Day 4	9:00 AM	1st smear
		4:30 PM	2nd smear
	Day 5	9:00 AM	3rd smear

Experimental

Establish a dose response curve with a standard HCG preparation.

EXPERIMENT 10–15

The Assay of Prolactin by the Pigeon Crop Sac Method*

The classical assay for prolactin is by its effect on the crop sac of the pigeon. The assay is extremely simple and involves injecting the test material by either an intramuscular or intradermal route and measuring either the weight or area of the crop sac after 4 days of treatment. A two-point assay is sufficient, using four birds per point (Fig. 10-11).

Procedure

Pigeons (260–340 gm) are injected for 4 days with 0.1 ml per day of material to be tested, either by intramuscular (pectoral) or intra-dermal injections. If intradermal injections are made, an area on the skin over the crop sac should be marked with methylene blue to localize the injection spot.

Assay by Intramuscular Injection

Animals are killed on day 5; the crop sac is dissected out, freed from fatty tissue, and weighed to the nearest 0.01 gm. (The crop sac forms a

* Cf. references (6, 17, 50, 62).

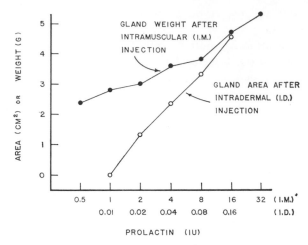

Fig. 10-11. The assay of prolactin by the pigeon crop method.

thin membranous pouch across the breast of the bird and is shaped vaguely into two lobes.) A standard curve must be established with prolactin of known purity.

Assay by Intradermal Injection

Animals are killed on day 5, the tissue is dissected out and stretched on a glass plate. A second glass plate is placed on top of the tissue and the "sandwich" is illuminated from below. The outline of the area of proliferation of the crop sac is traced with a planimeter. A standard curve must be established with prolactin of known purity.

Experimental

1. Establish dose-response curves for prolactin using both the local and intramuscular route of injection.

2. Assay the prolactin content of the pituitary gland from a normal rabbit and from a rabbit during the first week of lactation.

EXPERIMENT 10–16

Diagnosis of Pregnancy by the Presence of HCG in Urine

Most of the diagnostic tests for pregnancy in the human being involve the detection of HCG in urine (4, 5, 10, 33, 37–40, 75, 84, 93, 94). The hormone makes its appearance at about 30–40 days of gestation and reaches a peak soon thereafter. After about 80 days, the level of the hormone in the blood declines and remains relatively low until the last trimester, when a slight rise is noted. From the time of its appearance until after delivery, urinary HCG can be detected with ease by bioassay. Another method of diagnosis of pregnancy in humans is the measure of pregnanediol excretion in the urine. Recently a pregnancy test based upon the administration of progestogens has been suggested. In this test oral progestogens are administered for several days. If menstruation does not occur after withdrawal of the progestogen, the test is positive for pregnancy.

Preparation of Urine

1. Filter a morning sample of urine from a woman pregnant at least 6 weeks.

2. If sample is alkaline, acidify 25 ml of urine with 6% acetic acid, using litmus paper as an indicator.

3. Extract urine with 75 ml of ether in a separatory funnel and discard the ether layer (ether extraction is not always essential).

4. Evaporate the ether from the aqueous layer (without heat) by vacuum.

I. ASCHHEIM-ZONDEK TEST*

Procedure

Immature female mice, age 3–4 weeks, weight 6–8 gm, are used. Three samples of urine, prepared as above, are to be tested. At least one sample will be from a pregnant woman. Each sample is to be injected into a group of three mice. Two additional mice are to be used as controls. Injections are to be made subcutaneously, each mouse receiving 0.1 ml of urine per injection using the following treatment schedule:

	Day 1	1:30 PM
		4:30 PM
	Day 2	9:00 AM
		1:00 PM
		4:30 PM
	Day 3	9:00 AM
Vaginal smears are to be obtained	Day 4	9:00 AM
	Day 5	9:00 AM
Postmortem examination of ovaries and uterus	Day 6	4:00 PM

In clinical work, the mice are routinely injected with two volumes of the urine sample, i.e., two mice receive 0.4 ml of urine per injection and

* Cf. references (4, 5).

two receive 0.3 ml of urine per injection. Furthermore, vaginal smears are not taken. The reaction is evaluated as shown below:

Positive test

1. ++ Ovary positive; uterus positive
2. + Ovary positive; uterus negative

Negative test

1. — Ovary negative; uterus positive
2. ⊥— Ovary negative; uterus negative

A "positive" ovary is one in which hemorrhagic follicles or corpora lutea are observed. A "positive" uterus is one in which marked vascularity and an increase in size is observed (Table 10–5).

TABLE 10–5

REACTIONS AFTER THE INJECTION OF PREGNANCY URINE IN FEMALE MICE

Ovary	Uterus	Vagina	Vaginal smear	Hormone action	Pregnancy diagnosis
Negative	Small	Closed	Negative	None	Negative
Macro- and microscopically negative	Large	Open	Positive	Estrogenic	Negative
Macroscopically not too decisive, microscopically only large follicles	Enlarged	Open	Positive	APL[a]	Negative (second examination of urine necessary)
Macroscopically corpora hemorrhagica or corpora lutea or both	Large	Open	Positive	APL	Positive
Macroscopically corpora hemorrhagica or corpora lutea or both	Small	Closed	Negative	APL	Positive

[a] Anterior pituitary-like substance.

II. FRIEDMAN TEST

The Friedman test for pregnancy (37, 38), essentially a modification of the Aschheim-Zondek test, is based on the observation that ovulation can be induced in the adult rabbit by the injection of human pregnancy urine. Both the Friedman and the Aschheim-Zondek tests have an accuracy of about 98%, but the former has supplanted the latter because of the speed of completion of the test. Whereas the Aschheim-Zondek test requires 96 hours, the Friedman test can be completed in 48 hours.

Procedure

1. Inject 4.0–10.0 ml of the urine, previously prepared, intravenously into an adult female rabbit that has been isolated for one month from other rabbits. If there is any doubt about the animal, a laparotomy should be performed and the ovaries examined. Only rabbits which contain ovaries with follicles (not corpora lutea) should be used.

2. Twenty-four hours after the first treatment, a second intravenous injection is made, using 4.0–10.0 ml of urine.

3. Forty-eight hours after the first injection, a laparotomy is performed and the ovaries are examined. The presence of fresh corpora lutea or corpora hemorrhagica indicates a positive reaction.

III. XENOPUS TEST*

Procedure

Mature female frogs (*Xenopus laevis* Daudin) are injected in the dorsal lymph sac with 1.0 ml of pregnancy urine and placed in covered containers with water covering all but their heads. A positive reaction is indicated by the presence of ova in the container within 6–24 hours after the injection. Animals should be kept in a quiet environment.

IV. MALE FROG TEST†

Procedure

1. Inject 2.0–4.0 ml of urine (using a 25-gauge needle) into the dorsal lymph sac.

2. Place the animal in a clean, dry jar.

3. Allow to rest for 2–4 hours.

4. At the end of this time, urine should be present in the jar. If not, grasp the frog by the head and shoulders and gently express the urine by pressing on the abdomen.

5. Place a drop of urine on a slide and examine under the microscope for the presence of spermatozoa. The spermatozoa of frogs are cigar-shaped with transparent flagella.

6. The presence of sperm is a positive reaction.

Test the three samples of urine in two frogs each. Use two controls.

* Cf. references (10, 84, 93).
† Cf. references (75, 94).

V. HYPEREMIA OF THE OVARY*

Procedure

Immature female rats (3–4 weeks old) are injected subcutaneously with 2.0 ml of urine 4–6 hours prior to autopsy. A positive reaction is indicated by a hyperemia of the ovary of the treated animals when compared with uninjected controls. The rats are killed by ether asphyxiation; the ovaries are removed and placed on wet blotting paper and examined under an ordinary desk lamp. Ovaries from rats that fail to show a positive response are light yellow in color; whereas a pink to deep red ovary indicates a positive reaction.

VI. IMMUNOLOGIC TEST FOR PREGNANCY

This test depends upon the *in vitro* inhibition by HCG of the hemagglutination reaction of HCG-treated red blood cells with antiserum.

The concentration of HCG in the urine (or serum) is then determined by comparison with standards of known dilutions. With due precaution for "false positives" owing to the presence of large amounts of human pituitary LH, it is possible to achieve true diagnoses 99.8% of the time. An excellent discussion of this type of test is presented by Wide (93a).

Experimental: Tests I–VI

Test different samples of urine from pregnant and nonpregnant women by several of the pregnancy tests.

References

1. Albert, A. 1955. Procedure for routine clinical determination of urinary gonadotropin. *Proc. Staff Meetings Mayo Clinic* 30: 552–555.
2. Albert, A. 1961. Extraction of gonadotropic material from urine, *in* "Human Pituitary Gonadotropins" (A. Albert, ed.), pp. 6–10. Thomas, Springfield, Illinois.
3. Aldred, J. P., Sammelwitz, P. H., and Nalbandov, A. V. 1961. Mechanisms of formation of corpora lutea in guinea pigs. *J. Reprod. Fertility* 2: 394–399.
4. Aschheim, S. 1930. The early diagnosis of pregnancy, chorionepithelioma and hydatidiform mole by the Aschheim-Zondek test. *Am. J. Obstet. Gynecol.* 19: 335–342.
5. Aschheim, S., and Zondek, B. 1928. Die Schwangerschaftsdiagnose aus dem Harn durch Nachweis des Hypophysenvorderlappenhormons. *Klin. Wochschr.* 7: 1453–1457.
6. Astwood, E. B. 1953. Tests for luteotropin. *Ciba Found. Colloq. Endocrinol.* 5: 74–85.

* Cf. reference (33).

7. Astwood, E. B., and Greep, R. O. 1938. A corpus luteum-stimulating substance in the rat placenta. *Proc. Soc. Exptl. Biol. Med.* **38**: 713–716.

8. Barraclough, C., and Sawyer, C. H. 1959. Induction of pseudopregnancy in the rat by reserpine and chlorpromazine. *Endocrinology* **65**: 563–571.

9. Bastian, J. W., and Zarrow, M. X. 1955. A new hypothesis for the asynchronous ovulatory cycle of the domestic hen (*Gallus domesticus*). *Poultry Sci.* **34**: 776–788.

10. Bellerby, C. W. 1934. A rapid test for the diagnosis of pregnancy. *Nature* **133**: 494–495.

11. Benson, G. K., and Folley, S. J. 1956. Oxytocin as stimulator for the release of prolactin from the anterior pituitary. *Nature* **177**: 700.

12. Bogdanove, E. M., and Schoen, H. C. 1959. Precocious sexual development in female rats with hypothalamic lesions. *Proc. Soc. Exptl. Biol. Med.* **100**: 664–669.

13. Bradbury, J. T., Brown, E. S., and Brown, .W. E. 1949. Adsorption of urinary gonadotrophins on kaolin. *Proc. Soc. Exptl. Biol. Med.* **71**: 228.

14. Breneman, W. R. 1942. Action of prolactin and estrone on weights of reproductive organs and viscera of cockerel. *Endocrinology* **30**: 609–615.

15. Brown, P. S. 1955. The assay of gonadotrophin from urine of non-pregnant human subjects. *J. Endocrinol.* **13**: 59–64.

16. Cole, H. H., and Hart, G. H. 1930. The potency of blood serum of mares in progressive stages of pregnancy in effecting the sexual maturity of the immature rat. *Am. J. Physiol.* **93**: 57–68.

17. Cowie, A. T., and Folley, S. J. 1955. Physiology of the gonadotropins and the lactogenic hormone, *in* "The Hormones" (G. Pincus and K. V. Thimann, eds.), Vol. 3, pp. 309–387. Academic Press, New York.

18. Cowie, A. T., and Folley, S. J. 1961. The mammary gland and lactation, *in* "Sex and Internal Secretion" (W. C. Young, ed.), Vol. 1, pp. 590–642. Williams & Wilkins, Baltimore, Maryland.

19. Davies, J., Amoroso, E. C., and Dempsey, E. W. 1959. The subplacenta of the guinea pig. *Anat. Record* **133**: 266.

20. De Groot, J. 1959. The rat forebrain in sterotaxic coordinates. *Verhandel. Koninkl. Ned. Akad. Wetenschap.* **52**: 1–40. (Library of Congress Call Number 611.81-G876r-1959.)

21. Doggett, V. C. 1956. Periodicity in the fecundity of male rabbits. *Am. J. Physiol.* **187**: 445–450.

22. Elwers, M., and Critchlow, V. 1960. Precocious ovarian stimulation following hypothalamic and amygdaloid lesions in rats. *Am. J. Physiol.* **198**: 381–385.

23. Evans, H. M., and Simpson, M. E. 1950. Physiology of the gonadotrophins, *in* "The Hormones" (G. Pincus and K. V. Thimann, eds.), Vol. 2, pp. 351–404. Academic Press, New York.

24. Evans, H. M., Simpson, M. E., Lyons, W. R., and Turpeinen, K. 1941. Anterior pituitary hormones which favor the production of traumatic uterine placentomata. *Endocrinology* **28**: 933–945.

25. Evans, H. M., Simpson, M. E., Tolksdorf, S., and Jensen, H. 1939. Biologic studies of the gonadotropic principles in sheep pituitary substance. *Endocrinology* **25**: 529–546.

26. Everett, J. W. 1954. Luteotrophic function of autografts of the rat hypophysis. *Endocrinology* **54**: 685–690.

27. Everett, J. W. 1956. Functional corpora lutea maintained for months by auto-grafts of rat hypophyses. *Endocrinology* **58**: 786–796.
28. Everett, J. W. 1956. The time of release of ovulating hormone from the rat hypophysis. *Endocrinology* **59**: 580–585.
29. Everett, J. W. 1961. The mammalian reproductive cycle and its controlling mechanisms. *in* "Sex and Internal Secretion" (W. C. Young, ed.), Vol. I, pp. 497–555. Williams & Wilkins, Baltimore, Maryland.
30. Everett, J. W. 1961. The preoptic region of the brain and its relation to ovulation, *in* "Control of Ovulation" (C. A. Villee, ed.), pp. 101–121. Pergamon Press, New York.
31. Everett, J. W., and Sawyer, C. H. 1949. A neural timing factor in the mechanism by which progesterone advances ovulation in the cyclic rat. *Endocrinology* **45**: 581–595.
32. Flerkó, B., and Szentágothai, J. 1957. Oestrogen sensitive nervous structures in the hypothalamus. *Acta Endocrinol.* **26**: 121–127.
33. Frank, R. T., and Berman, R. L. 1941. A twenty-four hour pregnancy test. *Am. J. Obstet. Gynecol.* **42**: 492–496.
34. Fraps, R. M. 1954. Neural basis of diurnal periodicity in release of ovulation-inducing hormone in fowl. *Proc. Natl. Acad. Sci.* (*U. S.*) **40**: 348–356.
35. Fraps, R. M. 1961. Ovulation in the domestic fowl, *in* "Control of Ovulation" (C. A. Villee, ed.), pp. 133–162. Pergamon Press, New York.
36. Fried, P. H., and Rakoff, A. E. 1952. The effects of chorionic gonadotropin and of prolactin on the maintenance of corpus luteum function. *J. Clin. Endocrinol. Metab.* **12**: 321–337.
37. Friedman, M. H. 1929. Effect of injections of urine from pregnant women on ovary of the rabbit. *Proc. Soc. Exptl. Biol. Med.* **26**: 720–721.
38. Friedman, M. H., and Lapham, M. E. 1931. A simple, rapid procedure for the laboratory diagnosis of early pregnancies. *Am. J. Obstet. Gynecol.* **21**: 405–410.
39. Galli-Mainini, C. 1947. Pregnancy test using the male toad. *J. Clin. Endocrinol. Metab.* **7**: 653–657.
40. Galli-Mainini, C. 1948. Pregnancy test with male batrachia. *Endocrinology* **43**: 349–350.
41. Gellert, R. J., and Ganong, W. F. 1960. Precocious puberty in rats with hypothalamic lesions. *Acta Endocrinol.* **33**: 569–576.
42. Gorski, R. A., and Barraclough, C. 1962. Adenohypophyseal LH content in normal, androgen-sterilized and progesterone-primed sterile female rats. *Acta Endocrinol.* **39**: 13–27.
43. Greep, R. O. 1961. Physiology of the anterior hypophysis in relation to reproduction, *in* "Sex and Internal Secretion" (W. C. Young, ed.), Vol. I, pp. 240–301. Williams & Wilkins, Baltimore, Maryland.
44. Greep, R. O., and Fevold, H. L. 1937. The spermatogenic and secretory function of the gonads of hypophysectomized adult rats treated with pituitary FSH and LH. *Endocrinology* **21**: 611–618.
45. Greep, R. O., Fevold, H. L., and Hisaw, F. L. 1936. Effects of two hypophyseal gonadotropic hormones on the reproductive system of the male rat. *Anat. Record* **65**: 261–271.
46. Greep, R. O., van Dyke, H. B., and Chow, B. F. 1940. The effect of pituitary gonadotropins on the testicles of hypophysectomized immature rats. *Anat. Record* **78**: 88.

47. Greep, R. O., van Dyke, H. B., and Chow, B. F. 1941. Use of anterior lobe of prostate gland in the assay of metakentrin. *Proc. Soc. Exptl. Biol. Med.* **46:** 644–649.

48. Greep, R. O., van Dyke, H. B., and Chow, B. F. 1942. Gonadotropins of the swine pituitary. I. Various biological effects of purified thylakentrin (FSH) and pure metakentrin (ICSH). *Endocrinology* **30:** 635–649.

49. Greer, M. A. 1953. The effect of progesterone on persistent vaginal estrus produced by hypothalamic lesions in the rat. *Endocrinology* **53:** 380–390.

50. Grosvenor, C. E., and Turner, C. W. 1958. Assay of lactogenic hormone. *Endocrinology* **63:** 530–534.

51. Hall, C. E., and Hall, O. 1956. On the nature of parabiosis intoxication: shock as the precipitating cause. *J. Exptl. Med.* **103:** 263–272.

52. Hamburger, C. 1950. Gonadotropins, *in* "Hormone Assay" (C. W. Emmens, ed.), pp. 173–203. Academic Press, New York.

53. Harris, G. W. 1955. "Neural Control of the Pituitary Gland," pp. 60–102. Arnold, London.

54. Harris, G. W. 1961. The Pituitary Stalk and Ovulation, *in* "Control of Ovulation" (C. A. Villee, ed.), pp. 56–78. Pergamon Press, New York.

55. Heller, C. G., and Chandler, R. E. 1942. Gonadotropic hormone: modification of the alcohol-precipitation assay method. *J. Clin. Endocrinol.* **2:** 252–253.

56. Hill, R. T. 1932. Blood exchange and hormonic reaction in parabiotic rats. *J. Exptl. Zool.* **63:** 203–234.

57. Johnson, H. W., Poshyachinda, D., McCormick, G., and Hamblen, E. C. 1960. Lactation with a phenothiazine derivative (Temaril). *Am. J. Obstet. Gynecol.* **80:** 124–127.

58. Kawakami, M., and Sawyer, C. H. 1959. Neuroendocrine correlates of changes in brain activity thresholds by sex steroids and pituitary hormones. *Endocrinology* **65:** 652–668.

59. Klinefelter, H. F., Albright, F., and Griswold, G. C. 1943. Experience with quantitative test for normal or decreased amounts of follicle stimulating hormone in urine in endocrinological diagnosis. *J. Clin. Endocrinol.* **3:** 529–544.

60. Lyons, W. R. 1942. The direct mammotrophic action of lactogenic hormone. *Proc. Soc. Exptl. Biol. Med.* **51:** 308–311.

61. Lyons, W. R., Li, C. H., and Johnson, R. E. 1958. The hormonal control of mammary growth and lactation. *Recent Progr. Hormone Res.* **14:** 219–254.

62. Lyons, W. R., and Page, E. 1935. Detection of mammotropin in the urine of lactating women. *Proc. Soc. Exptl. Biol. Med.* **32:** 1049–1050.

63. Meites, J., and Sgouris, J. T. 1953. Can the ovarian hormones inhibit the mammary response to prolactin? *Endocrinology* **53:** 17–23.

64. Meites, J., and Sgouris, J. T. 1954. Effects of altering the balance between prolactin and ovarian hormones on initiation of lactation in rabbits. *Endocrinology* **55:** 530–534.

65. Moore, W. W., and Nalbandov, A. V. 1955. Maintenance of corpora lutea in sheep with lactogenic hormone. *J. Endocrinol.* **13:** 18–25.

66. Nalbandov, A. V. 1959. Neuroendocrine reflex mechanisms: Bird ovulation, *in* "Comparative Endocrinology" (A. Gorbman, ed.), pp. 161–173. Wiley, New York.

67. Nalbandov, A. V., Moore, W. W., and Norton, H. W. 1955. Further studies on the neurogenic control of the estrous cycle by uterine distention. *Endocrinology* **56:** 225–231.

68. Nikitovitch-Winer, M., and Everett, J. 1958. Comparative study of luteo-trophin secretion by hypophyseal autotransplants in the rat. Effects of site and stages of the estrous cycle. *Endocrinology* **62**: 522–532.

69. Opel, H., and Nalbandov, A. V. 1961. Follicular growth and ovulation in hypophysectomized hens. *Endocrinology* **69**: 1016–1028.

70. Opel, H., and Nalbandov, A. V. 1961. Ovulability of ovarian follicles in the hypophysectomized hen. *Endocrinology* **69**: 1029–1035.

71. Parkes, A. S., and Bruce, H. M. 1961. Olfactory stimuli in mammalian repro-duction. *Science* **134**: 1049–1054.

72. Parlow, A. F. 1958. A rapid bioassay method for LH and factors stimulating LH secretion. *Federation Proc.* **17**: 402.

·73. Parlow, A. F. 1961. Bioassay of pituitary luteinizing hormone by depletion of ovarian ascorbic acid, *in* "Human Pituitary Gonadotropins" (A. Albert, ed.), pp. 300–310. Thomas, Springfield, Illinois.

74. Riddle, O., Bates, R. W., and Dykshorn, S. W. 1933. The preparation, identi-fication and assay of prolactin—a hormone of the anterior pituitary. *Am. J. Physiol.* **105**: 191–216.

75. Robbins, S. L., and Parker, F., Jr. 1948. The use of the male North American frog (*Rana pipiens*) in the diagnosis of pregnancy. *Endocrinology* **42**: 237–243.

76. Rothchild, I. 1960. The corpus luteum—pituitary relationship: The associa-tion between the cause of luteotrophin secretion and the cause of follicular quiescence during lactation; the basis for a tentative theory of the corpus luteum-pituitary relationship in the rat. *Endocrinology* **67**: 9–41.

77. Rothchild, I., and Koh, N. K. 1951. The effects of a single preovulatory injec-tion of progesterone on indices of ovulation in women. *J. Clin. Endocrinol. Metab.* **11**: 789–790.

78. Rowan, W. 1925. Relation of light to bird migration and developmental changes. *Nature* **115**: 494–495.

79. Sammelwitz, P. H., Aldred, J. P., and Nalbandov, A. V. 1961. Mechanisms of maintenance of corpora lutea in pigs and rats. *J. Reprod. Fertility* **2**: 387–393.

80. Sawyer, C. H., and Kawakami, M. 1961. Interactions between the central nervous system and hormones influencing ovulation, *in* "Control of Ovula-tion" (C. A. Villee, ed.), pp. 79–100. Pergamon Press, New York.

81. Scheff, G. J., and Plagge, J. C. 1955. Use of fluorescein in testing the union of parabiotic rats. *Proc. Soc. Exptl. Biol. Med.* **88**: 559–561.

82. Schwartz, N. B., and Bartosik, D. 1962. Changes in pituitary LH content dur-ing the rat estrous cycle. *Endocrinology* **71**: 756–762.

83. Segal, S. J. 1957. Response of weaver finch to chorionic gonadotrophin and hypophyseal luteinizing hormone. *Science* **126**: 1242–1243.

84. Shapiro, H. A., and Zwarenstein, H. A. 1934. A rapid test for pregnancy on *Xenopus laevis*. *Nature* **133**: 762.

85. Simpson, M. E., Evans, H. M., and Li, C. H. 1950. Effect of pure FSH alone or in combination with chorionic gonadotropin in hypophysectomized rats of either sex. *Anat. Record* **106**: 247–248.

86. Simpson, M. E., Li, C. H., and Evans, H. M. 1942. Biological properties of pituitary interstitial cell-stimulating hormone (ICSH). *Endocrinology* **30**: 969–976.

87. Simpson, M. E., Li, C. H., and Evans, H. M. 1951. Synergism between pituitary follicle-stimulating hormone (FSH) and human chorionic gonadotropin (HCG). *Endocrinology* **48:** 370–383.

88. Smith, P. E., and White, W. E. 1931. The effect of hypophysectomy on ovulation and corpus luteum formation in the rabbit. *J. Am. Med. Assoc.* **97:** 1861–1863.

89. Steelman, S. L., and Pohley, F. M. 1953. Assay of the follicle-stimulating hormone based on the augmentation with human chorionic gonadotropin. *Endocrinology* **53:** 604–616.

90. Tanaka, A. 1955. A simple method of hypophysectomy on rats. *Shionogi Kenkyushi Nempo,* No. 5, p. 678.

91. Van Dyke, D. C., Simpson, M. E., Lepkovsky, S., Koneff, A. A., and Brobeck, J. R. 1956. Hypothalamic control of pituitary function and corpus luteum formation in the rat. *Proc. Soc. Exptl. Biol. Med.* **95:** 1–5.

92. van Tienhoven, A. 1961. Endocrinology of reproduction in birds, *in* "Sex and Internal Secretion" (W. C. Young, ed.), Vol 2, pp. 1088–1169. Williams & Wilkins, Baltimore, Maryland.

93. Weisman, A. I., and Coates, C. W. 1940. The frog test (*Xenopus laevis*) as a rapid diagnostic test for early pregnancy. *Endocrinology* **28:** 141–142.

93a. Wide, L. 1962. An immunological method for the assay of human chorionic gonadotrophin. *Acta Endocrinol. Suppl.* **70:** 1–111.

94. Wiltberger, P. D., and Miller, D. F. 1948. The male frog, *Rana pipiens,* as a new test animal for early pregnancy. *Science* **107:** 198.

95. Witschi, E. 1940. The quantitative determination of follicle-stimulating and luteinizing hormones in mammalian pituitaries and a discussion of the gonadotropic quotient, F/L. *Endocrinology* **27:** 437–446.

96. Wolfson, A. 1959. Ecologic and physiologic factors in the regulation of spring migration and reproductive cycles in birds, *in* "Comparative Endocrinology" (A. Gorbman, ed.), pp. 38–70. Wiley, New York.

97. Zarrow, M. X., Caldwell, A. L., Hafez, E. S. E., and Pincus, G. 1958. Superovulation in the immature rat as a possible assay for LH and HCG. *Endocrinology* **63:** 748–758.

98. Zarrow, M. X., and Wilson, E. D. 1961. The influence of age on superovulation in the immature rat and mouse. *Endocrinology* **69:** 851–855.

CHAPTER 11

Oxytocin, Vasopressin, and Melanocyte Stimulating Hormone

Part A. Hormones of the Neurohypophysis: Oxytocin and Vasopressin

The hypophysis of most vertebrates has been arbitrarily divided into two major structures on the basis of embryological origin: the adenohypophysis (sometimes referred to as the anterior pituitary gland) and the neurohypophysis (sometimes called the posterior pituitary gland). The neurohypophysis is intimately related to the central nervous system in that (a) the infundibular process arises from nervous tissue, (b) the gland remains attached to the hypothalamus throughout life by means of the infundibular stalk, and (c) in all probability the two hormones, oxytocin and vasopressin, are formed in certain nuclei of the hypothalamus.

Sites of Hormone Formation

The neurohypophysis develops in the embryo from the floor of the third ventricle of the diencephalon. In contrast, the pars anterior and pars intermedia originate from the roof of the buccal cavity (Rathke's pouch). The complex of tissues that comprise the neurohypophysis, i.e., the median eminence, infundibular stalk, and infundibular process, are all derivations of the hypothalamus and are functionally connected with it via several neural pathways.

Three major components comprise the organization of the posterior lobe of the pituitary gland: capillaries, derived from the inferior hypophyseal arteries, as the major vascular supply; pituicytes, modified glial cells, which may contain refractile granules; and unmyelinated nerve fibers, which originate primarily from the supraoptic and paraventricular nuclei of the hypothalamus and course into the posterior lobe as the hypothalamohypophyseal tract. The secretions of the posterior pituitary gland are thought to originate from these nuclei of the hypothalamus. Experiments in which lesions are placed in the areas of the supraoptic and paraventricular nuclei (Fig. 10-3), or across the hypothalamohypophyseal tract have been shown to impair the function of the posterior pituitary gland (29). Conversely, stimulation of the infundibular stalk or the hypothalamus results in increased hormonal activity (3, 11, 12, 29). Histological observations have disclosed that neurosecretory material accumulates at the proximal end of the cut pituitary stalk (5, 47), and extracts of hypothalamus and tuber cinereum have been shown to have vasopressor and oxytocic activity. Thus, the production of the neurohypophyseal hormones is believed to occur in the hypothalamus (17, 29). The hormones are thought to travel down the hypothalamohypophyseal tract to the posterior lobe, where they are stored or released. Table 11–1 lists the relative distribution of oxytocin and vasopression between the hypothalamus and posterior lobe as determined by extraction and assay of these tissues (66).

TABLE 11–1
DISTRIBUTION OF OXYTOCIN AND VASOPRESSIN BETWEEN
THE HYPOTHALAMUS AND POSTERIOR LOBE[a]

	Vasopressin		Oxytocin	
Ani al	Hypothalamus (%)	Posterior lobe (%)	Hypothalamus (%)	Posterior lobe (%)
Dog	15–20	80–85	2–8	92–97
Camel	0.4	99	1.2	98
Ox	0.2	99	0.3	99
Hog	0.5	99	0.5	99
Rat	3.0	97	1.0	99
Monkey	0.4	99	—	99
Man	0.7–1.7	98	2.5	97

[a] Data taken from van Dyke et al. (66).

Nature of the Neurohypophyseal Hormones

The hormones of the neurohypophysis are cyclic octapeptides of molecular weight of about 1000 and are very similar to each other in structure. In most vertebrates, two hormones are found, one containing primarily oxytocic activity and the other primarily the vasopressor and antidiuretic (ADH) action. In those nonmammalian vertebrates tested, a single compound, containing antidiuretic activity has been identified and found to consist of an amino acid sequence similar to both oxytocin and vasopressin. This structure has been termed arginine vasotocin (17, 54, 55). The amino acid sequences of oxytocin and vasopressin, determined by du Vigneaud *et al.* (18, 19) in 1953, have since been synthesized; several analogs, which also are active, have been prepared. Figure 11-1 depicts the amino acid sequences of oxytocin, two varieties of vasopressin, and vasotocin.

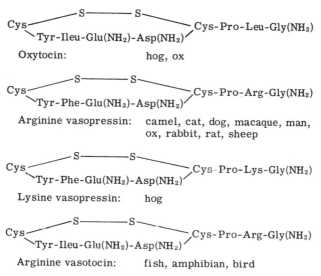

Fig. 11-1. The neurohypophyseal hormones: amino acid sequences.

Protein or polypeptide molecules of non-pituitary origin have also been found to possess oxytocic and vasopressor activity (13). Several such preparations and their respective properties are listed in Table 11–2.

Action of the Neurohypophyseal Hormones

Four major actions are ascribed to the hormones of the posterior pituitary gland. These are: (a) increase in contractility of the uterus, (b) milk ejection from the mammary gland, (c) water retention and electrolyte balance, and (d) vasopressor or depressor activity. Each of these activities is used as a parameter for the bioassay of oxytocic and vasopressor substances.

A. The Uterus

Oxytocin has a powerful contracting action on the uterus, both

TABLE 11–2

POLYPEPTIDES THAT EXHIBIT OXYTOCIC AND VASOPRESSOR ACTIVITY

Polypeptide	Source	Activity		
		Oxytocic	Vasopressor (VP) Vasodepressor (VD)	ADH
Bradykinin	Tryptic or snake venom digestion of blood serum or hypertensinogen	+	VD	
Pepsitensin	Digestion of hypertensinogen with pepsin	+	VP	
Pepsanurin	Peptic hydrolysis of residue left after conversion of hypertensinogen to hypertensin	+	−	+
Hypertensin	Digestion of blood serum by products of ischemic kidney	+	VP	+
Pepsitocin	Peptic hydrolysis of hypertensinogen	+	−	+
Kallidin	Enzymatic action of kallikrein on α-globulin fraction of serum	+		

in vivo and *in vitro*. This was first shown by H. H. Dale in 1909, who obtained stimulation of the smooth musculature *in vitro* with whole extracts of the posterior lobe (15). The response of the uterus is most striking in the animal primed with estrogen or in natural estrus. In the ovariectomized animal, or in animals during pregnancy or pseudo-pregnancy when the uterus is under progestogen domination, oxytocin is less effective (38, 56). From the second to the twenty-ninth day of gestation in the rabbit (the period corresponding to the time of progestogen domination) the threshold of the uterus to oxytocin increases 100-fold, but as the uterus becomes dominated by estrogen at the end of pregnancy, minimal doses of oxytocin can elicit the contractile response (60). This reaction, as observed in the rabbit, has been suggested as a bioassay of oxytocic substances (7, 24). The uterus of the human being responds similarly, but not in such a striking manner.

Oxytocin has been shown to cause a decrease in the membrane potential of the uterus of the parturient rabbit (41, 42). This action potentiates a train of discharges that result in a contraction of the myometrium. The response may be related to the concentration of extracellular calcium. Progesterone, administered at the end of pregnancy in the rabbit (and other mammals), inhibits the action of oxytocin on uterine contractility.

That a neurohumoral reflex arc exists for the release of oxytocin has been demonstrated by experiments in which uterine contractions are observed after various stimuli, including mating, manipulation of the external genitalia, mechanical stimulation of the uterine cervix by stretching or tapping, or electrical stimulation of the neurohypophysis. The response (uterine contraction) is abolished after posterior lobectomy, neurectomy of the region stimulated, spinal section, or anesthesia (20). The same neurohumoral arc has been definitely established for milk let-down (see Section B, Mammary Gland).

The action of vasopressin on the uterus is slight. Some effect has been observed in the cow late in pregnancy. In the nonpregnant and early pregnant human being, vasopressin may elicit uterine contractions, but the response may be a result of ischemia produced by vasoconstriction. Other substances which effect uterine contractions under specific conditions are epinephrine, norepinephrine, acetylcholine, and 5-hydroxytryptamine (26).

B. Mammary Gland

In the mammary gland that is actively secreting milk, oxytocin will cause the ejection of milk from the alveoli by effecting a contraction of the myoepithelial cells around each alveolus. The action can be evoked either by injection of the hormone, by stimulation of the hypothalamus, or by manipulation of the nipples of the mammae (3, 10–12, 20). Thus, a neural arc has been shown to exist for milk ejection in the lactating mother. The suckling stimulus activates the hypothalamus via an afferent pathway and causes the eventual release of oxytocin by the posterior pituitary gland. The reflex can be conditioned. Inhibition of the reflex is effected by local or general anesthesia, lesions in the hypothalamus, posterior hypophysectomy, fear, stressors, or release or injection of epinephrine. The inhibition effected by any of these means is overcome by the administration of oxytocin.

Other stimuli known to cause oxytocin release and milk ejection are mating; manipulation of the vulva, cervix, or uterus (goat and cow); labor (human being); and intracarotid injection of hypertonic saline. Pure vasopressin contains about 0.2 the activity of pure oxytocin when measured by the milk ejection assay in the rabbit.

The action of oxytocin on the mammary gland is evident only in the gland that is actively secreting milk; hence, its action is primarily on milk let-down (ejection) rather than on milk synthesis or secretion. The latter process, also under hormonal regulation, requires a rather delicate balance in secretions from the pituitary, ovary, thyroid, adrenal, pancreas, and parathyroid glands, as well as proper nutritional requirements.

There is some evidence to indicate that oxytocin may be involved in the release of prolactin from the pituitary gland, and thus indirectly participate in the regulation of milk secretion (50). However, these reports have not been confirmed (57).

C. THE KIDNEY AND INTEGUMENT

The antidiuretic action of vasopressin may possibly be elicited at three sites in the kidney: the descending loop of Henle, the distal convoluted tubule, and the collecting duct of the nephron (68). The hormone promotes the reabsorption of water from the kidney unit to the vasculature (and possibly the excretion of sodium and potassium), thus concentrating the urine and aiding in the maintenance of normal osmotic conditions. Removal of the posterior pituitary gland, or appropriately placed lesions in the hypothalamus or pituitary stalk, may result in severe permanent diuresis (diabetes insipidus). In the human being, the excretion of 10–20 liters of urine per day occurs after total destruction of the posterior pituitary gland by tumor or extirpation. The clinical signs of this disorder, known as diabetes insipidus, include polyuria, followed by polydipsia, and can be treated by administration of extracts of posterior pituitary gland or synthetic vasopressin.

That the control of the release of the antidiuretic hormone (ADH, vasopressin) is elicited by changes in osmotic pressure of the blood has been shown by experiments in which large volumes of water are injected into the general circulation, or hypertonic saline injected into the hypothalamus (3). In the former case, a water diuresis occurs until the injected volume of liquid is excreted; in the latter instance, antidiuresis and polydipsia, followed by polyuria may be observed. The polydipsia may occur as a result of stimulation of a specific thirst center; the polyuria follows as the ADH homeostatic mechanism is activated.

Removal of the anterior pituitary gland along with the posterior hypophysis ameliorates the symptoms of diabetes insipidus. However, if an extract of the anterior pituitary gland is administered, diabetes insipidus reappears. This phenomenon may be due to a return of the animal to a good metabolic state by the replacement therapy, not to a specific diuretic principle in the pars distalis. Administration of thyroid hormone increases the severity of diabetes insipidus.

The release of vasopressin from the pars nervosa is inhibited after administration of hydrocortisone-like steroids, epinephrine, or alcohol and after exposure to cold. Stressors, adrenal steroids, acetylcholine, morphine, barbiturates, nicotine, yohimbine, and ether stimulate the release of vasopressin from the posterior lobe (67). The water-loaded rat, under alcohol anesthesia, and the trained, unanesthetized, hydrated dog have been used as assay animals for substances possessing anti-diuretic activity.

The integument of some amphibians, known to participate in the regulation of salt and water balance in these animals, has been shown to be sensitive to vasopressin and oxytocin (6, 25, 32, 58, 63, 64). Administration of posterior pituitary extracts to frogs produces absorption and retention of water, measurable by an increase in weight of the animal. Presumably, the mechanism of action of vasopressin in this instance is similar to its action on the kidney of higher vertebrates. Pure oxytocin shows relatively little antidiuretic activity, and in fact may cause diuresis under certain conditions (21, 22).

D. The Smooth Muscle of the Vasculature

An increase in blood pressure of mammals is observed after stimulation of the posterior lobe of the hypophysis, injection of vasopressin, or stimulation of appropriate areas of the hypothalamus. The effect observed is a result of the action of vasopressin on the smooth musculature of the arteries and arterioles. After administration of a moderate dose of vasopressin, a preliminary rise in blood pressure is observed followed by a transient fall, and finally a sustained rise. The transient decrease in pressure is a result of a decreased cardiac output which occurs after temporary constriction of the coronary arteries. Larger doses of vasopressin mask the cardiac effect on blood pressure. Repeated administration of the hormone results in a tachyphylaxis or refractoriness, evidenced by a gradual decrease in the maximum response. Large doses of vasopressin constrict the afferent vessels of the renal corpuscle, thus reducing the blood flow through the kidney and subsequent urine formation. The pressor response of the dog and rat have been used as parameters for bioassay of vasopressin-like extracts.

Oxytocin has a very slight but definite effect on the blood pressure of mammals. However, in the bird, there is observed a decrease in pressure after administration of the oxytocic hormone (9). The vasodepressor response in the bird has been utilized as an assay for oxytocic substances. Vasopressin is about one-sixth as potent as oxytocin in this respect.

Many substances are known to effect changes in blood pressure and may therefore interfere with assays based upon pressor responses. Ergot alkaloids, epinephrine and norepinephrine, acetylcholine, sympatho- and parasympathomimetics, and tranquilizers are but a few.

E. OTHER ACTIONS OF THE POSTERIOR PITUITARY HORMONES

Extracts of posterior pituitary gland or its purified hormones have been shown under special conditions to: (a) increase sodium, potassium, and chloride excretion; (b) stimulate contraction of smooth muscle of intestine; (c) cause hyperglycemia and glycosuria and a decrease in liver glycogen; (d) cause a decrease in metabolic rate; (e) cause oviposition in the bird; (f) induce the spawning reflex in certain fish.

The Assay of Posterior Pituitary Hormones

Several bioassays have been developed for the measure of oxytocin and vasopressin (65). For oxytocic activity, measures of blood pressure

TABLE 11–3
SENSITIVITY OF VARIOUS ASSAYS FOR OXYTOCIN AND VASOPRESSIN

Assay	Potency[a]		Sensitivity	References
	Oxytocin	Vasopressin		
Rat uterus, *in vitro*	500	30	0.1–1.0 mU/ml (oxytocin)	(20, (26), (65)
Avian depression, iv	500	85	100 mU (oxytocin)	(9)
Milk ejection, rabbit, iv	500	100	0.5–2.0 mU (oxytocin) 3–10 mU (vasopressin)	(65)
Isometric contraction of mammary gland, rabbit, *in vitro*	—	—	0.1–0.5 mU/ml (oxytocin)	(53)
Pressor, rat, iv	7	600	4 mU (vasopressin) 300 mU (oxytocin)	(65)
Antidiuresis, dog, iv	3	600	0.25 mU (vasopressin) 50 mU (oxytocin)	(65)
Antidiuresis, mouse, iv	—	—	0.01 mU (vasopressin)	(33)
Antidiuresis, rat, iv	—	—	0.01 mU (vasopressin)	(2), (16), (27)
Antidiuresis, rabbit, iv	—	—	0.1 mU (vasopressin)	(48)

[a] USP units per milligram of pure hormone.

depression of the chicken, uterine contractility, mammary gland contraction, milk ejection, and parturition have been used. Vasopressin activity has been measured by elevation of blood pressure and by its antidiuretic action in various mammals. Since methods for high degree of purification and for artificial synthesis of the hormones have been developed, an accurate estimation of the potency of the pure hormones is now possible. Table 11–3 lists several of the bioassays for oxytocin and arginine vasopressin, the respective potencies of the pure hormones when measured by several of the assays listed, and the sensitivities of the assay procedures. The International Unit is equivalent to 0.5 mg of the standard powdered posterior pituitary gland, assayed by the avian depressor method for oxytocin, but applicable to antidiuretic and pressor activity also. Lysine vasopressin is about half as active as arginine vasopressin.

None of the assays are absolutely specific for either hormone, and thus some of the assays are not tenable when tissues containing high concentrations of the "contaminating" hormone are used. The guinea pig uterus has been used as an assay for oxytocin (instead of rat), and the pressor effect of vasopressin has been assayed in dogs and cats.

Biogenesis, Metabolism, and Mechanism of Action

It had originally been suggested that both of the posterior pituitary hormones might be produced in the neural lobe as a single large molecule or as a pair of molecules. Release of the hormones into the circulation was thought to be controlled by neurons from the hypothalamus. Presently, it is believed that both hormones of the pars nervosa are synthesized in the nerve cells of certain nuclei of the hypothalamus, either as the hormone or a precursor. These substances, in conjunction with a protein carrier, travel down the axons of the supraopticohypophyseal tract to the posterior lobe, where they are stored. Both oxytocin and vasopressin have been found in the area of the supraoptic and paraventricular nuclei of the hypothalamus, and stainable, secretory material thought to be the protein carrier of the two hormones has been observed in secretory neurons and in the axons of the hypothalamo-hypophyseal tract. It is also possible that changes in the hormones could occur in the axon and posterior lobe. Both hormones appear to be bound to the same protein carrier in the neural lobe (4, 14).

The forms in which the hormones are released into the blood and in which they circulate are not known. In most mammals the hormones are released simultaneously, but not in equimolar concentrations. Stimuli which effect release of oxytocin also cause release of vasopressin. The hormones may circulate as the "free" form or perhaps bound to plasma proteins (35), as are other hormones, e.g., the steroids and thyroxine. Oxytocin and vasopressin are inactivated by blood and by homogenates of such tissues as the small intestine, liver, or kidney. Inactivation in the normal animal may be accomplished in the liver or kidney. An enzyme "oxytocinase," obtained from the blood of pregnant women and from placentas, has been shown to inactivate oxytocin (8, 17). The concentration of this enzyme is relatively high during late pregnancy, reaching maximum levels prior to parturition (8).

Evidence suggests that the posterior pituitary hormones are excreted in the urine as substances of rather large molecular weight (1). The methods used to obtain these substances from urine are not effective for material with molecular weights around 1000.

The mechanisms of action of oxytocin and vasopressin are, at best, vaguely understood. In the uterus of the rabbit, it has been shown that a deficiency in calcium results in a lowering of the membrane potential and a depolarization of the membrane of the myometrial cell. Under these conditions, action potentials, and thus myometrial contractions, are abolished and cannot be restored by administration of oxytocin. The presence of trace amounts of the ion restores the actions of oxytocin on uterine contractility. However, under these conditions, the posterior pituitary hormone causes an *increase* in the potential of the membrane and the appearance of action potentials. The parturient and postparturient uterus of the rabbit in a normal ionic environment reacts to oxytocin by a *decrease* in the membrane potential, an increase in action potentials, and a wave of contractile activity. When the uterus is perfused with progesterone, the discharges of action potentials are abolished, the membrane potential increases slightly, and oxytocin is ineffective. In this system, it requires a longer time to render the uterus calcium free, a result suggesting that progesterone may bind the ion to the membrane. Thus, it appears that oxytocic activity may be dependent upon environmental calcium concentration and the presence and maintenance of a membrane potential at a level which can respond to the hormone (14, 28, 41, 42, 51, 52). Presumably, a similar type of activity might be postulated for the effect of the hormone on the myoepithelial cell of the mammary gland.

The mechanism of action of vasopressin on the kidney is thought by some investigators to be based on an ability of the hormone to increase the pore size of the renal tubule and thus allow passive transfer of water back into circulation (68). Evidence has been gathered in amphibians to suggest that this is the mechanism of action in the skin of these animals. Some investigators believe that the sites of action of the hormone are the descending limb, distal convoluted tubule, and collecting ducts. Other workers feel that antidiuretic action is confined to the distal segment of the nephron (59). Studies using the toad bladder indicate that an interaction of the —S—S—bonds of ADH with the —SH bonds of the tissue may be involved in a mechanism of action of the hormone in water resorption.

Part B. Hormones of the Intermediate Lobe of the Pituitary Gland: Melanocyte Stimulating Hormone (MSH)

The intermediate lobe of the pituitary gland is, in fact, derived from the adenohypophysis. Embryologically, the pars intermedia develops from Rathke's pouch rather than from the base of the diencephalon, which is the source of neurohypophyseal elements. The secretions of the pars intermedia, α- and β-MSH, are structurally related to hormones produced by the anterior lobe of the hypophysis.

Sites of Formation of MSH

The pars intermedia varies in the mammals from almost complete anatomic obscurity (whale) to a well defined tissue mass (mouse). The tissue is composed of all three main types of cells common to the anterior lobe, acidophils, basophils, and chromophobes; however, one or another of these cell types may predominate in different species. Secretory granules may be evident. In some species (man), vesicles that contain colloid may be present. Nerve fibers arising from the hypothalamus may permeate the substance of the intermedia. The tissue does not contain a rich vascular network.

Nature of the Hormones of the Pars Intermedia

The melanocyte stimulating hormones, α- and β-MSH (older terminology: melanophore expanding hormone, intermedin, chromatophorotropin, substance "B") are polypeptides remarkably similar to a portion of the ACTH molecule (30, 31). Figure 11-2 depicts the structures of

	1	2	3	4	5	6	7	8	9	10	11	12	13	14	⋯	39
α-MSH (pig)		R-Ser	Tyr-Ser	Met-Glu	-His	-Phe-Arg-Try-Gly	Lys	Pro	Val							
β-MSH (pig)	Asp-Glu -Gly -Pro	Tyr-Lys	Met-Glu	-His	-Phe-Arg-Try-Gly	Ser	Pro	Pro-Lys-Asp								
ACTH (pig)		Ser	Tyr-Ser	Met-Glu	-His	-Phe-Arg-Try-Gly	Lys	Pro	Val -Gly	⋯	Phe					

Fig. 11-2. Structures of α- and β-MSH in comparison with that of ACTH.

these hormones in comparison with ACTH. The structure of β-MSH varies slightly in different species.

Action of MSH

The classical effect of MSH is observed most readily in lower vertebrates. The hormone causes a dispersion of the melanin granules in melanocytes of the skin of fish, amphibians, and reptiles, with a resulting darkening of the skin (46). Both α- and β-MSH are effective; α-MSH is about two to five times as potent as β-MSH. In mammals, melanin dispersion is not as obvious, although the action has been noted (45). MSH also causes an increase in melanin synthesis (23).

The action of MSH on pigment dispersion in lower forms is evidenced in amphibians adapted to light or dark environments. The frog, adapted to a light environment, exhibits a lightening of the skin. Microscopically, the melanin granules of the melanocytes are aggregated at the center of the pigment cell in this animal (34). Darkening of the skin consists in a dispersion of the granules throughout the cell and occurs when the animal is placed in a dark environment or injected with MSH (Fig. 11-3). The hypophysectomized animal does not adapt when placed in

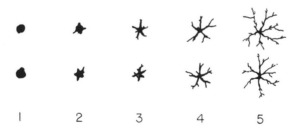

Fig. 11-3. Melanophore index. Adapted from Landgrebe and Waring (43).

darkened surroundings. Various drugs, such as caffeine, Metrazol, pilocarpine, and some barbiturates also cause pigment dispersion, but some of these are effective only in the animal with an intact pituitary gland, suggesting an action mediated through MSH release. The darkening of the frog skin can be reversed by melatonin, an extract of pineal origin (69), by norepinephrine, by glucocorticoids, or by hypophysectomy. Acetylcholine reverses only the dispersion caused by MSH.

Recently, it has been shown that β-MSH causes an increase in monosynaptic potentials in the spinal cord of the cat (40). The effect is not observed with ACTH, α-MSH, oxytocin, or vasopressin. The melanophoretic activity of both α- and β-MSH can be inactivated by incubation with extracts of brain, but not with liver or muscle homogenates (49).

Although both hormones are structurally similar to a portion of the ACTH molecule, only α-MSH has been shown to demonstrate ACTH activity (62). The hormones of the intermediate lobe, however, possess some inherent vasopressor action.

The Assay of MSH

The assay of MSH is based upon its principal action, the dispersion of melanin in the melanocytes of amphibians (43). The frog (*Rana pipiens*) or the South African toad (*Xenopus laevis*) are commonly used. Assay procedures vary from a subjective grading of skin color or microscopic observation of melanin dispersion (43) to measurement of the degree of darkening (under constant illumination) by a photoelectric reflectometer (61). *In vivo* assays are usually performed using hypophysectomized frogs or animals adapted to light environment for prolonged periods. *In vitro* assays utilize sections of skin immersed in physiological saline solution under constant conditions.

The International Unit of MSH is equivalent to the activity present in 1 μg of lyophilized standard posterior pituitary powder. Purified α-MSH may contain about 1 to 2×10^7 units per milligram. The activity of purified β-MSH is about 5×10^6 units per milligram.

Biogenesis, Metabolism, and Mechanism of Action

At present, nothing is known of the synthesis and metabolism of the hormones of the intermediate lobe. Because of the similarity in structures observed between MSH and ACTH, it has been thought that the biosynthesis of these two groups of hormones may be related. The hormone is believed to be formed in the intermediate lobe, is extractable from blood and urine, and has been shown to increase during pregnancy and in adrenal insufficiency (46).

The effect of MSH on melanin dispersion is dependent upon the presence of oxygen, and may require ATP, oxidative phosphorylation, and the cytochrome oxidase system. Factors that effect dispersion and aggregation of melanin granules in the cell may act through changes in the permeability of the cell membrane and the sol-gel framework of the cell (44, 46).

The action of MSH on melanin synthesis is thought to be mediated through its ability to increase tyrosinase activity. This enzyme facilitates the oxidation of tyrosine to dihydroxyphenylalanine, a precursor of melanin (39, 46).

Because the release of MSH from the pituitary glands of normal amphibians is dependent in a high degree on the external environment (light and temperature), it might be suspected that a neural link exists in the chain of events that result in the liberation of the hormone from the hypophysis (19a).

EXPERIMENT 11–1

Effect of Oxytocin and Vasopressin on Uterine Contractility

The ability of oxytocin to cause contractions of the uterus of the rat has been used as a criterion for bioassay of this hormone (37). The assay is feasible for tissue extracts that are rich in oxytocic activity and have been refined to eliminate nonspecific elements that may interfere with the response. Minimum concentrations of 10 mU are usually used for quantitative determinations unless the volume of the bath is reduced.

Procedure and Experimental

Follow the estrous cycles of rats (weighing 120–200 gm) until observations of the vaginal smears leave no doubt as to the stage of the cycle. Use only those animals that are in the first or second day of diestrus. The uterine horns are removed and a 1.5 cm section is attached to a kymograph lever system as depicted in Experiment 2–10. The lever ratio should be about 4:1, and the kymograph should rotate about 1 cm in 15 minutes or be moved manually. A modified Locke solution (see Appendix A–8), which contains only 25% of the calcium ions and half the amount of glucose, is used. The solution is aerated as in Experiment 2–10 with 5% CO_2 and 95% oxygen. The volume of the solution should be about 10 ml (at most) and should cover the entire uterine segment; thus a tube of proper diameter must be employed.

1. Allow the uterus to remain in solution about 10–20 minutes. Observe for spontaneous contractions. If these occur, the temperature of the bath may be lowered to about 28–30°C. The temperature must remain constant throughout the experiment.

2. Drain bath, flush, refill; wait 15 minutes.

3. Add 1 mU synthetic oxytocin (1.0 mU/0.1 ml) to the 10 ml bath.

4. Observe for uterine contractions for a period of 5 minutes.

5. Drain, flush, and refill tube; wait 15 minutes.

6. Follow Steps 3, 4, and 5 using dosages of 5 mU, 10 mU, 15 mU, and 20 mU oxytocin.

What is the minimum effective dose that will produce an observable contraction of the uterus?

Test the effect of solutions of epinephrine, vasopressin, and acetylcholine on uterine contractions.

The following procedure is usually used in assaying substances for oxytocic activity. The dose of standard oxytocin that gives a response 75% of the maximum contraction height is determined. A second dose, which gives a contraction height 25% less than the first, is also determined. For the assay, these two doses of the standard are first administered. Two identical doses of the test solution (judged to produce a response intermediate to the two standard dosages) are then administered. Finally, the two standard solutions (administered in *reverse* order) are introduced into the bath.

It is also possible to use the uteri of immature guinea pigs (body weight between 250 and 300 gm) in this experiment.

EXPERIMENT 11–2

Effect of Oxytocin on the Mammary Gland

The ability of oxytocin to cause milk ejection can be demonstrated easily *in vivo* and *in vitro*. This action is the humoral part of a neurohumoral reflex arc normally in effect in the lactating animal. The present experiment is an *in vitro* demonstration of the action of oxytocin on the mammary gland of the lactating rat.

Procedure and Experimental

1. The use of a lactating rat on the 7th–10th day post-partum is recommended. Remove the pups 24 hours prior to the experiment to permit engorgement of the mammary glands.

2. Place the rat under ether anesthesia and remove two or more mammary glands by the following procedure. Shave or clip the hair around the area of the gland. Cut through the skin adjacent to the gland and separate the skin from the muscle layer, making a flap that contains the mammary tissue. Holding the scissors parallel to the skin, slice or cut out mammary tissue. Place the tissue in a mammalian Ringer solution (Locke or Tyrode). The skin flap may be returned to position and sutures taken, if the animal is to be used again.

3. Wash the mammary gland two or three times with clean Ringer solution. Cut small sections (about 1 cm²) and place each section in a *small* dish or watch glass containing about 1–2 ml Ringer solution. Keep volumes of solution constant among the watch glasses.

4. To each sample of tissue, add one of the following and observe for at least 15 minutes. If possible, run duplicate samples of each dose level.

(a) Oxytocin: 1 U, 2 U, 4 U, 6 U
(b) Pituitrin (Parke Davis): 2 U, 6 U, 12 U
(c) Epinephrine (1:5000): 0.1 ml, 0.5 ml

5. Milk may be released as a faint halo around the slice, or the entire solution may turn milky. The expression of milk into the solution may be visualized easily if the watch glasses are placed upon a dark (or black) background. Grade the responses subjectively, i.e., 0, +1, +2, etc.

Similar experiments may be performed using the mouse or rabbit.

EXPERIMENT 11-3

Assay for Oxytocic Substances*

The standard USP assay for oxytocin is based upon blood pressure depression in the chicken. The assay is usually not sensitive to less than 100 mU of oxytocin (for quantitative determinations), and results may be erroneously high if more than 2.5 U vasopressin per unit oxytocin is present in tissue extracts being assayed.

Procedure and Experimental

White Leghorn chickens weighing between 1.8 and 2.2 kg are anesthetized by injecting intravenously sodium phenobarbital (200 mg/kg). The ischiadic artery is exteriorized by the following procedure:

1. Remove feathers from outer surface of left thigh.

2. A 7–8 cm incision is made in the skin parallel to and about 1.5 cm below the femur. This incision should expose the gluteus primus muscle. The lower edge of the incision is retracted to expose the edge of the gluteus primus muscle, which lies over the semitendinosus. This edge is freed for the length of the incision. Lift the free edge to expose the ischiadic artery and vein and crural vein lying along the edge of the semitendinosus. Cut across the gluteus primus near the proximal end of the skin incision, reflect the flap, and secure it to the upper thigh.

3. Dissect free the length of the ischiadic artery and crural vein. Cannulate the artery.

4. To record blood pressure, use a mercury manometer with an inside diameter of 2.5–3.0 mm with a float to operate a recorder-pointer. Anticoagulant (5–8.5% sodium citrate) is used to fill the manometer. The blood pressure should be about 105 mm Hg.

5. A slow-moving recording drum (1 cm in 5 minutes) is used to record changes in blood pressure.

6. Injections of solutions of oxytocin are made every 5 minutes into

* Cf. reference (9).

the crural vein, using a tuberculin syringe fitted with a 27-gauge needle. The time between injections should be constant. Inject the following solutions of oxytocin: 10 mU, 50 mU, 100 mU, 150 mU, 200 mU, 500 mU. All concentrations are contained in 0.1 ml solution.

EXPERIMENT 11–4

Action of ADH in the Frog

It has been observed that injection of pituitary extracts into frogs produces a temporary gain in weight as a result of absorption and retention of water. This phenomenon has been shown to be under the control of a posterior pituitary principle and to affect several amphibians (59, 59a, 63).

Procedure and Experimental

1. Two frogs are injected each with 0.5 ml of Pituitrin solution (approximately 12 mg Pituitrin per milliliter saline). The frogs are dried with a towel, and their urine is expelled by applying pressure on the abdomen. Weigh the animals to the nearest 0.1 gm.

2. Place the animals in a water container with enough water to cover their entire body surface with the exception of eyes and nostrils. A third frog (control) is injected with 0.5 ml frog Ringer solution (see Appendix A–8), handled in the same manner as the experimental animals, and placed in a similar container. (Be certain that identification of the animals is possible.)

3. Weigh the three animals in the manner described above every half hour for the first 3 hours after injection, and 6 and 24 hours after treatment. Note the darkening of the skin of the Pituitrin-injected specimens. To what hormone is this effect due? Does this action occur earlier than the imbibition effect? Is it observable after injection of pure vasopressin?

Note: Results can be improved by allowing the frogs to dehydrate by placing them in dry containers for 2 days prior to the experiment.

EXPERIMENT 11–5

The Assay of ADH in the Rat

The assay of ADH activity (16) can be performed in the suitably prepared cat, dog, rat, mouse, and rabbit. Sensitivity of some of these assays is as great as 0.01 mU vasopressin. The following procedure usually gives a good linear response between 10 and 50 mU of Pitressin (Parke, Davis) when plotted on a logarithmic scale.

Procedure and Experimental

Female rats (180–220 gm in weight), are fasted overnight but are allowed free access to water. The animals are administered an oral dose (by stomach tube) of 5 ml of tepid tap water per 100 gm body weight, followed 45 minutes later by an oral dose of 12% ethanol (5 ml/100 gm). When the animals are under alcohol anesthesia, they are secured to operating boards in a supine position. Catheterize the bladder of each animal. Place the board on a rack tilted at a 45-degree angle to permit drops of urine to fall from the catheter tube onto a flared end of a stylus. Thus each drop of urine is recorded by a blip which can be marked on a kymograph drum.

At approximately 45 minutes after the administration of the 12% ethanol, the rat is given an oral dose of 2% ethanol (4–5 ml/100 gm). When the urine flow becomes steady and reaches a magnitude of 3–8 ml per hour, the assay may begin. As the assay must be complete in one animal, a four-point procedure is utilized. Each rat receives two injections of a standard and two injections of the unknown preparation. The ratio between the doses must be the same for both preparations. These injections may be made into the jugular veins or into the saphenous vein of the leg. The antidiuretic potency (a) of the injected preparation is calculated as follows:

$$a = \frac{\text{No. of drops excreted during a 15-minute period (beginning 1 minute after the injection)}}{\text{No. of drops excreted in the 15 minutes preceding the above}}$$

The ratio (a) has a linear regression within the range of 10–50 mU Pitressin when the dosage is converted to logarithms.

Since the sensitivity of the animal to the hormone is influenced by the water load, it is advisable to replace the excreted fluid periodically, thus providing an equivalent water load for the four injections. This replacement fluid is 2% ethanol; as in all gavages, care must be taken to ensure that the stomach tube is inserted into the stomach, not into the lungs. If fluid is introduced into the lungs, the animal must obviously be discarded, as it is drowned.

EXPERIMENT 11–6

The Assay of MSH by Use of the Melanophore Index*

Several bioassays for MSH activity have been proposed and used with a high degree of confidence (61). The following experiment has the

* Cf. references (36, 43).

advantage of being extremely simple and requiring no assay equipment other than a low power dissecting microscope or magnifier.

Procedure and Experimental

Xenopus laevis toads are kept separately in white containers in water 4 inches deep. The containers are placed in a fairly well lit room at a temperature of about 16°C for several weeks prior to use. [For care and feeding, see F. W. Landgrebe, *J. Exptl. Biol.* **16**: 89 (1939).] Animals may be fed minced fresh rat liver once or twice a week. Containers must be cleaned after feeding.

1. Inject (with a 2-inch, 20-gauge needle), through the thigh muscles into the dorsal lymph sac of the frog at a point in the center of the back, aqueous solutions of constant volume (0.25 ml) containing MSH.

2. Maximum dose should give a melanophore index *peak* of 3.0.

3. Only dermal melanophores in the web of the foot are read every half hour for 3 hours under slight magnification.

4. The maximal melanophore index observed during the 3-hour period is the value to be recorded. The animals may be used over after a period of several days. (Cf. Fig. 11-3.)

References

1. Ames, R. G., Moore, D. H., and van Dyke, H. B. 1950. The excretion of posterior pituitary antidiuretic hormone in the urine and its detection in the blood. *Endocrinology* **46**: 215–227.
2. Ames, R. G., and van Dyke, H. B. 1952. Antidiuretic hormone in the serum or plasma of rats. *Endocrinology* **50**: 350–360.
3. Andersson, B. 1957. Polydipsia, antidiuresis and milk ejection caused by hypothalamic stimulation, *in* "The Neurohypophysis" (H. Heller, ed.), pp. 131–140. Butterworths, London.
4. Ascher, R., and Fromageot, C. 1957. The relationship of oxytocin and vasopressin to active proteins of posterior pituitary origin. Studies concerning the existence or non-existence of a single neurohypophyseal hormone, *in* "The Neurohypophysis" (H. Heller, ed.), pp. 39–50. Butterworths, London.
5. Bargmann, W., and Scharrer, E. 1951. The site of origin of the hormones of the posterior pituitary. *Am. Scientist* **39**: 255–259.
6. Barker-Jorgenson, C. 1950. The amphibian water economy, with special regard to the effect of neurohypophyseal extracts. *Acta Physiol. Scand. Suppl.* **78**: 1–79.
7. Berde, B., and Cerletti, A. 1958. Quantitative comparison of substances related to oxytocin: a new test. *Acta Endocrinol.* **27**: 314–324.
8. Caldeyro-Barcia, R., and Poseiro, J. J. 1958. Oxytocin and contractility of the pregnant human uterus. *Ann. N. Y. Acad. Sci.* **75**: 813–830.
9. Coon, J. M. 1939. A new method for the assay of posterior pituitary extracts. *Arch. Intern. Pharmacodyn.* **62**: 79–99.
10. Cowie, A. T., and Folley, S. J. 1957. Neurohypophyseal hormones and the

mammary gland, in "The Neurohypophysis" (H. Heller, ed.), pp. 183–201. Butterworths, London.

11. Cross, B. A. 1955. The hypothalamus and the mechanism of sympathetico-adrenal inhibition of milk ejection. J. Endocrinol. 12: 15–28.

12. Cross, B. A., and Harris, G. W. 1951. The neurohypophysis and "let-down" of milk. J. Physiol. (London) 113: 35P.

13. Croxatto, H., and Barnafi, L. 1960. Hormone and hormonelike activity of active polypeptides. Recent Progr. Hormone Res. 16: 263–308.

14. Csapo, A. 1961. The role of progesterone in the maintenance and termination of pregnancy, in "Brook Lodge Symposium" (A. C. Barnes, ed.), pp. 7–23. Brook Lodge Press, Augusta, Michigan.

15. Dale, H. H. 1909. The action of extracts of the pituitary body. Biochem. J. 4: 427.

16. Dicker, S. E. 1953. A method for the assay of very small amounts of antidiuretic activity with a note on the antidiuretic titre of rats' blood. J. Physiol. (London) 122: 149–157.

17. Dicker, S. E. 1961. Release and metabolism of the neurohypophyseal hormones. J. Pharm. Pharmacol. 13: 449–469.

18. du Vigneaud, V., Lawler, H. C., and Popenoe, E. A. 1953. Enzymatic cleavage of glycinamide from vasopressin and a proposed structure for this pressor-antidiuretic hormone of the posterior pituitary. J. Am. Chem. Soc. 75: 4880–4881.

19. du Vigneaud, V., Ressler, C., and Trippett, S. 1953. The sequence of amino acids in oxytocin with a proposal for the structure of oxytocin. J. Biol. Chem. 205: 949–957.

19a. Etkin, W. 1963. Metamorphosis-activating system of the frog. Science 139: 810–814.

20. Fitzpatrick, R. J. 1957. On oxytocin and uterine function, in "The Neurohypophysis" (H. Heller, ed.), pp. 203–220. Butterworths, London.

21. Frazer, A. M. 1937. The diuretic action of the oxytocic hormone of the pituitary gland and its effect on the assay of pituitary extracts. J. Pharmacol. Exptl. Therap. 60: 89–95.

22. Frazer, A. M. 1942. The action of the oxytocic hormone of the pituitary gland on urine secretion. J. Physiol. (London) 101: 236–251.

23. Frieden, E. H., and Bozer, J. M. 1951. Effect of administration of intermedin upon melanin content of the skin of Rana pipiens. Proc. Soc. Exptl. Biol. Med. 77: 35–37.

24. Fuchs, F., and Fuchs, A.-R. 1958. Induction and inhibition of labour in the rabbit. Acta Endocrinol. 29: 615–624.

25. Fuhrman, F. A., and Ussing, H. H. 1951. A characteristic response of the isolated frog skin potential to neurohypophyseal principles and its relation to the transport of sodium and water. J. Cellular Comp. Physiol. 38: 109–130.

26. Gaddum, J. H., and Hameed, K. A. 1954. Drugs which antagonize 5-hydroxy-tryptamine. Brit. J. Pharmacol. 9: 240–248.

27. Ginsburg, M., and Heller, H. 1953. The antidiuretic assay of vasopressin by intravenous injection into unanesthetized rats. J. Endocrinol. 9: 267–273.

28. Goto, M. 1960. The effects of oxytocin on the transmembrane potentials of the rat myometrium. Japan. J. Physiol. 10: 427–435.

29. Harris, G. W. 1955. "Neural Control of the Pituitary Gland," pp. 199–271. Arnold, London.

30. Harris, J. I., and Lerner, A. B. 1957. Amino acid sequence of the α-melanocyte-stimulating hormone. *Nature* **179:** 1346–1347.

31. Harris, J. I., and Roos, P. 1956. Amino acid sequence of a melanophore stimulating peptide. *Nature* **178:** 90.

32. Heller, H. 1941. Differentiation of an (amphibian) water balance principle from the antidiuretic principle of the posterior pituitary gland. *J. Physiol. (London)* **100:** 125–141.

33. Heller, H., and Blackmore, K. E. 1952. The assay of small amounts of antidiuretic activity by intravenous injections into mice. *J. Endocrinol.* **8:** 224–228.

34. Herrick, E. H. 1933. The structure of epidermal melanophores in frog tadpoles. *Biol. Bull.* **64:** 304–308.

35. Hipsley, E. H., and McKellar, J. W. 1959. The capacity of plasma for binding vasopressin in pregnant and non-pregnant human subjects. *J. Endocrinol.* **19:** 345–352.

36. Hogben, L., and Gordon, C. 1930. Studies on the pituitary. VII. The separate identity of the pressor and melanophore principles. *J. Exptl. Biol.* **7:** 286–292.

37. Holton, P. 1948. A modification of the method of Dale and Laidlaw for standardization of posterior pituitary extract. *Brit. J. Pharmacol.* **3:** 328–334.

38. Knaus, H. H. 1926. The action of pituitary extract upon the pregnant uterus of the rabbit. *J. Physiol. (London)* **61:** 383–397.

39. Kohn, R. R. 1953. On intermedin and melanin synthesis. *Endocrinology* **53:** 458–460.

40. Krivoy, W. A., and Guillemin, R. 1961. On a possible role of β-melanocyte stimulating hormone (β-MSH) in the central nervous system of the mammalia: an effect of β-MSH in the spinal cord of the cat. *Endocrinology* **69:** 170–175.

41. Kuriyama, H. A., and Csapo, A. I. 1959. The "evolution" of membrane and myoplastic activity of uterine muscle. *Biol. Bull.* **117:** 417–418.

42. Kuriyama, H., and Csapo, A. 1961. A study of the parturient uterus with the microelectrode technique. *Endocrinology* **68:** 1010–1025.

43. Landgrebe, F. W., and Waring, H. 1944. Biological assay and standardization of melanophore expanding pituitary hormone. *Quart. J. Exptl. Physiol.* **33:** 1–18.

44. Lerner, A. B., and Case, J. D. 1960. Melatonin. *Federation Proc.* **19:** 590–592.

45. Lerner, A. B., Shizume, K., and Bunding, I. 1954. The mechanism of endocrine control of melanin pigmentation. *J. Clin. Endocrinol. Metab.* **14:** 1463–1490.

46. Lerner, A. B., and Takahashi, Y. 1956. Hormonal control of melanin pigmentation. *Recent Progr. Hormone Res.* **12:** 303–320.

47. Leveque, T. F., and Scharrer, E. 1953. Pituicytes and the origin of the antidiuretic hormone. *Endocrinology* **52:** 436–447.

48. Lindquist, K. M., and Rowe, L. W. 1949. The antidiuretic activity of the posterior pituitary and its quantitative evaluation. *J. Am. Pharm. Assoc. Sci. Ed.* **38:** 227–231.

49. Long, J. M., Krivoy, W. A., and Guillemin, R. 1961. On a possible role of β-melanocyte stimulating hormone (β-MSH) in the central nervous system of the mammalia: enzymatic inactivation *in vitro* of β-MSH by brain tissue. *Endocrinology* **69:** 176–181.

50. McCann, S. M., Mack, R., and Gale, C. 1959. Possible role of oxytocin in stimulating release of prolactin. *Endocrinology* **64:** 870–889.

51. Marshall, J. M., and Csapo, A. I. 1959. The effects of calcium deficiency and

oxytocin on the membrane activity of uterine muscle as measured by the "Sucrose Gap" method. *Biol. Bull.* **117**: 419.

52. Marshall, J. M., and Csapo, A. I. 1961. Hormonal and ionic influences on the membrane activity of uterine smooth muscle cells. *Endocrinology* **68**: 1026–1035.

53. Mendez-Bauer, C., Cabot, H. M., and Caldeyro-Barcia, R. 1960. New test for the biological assay of oxytocin. *Science* **132**: 299–300.

54. Pickering, B. T., and Heller, H. 1959. Chromatographic and biological characteristics of fish and frog neurohypophyseal extracts. *Nature* **184**: 1463–1464.

55. Rasmussen, H., and Craig, L. 1961. The isolation of arginine vasotocin from fish pituitary glands. *Endocrinology* **68**: 1051–1055.

56. Reynolds, S. R. M. 1949. "Physiology of the Uterus." Harper (Hoeber), New York.

57. Rothchild, I., and Quilligan, E. J. 1960. The corpus luteum–pituitary relationship: on the reports that oxytocin stimulates the secretion of luteotrophin. *Endocrinology* **67**: 122–125.

58. Sawyer, W. H. 1951. Effect of posterior pituitary extracts on urine formation and glomerular circulation in the frog. *Am. J. Physiol.* **164**: 457–466.

59. Sawyer, W. H. 1957. The antidiuretic action of neurohypophyseal hormones in amphibia, *in* "The Neurohypophysis" (H. Heller, ed.), pp. 171–182. Butterworths, London.

59a. Sawyer, W. H. 1961. Comparative physiology and pharmacology of the neurohypophysis. *Recent Progr. Hormone Res.* **17**: 437–465.

60. Schofield, B. M. 1957. The hormonal control of myometrial function during pregnancy. *J. Physiol. (London)* **138**: 1–10.

61. Shizume, K., Lerner, A. B., and Fitzpatrick, T. B. 1954. *In vitro* bioassay for the melanocyte stimulating hormone. *Endocrinology* **54**: 553–560.

62. Steelman, S. L., and Guillemin, R. 1959. Adrenocorticotrophic activity of alpha melanocyte stimulating hormone (α-MSH). *Proc. Soc. Exptl. Biol. Med.* **101**: 600–601.

63. Steggerda, F. R. 1937. Comparative study of water metabolism in amphibians injected with pituitrin. *Proc. Soc. Exptl. Biol. Med.* **36**: 103–106.

64. Stewart, W. C. 1949. Effect of mammalian (posterior lobe) pituitary extract on water balance of frogs when placed in different osmotic environments. *Am. J. Physiol.* **157**: 412–417.

65. van Dyke, H. B., Adamsons, K., Jr., and Engel, S. L. 1955. Aspects of the biochemistry and physiology of the neurohypophyseal hormones. *Recent Progr. Hormone Res.* **11**: 1–35.

66. van Dyke, H. B., Adamson, K., Jr., and Engel, S. L. 1957. The storage and liberation of neurohypophyseal hormones, *in* "The Neurohypophysis" (H. Heller, ed.), pp. 65–76. Butterworths, London.

67. Walker, J. M. 1957. Release of vasopressin and oxytocin in response to drugs, *in* "The Neurohypophysis" (H. Heller, ed.), pp. 221–232. Butterworths, London.

68. Wirz, H. 1957. The location of antidiuretic action in the mammalian kidney, *in* "The Neurohypophysis" (H. Heller, ed.), pp. 157–169. Butterworths, London.

69. Wright, M. R., and Lerner, A. B. 1960. On the movement of pigment granules in frog melanocytes. *Endocrinology* **66**: 599–609.

CHAPTER 12

Parathormone

The physiology of the parathyroid glands involves primarily the regulation of calcium and phosphorus, elements that play a major role in the growth, development, and maintenance of bone. In addition, the parathyroids are concerned with homeostatic mechanisms in the body through their involvement in the maintenance of serum calcium and phosphorus levels. A deficiency in the secretory activity of the glands leads to severe disorders involving tetanic convulsions and death, while hyperactivity leads to rarefaction of bone and deposition of calcium in the soft tissues.

Site of Formation

The parathyroid glands are usually four in number (sometimes fewer) and are present in the neck region, adjacent to or embedded in the thyroid gland. The glands are extremely small: of the size of a pin head in the rat, or of a garden pea in man. In most mammals the parathyroid glands are embedded in the thyroid tissue and are usually removed when a total thyroidectomy is performed (Fig. 12-1). However, both the number and exact position of these glands vary to a great extent, even to being present outside the thyroid gland, but usually in

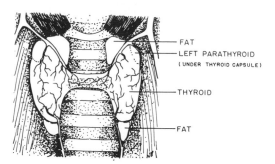

Fig. 12-1. Location of the parathyroid glands in the rat (Sprague-Dawley strain).

the neck region. In the domestic bird, for example, the parathyroids are usually found in an extrathyroidal position. In the rat, usually two glands are present, and these are embedded beneath the thyroid capsule.

The gland in birds and mammals appears well encapsulated and contains cords of cells separated by connective tissue and a fairly good vascular supply (cf. Fig. 12-2). Two kinds of epithelial cells have been

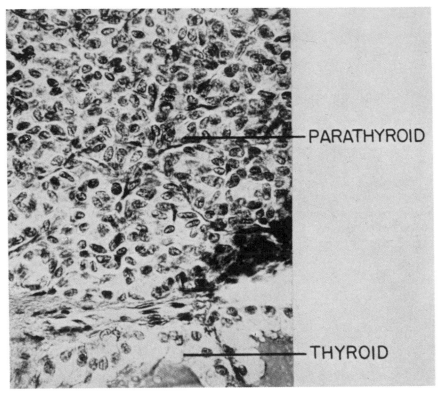

Fig. 12-2. Section through the parathyroid gland of the rat (from 215×).

described. These are the "chief cells" and the "oxyphil cells." The chief cells exhibit a cytoplasm with some glycogen, and a large vesicular nucleus. These are the principal cells present before puberty. After puberty, oxyphil cells appear and slowly increase in number with age. These cells contain no glycogen, but acidophilic granules are present in the cytoplasm, and hence these cells have also been termed acidophils. Although parathyroid cells are usually arranged in densely packed groups of cords, occasionally they are seen in the form of follicles, which may contain a colloid-like material. However, colloid in the parathyroid gland is devoid of iodine, unlike that of thyroid tissue. The functional relationships of the chief and oxyphil cells is at present unknown. No oxyphil cells have been found in rat parathyroid tissue.

Nature of Parathormone

The parathormone is a low molecular weight protein or polypeptide and was first extracted by Collip and his colleagues in 1925 (6). The hormone was found to cause an increase in calcium level of the serum and a decrease in phosphate content. In the several decades that followed, many attempts were made to isolate parathormone, all of which gave only partial success. Recently, Rasmussen and Craig (22) have reported the isolation of pure parathormone from beef parathyroids by countercurrent distribution techniques. The material was found to have a molecular weight of about 8500 and to contain a chain of 83 amino acid residues composed of 17 different amino acids. The exact sequence of the amino acids has not yet been established, but it has been shown that only 33 are required for the protein to exert its characteristic parathormone action. This product has been divided into at least three active fractions which behave as single substances when tested by ultracentrifugation, dialysis, and chromatography (Table 12–1) (13, 21, 22a). These fractions are called parathormone A, B, and C.

TABLE 12–1

CHARACTERISTICS OF THREE ACTIVE PARATHORMONE FRACTIONS[a]

Hormone	Molecular weight	Number of amino acids	Activity (units/mg)
Parathormone A	8500	75	2700
Parathormone B	7200	67	1800
Parathormone C	8600	74	2000–3000

[a] Data from Greep and Talmage (13), Rasmussen (21), and Rasmussen and Craig (22a).

Action of Parathormone

Parathormone is of major importance in the maintenance of homeostasis by virtue of its regulatory role in calcium and phosphorus metabolism. Calcium is required in such physiological activities as bone metabolism, blood coagulation, neuromuscular excitability, muscle contraction, membrane permeability, nerve function, and fertilization. In a similar fashion, phosphorus is involved in acid-base balance of the blood, is a constituent of various coenzymes, phospholipids, nucleoproteins, nucleic acid, and bone, and is a factor in carbohydrate metabolism. It is apparent, therefore, that the control of these elements is of paramount significance in the maintenance of the organism in a good physiological state.

The absence of parathormone leads to tetany and death in all animals if the calcium intake is restricted. The severity of the tetanic convulsions depends in measurable degree on the diet in some species. Although the decreased severity of parathyroidectomy in herbivorous animals may be associated with the high dietary intake of calcium and phosphorus, the diffuse nature of the gland in many of these animals makes complete parathyroidectomy, and thus evaluation of parathyroid action, difficult. In those animals particularly susceptible to parathyroid hormone deficiency (carnivores such as the cat and dog), the symptoms are quite marked and readily observed.

The first signs of decreased blood calcium levels in parathyroidectomized animals are manifested by an increased restlessness or irritability of the animal. In the dog, the rapid appearance of an anorexia, a drop in body temperature, an anuria, and a decrease in water intake is observed. As the deficiency increases, periodic muscle spasm and an irregular gait are observed. The muscular tremors first appear anteriorly 2 or 3 days after surgery and soon involve the entire body. Finally, continuous contractions of large muscle groups occurs and a seizure-like state ensues, the "parathyroid tetany."

The developing tetany causes a rise in body temperature, which in turn leads to *hyperpnea* with a resulting change in blood pH due to the loss of carbonic acid. As a consequence, a further drop in calcium ions occurs, which results in an exacerbation of the tetany. Seizures may be set off by external stimuli such as noise or gentle contact. Frequently death occurs during convulsions as a result of laryngeal spasm. The metabolic changes that occur are characterized by hypocalcemia (Fig. 12-3), decreased urinary calcium, hyperphosphatemia, decreased urinary phosphate, and a reduced blood citrate level. The decrease in extracellular calcium is the precipitating factor in the neuromuscular hyperexcitability, which is characterized by tremors and eventually tetanic convulsions.

Prolonged parathyroid deficiency may lead to bone decalcification, disturbance in dentition, and formation of cataracts in the eye. Many of these symptoms are alleviated by intravenous injection of calcium salts, or by administration of parathormone extracts. The symptoms are all a result of the decreased serum calcium level.

Hyperparathyroidism leads to a hypercalcemia, hypercalciuria, hypophosphatemia, and hyperphosphaturia. An increase in serum citrate and

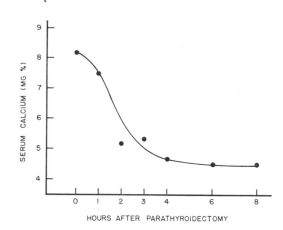

Fig. 12-3. Serum calcium levels in the parathyroidectomized rat. From Munson (17).

alkaline phosphatase has also been observed. Prolonged hyperparathyroidism will eventually create a metastatic deposition of calcium in the soft tissue and a rarefaction of the bone as a result of calcium resorption. Parathormone, in combination with other hormones, is also necessary for the maintenance of good lactation (29).

In the bird, parathormone produces an increase in the serum calcium levels of 2–8 mg/100 ml, whereas estrogens increase the level by 70–80 mg/100 ml (3). However, the action of estrogen is not observed following removal of the parathyroid gland (19). Large amounts of calcium are stored in bone, which apparently acts as a reservoir for utilization in the formation of the egg shell. Mobilization of this calcium occurs during egg shell formation.

The symptomatic effects produced by parathormone or its lack are the result of changes in calcium and phosphate levels in the body. A major source of these products is bone, in which the salts exist primarily as calcium phosphate and carbonate in a form such as hydroxyapatite $[3Ca_3(PO_4)_2 \cdot CaCO_3]$ and perhaps other more soluble forms, such as citrate. The extracellular fluids such as blood also contain small amounts of calcium and phosphate.

Experiments in mammals have shown that there exists a close relationship between the calcium and phosphate levels of bone and those of blood. In animals which are parathyroidectomized and nephrectomized, blood calcium levels "stabilize" at a value of about 7 mg/100 ml. Washing out the body fluids of these animals by peritoneal lavage reduces the serum calcium levels, but these soon return to the stabilized level as a result of calcium exchange from bone to blood. Thus, in the parathyroidectomized animal, an equilibrium apparently exists between blood and bone with respect to calcium level. The administration of parathormone increases the level of serum calcium, thus in effect "supersaturating" the blood with respect to bone. Normally in most mammals, serum calcium level is about 10–12 mg/100 ml.

Within the blood, calcium exists in several forms: approximately 50% as a nondiffusible protein-bound material, and the rest as a diffusible form which may or may not be ionized. It has been shown that an inverse relationship exists between the ionized form of blood calcium and phosphate: an increased blood calcium may be associated with a decreased serum phosphate. This phenomenon occurs after the injection of parathormone, but the fall in serum phosphate appears only after a rise in urinary excretion of this ion. The reciprocal relation between the ionized, diffusible blood calcium and phosphate is relatively constant and can be expressed as a solubility product equation: $Ca^{++} \times HPO_4^{--} = K$. Thus, if an increase in blood calcium is observed, usually a corresponding decrease in phosphate occurs. It has been postulated, therefore, that the effect of parathormone may be dual: (a) an action on the kidney to increase urinary phosphate excretion, and (b) an action on bone to mobilize calcium and phosphate. The former action would decrease serum phosphate levels, and "balance" the latter action, an increase in calcium and phosphate in serum. Thus, a constant $Ca^{++} \times HPO_4^{--}$ product in serum would be maintained. In fact, both these effects are observed under suitably controlled experiments, indicating that parathormone has a direct action on bone as well as kidney (10, 13, 15, 20).

Among the controlling elements involved in calcium and phosphorus metabolism, besides parathormone, are the vitamins D. The actions of the hormone and the vitamins appear to complement each other somewhat. The vitamins D act (a) primarily, by stimulating the absorption of calcium (and indirectly, phosphate) from the small intestine, and (b) possibly, by promoting the retention of phosphate and excretion of calcium in urine. Large doses of vitamin D may cause resorption of calcium and phosphate from bone and may increase the urinary excretion of those ions. Conversely, it has been suggested that parathormone may cause an increased absorption of calcium from intestine, in addition to its action on bone and kidney. Although the D vitamins can act in the absence of parathormone, it appears that the hormone may require the presence of the vitamin for normal activity.

The increased urinary excretion of phosphate after parathormone treatment may be the result of an increased glomerular filtration rate or an increased tubular secretion (15). In the normal animal with an active parathyroid, the phosphate loss is opposed by a tubular reabsorption of the ion, in part controlled by vitamin D. Thus it has been postulated that the vitamin regulates the levels of calcium and phosphate ions in the body by its action on intestinal absorption and urinary excretion, thus favoring absorption of calcium and retention of phosphate. Although parathormone may increase intestinal absorption of calcium, its major action is by regulation of the blood levels of calcium and phosphate by increasing resorption of these substances from bone and increasing urinary phosphate excretion. The balance of these two systems control intake, ratio, utilization, and excretion of calcium and phosphate.

Regulation of parathormone release is thought to be a result of the level of diffusible calcium in extracellular fluids. Hypertrophy of the parathyroid gland can be obtained by the maintenance of a low level of diffusible serum calcium or by infusion of blood from hypocalcemic animals. The volume of the parathyroid glands has been shown to be inversely related to the level of diffusible serum calcium (25, 28).

Evidence has been presented to indicate the presence of a fast-acting hormone from the parathyroid gland that lowers blood calcium. This substance has been called calcitonin; it is thought to regulate blood calcium levels by acting as a hypocalcemic factor. Calcitonin is released during hypercalcemia (6a,b).

Assay of Parathormone

For many years the only assay for parathormone of any value was a measure of the rise in serum calcium in the normal or parathyroidectomized dog. Assays based upon blood calcium changes in the rabbit and rat appeared to offer no promise (12). Recently, however, it has been shown that a good dose-response curve can be obtained with a parathyroidectomized rat on a calcium-deficient diet (16, 17). The animal is first placed on a calcium-deficient diet; 4 days later it is parathyroidectomized by electrocautery. Different doses of the hormone are injected, and the serum calcium levels are determined 6 hours later. This assay has been used very successfully to measure the potency of purified extracts of the parathyroid glands.

The phosphate diuresis induced by parathormone has also been utilized as an assay for the hormone. Groups of 16 mice each weighing between 20 and 25 gm are hydrated with 1 ml of 0.9% NaCl per 5 gm body weight injected intraperitoneally, and the urine is collected for $3\frac{1}{2}$ hours. The hormone is administered just prior to the urine collection period, and the urinary phosphate excretion is determined. A good regression line is obtained over the range of 0.5–1.5 USP units (7).

A new method proposed for the assay of parathormone involves the utilization of isotopic calcium (5). Rats are fed a calcium-free diet for

3 days and then injected with 100 μc Ca⁴⁵. The animals are then maintained on a regular diet for 45 days to allow for the deposition of a constant level of radioactive calcium in the bone and to ensure that radioactive calcium, rather than stable calcium, will be mobilized after hormone treatment. Prior to the assay, the animals again are placed for 5 days on a calcium-free diet; the urinary calcium is determined for a 24-hour period before the injection of parathormone and for a 24-hour period following the injection of the hormone. The assay can detect 2 USP units.

A measure of the increased height of leg muscle contraction, as a result of parathormone treatment in the frog, also has been suggested as an assay for the hormone (11). This response is based upon the effect of parathormone on calcium levels at the neuromuscular junction.

As no international standard has been prepared for parathormone, an absolute measure of potency is not available. However, the biological response of the dog has been utilized as a basis for comparison of extracts. The USP unit is defined as 1/100 of the amount of an extract required to raise the serum calcium of a dog weighing 20 kg by 5 mg/100 ml within 16–18 hours after the administration of the preparation.

Biogenesis, Metabolism, and Mechanism of Action

Little information is available on the biogenesis, metabolism, and degradation of parathormone. Like most hormones, it appears to be degraded in the liver. Autotransplantation of parathyroid glands of the rat to the spleen fails to cause hypertrophy of the parathyroids, but it does result in an inability to maintain the calcium level in the peritoneal fluid following peritoneal lavage (8).

Concerning the mechanism of action of the hormone, many theories have been proposed. Early work indicated that the initial action following parathormone injection was a phosphate diuresis followed by a drop in serum phosphate and a subsequent rise in serum calcium. This led to the suggestion that the primary site of action was on the kidney and that the resorption of bone following parathormone treatment was secondary in an attempt to maintain the solubility product (1). Small amounts of parathormone injected into one renal artery in a dog caused a unilateral or preferentially unilateral phosphaturia with no systemic change in renal hemodynamics or plasma phosphate concentration (20). The original concept, on the other hand, proposed that the main action of parathormone was on bone proper. That the kidney is not essential to the action of the parathormone on bone has been amply demonstrated in experiments utilizing the technique of peritoneal lavage. Under such conditions, parathormone restores to normal the concentration of the calcium in the peritoneal washings of a parathyroidectomized, nephrectomized rat.

A wealth of data has been obtained to indicate a direct action of parathormone on bone. This consists of the demonstration of a local action of parathormone. In these experiments it has been shown that parathyroid tissue, transplanted directly to cranial bone, causes local resorption of the bone (4). Similar results have been obtained in tissue culture using both parathyroid tissue and the pure hormone (9).

It is generally agreed that the parathyroids secrete a hormone that acts directly on bone and kidney. It has been suggested that the main effect of parathormone on the bone is to cause the production or accumulation of citrate, lactate, or carbonic acid (8a). The local change in pH has been thought to provide an adequate substrate to facilitate the dissolution of calcium. In the kidney, it has been suggested that parathormone acts directly on the renal tubule and produces a phosphaturia by depressing phosphate reabsorption, or by stimulating tubular secretion of phosphate. The synthesis of this information into a theory for the mechanism of action of parathormone and its relationship to vitamin D remains to be established.

EXPERIMENT 12–1

Parathyroidectomy*

For many years parathyroidectomy was performed by removal of the thyroid gland, and hence the parathyroids also, since the latter are usually embedded in the former. This operation is, in reality, called a thyroparathyroidectomy and is surgically adequate but requires that the animal be maintained on thyroxine so that the results of parathyroid deficiency are not complicated by the lack of thyroid hormone. By careful dissection, it is possible to remove surgically the single pair of parathyroid glands in the rat. Recently, however, another excellent method has been employed successfully: that of using electrocautery as a means of destroying the tissue.

Procedure

A. *Surgical Procedure in the Rat* (Figs. 8-5 and 12-1)

1. Place the rat under barbiturate anesthesia (Nembutal).

2. After it has lost consciousness, place the rat on an operating board and secure it firmly as if for thyroidectomy.

* Cf. references (12, 24, 27).

3. Swab the neck region with Zephiran and expose the thyroid gland. Use retractors to keep the area clearly exposed.

4. Using a dissecting microscope (15×), carefully dissect free the lateral edges of the thyroid gland to expose the single pair of parathyroid glands: whitish bodies on the lateral edges of the anterior poles of the thyroid gland.

5. Carefully destroy each gland by electrocautery.

6. Remove retractors and close the skin with several sutures.

B. Surgical Procedure in the Pigeon (Fig. 12–4)

1. Anesthetize the pigeon with Nembutal (25 mg per kilogram body weight) via the radial vein.

2. Place the bird on the operating board and restrain it with rubber straps in such a position that its head is nearest the operator.

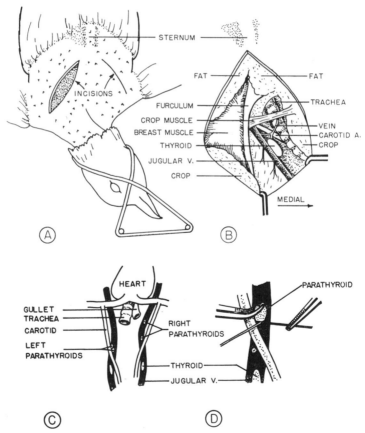

Fig. 12-4. Parathyroidectomy in the pigeon. Adapted from Smith (24).

3. Pluck the feathers over the neck and crop sac areas and make an incision 6 cm long through the skin on the left side from shoulder to sternum.

4. Separate the crop sac from the furculum and push gently to the midline.

5. Puncture and tear open the air sac.

6. Fasten the bird's head securely to the board. Strangulation is not a problem since the bird can breathe through the open air sac.

7. Pull the trachea to the midline with retractors.

8. Retract the crop sac and skin out of the area.

9. Clear the region posterior to the thyroid and expose the carotid artery and jugular vein.

10. The parathyroids are usually seen together. They may lie on the jugular vein and under the carotid artery at a point where the two vessels cross.

11. The gland can be partly freed, ligated, and lifted out after careful separation. Care must be taken not to tear the jugular vein.

12. The operation is completed by closing the skin with sutures and swabbing out the animal's mouth to remove mucus.

13. The right parathyroids are removed in a similar fashion, except that the gullet is retracted and the bird's head is strapped down on the right side of the board.

It is suggested that the operation be carried out in two stages 1 week apart to reduce operative trauma and make it easier to control the resulting tetany.

EXPERIMENT 12–2

Withdrawal of Blood*

Procedure

A. Chicken

Blood may be obtained from the wing vein of the chicken if small samples are required. However, only a limited number of samples can be obtained in this manner since repeated cutting of the vein will lead to damage. Large amounts of blood may be obtained directly from the heart, and this route may be used repeatedly without damage to the bird. The bird is placed on its back and tied to a board with the head hanging over the edge. The feathers are plucked from the skin overlying the clavicular region and the skin is cleaned with 70% alcohol. A 3–4

* Cf. references (2, 26).

inch 16- or 18-gauge needle is inserted into the thoracic cavity via the triangular opening formed by the coracoid bones. The initial insertion is on the median plane at a slightly downward angle; the needle is then directed horizontally until it enters the heart. The syringe is then filled and the needle is quickly withdrawn with a single movement.

B. Rabbit

Blood may be obtained with ease either from the marginal ear vein or the heart of the rabbit. If the ear vein is to be used, the animal is placed in a rabbit box which permits access to the head and ears. An ear is shaved and the marginal vein is dilated with heat from an incandescent lamp, by the application of xylene, or by rubbing or flicking the ear with the fingers. If xylene is used, then the ear should be cleansed with 70% alcohol before blood withdrawal since the xylene is very irritating and will damage the tissue. After the vessel is dilated, the vein is nicked with a sharp blade and the blood is collected as it drips from the cut vessel. The bleeding can be stopped by clamping a bit of cotton to the cut with an artery clamp. This may be removed within 10–15 minutes.

For cardiac puncture, the rabbit is strapped on its back to a board, its head and legs firmly tied. The position of the heart may then be palpated with the fingers of the left hand. When the heart is located, a syringe fitted with an 18-gauge needle (3 inches long) is inserted between the ribs into the heart. The blood is withdrawn slowly with light negative pressure.

C. Rat or Mouse

Blood is usually obtained from the tail in the rat or mouse. It is essential that the tail be cleansed first and then warmed under an incandescent bulb for 5–10 minutes. This is necessary in order to ensure good flow. When the tail has been warmed sufficiently, a nick may be made in the tail with a sharp blade, or a small portion may be cut off the tip of the tail. A sufficient amount of blood can be obtained by this means to do blood counts, blood sugars, etc. Cessation of blood flow from the tip of the tail may be obtained by placing an arterial clamp on the end of the tail or dipping the tail into collodion.

Cardiac puncture is the usual procedure when large volumes of blood are required. The procedure for the rat is comparable to that for the rabbit. The animal may be lightly anesthetized and tied down or simply anesthetized; afterward, a syringe fitted with a 24-gauge needle is inserted between the ribs over the heart. The operator can usually feel the heart beat when the needle enters the heart and if the syringe plunger is pulled back slightly, blood will enter the syringe when the needle enters the ventricle.

Heart puncture in the rat can also be done between the xiphoid process and costal angle.

It has been suggested that blood can be obtained via the orbital sinus with greater ease than by way of heart puncture. A glass tubing 6–8 inches in length and 4–6 mm in diameter, drawn out to pipette form is again drawn to provide a capillary puncturing end about 1 inch long. The bore of the puncture end should easily permit the free flow of blood. The animal is held immobile on its side against a table top by a firm grip, permitting the head to be pressed down with the thumb and forefinger. The capillary end of the glass tubing is inserted into the orbit at the anterior angle formed by the lids and the nictitating membrane. A short thrust past the globe will permit entry into the slightly resistant, thorny membrane of the sinus. The eyeball itself remains uninjured. As soon as the sinus is punctured, blood enters the tubing by its own pressure.

The tube then can be sealed and the blood centrifuged without transfer. Heparinization of the tubes permits the taking of larger samples. Stress to the animal can be reduced by the administration of 2 drops of 2% cocaine administered topically to the eye before beginning.

EXPERIMENT 12–3

Parathyroidectomy, Survival Time, and Serum Calcium Levels*

This experiment is carried out best in the cat or dog, since the operation is fatal in these animals. However, the rat may be used if the animal is placed on a calcium-free diet.

Procedure and Experimental

1. Maintain rats on a calcium-free diet for 10–20 days prior to the experiment.

2. Parathyroidectomize several rats.

3. Obtain blood serum at the time of the operation and at 2-hour intervals until death, which occurs in 6–12 hours. If a flame photometer is available for calcium analysis, then blood may be obtained from the tail vein since 0.1 ml of serum is adequate and the same rat can be used over again. However, if serum calcium is determined by the chemical technique, it will be necessary to use one rat per determination. If a

* Cf. references (14, 16–18).

limited number of rats are available, the values obtained at time 0 and 3–6 hours after parathyroidectomy will give adequate results.

A. Determination of Calcium in the Blood by the Permanganate Method

1. Place 2 ml of serum in a 15-ml centrifuge tube.
2. Add 2 ml of distilled water.
3. Add 1 ml of 4% ammonium oxalate.
4. Shake by circular movement and tapping.
5. Let stand at least 30 minutes (or overnight) in the refrigerator.
6. Shake the tubes.
7. Centrifuge for 10 minutes at high speed.
8. Carefully pour off the supernatant; invert the tubes and let them drain on filter paper for 10 minutes.
9. Wipe the mouth of the tube.
10. Break up the precipitate and wash the sides of the tube with 3 ml of dilute ammonium hydroxide (dilute the concentrated NH_4OH to 1:50).
11. Centrifuge and drain as before (Steps 7–9).
12. Add 2 ml of 1.0 N H_2SO_4.
13. Place in a boiling water bath for 1 minute.
14. Titrate with 0.01 N $KMnO_4$ to a pink color. The titration should be carried out while the tube is warm.

Notes: (a) After adding the first drops of permanganate, a pink color may develop and then fade. This is not the end point. (b) Always run 1 blank which contains water in place of the serum. (c) Standardize the $KMnO_4$ against 0.01 N sodium oxalate. (d) One milliliter of 0.01 N $KMnO_4$ is equivalent to 0.2 mg of calcium.

Calculation

$$(x - b)\,(y) \times 100/z = \text{mg/100 ml calcium}$$

$x = $ milliliters of $KMnO_4$ required in titration

$b = $ blank

$y = $ milligrams calcium equivalent to 1 ml of 0.01 N $KMnO_4$ ($=0.2$)

$z = $ milliliters of serum (2 ml is used in this procedure, although 1 ml is sufficient)

B. Determination of Serum Calcium Using Small Amounts of Serum Reagents

Reagents

These reagents are stable at room temperature for 6 months.

1. *Calcium* (standard), 5 mEq/liter. Dissolve 0.2502 gm $CaCO_3$ in 1 ml of 6 N HCl and make up to 1 liter with double-distilled water.

2. *Ethylenediamine tetraacetate (EDTA), stock*, 5 mEq/liter. Dissolve 0.9306 gm of sodium-EDTA·$2H_2O$ in 1 liter of double-distilled water containing 0.1% phenol.

3. *EDTA, titration*, 0.5 mEq/liter. Dilute stock EDTA 1:10.

4. *NaOH*, 0.8 N. Dissolve 32 gm NaOH in 1 liter of double-distilled water. Adjust normality, if necessary, so that the standard curve will pass through the origin.

5. *Cal-Red (indicator)*. Dissolve 400 mg of Cal-Red [2 hydroxy-1-(2-hydroxy-4-sulfo-1-naphthylazo)-3-naphtholic acid] in 100 ml 95% ethanol. Let stand overnight and filter.

Titration

1. Place 0.1 ml of serum in a small Erlenmeyer flask.

2. Add 0.5 ml of the 0.8 N NaOH.

3. Titrate with the EDTA (0.5 mEq/liter) within 10 minutes, using a white background or incandescent light.

Note: Addition of a few drops of methyl red (4 mg/100 ml 95% ethanol) changes the end point to blue green, which may be seen with greater ease by some students.

Calculation

1. Run the titration with the calcium standard in place of the serum. One milliliter of the EDTA (0.5 mEq/liter) is equivalent to a serum calcium of 5 mEq/liter.

EXPERIMENT 12–4

Effect of Parathormone on Serum Calcium*

It has been shown that the serum calcium level falls rapidly after parathyroidectomy in the rat if the animal has been on a calcium-free diet. The rat, under these conditions, has been used extensively as an assay animal and has thus facilitated the work on the purification and identification of parathormone. Treatment of such animals with parathormone results in an increase in serum calcium levels (Fig. 12-5).

Procedure

1. Young adult male rats (180–200 gm body weight) are maintained on a calcium-deficient diet for 4 days prior to parathyroidectomy.

* Cf. references (14, 16).

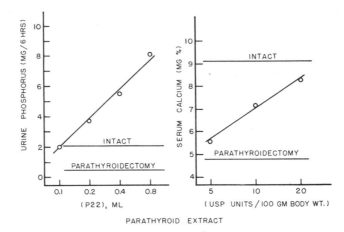

Fig. 12-5. Effect of parathormone on serum .calcium and urinary phosphorus in the rat. From Munson (16).

2. Remove the parathyroid glands by electrocautery (see Experiment 12–1).

3. Immediately after the operation, inject subcutaneously into different groups of rats the various preparations listed below.

4. Exactly 6 hours later, anesthetize the animals with ether and obtain blood by cardiac puncture. Centrifuge the blood and carefully remove the serum for analysis.

5. Determine the calcium present in the serum (see Experiment 12–3).

Experimental

1. Test the following substances: (a) saline, (b) 5 USP units of parathormone, (c) 10 USP units of parathormone, (d) 20 USP units of parathormone, and (e) any available unknown extract of parathyroid gland.

Note: The dosages suggested above for the parathormone are per 100 gm body weight.

2. Plot a dose-response curve. Determine the potency of an unknown extract.

EXPERIMENT 12–5

Self-Selection of Calcium

This experiment is designed to demonstrate the ability of the animal to select a diet essential for the maintenance of life. Richter in 1937 showed that rats selected a diet rich in calcium if the parathyroid glands were absent (23). This finding has been extended to include other essential elements such as increased NaCl intake in adrenal deficiency.

Procedure and Experimental

1. Expose rats to a choice of tap water or 2% calcium lactate in tap water and record daily fluid intake of each liquid throughout the entire experiment.

2. After 1–2 weeks, parathyroidectomize the rats and maintain records of fluid intake for approximately 2 more weeks.

3. Inject the rats with 20–50 USP units of parathormone per 100 gm body weight for 1–2 weeks more and record fluid intake.

4. Plot the daily fluid intake of each liquid over the entire period, denoting the times of operation and replacement therapy.

Note: This experiment may be performed in conjunction with experiments on thyroidectomy in the rat.

References

1. Albright, F. 1941. The parathyroids: physiology and therapeutics. *J. Am. Med. Assoc.* **117**: 527–533.
2. Armaghan, V., Pavlech, H. M., and Olsen, N. O. 1953. Collection and storage of chicken plasma for tissue culture. *Science* **117**: 156–158.
3. Baldini, J. T., and Zarrow, M. X. 1952. Estrogen and serum calcium level in the bobwhite quail. *Poultry Sci.* **31**: 800.
4. Chang, H. 1950. Localized resorption of bone adjacent to parathyroid grafts. *Anat. Record* **106**: 266–267.
5. Clark, I., Bowers, W., and Geofrey, R. 1960. A new method for the bioassay of the calcium mobilizing fraction of parathyroid extracts. *Endocrinology* **66**: 527–532.
6. Collip, J. B. 1925. The extraction of a parathyroid hormone which will prevent or control parathyroid tetany and which regulates the level of blood calcium. *J. Biol. Chem.* **63**: 395–438.
6a. Copp, D. H., and Davidson, A. G. F. 1961. Direct humoral control of parathyroid function in the dog. *Proc. Soc. Exptl. Biol. Med.* **107**: 342–344.
6b. Copp, D. H., Cameron, E. C., Cheney, B. A., Davidson, A. G. F., and Henze, K. G. 1962. Evidence for calcitonin—a new hormone from the parathyroid that lowers blood calcium. *Endocrinology* **70**: 638–649.
7. Davies, B. M. A., Gordon, A. H., and Mussett, M. V. 1955. A mouse urine phosphate assay for parathyroid hormone with certain applications. *J. Physiol. (London)* **130**: 79–95.
8. Davis, R., and Talmage, R. V. 1960. Evidence for liver inactivation of parathyroid hormone. *Endocrinology* **66**: 312–314.
8a. Firschein, H. E., Neuman, W. F., Martin, G. R., and Mulryan, B. J. 1959. Studies on the mechanism of action of the parathyroid hormone. *Recent Progr. Hormone Res.* **15**: 427–454.
9. Gaillard, P. J. 1955. Parathyroid gland tissue and bone *in vitro. Exptl. Cell. Res. Suppl.* **3**: 154–169.

10. Gaillard, P. J. 1959. Parathyroid gland and bone *in vitro*. *Develop. Biol.* **1**: 152–181.

11. Gellhorn, E. 1935. The influence of parathormone on the neuromuscular system: an experimental analysis. *Am. J. Physiol.* **111**: 466–476.

12. Greep, R. O. 1948. Physiology and chemistry of parathyroid hormone, *in* "The Hormones" (G. Pincus and K. V. Thimann, eds.), Vol. 1. Academic Press, New York.

13. Greep, R. O., and Talmage, R. V. 1961. "The Parathyroids." Thomas, Springfield, Illinois.

14. Hawk, P. B., Oser, B. L., and Summerson, W. H. 1947. "Practical Physiological Chemistry," 12th ed. McGraw-Hill (Blakiston), New York.

15. Levinsky, N. G., and Davidson, D. G. 1957. Renal action of parathyroid extract in the chicken. *Am. J. Physiol.* **191**: 530–536.

16. Munson, P. L. 1955. Studies on the role of the parathyroids in calcium and phosphorus metabolism. *Ann. N. Y. Acad. Sci.* **60**: 776–795.

17. Munson, P. L. 1960. Recent advances in parathyroid research. *Federation Proc.* **19**: 593–601.

18. Pappenhagan, A. R., and Jackson, H. D. 1960. Modified method for the determination of serum calcium in the presence of magnesium using Cal-Red indicator. *Clin. Chem.* **6**: 582–584.

19. Polin, D., and Sturkie, P. D. 1958. Parathyroid and gonad relationship in regulating blood calcium fractions in the chicken. *Endocrinology* **63**: 177–182.

20. Pullman, T. N., Lavender, A. R., Aho, I., and Rasmussen, H. 1960. Direct renal action of a purified parathyroid extract. *Endocrinology* **67**: 570–581.

21. Rasmussen, H. 1959. Stability *in vitro* of parathormone. *J. Biol. Chem.* **234**: 547–550.

22. Rasmussen, H., and Craig, L. C. 1959. Purification of parathyroid hormone by use of countercurrent distribution. *J. Am. Chem. Soc.* **81**: 5003.

22a. Rasmussen, H., and Craig, L. C. 1962. The parathyroid polypeptides. *Recent Progr. Hormone Res.* **18**: 269–295.

23. Richter, C. P., and Eckert, J. F. 1937. Increased calcium appetite of parathyroidectomized rats. *Endocrinology* **21**: 50–54.

24. Smith, G. C. 1945. Technique of parathyroidectomy in pigeons. *Anat. Record* **92**: 81–86.

25. Stoeck, H., and Carnes, W. 1945. The relation of the dietary Ca:P ratio to serum Ca and to parathyroid volume. *J. Nutrition* **29**: 43–50.

26. Stone, S. H. 1954. Method for obtaining venous blood from the orbital sinus of the rat or mouse. *Science* **119**: 100.

27. Sturkie, P. D. 1954. "Avian Physiology." Cornell Univ. Press (Comstock), Ithaca, New York.

28. Törnblom, N. 1949. On the functional relationship between the pituitary gland and the parathyroids. *Acta Endocrinol. Suppl.* **4**: 1–76.

29. von Berswordt-Wallrabe, R., and Turner, C. W. 1960. Successful replacement therapy in lactating thyro-parathyroidectomized rats. *Proc. Soc. Exptl. Biol. Med.* **104**: 113–116.

CHAPTER 13

Insulin and Glucagon

The endocrine role of the pancreas and its relation to insulin insufficiency and diabetes mellitus is a well known and classical example of a metabolic disorder arising from a hormonal deficiency. Though the disease had been known since early times, only in the latter part of the nineteenth century was the disorder related to the function of the pancreas. In 1889, von Mering and Minkowsky produced diabetes in the dog by pancreatectomy. In 1921, Banting and Best reported the isolation of an active extract of the pancreas that could control the hyperglycemia of diabetes mellitus. The work of Banting and Best and associates (4) gave such impetus to the research on insulin that the reports of a pancreatic hyperglycemic factor (originally called HGF and now glucagon) were overshadowed. However, the crystallization of glucagon was reported in 1953, and this was soon followed by the determination of its amino acid sequence (12). Recent advances in our knowledge of the role of the pancreatic hormones include the clarification of the structure of the hormones and indications of the sites in the metabolic pathways at which the action of the hormones takes place.

Sites of Formation

The pancreas is a large, well defined lobular gland in most mammals and is formed embryologically from two outpocketings of the duodenum. The gland is grossly divided into three portions: the head, lying near the duodenum, and the body and tail extending toward the spleen. The main pancreatic duct (Wirsung's duct) runs the entire length of the gland and empties the exocrine secretions into the duodenum. The relative compactness of the gland makes extirpation a comparatively simple operation in some mammals (37). However, the pancreas of the rat is so diffuse that extirpation is difficult. In this species, the gland lies in the gastrosplenic ligament and has many separate lobules along the length of the common bile duct. As many as 10–17 separate ducts enter the common bile duct (69).

The exocrine and endocrine portions of the pancreas are histologically well defined and distinct (Fig. 13-1). The exocrine portion of the

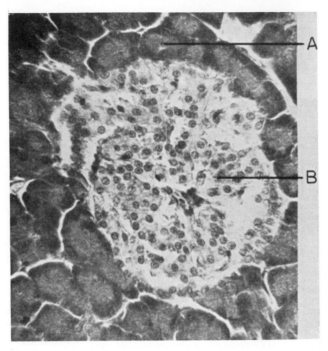

Fig. 13-1. Pancreas of the rat; *A*, exocrine pancreas; *B*, islet of Langerhans. (From 215×.)

pancreas is composed of compound acinar (alveolar) glands; the acini consist of single layers of pyramidal epithelial cells on a reticular membrane around a central lumen. Separate and distinct from the acini are the richly vascularized cells of the islets of Langerhans. The islet tissue is the endocrine portion of the pancreas and is composed of several types of cells. The α-cells are few in number and contain alcohol-insoluble granules. The β-cells compose the major part of the islet cells and contain alcohol-soluble granules. Nongranular γ-cells are found in some species. The δ(delta, D)-cells contain granules which stain differently from those of the α- or β-cells, and it has been suggested that the δ-cells represent a stage in the development of the α- or β-cells.

The histological appearance of the pancreas following the onset of diabetes mellitus or the administration of various agents has aided in the identification of the cells responsible for the secretion of insulin and

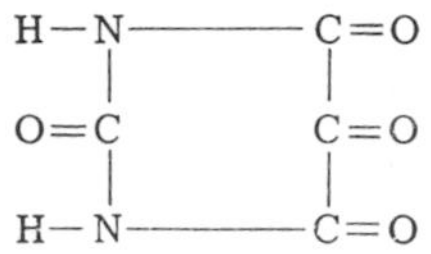

```
H—N————————C=O
 |           |
O=C         C=O
 |           |
H—N————————C=O
```

Fig. 13-2. Structure of alloxan.

glucagon. The discovery that the administration of alloxan (Fig. 13-2), an oxidation product of uric acid, induced degenerative changes in the pancreas and symptoms of diabetes mellitus (22, 30, 41) offered a simple means whereby diabetes mellitus could be produced easily. The nature of the alloxan-induced degenerative changes suggested that the β-cells were the site of insulin production. Rats, dogs, fish, and other animals have been treated with alloxan, and the symptoms of insulin deficiency have been associated with a degranulation and specific damage to the β-cells. Contrary to results obtained in most experimental animals, the pancreas of the guinea pig (1) and of many birds (50, 68) appears to be resistant to administered alloxan. In addition, the symptoms of diabetes mellitus found after the administration of pituitary gland extracts or growth hormone (29, 37, 38, 45) is associated with damage to the β-cells of the pancreas. The insulin deficiency following alloxan administration is a result of a direct damage to the β-cells, but that following treatment with pituitary extracts is considered to be a response from overstimulation and final exhaustion of the β-cell activity. Such evidence has been found sufficient to associate the β-cells of the islets of Langerhans with the site of insulin production.

The α-cells of the islet tissue are considered generally to be the site of glucagon formation although the evidence linking these cells with the hormone is not as complete as that relating insulin with the β-cells. Glucagon has been isolated not only from the pancreas, but, in addition, extracts of various organs from different species have suggested the presence of glucagon-like activity in the gastric mucosa, tongue, spleen, abdominal lymph nodes, and skin (8). Evidence for the role of the pancreas in the secretion of glucagon has been noted from (a) the isolation of hyperglycemic-glycogenolytic activity from pancreatic blood and (b) from cross circulation experiments where the physiological effects of glucagon have been found in a recipient animal linked to the pancreatic venous blood of a donor animal (27, 28). In addition, the administration of such chemicals as cobalt chloride and Synthalin-A (decamethylenediguanidine dihydrochloride) destroy the α-cells with a resultant loss in glucagon content (6, 8, 19, 35), but the results of these experiments have not been clear cut. In cases where the administration of cobalt chloride produced only moderate α-cell destruction, no decrease in pancreatic glucagon was found. However, when severe α-cell necrosis followed the treatment, the glucagon content of the gland was markedly reduced (8). In other experiments (9, 10), partial pancreatectomy of the dog (leaving intact the processus uncinatus which is devoid of α-cells) results in a gland that possesses no glucagon activity (Table 13–1). These studies support the concept that glucagon arises

TABLE 13–1

HYPERGLYCEMIC EFFECT OF EXTRACTS OF DOG PANCREAS ON BLOOD SUGAR
LEVELS OF THE CAT: EFFECT OF EXTRACTS
OF GLAND WITH AND WITHOUT α-CELLS[a]

Time after treatment[b] (minutes)	Blood sugar level (mg/100 ml)	
	Whole pancreas (α-cells present)	Uncinate portion (α-cells absent)
0	122	112
5	172	110
10	204	108
15	200	100
20	—	85
25	164	67

[a] Taken from Bencosme et al. (9).
[b] Treatment equivalent to 1 gm wet weight of pancreas.

from the α-cells. In addition, the results indicate that the various cells of the islets are independent of each other, since in the absence of α-cells the remaining cells in the uncinate portion of the pancreas of the dog do not give rise to new α-cells. These studies also point out the difficulty of establishing the endocrine nature of glucagon along classical lines, for the animal devoid of α-cells (8–10) does not show any physiological symptoms of glucagon deficiency. However, completely pancreactectomized birds show a hypoglycemia which can be corrected by glucagon (37, 47).

Nature of Insulin and Glucagon

Both insulin and glucagon are protein hormones of known amino acid composition. The protein nature of insulin presented a difficulty in the extraction of the hormone from the pancreas due to the presence of the proteolytic enzymes in the exocrine portion of the gland. The historic work of Banting and Best in extracting the active insulin fraction was achieved only when the acinar portion of the pancreas was degenerated (4). Subsequently, workers were able to crystallize both insulin and glucagon and ultimately determine the amino acid sequences of these proteins.

For many years, insulin was thought to be composed of 4 chains of amino acids made up of 2 pairs of identical chains (chains A and B), with a molecular weight of 12,000. The remarkable studies of Sanger culminated in the determination of the amino acid sequence of insulin, for which he was awarded the Nobel prize (67). Sanger showed that insulin consists of 2 chains of amino acids instead of 2 pairs of chains (Fig. 13-3); this finding corresponded with other studies that showed

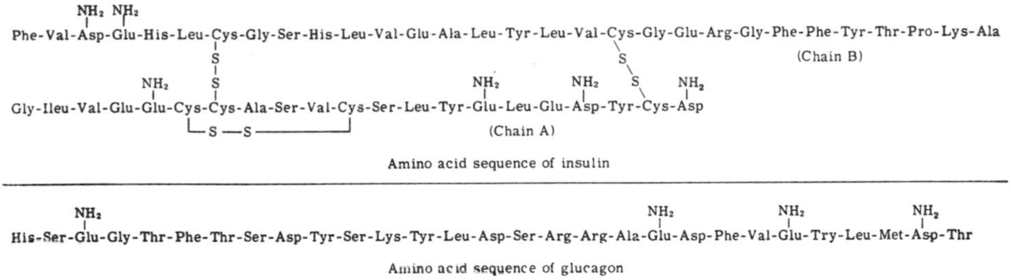

$$NH_2 \quad NH_2$$
Phe-Val-Asp-Glu-His-Leu-Cys-Gly-Ser-His-Leu-Val-Glu-Ala-Leu-Tyr-Leu-Val-Cys-Gly-Glu-Arg-Gly-Phe-Phe-Tyr-Thr-Pro-Lys-Ala
                        S   S   (Chain B)

$$NH_2 \quad S \qquad\qquad\qquad NH_2 \qquad NH_2 \quad S \quad NH_2$$
Gly-Ileu-Val-Glu-Glu-Cys-Cys-Ala-Ser-Val-Cys-Ser-Leu-Tyr-Glu-Leu-Glu-Asp-Tyr-Cys-Asp
        └─ S ─ S ──────────┘   (Chain A)

Amino acid sequence of insulin

$$NH_2 \qquad\qquad\qquad\qquad\qquad NH_2 \qquad NH_2 \qquad\qquad NH_2$$
His-Ser-Glu-Gly-Thr-Phe-Thr-Ser-Asp-Tyr-Ser-Lys-Tyr-Leu-Asp-Ser-Arg-Arg-Ala-Glu-Asp-Phe-Val-Glu-Try-Leu-Met-Asp-Thr

Amino acid sequence of glucagon

Fig. 13.3. Structure of pancreatic hormones.

the correct molecular weight of insulin to be near 6000. Two disulfide linkages connect the chains, and some of the reversible biological inactivations of the molecule are associated with the reduction of these —S—S— bonds. The insulin obtained from various species appears to be identical on the basis of immunological tests, thus indicating a lack of species specificity for this hormone (87). However, structural differences appear to exist between the insulin obtained from several species of fish and that isolated from beef (89).

Following the lead of Sanger, the amino acid sequence of glucagon was also established (12). The molecule of glucagon is a single chain of 29 amino acids, which, like insulin, has several amide groups (Fig. 13-3). A molecular weight of 3350 was obtained experimentally for glucagon. This value is in good agreement with that of 3485 derived from the empirical formula. The lack of —S—S— linkage in the glucagon molecule makes it resistant to alkali reagents. Thus the residual insulin activity present in a glucagon preparation may be removed by treatment with alkali.

Action of the Pancreatic Hormones

While the primary actions of the pancreatic endocrine secretions are on carbohydrate metabolism, these hormones also exert an influence on fat and protein metabolism by both a direct and indirect action. The metabolic pathways involved in the oxidation of carbohydrates are linked with those of fat and protein metabolism, hence modification of carbohydrate metabolism would be expected to reflect some change in fat and protein utilization. With respect to protein metabolism, it has been shown that insulin stimulates incorporation of amino acids into the protein of liver and muscle. The hormone has a limited effect even in the absence of the hypophysis (45a).

The effects of insulin administration may be summarized as follows (33): (a) an increased conversion of glucose to glycogen in liver and muscle; (b) an increased uptake and oxidation of glucose by peripheral tissues; (c) an increased rate of conversion of carbohydrate to fat; (d) an increased rate of protein synthesis.

Although insulin has an effect on liver, muscle, and other tissues, the primary action of glucagon is in the conversion of liver glycogen to glucose. The influence of glucagon on glycogenolysis has been definitely established, and some evidence indicates that glucagon also may influence the peripheral utilization of glucose, with secondary effects on fat and protein metabolism. However, it has also been reported that glucagon has no greater effect on increasing peripheral carbohydrate utilization than that seen following hyperglycemia (8, 28).

Administration of glucagon has been reported to increase fatty acid oxidation, ketone formation, and urinary nitrogen excretion. Whether these effects are attributable to glucagon is still in doubt. Other physiological influences of glucagon are seen in the reduction of gastric motility and secretion and in lowered pancreatic exocrine secretion following hormone treatment (8). In its gastrointestinal action, glucagon reverses the action of insulin.

The observations that glucagon counteracts some of the physiological actions of insulin have led to its characterization as an anti-insulin or insulin antagonist, a term that is objectionable to many investigators. Though glucagon does tend to oppose the action of insulin on the blood sugar level, both hormones appear to stimulate peripheral glucose utilization. While the mechanism by which glucagon does stimulate the uptake of glucose by peripheral tissue is in doubt (either by a direct action of glucagon or by virtue of its hyperglycemic action), nevertheless the combined action of insulin and glucagon on peripheral carbohydrate utilization is greater than that found with either hormone alone. As Hall (33) suggests, the counterbalancing action of the two hormones may serve as a more delicate homeostatic mechanism in the maintenance of blood sugar with a simultaneous stimulatory action of both agents on the peripheral use of glucose.

Much information on the role of insulin in physiological processes has been derived from the study of cases of natural and induced insulin insufficiency. It has been pointed out many times that the relation between insulin insufficiency and diabetes mellitus has been well established and that recent studies have given indications of the site of action of insulin. However, in the case of glucagon, a definite endocrine disorder has not been associated with a lack of this factor. Though experiments have indicated a release of glucagon by the pancreas, with one exception (47), removal of the gland has failed to produce an endocrinopathy ascribable to lack of glucagon. In part, this failure to induce symptoms of glucagon insufficiency may be related to the hyperglycemic factor produced by other organs.

A. DIABETES MELLITUS

The symptoms of insulin insufficiency seen in the diabetic human being have been reproduced in experimental animals including the pancreatectomized or alloxan-treated dog, cat, and rat. The symptoms develop from a reduction of available insulin and include a markedly increased blood glucose level (Table 13–2) which, after exceeding the renal threshold, leads to glucosuria. A typical reduced glucose tolerance curve is shown in Fig. 13-4. Since the diabetic animal is incapable of normal glucose utilization, the energy metabolism is impaired, and both an electrolyte imbalance and a dehydration are noted. The insulin insuffi-

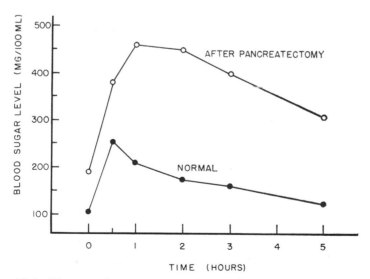

Fig. 13-4. Glucose tolerance curves of normal and pancreatectomized rats. Redrawn from Treadwell and Roe (80).

TABLE 13–2

BLOOD SUGAR IN THE NORMAL, DEPANCREATIZED, AND DIABETIC ANIMAL

Species	Normal blood glucose (mg/100 ml)	Treatment[a]	Post-treatment blood glucose (mg/100 ml)	Reference
Catfish	59	A	120–200	(55)
Toadfish	54	A	100–328 (died in 133 days)	(40)
Lizard	74–113	A	150–209	(48)
Bullfrog	13.5[d]	A	No effect	(92)
Toad	23	P[b]	104 (54–162)	(21)
Barn owl	130 (100–146)	A	Increase 10–30	(68)
Horned owl	155–226	A	No change	(68)
Horned owl	220–350	P	1000–1200	(56)
Pigeon	160	A	300 (with ensuing death)	(68)
Duck	108 (97–133)	A	126	(50)
			123	
			118	
Duck	100–125	P	200	(75)
			100–125	
Mouse	94	A	111–371	(54)
Rat	90–160	A	396–933	(48)
Rat	54	P	367	(69)
			181	
Rat	105	P	185	(80)
Rat	101	P	135	(72)
		P[c]	213	
Guinea pig	160	A	No effect	(1)
Rabbit, fasting	60–120	A	476–581	(31)
		P	400–500	
Sheep	30–50	A	140–200	(39)
Goat	35	P	75–165	(44)
Cat	108	P	592(338–1050)	(43)
Dog fasting	100–110	P	475–510	(25)
		P + insulin	100–150	
Monkey	75–80	P	200–400	(53)

[a] A = alloxan diabetes; P = pancreatectomy.
[b] Subtotal pancreatectomy.
[c] By electrocautery.
[d] 23% showed no measurable blood glucose.

ciency is directly or indirectly associated with abnormal metabolism of proteins and fats which leads to the crisis of the disease, acidosis. The diabetic animal may show the impaired fat metabolism by a high rate of ketone body formation leading to a ketonemia and ketonuria with eventual acidosis and death.

Early studies involving insulin and fatty acid metabolism led to the suggestion that complete oxidation of fatty acids without ketone formation could not be carried out unless an adequate supply of carbohydrate was present. This was expressed by the statement that "fat burns in the flame of carbohydrate." Later when the nature of the biochemical mechanisms of metabolism were more completely outlined, the relationship between fatty acid metabolism and carbohydrate oxidation and ketone formation was more clearly defined, and the suggestion was made that impaired carbohydrate metabolism in the diabetic animal led to a reduced energy supply which shifted the metabolic balance to favor the catabolism of fatty acids. Such a shift was seen to result in an excess formation of 2-carbon acetate fragments. Thus the tissues appeared to be flooded with more substrate than could be utilized, and the excess acetate molecules condensed to form the acidic ketone bodies, acetone, acetoacetic acid, and β-hydroxybutyric acid. Now evidence is available to indicate that insulin itself exerts a direct modification on fatty acid metabolism to account for the ketone formation. However, ketone body formation does occur in normal animals on low carbohydrate intake, as a result of a metabolic shift favoring fatty acid catabolism. Glucagon also appears to influence fatty acid metabolism, but the effect seems to be secondary to its carbohydrate effect.

While the symptoms of diabetes mellitus are associated with an insulin insufficiency, the exact cause of the reduced hormonal activity is unknown. Genetic and dietary factors play a role in the development of the disorder. Studies of diabetic patients and their relatives have revealed that a tendency toward diabetes may be inherited. Secondly, in adult diabetes, obesity is frequently associated with the disease. From studies of the diabetic patients and their symptoms, the subjects have been grouped into two general classes, the juvenile-type and adult-type diabetics. The juvenile type of diabetes is more severe than the adult type, and relatively high levels of exogenous insulin are required to control the acidosis from excessive ketone body formation.

Mirsky and co-workers (51) have studied the inactivation of insulin by the enzyme insulinase found in various tissues. In addition to this factor, several other insulin inhibitors have been found (20, 26, 85). A few diabetic patients respond to exogenous insulin treatment by the production of antibodies which are found to be associated with the γ-globulin fraction of blood protein. These antibodies have a protective action in mice against a convulsive dose of exogenous insulin. Another anti-insulin factor has been found in the α_1-globulin fraction of blood protein obtained from subjects at the onset of the disease. However, this factor is found only in acidotic subjects (26). Another group of workers (85, 86) have found an insulin inhibitor associated with the albumin fraction of blood protein of diabetic patients. Interestingly enough, this inhibitor disappears from the blood of human diabetics and depancreatized cats after hypophysectomy. In the latter animals, the insulin inhibitor reappears after cortisone treatment. Thus not only may the secretory level of the pancreas and metabolic requirement for insulin exert an influence in production of the disease, but the possible presence of insulin inhibitors can reduce the effective level of the circulating hormone.

Plasma insulin assays carried out on the two groups of diabetic human beings have revealed differences in blood hormone levels (86). The plasma from young, insulin sensitive, ketotic patients has been found to be devoid of insulin activity. However, treatment with insulin restores the blood hormone level toward that found in normal subjects. Assay of blood from the mature diabetic shows a normal level of insulin. In these subjects, administration of insulin fails to bring about an increase in circulating hormone. These findings lend further support to the evidence that the presence of insulin antagonists may play a role in diabetes mellitus. In addition, glucose administration increases the plasma insulin level in normal subjects (85, 86) (Table 13–3).

TABLE 13–3

PLASMA INSULIN LEVELS IN MAN[a]

| | Insulin level (microunits/ml) | | | |
| | | After glucose | | |
Sample	Fasting level	Hours	Level	Assay level
Plasma	0.001	2½	0.24–0.40	ADHA[b]
Plasma	0.03–0.08	1	0.13–0.80	Rat diaphragm
Plasma	0.06	1	0.10	Rat diaphragm
Whole blood	0.2	—	—	HA[c]
Plasma	0.05–0.35	—	—	Epididymal fat pad

[a] Taken from Vallance-Owen and Wright (86).
[b] Alloxan-diabetic-hypophysectomized-adrenalectomized rat.
[c] Hypophysectomized-adrenodemedullated rats.

Since insulin is a protein and is destroyed by the digestive enzymes, it is ineffective if administered orally. Several orally active hypoglycemic compounds have become available, e.g., tolbutamide and chloropropamide (Fig. 13-5). Both compounds are derivatives of arylsulfonureas and appear to act by stimulating the release of insulin from the β-cells of

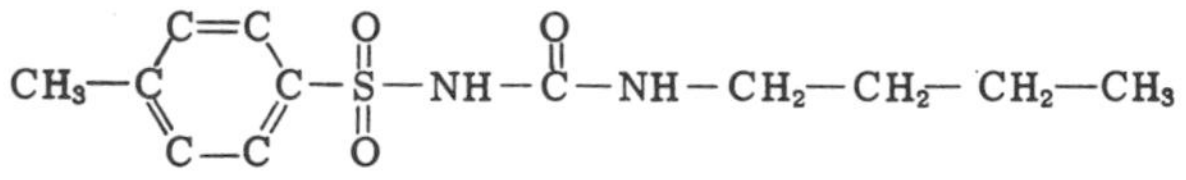

$$CH_3-\overset{C=C}{\underset{C-C}{\bigcirc}}C-\overset{O}{\underset{O}{\overset{\|}{S}}}-NH-\overset{O}{\overset{\|}{C}}-NH-CH_2-CH_2-CH_2-CH_3$$

Tolbutamide

$$Cl-\overset{C=C}{\underset{C-C}{\bigcirc}}C-\overset{O}{\underset{O}{\overset{\|}{S}}}-NH-\overset{O}{\overset{\|}{C}}-NH-CH_2-CH_2-CH_3$$

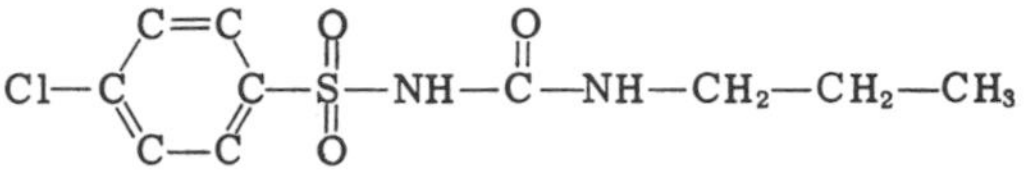

Chlorpropamide

Fig. 13.5. Structure of oral antidiabetic agents: tolbutamide and chloropropamide.

the pancreas and decreasing glucogenesis by the liver (88). Though some evidence indicates that these compounds may reduce insulin degradation, usually this effect is found at doses above the therapeutic level. In addition, these agents may have a direct effect on the liver and produce a hypoglycemia, though this effect occurs only in the presence of insulin. The general concensus indicates that the oral hypoglycemic agent stimulates the β-cells to release insulin since the compounds are generally ineffective in depancreactomized or alloxanized animals. Hence, the use of such compounds is limited to subjects with the adult type of diabetes. The ineffectiveness of the drugs in subjects with the juvenile-type disease lends further support to the concept that in this group of diabetics, the β-cells of the pancreas are not functioning.

B. INTERACTION BETWEEN PANCREATIC AND OTHER ENDOCRINE SECRETIONS

Among the classical studies on the metabolism of carbohydrates in normal and pancreatectomized animals are those that revealed the influence of the anterior pituitary and adrenal glands on this process. Cori and Cori (17) showed that adrenalectomy lowered the blood sugar and liver glycogen levels in rats but had no effect on muscle glycogen. Hypophysectomy in rats was found to bring about an increase in the loss of carbohydrate (64). Houssay first described the amelioration of diabetes mellitus in the depancreatized dog following hypophysectomy. This preparation is now known as the Houssay dog. In the diabetic animal, the blood sugar level, excretion of carbohydrate, and rate of ketosis are reduced following hypophysectomy (20, 36–38, 43, 64, 72), and the animal shows an increased sensitivity to insulin. Although fractions of the anterior pituitary gland and the purified pituitary hormones, growth hormone (STH) and corticotropin, are diabetogenic by inducing β-cell exhaustion (24, 29, 45, 49, 93) in many animals, the exact mechanism of interaction is in question. In the rat, growth hormone has no effect on the insulin requirement of the diabetic animal, and insulin treatment does not increase the body weight or composition of hypophysectomized-force fed rats (70, 71), but insulin is necessary for the anabolic action of growth hormone in the depancreatized rat. However, hypophysectomy, or adrenalectomy, does reduce the insulin requirements of the completely depancreatized rat.

The relief of diabetic symptoms following adrenalectomy (37, 42, 43) is in part related to the reduced stimulation of glycogenesis in the absence of adrenocorticoids. Adrenal cortical extracts or corticoids administered to depancreatized-adrenalectomized rats increase the severity of diabetic symptoms. Though STH cannot stimulate ketosis and the formation of fatty livers in rats, such effects can be induced by administration of ACTH and adrenocorticoids. Diabetic symptoms in animals can be produced with corticoid treatment, though the ability to promote the symptoms and the degree of severity varies with corticoids, dosage, length of treatment, and animals treated. This has been shown quite dramatically in the bird, where the administration of 11-dehydro-17-hydroxycorticosterone is virtually ineffective whereas diabetic symptoms can be produced easily with 17-hydroxycorticosterone (32).

The glycogenolytic, hyperglycemic effect resulting from administration of glucagon is followed by a secondary rise in liver glycogen concentration. Though this effect may be exerted through stimulation of insulin release by the hyperglycemia, the adrenal corticoids appear to exert a permissive action on the liver to allow this secondary deposition of liver glycogen (8).

Some evidence of sexual dimorphism has been obtained regarding the severity of diabetes in male and female rats (5, 37). After subtotal pancreatectomy, the incidence of diabetes is greater in male than female rats and androgen administration increases the severity of the diabetic response. In the bird (32), testosterone administration is without effect on the blood sugar levels. The variation in response of animals to estrogens and adrenocorticoids has been reviewed by Houssay (37). Though treatment wtih both types of compounds first increase the severity of diabetic symptoms, a later preventive action on the incidence of diabetes is noted.

The general findings indicate that the administration of hypophyseal, thyroid, or adrenocortical hormones induces a transient diabetes if treatment is discontinued after a short time. Prolonged treatment induces a permanent diabetic state. The diabetic state induced by hormone administration is identified by the prefix "meta" added to the hormone name, as metathyroid or metasomatotropic diabetes. Though the exact points of interaction through which various endocrine glands influence the response of an animal to insulin or insulin lack is unknown, the effects appear related to a direct action on the pancreas or by reflection through action on various phases of metabolism.

C. Methods of Study of Insulin and Glucagon: Species Variation in Response

A study of the physiological effects of insulin deficiency may be carried out in pancreatectomized animals or intact animals after treatment with alloxan or phlorizin (5, 39, 41, 43, 44, 57). The response of birds appears to differ from that of mammals (35, 68). In general, birds are resistant to alloxan treatment except for the pigeon, which dies shortly after treatment without indication of pancreatic pathology (68). However, treatment of birds with agents that are toxic to the α-cells produces some hypoglycemia (6, 35). The domestic fowl also responds to the antidiabetic drugs with a lowering of blood sugar (35, 52). Nevertheless after such treatment the animals respond to glucagon, a response indicating that the glycogenolytic path is not blocked by the drug.

While alloxan is quite effective in the rat and carnivorous mammals, the effect of the drug and of pancreatectomy itself is reduced in herbivorous mammals (37, 39, 44). Pancreatectomized goats, lambs, pigs, and calves show a rather mild degree of diabetes mellitus, with a slight change in glucose tolerance curves and ketosis. In adult sheep, total pancreactomy produces a severe diabetic state with hyperglycemia and ketosis, to varying degrees. Though the administration of alloxan to herbivores produces the usual severe diabetic symptoms, ketosis is generally reduced.

The onset of diabetes following alloxan administration is characterized by specific physiological changes. Shortly after the initiation of treatment, the animal shows a hyperglycemia which is followed by a hypoglycemic state. Finally a permanent diabetic state is produced showing the usual symptoms of this disorder (30, 41). One point of interest is that glucagon administration prior to alloxan treatment can prevent the diabetic action of the drug (2), but the protection can be offset by insulin injection. The evidence indicates that the blood glucose level at the pancreas may regulate the sensitivity of the gland to alloxan.

Assay of Pancreatic Hormones

A. INSULIN

The techniques employed for the bioassay of insulin are based on the hypoglycemic response and stimulation of peripheral glucose utilization brought about by the hormone. Hypoglycemic convulsions produced in normal intact mice and the hypoglycemia induced in rabbits are the most commonly used assays. In the former, the mouse unit (MU) is defined as the quantity of insulin required to produce convulsions in one-half the number of animals treated (see Experiment 13-4). The assay employing rabbits is usually carried out in 2 kg animals fasted 18–24 hours. One-half the number of animals receive the standard insulin preparation while the remainder receive the test preparation. The glucose level is determined in blood samples at 1.5, 3, and 5 hours after treatment. The cross-over technique is used in this assay: several days later the group given the standard insulin preparation now is administered the test hormone and the second group is given the standard insulin. Calculation of insulin activity in the unknown preparation is made by comparing preparations for their ability to lower blood sugar.

Other test animals have been used to determine the *in vivo* activity of insulin preparations. Opdyke (59) has found a linear relation between the hypoglycemic action of insulin and the logarithm of the dose of insulin when the hormone is administered to chicks fasted 14 hours (Fig. 13-6). Preparations other than intact animals have been used in assays to increase the sensitivity of the animal to insulin. Such assays have employed hypophysectomized-adrenodemedullated-alloxan diabetic rats as test animals (84). These animal preparations are sensitive to insulin doses of 0.001–1 IU/100 gm body weight and have been used to estimate the plasma levels of insulin. The results indicate a variation in the blood hormone content dependent upon the dietary state of the species and the test animal preparation used for the assay (84). However, such studies have shown that a rise in blood insulin level occurs after glucose administration (Table 13-3). Though glucose does increase the circulating level of insulin, only a major change in blood sugar concentration seems able to stimulate pancreatic activity, and some mech-

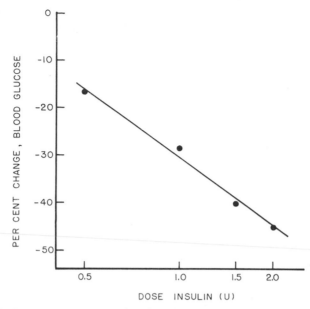

Fig 13-6. Dose-response curve for the effect of insulin on the blood sugar of chicks. Chicks are fasted 14 hours, and blood samples are obtained 1.5 hours after injection. Taken from Opdyke (59).

anism other than glucose level may be responsible for insulin release (13, 86).

The *in vitro* effect of insulin on stimulating glucose uptake and glycogen deposition in the isolated rat or mouse diaphragm has been used to establish insulin levels (60, 75, 83, 84). Minute quantities of insulin are

TABLE 13–4

Effect of Insulin on Glucose Consumption by Isolated Rat Diaphragm[a]

Insulin concentration[b]	Number of hemidiaphragms	Mean glucose uptake[c]	Insulin effect[d]
0	148	7.75 ± 1.2	—
0.01	50	9.13 ± 1.6	1.38
0.10	57	11.15 ± 1.9	3.40
1.00	147	13.83 ± 1.9	6.08

[a] Taken from Vallance-Owen and Wright (86).

[b] Insulin, bovine, microunits per milliliter of saline.

[c] Micrograms sugar per gram wet weight of muscle in 10 minutes; $\pm$ standard deviation.

[d] Mean uptake with insulin minus mean uptake without insulin.

capable of inducing marked increases in glucose uptake by the muscle tissue (56, 61, 86, 91) (Table 13–4). Another *in vitro* test preparation for insulin assay has involved the use of the adipose tissue of the rat (46, 89). The epididymal fat of the rat is quite sensitive to insulin: an increase in the uptake of glucose by the tissue and the conversion of the sugar to fat and carbon dioxide is observed.

B. GLUCAGON

The action of glucagon in stimulating glycogenolysis has been used as a demonstration of the endocrine nature of the hormone and as an assay. Cross-circulation techniques (28) have shown that glucagon is released into the pancreatic venous circulation, as indicated by the hyperglycemic response of dogs receiving such blood. This hyperglycemic response is the end point by which the potencies of glucagon preparations were first measured. In cats and dogs, the technique is based on the ratio of increases in blood sugar levels of animals given standard and unknown preparations of the hormone. Cats appear to be more sensitive test animals (8). In the bird, glucagon has been assayed by determining the time after treatment required to obtain maximum hyperglycemia (7).

The increase in activation of the enzyme, liver phosphorylase, after glucagon treatment and the resultant glycogen depletion in the liver are the bases for other assay methods for this hormone. One method is based

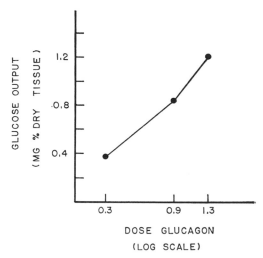

Fig. 13–7. Glucagon assay curve: increase in glucose output of the liver as a function of glucagon level. Redrawn from Tyberghein and Williams (82).

on the glucose output of the excised rabbit liver as a function of glucagon concentration (82) (Fig. 13-7). With this method, the presence of a glucagon-like material in rabbit plasma has been noted. Measurement of liver phosphorylase concentration in liver homogenates incubated with graded amounts of glucagon yield a proportional increase in enzyme concentration with increasing amounts of the hormone (79). This assay method appears to be more sensitive and less complex than the measurement of glucose released by liver slices (86).

Metabolism and Mechanisms of Action

A. Summary of Metabolic Pathways

The metabolism of a molecule of glucose depends on the ability of the molecule to enter a cell, where, under the influence of the enzyme glucohexokinase and of adenosine triphosphate (ATP), it is phosphorylated to form glucose 6-phosphate (G-6-P). From this point, several paths are available for the metabolism of glucose: oxidation with energy production, deposition as glycogen, or conversion to fat, with some carbon fragments serving as skeletons for amino acid synthesis. Insulin appears to act (a) by influencing the ability of glucose to enter the cell or (b) by influencing the ability of hexokinase to phosphorylate the molecule and (c) at the point coupling carbohydrate and fat metabolism, i.e., acetate. Attention to glucagon is drawn in the relation of this hormone to liver glycogen deposition.

The biochemical reactions involved in the formation of glycogen are outlined in Fig. 13-8. Once a molecule of glucose or fructose is phos-

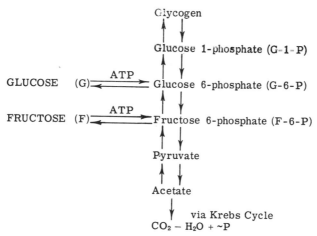

Fig. 13-8. Pathway for glycogen formation and glucose oxidation.

phorylated, it may be deposited as glycogen via glucose 6-phosphate, if not utilized for oxidation and energy production. For further oxidation, glucose 6-phosphate is converted through fructose 6-phosphate to fructose 1,6-diphosphate. This molecule is split into two 3-carbon fragments, one of which undergoes dehydrogenation to form pyruvic acid. Decarboxylation of pyruvic acid results in a 2-carbon fragment, acetate, which then couples with coenzyme A for further biochemical reactions. It is at this point, acetyl-coenzyme A (acetyl-CoA), that the metabolic paths of carbohydrates and fatty acids merge. Glucose oxidation is completed through the union of acetyl-CoA with oxalacetate where, with successive decarboxylation and dehydrogenation in the biochemical reactions of the Krebs or tricarboxylic acid cycle, the oxidation is completed and oxalacetate is regenerated (Fig. 13-9).

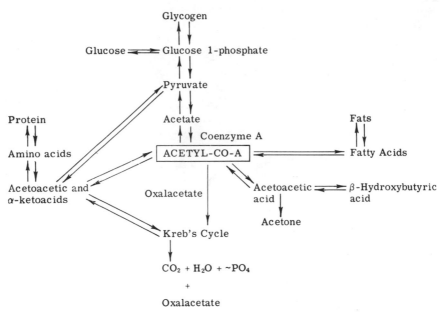

Fig. 13-9. Interrelation of pathways of the metabolism of carbohydrates, fats, and proteins through the formation of acetyl coenzyme A.

The coupling of fatty acid and carbohydrate pathways occurs with the formation of acetyl-CoA since this is a product of oxidation common to both foodstuffs. Fatty acids are catabolized by the successive oxidation of the β-carbon of a fatty acid, splitting off a 2-carbon fragment coupled with coenzyme A and the formation of a fatty acid with 2 carbons less than the original fatty acid (Fig. 13-10). The oxidation of

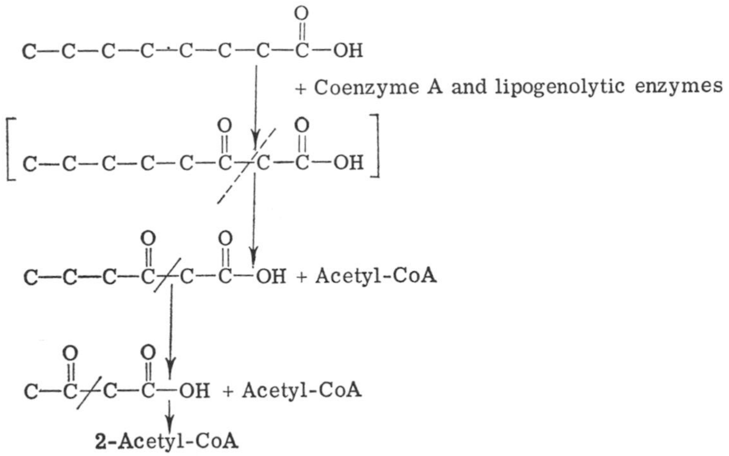

Fig. 13-10. Degradation of fatty acid chain by β-oxidation.

the β-carbon is repeated successively until a residual 2- or 3-carbon fragment of the fatty acid remains. While the routes for fatty acid anabolism and catabolism generally have been considered to be identical, a review of the evidence indicates a dissimilarity (14, 16, 75).

B. ACTION OF PANCREATIC HORMONES IN METABOLIC PATHWAYS

1. Glucagon

The influence of glucagon on glycogenolysis is exerted on the phosphorylase enzyme of the liver involved in the conversion of glycogen to glucose 1-phosphate. Reviews of recent studies indicate that the concentration of active liver phosphorylase (LP) is a function of the balance between the active (phosphorylated) and inactive (dephosphorylated) forms of this enzyme (8, 79). Two cellular factors have been found that control this balance. An enzyme, liver phosphorylase phosphatase (LPP), promotes inactivation of the liver phosphorylase while another enzyme, dephosphophosphorylase kinase (DPPK) stimulates activation of the liver phosphorylase. Glucagon, in combination with a factor from the particulate fraction of the liver cell (adenosine monophosphate, 3',5'-AMP), either supports the action of DPPK or inhibits the action of LPP to bring about a net increase in the concentration of liver phosphorylase. The resulting increase in LP promotes a shift to favor the breakdown of liver glycogen to glucose 1-phosphate and subsequent formation of glucose (Fig. 13-11). This action of glucagon has been demonstrated in liver slices and in cell-free liver preparations, where the increased level of

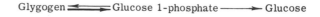

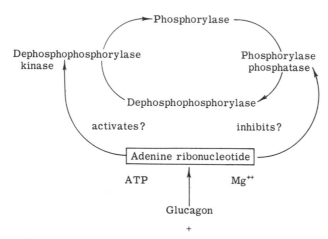

Fig. 13-11. Point of action of glucagon in the stimulation of hepatic glycogenolysis. Adapted from Behrens and Bromer (8).

LP has been observed. Like glucagon, epinephrine is capable of producing an active factor to promote an increase in liver phosphorylase
concentration (79). However, the rapidity of the response seems to vary.
Epinephrine induces a decrease in liver glycogen in as little as 20
minutes whereas the response to glucagon may require 1–2 hours (27).

2. *Insulin*

One of the first points considered for the influence of insulin to be
exerted on carbohydrate metabolism was the entrance of glucose into
the cell and its phosphorylation to glucose 6-phosphate. Early studies
indicated that a relation existed between insulin and the glucohexokinase
enzyme involved in the initial phosphorylation of glucose. Some workers
postulated that the activity of the hexokinase was reduced by a pituitary
factor and that insulin removed the inhibition, permitting the formation
of glucose 6-phosphate (18, 63). Stadie *et al.* (76) investigated the relation between insulin and glucohexokinase in rabbit muscle and failed
to find any influence of the pancreatic or adrenal hormones on the
enzyme. More recently attention has been drawn to the enzyme glucose
6-phosphatase. In rat liver slices, the release of glucose from glucose
6-phosphate is related to the activity of the glucose 6-phosphatase (3).

Administration of adrenal glucocorticoids have been found to increase the activity of the enzyme whereas insulin reduces its activity.

The phosphorylation of glucose is required before subsequent metabolic reactions can take place, but prior to this step the carbohydrate must gain entrance to the cell. Initially, insulin is rapidly bound to the tissue (74, 75, 77). This binding is followed by a marked increase in glucose transport into the cell. In eviscerated dogs, the effect of insulin on the distribution of galactose and related sugars was studied and the hormone was found to facilitate the transport of the sugars from the blood to the tissues (62, 65, 66). The chemical structure on the first three carbon atoms of the sugars which responded to the insulin treatment was identical with that of glucose. The conclusion was that a transport system acted to control the passage of sugar into the muscle. Additional evidence for this role for insulin has come from studies on the rate of penetration of substances from the blood into the aqueous humor of the eye (65, 66). In the alloxanized rabbit, the transfer of glucose into the aqueous humor was reduced by half and insulin treatment restored the permeability of the tissue to the sugar. Results of studies using isotopic glucose and the isolated rat diaphragm also have supported the concept that insulin influences sugar transport before hexokinase activity. In the isolated rat muscle, the concentration of unphosphorylated isotopic glucose was increased in the presence of insulin (61). Thus, insulin appears to modify the transport of glucose into the cell of the peripheral tissue.

It should be kept in mind that the mechanism of action for insulin may be different for the various target tissues. In peripheral tissue, such as the rat diaphragm, exposure to insulin for as little as 10 minutes produces an increased glucose uptake (75, 77) whereas insulin action in the liver and adipose tissue is much slower. Incubation of muscle tissue from normal or diabetic rats, or of liver from normal rats in the presence of insulin, results in a pronounced glucose uptake and glycogen deposition. However, with liver slices from diabetic animals, incubation with insulin fails to show any marked effect.

Two distinct metabolic disorders appear to occur in the liver of a diabetic animal. Glucose metabolism is impaired and fatty acid synthesis is reduced. The results of *in vitro* studies on the livers from diabetic animals have shown that the glucose uptake and conversion to carbon dioxide is markedly reduced, as is glycogen formation. Simultaneously, however, the production of glucose from other metabolites is increased. It has been found that the first metabolic block in the liver of the diabetic animals occurs between glucose and the formation of fructose 6-phosphate (14–16, 75). Fructose and subsequent products of metabolism are oxidized readily in the diabetic liver as indicated by the production of carbon dioxide. However, the utilization of glucose is impaired. Moreover, though the oxidation of fructose is virtually complete, including the formation of acetate, the 2-carbon fragments cannot be utilized for fatty acid synthesis. Thus the second metabolic block in the hepatic tissue of the diabetic animal is related to fatty acid synthesis. In cats (11), pancreatectomy results in a virtual abolishment of the incorporation of acetate into fatty acids and the rate of ketone body formation is increased fivefold (75, 78). In such pancreatectomized animals, hypophysectomy reduces the rate of ketone formation and restores the ability of the liver to synthesize fatty acids from the acetate fragment. As in the oxidation of fatty acids, the synthesis of the fatty acid involves a coupling of molecules of acetyl-CoA to build up the molecular chain. The first step in the formation of the fatty acids is the condensation of two molecules of acetyl-CoA to form butyryl-CoA, a 4-carbon chain, with which another acetyl-CoA is condensed to form a 6-carbon chain. Studies on the livers of diabetic animals have shown the fatty acid synthesis is possible when the substrate is butyryl-CoA but is not possible when the substrate is acetyl-CoA. Thus the block in fatty acid synthesis appears to occur between the coupling of two molecules of acetyl-CoA and the formation of the 4-carbon chain. In view of the stimulation of fatty acid synthesis following hypophysectomy of diabetic animals, fatty acid synthesis appears to be under the influence of both insulin and pituitary factors. Schemes have been devised (23) to show the interrela-

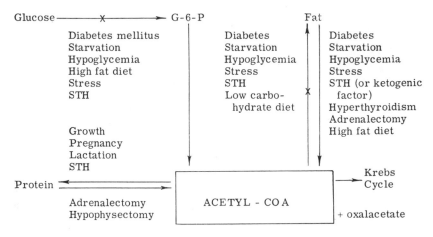

Fig. 13-12. Scheme for the interrelation of factors that influence ketogenesis; →×↔→ = inhibition. From Engel (23).

tion between endocrine and other factors involved in ketogenesis and antiketogenesis (Figs. 13-12, 13-13).

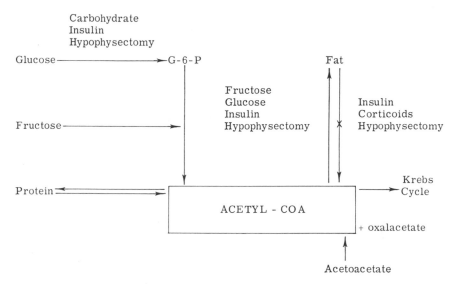

Fig. 13-13. Scheme for factors that influence antiketogenesis; →×↔ = inhibition. From Engel (23).

That other metabolic abnormalities occur in diabetic animals is evidenced by phosphate metabolism and the activities of various enzymes. The mitochondria from the liver of diabetic animals have been found to show a defective phosphate metabolism (75). In such preparations, the oxygen uptake and the rate of formation of the "high energy phosphate" compounds are markedly reduced. These abnormalities are reversed by insulin. As has been pointed out, the rat diaphragm, incubated with insulin or taken from an animal administered insulin, shows a rapid increase in uptake of glucose and formation of glycogen within 1–2 minutes after insulin is given. However, with the liver, 6–24 hours is required after insulin injection for the tissue to show a response in glucose oxidation and fatty acid synthesis.

Thus, the physiological effects of the pancreatic hormones are manifested through actions on metabolic activities at the cellular level. However, while the action of glucagon on hepatic tissue appears to be in the activation of a single enzyme, the action of insulin varies in different tissues. Since no single mechanism of action would seem to account for the responses to insulin, Stadie (75) has made an attempt to correlate the actions of the hormone to form a unified concept of action (Table 13–5). The rapidity of the response of muscle to insulin, both in the

TABLE 13–5

UNIFYING CONCEPT FOR THE ACTION OF INSULIN ON TISSUE[a]

Tissue	Mechanism of action	Site of action	Metabolic effect
Muscle	Combination	Cell surface	Glucose transport
Liver	Adaptation	Enzyme system	Glucose oxidation; fatty acid synthesis; oxidative phosphorylation
Adipose	Adaptation	Enzyme system	Glucose oxidation; fatty acid synthesis

[a] From Stadie (75).

binding of the hormone and in glucose uptake and glycogen deposition, seems to indicate that the hormone acts at the cell surface to aid glucose transport. Although a similar action may occur in hepatic tissue, indications are that the hormone has other influences in this tissue. In the diabetic liver, two metabolic blocks exist. Incubation of liver from diabetic animals with insulin has failed to bring about a reversal of the metabolic blocks resulting from the lack of the hormone. However, administration of the hormone to the intact diabetic animal does result in a reversal of abnormal metabolism, though considerable time is required: 6–24 hours. The time required for insulin treatment to correct the disorders appears to be related to the development or activation of enzyme systems inhibited by the hormone lack. Thus, in the liver, the action of insulin may involve a metabolic adaptation to restore the enzyme systems necessary to rebalance the carbohydrate and fat metabolism toward normal with the production of the proper oxidative phosphorylation mechanisms for production of energy. This unified concept involving the cell transport of glucose and stimulation of enzyme systems does not present the final answer to the mechanism of action of insulin, but it does correlate the known facts and point toward a possible solution.

EXPERIMENT 13–1

Pancreatectomy in the Rat*

The complete removal of the pancreatic tissue of the rat has presented a difficulty because the gland is so diffuse, lying in the gastrosplenic mesentery and in the mesenteric loop of the duodenum. Through

° Cf. references (34, 69–72, 80)

the use of electrocautery techniques, the destruction of most of the pancreatic tissue and subsequent induction of the diabetic condition in the rat is possible. Recent surgical methods utilize a gentle rubbing or scraping of the mesentery with swabs to remove the pancreas. Scow has combined the rubbing technique with electrocautery to bring about nearly complete removal of the pancreas and a severe diabetic state. The postoperative care of the animals is critical, and death may result from ketosis or from an overdose of insulin. The method of Treadwell brings about the removal of a large portion of the pancreas and a slower development of a less severe diabetic state, so that postoperative care is less critical. The operative procedure utilized here is devised after that described by Treadwell. It is recommended that the pancreatectomy as described by Scow be attempted after experience with the Treadwell technique has been obtained.

Procedure

Prior to pancreatectomy, the animals are placed on a low-residue diet to reduce the solid material content of the gastrointestinal tract.

LOW RESIDUE DIET

Component	Per cent by weight
Casein	30
Lard	25
Starch	14
Sucrose	14
Salt mixture	5
Brewers' yeast	10
Cod liver oil	2

Surgical Items

The following surgical items are needed in addition to the routine instruments:

1. *Swabs,* about 30 round tooth picks with a small amount of cotton twisted around one end.

2. *Sterile saline* (0.85%). This is used to keep the exposed organs and fingers of the operator moist during the operation. Removal of the pancreatic tissue is hastened by keeping the tissue moist.

3. *Zephiran solution.* (See Appendix A–9.)

Removal of Blood for Sugar Determination

Blood may be obtained by cutting off a small portion of the tail of the rat. For ease of handling, the animal may be wrapped up in a towel or placed in a plastic restraining cage. The tail is heated under a lamp or in hot water and rubbed to increase blood flow. After this, a small portion of the tip of the tail is cut off with a sharp razor, and the blood is collected. The blood flow may be stopped by applying cotton to the cut end of the tail or dipping the tail in collodion (see bleeding techniques, Experiment 12–2).

Operative Procedure

Select rats weighing 200–300 gm. Place them on the low-residue diet for 3 days, then fast the animals for 24 hours prior to surgery. Anesthetize the rats with Nembutal supplemented with ether if necessary. Moisten the abdomen with some Zephiran and open with a midline incision extending about 3.5 cm caudally from the xiphoid process. Draw out the stomach and turn it upward so that the anterior surface lies on the thorax. If the spleen is not drawn out with the stomach, expose it by drawing out the mesentery between the spleen and stomach. Push the transverse colon in a caudal direction to expose the origin of the pancreatic and splenic blood vessels and the attachment of the mesentery to the posterior abdominal wall. Remember to keep the tissues moist.

Hold the mesentery on the ball of the index finger and gently rub the exposed *moistened* surface with a swab to roll the pancreatic tissue out of the mesentery. Removal of the gland in this area is begun by rubbing upward and outward on the mesentery from its point of attachment to the posterior wall of the abdomen. Continue this removal upward to the spleen and centrally to the greater curvature of the stomach. Though care must be taken to preserve the splenic blood vessels, the vessels may be rubbed with little damage as they rest on the index finger. Particular attention is to be paid to the complete removal of the pancreas tissue about the plexus leading into the hilum of the spleen and that immediately adjacent to the stomach.

The rubbing process is carried downward along the greater curvature of the stomach to the pyloric end, care being given to the gastroduodenal and gastroepiploic arteries. To ensure complete removal of the pancreatic tissue, rub out most of the fat also, so that only the larger blood vessels remain. Disruption of the small vessels leading to the pancreas may be incurred without severe hemorrhage. At this point return the spleen to its normal position. Then exert traction on the duodenum at the pyloric end and expose the first loop of the small intestine, the mesentery of which contains the remainder of the pancreas.

Rotate the animal so that its head points to the operator's right. Use the swab to gently free the duodenal loop from the attachment to the transverse colon. Be cautious at this point since the portal vein is exposed and may be ruptured if care is not taken. Now determine the course of the bile duct (note the many small ducts) by holding up the intestinal loop. Observe the duct passing obliquely through the mesentery near the pylorus until it enters the duodenum. First remove the 5% of the pancreas lying between the bile duct and the duodenum. Start the gentle rubbing of the mesentery at the point of attachment of the stomach and work downward parallel to the bile duct. Next remove the pancreas from the rest of the mesentery within the loop by starting along the line of the portal vein and working upward and outward. After the pancreas on one side has been removed, turn the animal to the operator's left and rub the opposite side of the mesentery to remove the remainder of the pancreas. Be certain to remove entirely that part of the pancreas which lies against the inner curvature of the duodenal loop.

Return the organs to the abdominal cavity. Close the peritoneum and muscle layer together with a continuous suture. The cutaneous layer is closed with individual stitches. Immediately give the rat an 8-ml injection of isotonic saline by subcutaneous injection in the dorsal region. Then inject 300 units of penicillin in 0.1 ml subcutaneously in the lateral aspect of the thigh. Maintain the animal at 35°C for 72 hours and without food or water for the first 24 hours. Give the animal saline drinking fluid for the next 48 hours. The low residue diet should be again initiated on the second postoperative day and maintained until day 7 when the standard laboratory diet may be given.

EXPERIMENT 13–2*

Analysis of Urine and Blood

Insulin deficiency may result in an abnormal protein and fat metabolism in addition to the impairment of carbohydrate metabolism. Thus, increased catabolism of fatty acids, a block in the synthesis of fatty acids, and the decreased ability to utilize glucose causes an accumulation of metabolites in blood, and their subsequent excretion in urine. Analyses of blood and urine reveal an increased level of glucose and ketone bodies such as acetone and acetoacetic acid.

Qualitative Determination of Acetone, Acetoacetic Acid and Reducing Sugars in Urine

I. TEST FOR ACETONE

1. Add a few drops of freshly prepared 5% sodium nitroprusside solution to 2–5 ml of urine.

* Cf. reference (34).

2. Add dilute sodium hydroxide until the solution is alkaline (a red color will appear).

3. Add a few drops of acetic acid until the solution is acid.

4. If acetone is present, the red color is intensified; if not, the color changes to yellow.

II. TEST FOR ACETOACETIC ACID

1. Add a solution of 5% ferric chloride drop by drop to 5 ml of urine in a test tube until the precipitate of ferric phosphate ceases to form.

2. Filter the solution and add more ferric chloride to the filtrate. The presence of acetoacetic acid is indicated by the development of a deep red color.

III. TEST FOR REDUCING SUGARS

1. Place 5 ml of Benedict's Qualitative Reagent in a test tube.

Benedict's Reagent

Copper sulfate	17.3 gm
Sodium citrate	173.0 gm
Sodium carbonate	100.0 gm
Distilled water to make	1 liter

2. Add exactly 8 drops of urine.

3. The mixture may be boiled cautiously, not vigorously, over a flame for 1–2 minutes (or mixed thoroughly and placed in a boiling water bath for 5 minutes).

4. After heating, allow the tube to cool in *air*. If glucose is present the solution will show a precipitation or colloidal precipitate, green, yellow, or red in color. If glucose is absent, color change will not occur though slight precipitation of ureates may be noted.

Quantitative Determinations of Blood Glucose*

I. NELSON-SOMOGYI METHOD

Procedure

Reagents

1. *Copper reagent*

Na_2HPO_4 (anhydrous)	28 gm
Rochelle salt (potassium sodium tartrate)	40 gm
Dissolve in 700 ml water	

* These methods may be used in conjunction with Experiment 7-12 for determination of liver glycogen.

1.0 N NaOH	100 ml
10% CuSO₄	80 ml
Na₂SO₄ (anhydrous)	180 gm

1.0 N NaOH — 100 ml
10% $CuSO_4$ — 80 ml
Na_2SO_4 (anhydrous) — 180 gm

Dissolve the Rochelle salt and Na_2HPO_4 first, then add the NaOH, $CuSO_4$, and the Na_2SO_4 in that order. Make up to 1 liter, let stand for 24–48 hours, then filter.

2. Arsenomolybdate reagent

Ammonium molybdate   25 gm in 450 ml H_2O
H_2SO_4 (conc.)   21 ml
$Na_2AsO_4 \cdot 7\ H_2O$ 3 gm in 25 ml

Mix and incubate at 37°C for 24–48 hours. Store in dark glass-stoppered bottle.

3. Deproteinizing reagents

$ZnSO_4$ 5%
$Ba(OH)_2$ 0.3 N

Adjust concentrations so that 5 ml $ZnSO_4$ is equivalent to 4.7–4.8 ml of barium hydroxide. Dilute 5 ml of zinc sulfate to 25 ml and titrate with barium hydroxide, using phenolphthalein as indicator. The actual concentrations of the barium hydroxide and zinc sulfate are not important; the equivalence of both solutions is important.

4. Sugar standards

Prepare a stock glucose solution by dissolving 100 mg/100 ml of reagent grade glucose in saturated benzoic acid solution. Dilute the stock solution to prepare sugar standards of 0.05 mg/ml (1:20 dilution) and 0.10 mg/ml (1:10 dilution). Use the saturated benzoic acid solution as the diluent. Other standard solutions ranging from 0.01 mg/ml to 0.15 mg/ml may be prepared for use in determining the validity of the Beer's law relation for this procedure (plot absorbancy versus concentration).

Blood Filtrate

1. Mix 0.1 ml of blood and 3.1 ml of H_2O; rinse pipette by drawing water into tube and expelling.
2. Add 0.4 ml of barium hydroxide.
3. Mix and let stand 10 minutes.
4. Add 0.4 ml of zinc sulfate after the mixture has turned brown.
5. Stopper and shake.
6. Centrifuge or filter (this results in a blood dilution of 1:40).

Determination of Glucose

1. Add 1 ml of filtrate (or 1 ml glucose standard) to Folin-Wu tube.

2. Add 1 ml of copper reagent.

3. Place in boiling water bath for exactly 20 minutes. (A glass bead or marble should be used to close the mouth of the Folin-Wu tube.)

4. Cool in running water.

5. Add 1 ml of arsenomolybdate reagent.

6. Dilute to the 25 ml mark.

7. Mix.

8. Determine the absorption spectrum in a spectrophotometer at wavelengths between 500 and 550 mμ (540 mμ is given as usual maximum); set the instrument with a blank prior to each reading (or use Klett photoelectric colorimeter with the green filter)

$$\text{mg/100 ml blood sugar} = (R_U/R_{St}) \times St \times dil. \times 100$$

R_U = Klett reading of unknown
R_{St} = Klett reading of standard
St = milligrams sugar in standard
dil. = 40

Always use two sugar standards: 0.05 mg/ml, 0.10 mg/ml.

II. ANTHRONE METHOD

This method (71a) requires great care in performing the technical procedures. Use only clean glassware, rinse mouth and hands before pipetting, and measure all reagents carefully.

Procedure

Blood Filtrate

1. Discharge 0.1 ml of each blood sample into marked centrifuge tubes containing exactly 10 ml of *freshly prepared* 4% trichloroacetic acid (TCA). (Rinse the blood pipette back and forth by keeping the tip immersed and alternately drawing up and blowing back two or three times.)

2. Let tubes stand 15 minutes.

3. Centrifuge at moderately high speed for 10 minutes.

4. Decant the supernatant fluid into a clean dry test tube. (If tubes are stoppered and refrigerated, they will be stable for 3–4 days. Store the samples if the experiment cannot be completed the same day.)

Determination of Glucose

1. Carefully pipette duplicate 2.0-ml portions of each supernatant into 16 × 150 mm Pyrex test tubes.*

2. The test tubes should be in a rack for all the following steps. With a 5.0-ml syringe fitted with a 2-inch, 18-gauge needle, rapidly add into each tube exactly 4.0 ml of the anthrone reagent (0.2% anthrone in concentrated sulfuric acid, *prepared fresh* within 3 hours of use). The tubes become very hot. Mix vigorously with a stirring rod. Use a clean, oven-dried stirring rod for each sample.

3. Allow tubes to cool: read in a colorimeter, at a wavelength of 620 $m\mu$, no earlier than 10 minutes after color development, using a reagent blank which contains distilled water instead of the blood filtrate.

4. Each set of determinations should be accompanied by glucose standard controls, prepared in distilled water and containing, in duplicate, the equivalents of 50 and 100 mg blood sugar per 100 ml. By this method, 20 μg of standard glucose per 2.0 ml sample are equivalent to 100 mg blood sugar per 100 ml.

Experimental

1. Determine the blood sugar levels in the rat prior to and following pancreatectomy.

2. Examine the urine of these animals for the presence of ketone bodies and reducing sugars.

EXPERIMENT 13–3

Alloxan Diabetes†

The experimental study of diabetes mellitus was facilitated by the discovery of a specific chemical, alloxan, which can induce necrosis of

---

* In cases where very *high* levels of blood glucose are expected, it is often necessary to use less supernatant. The following dilutions are convenient.

Supernatant (ml)	Water (ml)	Total volume (ml)	Factor
1.0	1.0	2.0	2
0.5	1.5	2.0	4
0.4	1.6	2.0	5

If this is done, multiply the final blood glucose value (obtained from the standard curve) by the appropriate factor.

† Cf. references (22, 30, 39–41, 50, 54).

the β-cells of the pancreas. Not only did the studies involving alloxan offer a means of extending the physiological investigations of insulin insufficiency, but also they presented early evidence that the hormone originated from a specific cell in the pancreas.

Procedure and Experimental

For best results, use rats that weigh 120–150 gm and have been fasted for 24 hours. The initial blood sugar level of the animals should be determined before the alloxan is administered. Prepare a 2% solution of alloxan monohydrate in saline and administer the agent to each of two groups of rats at two dose levels; 50 and 100 mg per kilogram body weight. A third group of animals are used as controls. The drug is to be administered by intravenous injection into the tail vein (or saphenous vein) of the animals. Subcutaneous injection may be used if the dosage is raised to between 150 and 200 mg/kg.

For injections into the tail vein, place the rat in a restraining cage or wrap securely in a towel. Swab the tail with xylene, then immediately wash the tail with alcohol. This is necessary in order to remove the xylene, which is extremely irritating. The tail veins should be clearly visible, if they are not, a lamp may be used to heat the tail. (In large animals, washing the tail with warm water and soap will aid in making the vessels visible). Inject the alloxan with a 27-gauge needle, inserting the needle at a slight angle under the scale of the tail parallel to a vein. Always start the injection near the tip of the tail since the vessels are easier to enter at this point, and, in addition, if any difficulty develops in the injection, that portion of the vein anterior to the initial injection site can still be used.

If the injection is to be made into the saphenous vein, roll the rat tightly in a cloth towel with the hind legs exposed. Shave one leg and wash it with Zephiran. Then hold the leg firmly to occlude the circulation. Make the injection into the exposed vein at the level of the foot.

During the 2-week period following treatment, record the daily water intake of each animal, both treated and control rats. Determination of fluid intake is facilitated by using a calibrated drinking tube for each animal. After 2 weeks, determine the blood sugar levels of the rats to determine the severity of the diabetes.

Since it is possible to obtain enough blood from one rabbit for an entire class to use for blood sugar determination, it is valuable to repeat the experiment on alloxan diabetes in this animal. Fast a rabbit for 24 hours; then inject the animal intravenously in an ear vein with alloxan (10%) at a dose of 150 mg per kilogram body weight. Student groups will be assigned the days on which blood is to be obtained and the glucose level determined.

Review the symptoms that accompany the development of alloxan diabetes and the possible role of glucose level in resisting alloxan damage to the pancreas.

EXPERIMENT 13–4

Insulin Convulsions in Mice

The ability of insulin to decrease blood sugar offers a ready means for detecting the activity of the hormone. If the insulin titer becomes too great, a hypoglycemic shock ensues which is accompanied by severe muscular spasms (presumably associated with the degradation of muscle glycogen). Insulin convulsion in the mouse has been used as a routine screening assay for the potency of insulin preparations.

Procedure and Experimental

Mice, weighing less than 20 gm, are fasted for 24 hours. Insulin, 0.5–1 unit in a volume of 0.1 ml, is injected subcutaneously. Immediately place each animal into a separate compartment surrounded by water at 38°C. (Why is the temperature important?) Observe the mice at 5-minute intervals; pick up each mouse and allow it to drop from a height of 2 inches. Make observations quickly, and return the animal to its compartment. Record the changes and compare the times at which convulsions first appeared in the mice throughout the laboratory.

When the convulsions appear, inject one mouse subcutaneously with 0.05 ml of 10% glucose and inject the other with 0.1 ml of epinephrine (1:1000). Return the animals to the compartments and observe the changes. Compare the effects of epinephrine and glucose.

Continue the observations on the mice after the above treatments. Do convulsions reappear? If so, why? If convulsions do reappear inject more glucose or epinephrine and repeat until convulsions do not appear for 1 hour.

Why are the animals dropped from a height of 2 inches? What initiates the convulsions? What tissues are involved? Explain any differences in the responses of the mice to insulin. Compare the physiology involved in the response of the insulin-treated mice to epinephrine and glucose. How might glucagon affect insulin-treated mice?

If a sufficient number of mice are available, inject groups of 15–20 with various amounts of insulin (e.g., 0.2 U, 0.5 U, 1 U, 2 U, etc.) and establish a dose-response curve by plotting the percentage incidence of convulsions in each group of mice against the dose of insulin.

EXPERIMENT 13–5

Insulin Hypoglycemia in the Rabbit

In the preceding experiment, the hypoglycemic action of insulin in mice was detected by the convulsion resulting from the low blood sugar level. Similar responses occur in larger animals, however, the decrease in blood sugar is more gradual. Observations on the blood glucose level in the rabbit before and after insulin administration can illustrate clearly the effect of the hormone on carbohydrate metabolism. In this experiment, it is important to observe the precautions of keeping the animal warm and to have available glucose for injection if the animal goes into hypoglycemic coma. The response of an animal in hypoglycemic shock to glucose is dramatic.

Procedure and Experimental

A young, immature rabbit, approximately 1 kg in body weight, is fasted for 24 hours and injected with insulin (50–100 IU/kg) intramuscularly. Blood for glucose determination may be taken from the marginal ear vein prior to treatment and at every 15 minutes or half-hour after treatment until convulsions appear.

The animal should be kept warm throughout the experiment and a 5% glucose solution must be available for intravenous injection to prevent death from hypoglycemic shock. When convulsions appear, inject the glucose solution into the ear vein. Record the amount of glucose administered and the frequency of treatments. One laboratory group may be assigned to observe the animal during the evening in case subsequent glucose treatment becomes necessary.

Plot the change in blood sugar level as a function of time; note on the graph the point at which convulsions and/or coma occurred.

EXPERIMENT 13–6

Insulin Hypoglycemia in Fish

Insulin, as far as is known, lacks species specificity with the possible exception of some species of fish. While the hormone is protein in nature and is destroyed by digestive enzymes, like many proteins, it can be absorbed through mucous membranes. In this experiment, fish are bathed in an insulin solution to determine the ability of various concentrations of the hormone to induce hypoglycemic shock.

Procedure and Experimental

Distribute minnows or goldfish into 5 bowls containing the following dilutions of insulin (IU/100 ml): 100, 200, 300, 400, and 500.

Determine the time required for each concentration of insulin to produce cessation of activity and the failure of the fish to right itself. As soon as the insulin shock is manifested, transfer the fish to bowls containing 5% glucose. Note that all the solutions will not induce hypoglycemic shock, hence the experiment should be terminated after 1-2 hours.

EXPERIMENT 13-7

Glucose Tolerance Response in Rats*

Under conditions where the endogenous production of insulin is decreased, the metabolism of carbohydrates is also reduced. The glucose tolerance response is an attempt to measure the ability of an animal to metabolize carbohydrates and thus is a reflection of insulin release. The administration of glucose to a fasted, normal animal, is followed by a rapid rise in blood sugar with a slower return to the normal level. In diabetic or insulin-insufficient animals, the increased blood sugar level is maintained for a prolonged period before the return to normal or pretreatment level (see Fig. 13-4). Thyroxine and other agents that modify carbohydrate metabolism also influence the glucose tolerance curve.

Procedure and Experimental

The blood glucose tolerance experiment is usually carried out in unanesthetized animals. However, for ease of handling, the rats may be anesthetized lightly with Nembutal (25 mg per kilogram body weight). Also the animals should be fasted for 24 hours.

Lightly anesthetize the animal with Nembutal and wrap the animal in a cloth towel or place it in a plastic restraining cage with the tail extended. After the animal has been anesthetized for 15-20 minutes obtain a sample of blood (0.1 ml) from the tail vein. The tail may have to be heated under a lamp to increase the blood flow. Inject the animal with glucose (350 mg/100 gm body weight intraperitoneally) and obtain

* Cf. reference (80).

tail vein blood at 10, 30, 60, and 120 minutes after treatment (see Experiment 12–2 for blood withdrawal techniques). Determine the blood glucose level in all samples and draw a glucose tolerance curve. Compare the glucose tolerance curve for normal and diabetic animals and account for the differences.

Normal, diabetic, and thyroxine-treated rats may be used for the various curves compared.

Too much struggling on the part of the animal will change the shape of the curve. Why?

EXPERIMENT 13–8

Effect of Insulin on the Uptake of Glucose by Isolated Muscle*

One of the effects of insulin that has been demonstrated many times is the ability of this hormone to increase the penetration of sugars into muscle tissue. Stadie and co-workers showed that not only did insulin increase the sugar accumulation in the isolated tissue, but the hormone was actually bound to the muscle. This response to the hormone has served as an *in vitro* assay for insulin preparations and for the estimation of plasma insulin levels. In addition, this technique has been utilized to show the effect of other endocrine secretions on the accumulation of glucose in the diaphragm and of xylose in the intact frog peroneus muscle.

Procedure and Experimental

In the technique described here either one rat or five mice may be used. The hemidiaphragms are obtained from the animals and one rat hemidiaphragm (or 5 mice hemidiaphragms) are incubated with the insulin-glucose solution while the other hemidiaphragm is incubated with the glucose alone as a control. At the end of the experiment, the glucose remaining in the incubation media is determined in order to evaluate the rate of sugar uptake by the isolated muscle.

Materials

1. *Animals:* rats 150 gm (mice 25–30 gm), all of the same sex fasted for 24 hours.

2. *Krebs-Ringer Bicarbonate solution* (KRB) (see Appendix A–8).

3. *Glucose solution.* Dissolve glucose in KRB solution to prepare a concentration of 3 mg glucose per milliliter. This is the GKRB solution (see Appendix A–8).

* Cf. references (58, 60–62, 75, 77, 83, 90, 91).

4. *Insulin.* Dissolve purified insulin in a 0.9% saline solution (pH 3) to produce a concentration of insulin of 50 units/ml. Prepare insulin standard by diluting the insulin with GKRB to a concentration of 1 unit of insulin/ml GKRB. Prepare serial dilutions of insulin to 10^{-5} units per milliliter of GKRB.

Method

Kill the animal by a sharp blow on the head; rapidly expose the diaphragm with as little trauma as possible. Excise the diaphragm with iridectomy scissors and place the muscle in *ice cold* KRB. (*Note:* no glucose is present.) Allow the tissue to remain in the cold KRB 15–20 minutes. While in the cold KRB, the diaphragm may be cut in half; the thick posterior portion and any adipose tissue is discarded. (If mice are used, the KRB solution should be oxygenated continuously with 95% O_2 and 5% CO_2 during this period. In addition, the diaphragms may be cut in half after this preliminary incubation in the cold.)

Remove the diaphragms and rinse with fresh medium (KRB), then blot dry. Place 1 hemidiaphragm (or 5 mouse hemidiaphragms) in a Warburg vessel with 2.0 ml GKRB solution containing a known concentration of insulin. The control muscle is placed in another cup (Warburg) with 2.0 ml of the GKRB solution alone. Attach the cups to the Warburg manometer and gas with 95% O_2–5% CO_2. Incubate at 37°C for 90 minutes at 90 oscillations per minute. At the end of the incubation period, determine the residual glucose in the media. (Make duplicate determinations using one of the techniques described in Experiment 13–2.)

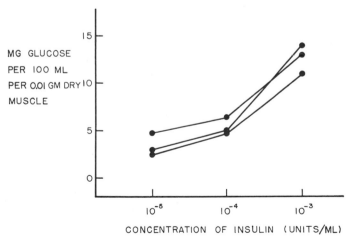

Fig. 13-14. Effect of insulin on the glucose uptake by the isolated rat diaphragm. Redrawn from Vallance-Owen and Hurlock (83).

Remove the hemidiaphragms, rinse in water, dry at 105°C for 2 hours, then weigh. Be sure to allow the tissue to cool before weighing, in order to obtain an accurate weight. Calculate the glucose uptake in terms of milligrams glucose per 100 ml per 10 mg dry weight. Plot the glucose uptake against concentration of insulin (Fig. 13-14) and determine the insulin effect (Table 13–4).

EXPERIMENT 13–9

Hyperglycemic Agents*

Both glucagon and epinephrine bring about an increase in blood sugar by essentially the same mechanism. However, the response to epinephrine is usually more rapid than that for glucagon. Any of the common laboratory animals, such as bullfrog, rabbit, rat, may be used in this experiment to demonstrate the action of hyperglycemic agents. In general, it is best to use a light anesthesia to minimize the endogenous release of epinephrine as a result of the animal struggling.

Procedure and Experimental

Obtain a bullfrog (*Rana catesbiana*); either pith the animal posteriorly or anesthetize it with 10% urethan. Secure the animal to a frog board and insert a 22-gauge needle into the right ventral aorta. Leave the needle in place for subsequent injections and blood withdrawals. Inject the animal with heparin (5 mg per kilogram body weight). For a class experiment, various student groups may be assigned dosages of glucagon (varying from 5 to 200 μg/kg) and epinephrine (50–100 μg/kg) for administration to the animals.

Determine the initial blood sugar level (time zero). Then determine the blood sugar levels at various intervals after administration of the hyperglycemic agent (20, 30, 60, and 90 minutes). Tabulate the results. Compare the rapidity and degree of response to the two hyperglycemic agents. Review the mode of action of these hormones.

References

1. Allergretti, N., Est, M., and Uriac, D. 1956. Alloxan administration in the guinea pig with acinous tissue atrophic rendered by ligature of the pancreatic duct. *Endocrinology* **59**: 131–134.
2. Arteta, J. L., and Carballido, A. 1957. The preventive effect of glucagon (HGF) against the diabetogenic action of alloxan and its antagonism by insulin. *J. Endocrinol.* **15**: 243–247.

* Cf. references (8, 79, 82, 91, 92).

3. Ashmore, J., Hastings, A. B., Nesbett, F. B., and Renold, A. E. 1956. Studies on carbohydrate metabolism in rat liver slices. Hormone factors influencing glucose-6-phosphatase. *J. Biol. Chem.* **218**: 77–88.

4. Banting, F. G., Best, C. H., and Macleod, J. J. R. 1922. The internal secretion of the pancreas. *Am. J. Physiol.* **59**: 479.

5. Beach, E. F., Bradshaw, P. J., and Blatherwick, N. R. 1951. Alloxan diabetes in the albino rat as influenced by sex. *Am. J. Physiol.* **166**: 364–373.

6. Beekman, B. E. 1956. The effect of Synthalin A on blood sugar and pancreatic alpha islet cells of the fowl. *Endocrinology* **59**: 708–711.

7. Beekman, B. E. 1958. A bioassay for glucagon based on the hyperglycemic response of the fowl. *Poultry Sci.* **37**: 595–599.

8. Behrens, O. K., and Bromer, W. W. 1958. Glucagon. *Vitamins Hormones* **16**: 263–301.

9. Bencosme, S. A., Liepa, E., and Lazarus, S. S. 1955. Glucagon content of pancreatic tissue devoid of alpha cells. *Proc. Soc. Exptl. Biol. Med.* **90**: 387–389.

10. Bencosme, S. A., Mariz, S., and Frie, J. 1957. Changes in dogs devoid of A-cells. *Endocrinology* **61**: 1–11.

11. Brady, R. O., Lukens, F. D. W., and Gurin, S. 1951. Synthesis of radioactive fatty acids *in vitro* and its hormonal control. *J. Biol. Chem.* **193**: 459–464.

12. Bromer, W. W., Staub, A., Diller, E. R., Bird, H. L., Sinn, L. G., and Kehrens, O. K. 1957. The amino acid sequence of glucagon. *J. Am. Chem. Soc.* **79**: 2807–2811.

13. Brown, E. M., Dohan, F. C., Freedman, L. R., DeMoor, P., and Lukens, F. D. W. 1952. The effects of prolonged infusion of the dog pancreas with glucose. *Endocrinology* **50**: 644–656.

14. Chernick, S. S., and Chiakoff, I. L. 1951. Two blocks in carbohydrate utilization in the liver of diabetic rats. *J. Biol. Chem.* **188**: 389–396.

15. Chernick, S. S., and Scow, R. O. 1959. Early effects of "total" pancreatectomy on fat metabolism of the rat. *Am. J. Physiol.* **196**: 125–131.

16. Chaikoff, I. L. 1951–1952. Metabolic blocks in carbohydrate metabolism in diabetes. *Harvey Lectures* **47**: 99–125.

17. Cori, C. F., and Cori, G. T. 1927. The fats of sugar in the animal body. VII. The carbohydrate metabolism of adrenalectomized rats and mice. *J. Biol. Chem.* **74**: 473–494.

18. Cori, C. F. 1945–1946. Enzymatic reactions in carbohydrate metabolism. *Harvey Lectures* **41**: 253–272.

19. Davis, J. C. 1952. Hydropic degeneration of the α-cells of the pancreatic islets produced by Synthalin-A. *J. Pathol. Bacteriol.* **64**: 575–584.

20. De Bodo, R. C., and Altszuler, N. 1958. Insulin hypersensitivity and physiological insulin antagonists. *Physiol. Rev.* **38**: 389–445.

21. Dosne, C. 1943. Study of interrelationship of pancreatic diabetes with endocrine glands in toad. *Endocrinology* **33**: 224–228.

22. Dunn, J. S., Shoehan, H. L., and McLetchie, N. G. B. 1943. Necrosis of the islets of Langerhans produced experimentally. *Lancet* **i**: 484–487.

23. Engel, F. L. 1957. The influence of the endocrine glands on fatty acid and ketone body metabolism. *Am. J. Clin. Nutrition* **5**: 417–430.

24. Engel, F. L., Albertson, T., Fredricks, J., and Lopez, E. 1958. Evidence for stimulation of insulin secretion by growth hormone in the rat. *Endocrinology* **63**: 99–105.

25. Feller, D. D., Chiakoff, I. L., Strisower, E. J., and Searle, G. L. 1951. Glucose utilization in the diabetic dog studied with C-14 glucose. *J. Biol. Chem.* **188**: 865–880.

26. Field, J. B., and Stetten, D. 1956. Humoral insulin antagonism associated with diabetic acidosis. *Am. J. Med.* **21**: 330–343.

27. Foà, P. P., Galansino, G., and Pozza, G. 1957. Glucagon: a second pancreatic hormone. *Recent Progr. Hormone Res.* **13**: 473–510.

28. Foà, P. P., Weinstein, H. R., and Smith, J. R. 1949. Secretion of insulin and of a hyperglycemic substance studied by means of pancreatic-femoral cross circulation technique. *Am. J. Physiol.* **157**: 197–204.

29. Foglia, V. O. 1941. Hormonal action of the toad hypophysis in mammals. *Endocrinology* **29**: 503–513.

30. Goldner, M. G., and Gomori, G. 1944. Studies on the mechanism of alloxan diabetes. *Endocrinology* **35**: 341.

31. Greeley, P. O. 1937. Pancreatic diabetes in the rabbit. *Proc. Soc. Exptl. Biol. Med.* **37**: 309–312.

32. Greenman, D. L., Elton, R. L., and Zarrow, M. X. 1959. Steroid diabetes in the chicken. *Anat. Record* **134**: 573–574.

33. Hall, P. F. 1959. "The Functions of the Endocrine Glands." Saunders, Philadelphia, Pennsylvania.

34. Hawk, P. B., Oser, B. L., and Summerson, W. H. 1954. "Practical Physiological Chemistry," 13th ed. McGraw-Hill, New York.

35. Hazelwood, R. L., and Lorenz, F. W. 1957. Responses of the domestic fowl to hyper- and hypoglycemic agents. *Endocrinology* **61**: 520–527.

36. Houssay, B. A. 1940. Advancement of knowledge of the role of the hypophysis in carbohydrate metabolism during the last twenty-five years. *Endocrinology* **30**: 884–896.

37. Houssay, B. A. 1958. Comparative physiology of the endocrine pancreas, *in* "Comparative Endocrinology" (A. Gorbman, ed.). Wiley, New York.

38. Houssay, B. A., and Anderson, E. 1949. Diabetogenic action of anterior pituitary hormones. *Endocrinology* **45**: 627–629.

39. Jarret, I. G. 1946. Alloxan diabetes in a ruminant. *Nature* **197**: 441–442.

40. Lazarow, A., and Berman, J. 1948. The production of diabetes in the toadfish with alloxan. *Anat. Record* **100**: 688.

41. Lazarow, A., and Polcey, S. L. 1946. The production and course of alloxan diabetes in the rat. *J. Lab. Clin. Med.* **31**: 1104–1105.

42. Long, C. N. H., Katzin, B., and Fry, E. B. 1940. The adrenal cortex and carbohydrate metabolism. *Endocrinology* **26**: 309–344.

43. Long, C. N. H., and Lukens, F. D. W. 1936. The effects of adrenalectomy and hypophysectomy upon experimental diabetes in the cat. *J. Exptl. Med.* **63**: 465–490.

44. Lukens, F. D. W. 1938. Pancreatectomy in the goat. *Am. J. Physiol.* **122**: 729–733.

45. Lukens, F. D. W., and Dohan, F. C. 1942. Pituitary diabetes in the cat; recovery following insulin or dietary treatment. *Endocrinology* **30**: 175–202.

45a. Manchester, K. L., and Young, F. G. 1961. Insulin and protein metabolism. *Vitamins Hormones* **19**: 95–132.

46. Martin, D. B., Renold, A. E., and Dagenais, Y. M. 1958. An assay for insulin-like activity using rat adipose tissue. *Lancet* **ii**: 76–77.

47. Miahle, P. 1955. Importance du glucagon dans la régulation de la glycémie chez le canard. *Compt. Rend. Acad. Sci.* **241:** 1851–1853.
48. Miller, M. R., and Wurster, D. H. 1956. Studies on the blood glucose and pancreatic islets of lizards. *Endocrinology* **58:** 114–120.
49. Miller, R. A. 1942. Effects of anterior pituitary preparations on insulin of islet cells of pigeon pancreas. *Endocrinology* **31:** 535–544.
50. Mirsky, I. A. 1945. Alloxan administration to the duck. *Proc. Soc. Exptl. Biol. Med.* **59:** 35–37.
51. Mirsky, I. A. 1956. The role of insulinase and insulinase inhibitors. *Metab. Clin. Exptl.* **5:** 138–143.
52. Mirsky, I. A., and Gitelson, S. 1957. Comparison of the hypoglycemic action of tolbutamide in the fowl and other species. *Endocrinology* **61:** 148.
53. Mirsky, I. A., Nelson, N., Grayman, I., and Elgart, S. 1942. Pancreatic diabetes in the monkey. *Endocrinology* **31:** 264–270.
54. Mount, L. E. 1952. The effects of graded doses of alloxan on the blood sugar of the mouse. *J. Physiol. (London)* **115:** 52p.
55. Murrell, L. R., and Nace, R. F. 1959. Experimental diabetes in the catfish: Normal and alloxan-diabetic blood glucose and pancreatic histology. *Endocrinology* **64:** 542–550.
56. Nelson, N., Elgart, S., and Mirsky, I. A. 1942. Pancreatic diabetes in the owl. *Endocrinology* **31:** 119–123.
57. Newey, H., Parsons, B. J., and Smyth, D. H. 1959. The site of action of phlorrhizin in inhibiting intestinal absorption of glucose. *J. Physiol. (London)* **148:** 83–92.
58. Norman, D., and Hiestand, W. A. 1960. Hormones and sugar penetration in skeletal muscle. *Comp. Biochem. Physiol.* **1:** 167–169.
59. Opdyke, D. F. 1942. Response of fasted and non-fasted chicks to insulin. *Endocrinology* **31:** 363.
60. Oyama, J., and Grant, R. L. 1959. Effect of insulin on glucose uptake by mouse diaphragm tissue. *Proc. Soc. Exptl. Biol. Med.* **100:** 91–92.
61. Park, C. R., Bornstein, J., and Post, R. L. 1955. Effect of insulin on free glucose content of rat diaphragm *in vitro*. *Am. J. Physiol.* **182:** 12–17.
62. Park, C. R., and Johnson, L. H. 1955. Effect of insulin on transport of glucose and galactose into cells of rat muscle and brain. *Am. J. Physiol.* **182:** 17–23.
63. Price, W. H., Cori, C. F., and Colowick, S. P. 1945. The effect of anterior pituitary extract and of insulin on the hexokinase reaction. *J. Biol. Chem.* **160:** 633–634.
64. Russell, J. A. 1936. Carbohydrate levels in fasted and fed hypophysectomized rats. *Proc. Soc. Exptl. Biol. Med.* **34:** 279–280.
65. Ross, E. J. 1952. The influence of insulin on the permeability of the blood-aqueous barrier to glucose. *J. Physiol. (London)* **116:** 414.
66. Ross, E. J. 1953. Insulin and the permeability of cell membranes to glucose. *Nature* **171:** 125.
67. Sanger, F. 1959. The chemistry of insulin. *Science* **129:** 1340–1344.
68. Scott, C. C., Harris, P. N., and Chen, K. K. 1945. Effects of alloxan on birds. *Endocrinology* **37:** 201–207.
69. Scow, R. O. 1957. "Total" pancreatectomy in the rat: Operation, effects and postoperative care. *Endocrinology* **60:** 359–367.
70. Scow, R. O., Wagner, E. M., and Cardeza, A. 1957. Effect of hypophysectomy

on the insulin requirement and response to fasting of "totally" pancreatectomized rats. *Endocrinology* **61**: 380–391.

71. Scow, R. O., Wagner, E. M., and Ronov, E. 1958. Effect of growth hormone and insulin on body weight and nitrogen retention in pancreatectomized rats. *Endocrinology* **62**: 593–604.

71a. Seifter, S., Dayton, S., Novic, B., and Muntwyler, E. 1950. The estimations of glycogen with the anthrone reagent. *Arch. Biochem.* **25**: 191–200.

72. Shapiro, R., and Pincus, G. 1936. Pancreatic diabetes and hypophysectomy in the rat. *Proc. Soc. Exptl. Biol. Med.* **34**: 416–419.

73. Sprague, R., and Ivy, A. C. 1936. Studies in avian carbohydrate metabolism. *Am. J. Physiol.* **115**: 389–394.

74. Stadie, W. C. 1954. Current concepts of the action of insulin. *Physiol. Rev.* **34**: 52–100.

75. Stadie, W. C. 1957. Newer concepts of the action of insulin. *Am. J. Clin. Nutrition* **5**: 393–403.

76. Stadie, W. C., Haugaard, N., and Hills, A. G. 1947. The effect of insulin and adrenal cortical extract on the hexokinase reaction in extracts of muscle from depancreatized cats. *J. Biol. Chem.* **184**: 617–626.

77. Stadie, W. C., Haugaard, N., Marsh, J. B., and Hills, A. G. 1949. The chemical combination of insulin with muscle (diaphragm) of normal rat. *Am. J. Med. Sci.* **218**: 265–280.

78. Stadie, W. C., Zapp, J. A., and Lukens, F. D. W. 1940. The effects of insulin on the ketone metabolism of normal and diabetic cats. *J. Biol. Chem.* **132**: 423–443.

79. Sutherland, E. W., and Cori, C. F. 1951. Effect of hyperglycemic-glycogenolytic factor and epinephrine on liver phosphorylase. *J. Biol. Chem.* **188**: 531–543.

80. Treadwell, C. R., and Roe, J. H. 1954. Technic for complete pancreatectomy in the rat. *Proc. Soc. Exptl. Biol. Med.* **86**: 878–881.

81. Turner, C. D. 1960. "General Endocrinology." Saunders, Philadelphia, Pennsylvania.

82. Tyberghein, J. M., and Williams, R. H. 1959. Assay of glucagon in rabbit plasma. *Metab. Clin. Exptl.* **7**: 635–645.

83. Vallance-Owen, J., and Hurlock, B. 1954. Estimation of plasma insulin by the rat diaphragm method. *Lancet* **i**: 68–70.

84. Vallance-Owen, J., Hurlock, B., and Please, N. W. 1954. Estimation of plasma insulin. *Lancet* **i**: 983–984.

85. Vallance-Owen, J., and Lukens, F. D. W. 1958. Studies on insulin antagonism in plasma. *Endocrinology* **60**: 625–633.

86. Vallance-Owen, J., and Wright, P. H. 1960. Assay of insulin in blood. *Physiol. Rev.* **40**: 218–245.

87. Wasserman, P., and Mirsky, I. A. 1942. Immunological identity of insulin of various species. *Endocrinology* **31**: 115–118.

88. Williams, R. H., Pollen, R. H., Tanner, D. C., and Barnes, R. H. 1959. Oral antidiabetic therapy. *Ann. Internal Med.* **5**: 1121–1133.

89. Wilson, S., and Dixon, G. H. 1961. A comparison of cod and bovine insulins. *Nature* **191**: 876–879.

90. Winegrad, A. I., and Renold, A. E. 1958. Studies on rat adipose tissue *in vitro*. *J. Biol. Chem.* **233**: 267–272.

91. Wright, P. H. 1957. Plasma insulin estimation by the rat diaphragm method. *Lancet* **ii**: 621–624.
92. Wright, P. H. 1959. Blood sugar studies in the bullfrog *Rana catesbiana*. *Endocrinology* **64**: 551–558.
93. Young, F. G. 1940. The pituitary gland and carbohydrate metabolism. *Endocrinology* **26**: 345–351.

CHAPTER 14

The Invertebrate Hormones

The endocrine activities of invertebrates described in this chapter are representative descriptions of the most widely studied systems. Evidence of hormonal or endocrine control of physiological processes has been suggested for every major invertebrate phylum. While some of the reports are largely observational, experimental tests have been performed in the Annelida (23, 24), the Mollusca (36, 38, 56, 57), and the Arthropoda. Of these the most thoroughly studied has been the phylum Arthropoda. This chapter will, therefore, give major emphasis to endocrine regulation in this largest of the invertebrate phyla.

The major portion of arthropod endocrinology has been concerned with regulation of such long-term phenomena as growth, molting, and regeneration. Except for the large number of experiments on the regulation of cephalopod and crustacean chromatophores, relatively less attention has been given to the regulation of processes that are more important to the minute-to-minute, hour-to-hour, or day-to-day physiology of the animals, such as regulation of the rate of heart beat (45), activity rhythms, blood carbohydrate concentration, or water metabolism (40). It would appear that these areas are likely to be studied more intensively in the future, and thus a brief discussion of the endocrinology of each of these processes is included.

Regulation of Molting and Growth in the Insecta

The publication of two excellent reviews in 1963 (30) and 1964 (51) and the availability of earlier reviews (49, 55, 59, 60) obviate the need for extensive bibliographic citation in this section. The student is advised to examine the above-cited reviews for detailed information and complete coverage of the literature. The present discussion will list only selected references.

A. Prothoracotropic Hormone or Brain Hormone

While the growth of many tissues of the arthropod is more or less continuous, the hard exoskeleton is shed in periodic molts. Kopeč (35) was the first to show that control of the molting process is humoral. By ligating the last-stage caterpillar of *Lymantria* he was able to prevent pupation in the region posterior to the ligature, but not in more anterior regions. Section of the nerve cord did not prevent molting of the whole animal. Similar results were obtained by other workers with the fly *Calliphora* (16) and in decapitated larvae of the bug *Rhodnius*. Confirmatory evidence was obtained from the experiments in which epidermal tissues of one insect, transplanted to the external surface of another, molted simultaneously with the host; and also from experiments in which fragments of adult cuticle were transplanted into the body cavity of juvenile hosts and molted synchronously with the larvae.

The experiments of Kopeč suggested that the critical anterior organ is the supraesophageal ganglion or brain since removal of the brain prevented molting of the entire animal just as isolation by ligation of the region containing the brain prevented molting in the brainless portion. The reciprocal experiment in which brainless animals were induced to molt by implantation of brains was, however, more difficult. In the moth *Ephestia,* only a very small fraction of brainless animals molted after implantation of brains. The experiments which gave the first clue to the explanation of these puzzling results were obtained from the observations that pupation of the sawfly *Trypoxylon* can be prevented by removal of the brain or by ligation; and that the block to pupation can be reversed by implantation of the brain of a molting animal or by injection of blood from larvae in the course of pupation. These experiments indicated that activation following either implantation of brains or injection of body fluids is successful only when the implanted tissues or body fluids are taken from animals in the stage of active production or secretion of the necessary humoral factor.

Selective extirpations of small areas of the brain have shown that the hormone is synthesized in the medial neuroendocrine cells of the pars intercerebralis. The number of cells, although constant in any one species, varies among the species examined from a relatively small number of 26 in the cecropia moth, *Hyalophora cecropia* to over 2000 in locusts (25). Furthermore, in some species lateral groups of neurosecretory cells seem also to be involved in the secretory process. In all cases the neurosecretory material occurs as granules about 1500 Å in diameter, surrounded by a 70 Å membrane (61). Neurosecretory granules have been isolated also by differential centrifugation.

The chemical nature of the brain hormone is, at present, a subject of considerable controversy. Kobayashi has claimed that it is indistinguishable from cholesterol and, indeed, that its effects can be mimicked by purified cholesterol from a variety of sources. Ichikawa, on the other hand, finds that the hormone is water soluble and lipid insoluble. Objections have been raised to the specificity of the assay methods used by Kobayashi and collaborators since substances not found in insects, such as epinephrine, are capable of mimicking the activation normally caused by the brain in his test animals. As many investigators have pointed out, a variety of steroids, sterols, and steroid precursors are capable of mimicking the effects of the brain hormone in certain insect test systems (51). In the most critical system, the brainless, diapausing cecropia moth, however, neither cholesterol nor any other lipid-soluble extract has proved to be capable of activating the thoracic glands.

B. Ecdysone

Brainless animals are capable of surviving for weeks, months, or even years in a state of developmental arrest. The next clues to the nature of the humoral control of development came from experiments performed on animals in a physiological state of developmental arrest, the diapausing state. Williams (62) was able to show that when saturniid moths which have a normal pupal diapause are debrained or when, more simply, the abdomen is isolated from more anterior portions, the resulting abdomens do not develop. Activation of the brain in these species depends upon exposure of the animal to low temperatures. Implantation of activated brains into brainless animals evoked development, but curiously enough, implantation of similar brains into isolated abdomens did not. Similar experiments had been performed with *Drosophila*. Further investigation showed that the brain hormone does not act directly upon all the tissues of the animal, but, rather, that it is a tropic hormone acting upon a second endocrine gland located in the thorax.

Thoracic glands have now been identified as endocrine organs in a large number of insect species. In many cases their anatomy was already known before their function was elucidated (a situation common in vertebrate endocrinology, but rare among invertebrates). For this reason they have a variety of names including: prothoracic glands, ventral glands, and peritracheal glands. In all cases that have been carefully investigated, the implantation of activated thoracic glands into parts of the insect body causes molting of the host fragment in the absence of brain or other endocrine organs. The converse experiment, ablation of the thoracic glands and consequent molting block, is technically more difficult since the glands are frequently diffuse and may consist, in part, of isolated cells. Critical ablation experiments have been performed in locusts, which never molt after removal of the glands.

In 1954, Butenandt and Karlson isolated and crystallized what is probably the hormone of the prothoracic gland. These investigators used as an assay procedure the induction of puparium formation in isolated dipteran abdomens (see Experiment 14–1) and were able to induce puparium formation in *Calliphora* pupae with concentrations of slightly less than 0.01 μg per abdomen (30). The chemical data and proposed structural formula for ecdysone are given in Fig. 14-1; the positions of four of the hydroxyl groups are not known.

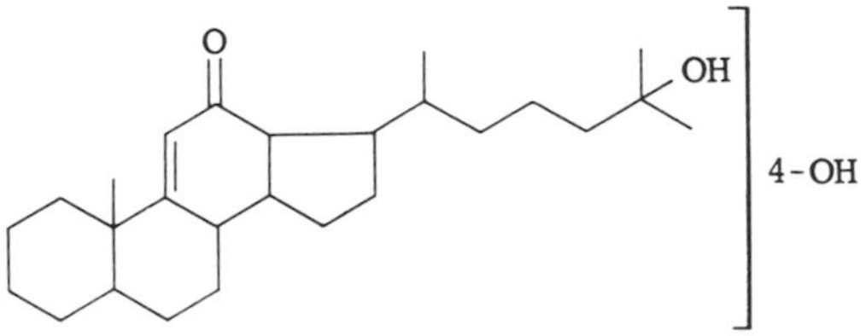

Fig. 14-1. Preliminary structural formula of ecdysone. Molecular weight, 464. Empirical formula, $C_{27}H_{44}O_6$. The position of the 4-OH groups shown on the right is not known. Taken from Karlson (31).

No insect species that has been carefully studied has been found to be capable of synthesis of steroids from acetate, hence it seems probable that ecdysone is formed by degradation of essential dietary steroids. Evidence that this is the case has been obtained from experiments in which crystalline ecdysone of constant specific activity was extracted from *Calliphora* larvae which had been injected with labeled H^3-cholesterol.

Ecdysone has been shown to mimic the known functions of the thoracic gland, including the induction of molts, termination of diapause, puparium formation, and, most interesting, the induction of "puffing" in the polytene chromosomes of diptera. The "puffing" phenomenon deserves special mention, since it indicates one mechanism by which steroid hormones may act to induce the production of the messenger RNA which directs the course of protein synthesis in cells. As Beerman (4) first suggested in 1952, the "puffs" of polytene chromosomes represent sites of high rates of synthesis of RNA. Certain "puffs" appear in larvae of the midge *Chironomus tentans* only in the period just preceding the molt when ecdysone is exerting its effects. These same puffs also appear in animals which have been injected with ecdysone in concentrations sufficient to bring about premature molting (12). These observations suggest a direct connection between the hormone and the activation of the genetic machinery responsible for the control of protein synthesis. Evidence has been presented to show that two of the proteins synthesized under genetic control at the time of molting are involved in the formation of and activation of the enzymes involved in the tanning of the cuticle (sclerotization). It has also been demonstrated that these enzymes are induced by ecdysone, presumably through activation of specific genetic sites.

Regardless of the mechanism by which the secretory product of the thoracic glands is presumed to act, the end results of secretion appear, in all species studied, to have effects that can best be described as furthering the initiation of molting. These gross effects include the synthesis of proteins, increase in amino acid incorporation into tissues, synthesis of RNA, and initiation of cuticular tanning. This last phenomenon seems to be initiated by ecdysone acting to induce the formation of one enzyme and to activate another.

Except for the control of sclerotization, most of the other effects of ecdysone can also be produced by wounding the insects. Hence it is likely that most of the biochemical effects of ecdysone are secondary or tertiary rather than primary effects of the hormone.

C. JUVENILE HORMONE

The reactions of the tissues to stimulation by ecdysone are modulated by a third hormone, secreted by the corpora allata. Wigglesworth showed in 1934 that when animals molt in the presence of a hormone secreted by these glands a juvenile stage follows the molt. If the gland is extirpated before one of the early juvenile molts, a premature adult develops in the molting process. Conversely, if juvenile glands are implanted into animals preparing for metamorphosis into the adult stage, they undergo a supernumerary juvenile molt (see Fig. 14–2).

Following purification of the juvenile hormone from the abdomens of adult male cecropia moths (63), further studies disclosed that substances which act in the same way as the natural hormone are present in plants, microorganisms, and animals other than insects. A juvenile hormone-like substance has been found even in certain parasites that infect many insects. These parasites produce a sufficient amount of hormone-like substance to prevent adult metamorphosis of the host (15). The only other instance in which an exogenous source of juvenile hormone has been suspected of a physiological role was in experiments where derivatives of farnesol appeared in the feces of insects; they are believed to have had a juvenilizing effect in colonies of social insects (50) (Experiment 14–11).

A large number of terpenoids, steroids, and related compounds also

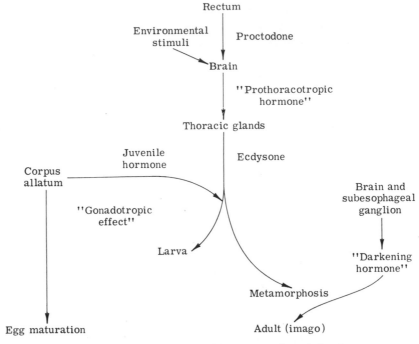

Fig. 14-2. Hormonal regulation of insect growth and development.

are capable of promoting the retention of juvenile characteristics by insect tissues. Some of these compounds are capable of mimicking activities of the prothoracotropic brain hormone or of the hormone of the thoracic gland. Since the precise nature of the effect depends upon such factors as concentration, previous history of the animal used for assay, and species, investigations have failed to give unequivocal data on the specific hormone secreted. When farnesol was isolated from insect feces and found to have some of the effects of juvenile hormone preparations (50), it was hoped that this substance or one of its derivatives was the juvenile hormone of insects. Unfortunately, it is not effective when injected, but only on topical application. Furthermore, farnesol and other substances with juvenile hormone activity also have other, unrelated, functions in insects, such as stimulation of the brain and prothoracic glands.

The central position of farnesyl pyrophosphate in biosynthetic pathways for sterols, carotenoids, and terpenoids tempts one to speculate that all the compounds which have been found to be active in endocrine regulation in insects are first metabolized to some common precursor of insect hormones and that the specificity of observed effects depends upon the metabolic capabilities of the tissues of the insect used for assay. The steroid nature of ecdysone certainly suggests that such an explanation would serve for the molt-initiating effects of some terpenoids.

D. THE DARKENING FACTOR OF THE BRAIN

A second hormone has been reported in the brain and appears to act directly on the tissues rather than as a tropic hormone for some other gland (13, 17). In some flies, the sequence of events following the final molt to the adult stage (imago) is interrupted before sclerotization (hardening and darkening) of the cuticle. During the period after the adult is formed, but before the cuticle is fully hard, the flies escape from the puparium and (for those which pupate beneath the soil or other substratum) make their way to the surface. If the adults are kept within the puparium or in another restricted space, the cuticle remains soft and white. By ligating newly emerged adults, it can be shown that the tanning requires the presence of substances from the anterior region; and the hormonal nature of the control can be demonstrated by injection of body fluid from flies which have just darkened or are in the process of darkening.

Further localization (17) of the site of production of the "darkening hormone" shows that it is derived from the median neurosecretory cells of the brain and from two groups of neurosecretory cells in the thoracic ganglia. A variety of experiments indicate that the hormone is not identical with the prothoracotropic hormone of the brain nor with ecdysone. Chemical studies (13) indicate that this "darkening factor" is probably a large polypeptide since it is not dialyzable and is inactivated by the bacterial protease subtilisin.

That the hormone is of general importance is indicated by the fact that blood of *Schistocerca* (a locust), of *Periplaneta* (a cockroach), and of a number of dipteran species all contain factors that will initiate the darkening process in the test animal. Apparently the substance is released from the brain and thoracic ganglia in response to appropriate sensory stimuli, since section of the nerve cord posterior to the thoracic ganglia prevents release of the hormone.

E. PROCTODONE AND REGULATION OF PROTHORACOTROPIC HORMONE SECRETION

Whereas the initiation of the processes of molting appears always to be stimulated by the secretion of ecdysone in response to secretion of the prothoracotropic hormone of the brain, the secretion of the latter hormone appears to be under the control of a variety of stimuli. In *Rhodnius,* the effective control resides in nervous impulses resulting from distention of the crop. In other species, in which the arrested development of diapause is reversed by day-length stimuli, there is evidence of resumption of growth and molting initiated by hormonal secretion from the hindgut. In the European corn borer (3), the hormone proctodone is secreted by specialized epithelial cells in the seventh and eighth segments and stimulates molting. There is evidence that it is effective even in such nondiapausing species as the wax moth *Galleria.*

Regulation of Molting and Growth in the Crustacea: X-Organ and Y-Organ Hormones

The regulation of molting and growth in crustacea has many similarities to the processes in insects, but differs enough to offer interesting comparisons. If one removes the eyestalks of any of a large number of species of crustacea, nearly all the operated animals will undergo a prompt and precocious molt. This procedure is commonly used to prepare soft-shell (i.e., newly molted) crabs for the table and crayfish for fishing bait. Since implantation of eyestalks into other sites of the animal prevents the molt, these structures must contain a source of molt-inhibiting hormone. It has been shown that the hormone is a neurosecretory product of a group of cells whose axon terminals form the sinus gland in the eyestalks and whose cell bodies lie on the surface of the brain as the "medulla terminalis X-organ" (44) (Fig. 14-7).

Unlike the thoracic glands of insects the hormones of the eyestalk structures do not act directly upon the crustacean tissues. Instead stimulation of molting in crustacea is due to the secretion of another endocrine organ, the ventral gland or "Y-organ," which lies ventrally beneath the mandibular muscles (18). When the Y-organ is removed, molting does not occur.

Investigations of interaction between the molt-inhibition by the X-organ and the molt stimulation by the Y-organ have shown that the neurosecretory cells of the X-organ cease secreting just before the molt, at which time the Y-organ becomes activated. The neurosecretory cells of the X-organ then resume secretion just at the time that the Y-organ stops secreting. From the results of implantation studies and because section of the nerve running from the X-organ to the Y-organ is without effect on these interrelations, it is probable that the neurosecretory products of the X-organ are released into the extracellular fluid rather than moving by direct axonal transport.

In addition to the functional similarities between the Y-organ of crustacea and insect thoracic glands, both tissues have similarities in embryologic development and histological structure. The homologies are striking even on the chemical level, since ecdysone isolated from silkworms can induce molting in crustacea. Since many of the terpenoids may also act to regulate various developmental processes in the arthropods this action of ecdysone should not be taken as proof that the molting hormone is the same both in insects and crustacea.

Regulation of Reproduction; Hormones of the Corpus Allatum, X-Organ, and Medial Neurosecretory Brain Cells in Insects and Crustacea

A. EGG MATURATION IN INSECTS

Control of reproduction in insects seems to be a function of the corpora allata. In the majority of insect species, the continued presence of these glands during adult life is essential for egg maturation and, in several cases, for oviposition. Only in those species which have a brief adult life or in which the adults do not eat, do the glands appear to complete their function in late larval or early pupal life and to be dispensable in adult life (65).

A commonly observed action of the corpus allatum hormone is an increased rate of biosynthesis of protein at the expense of fat deposition. The newly formed proteins are laid down in the egg. It has been suggested that the crucial reactions might be stimulation of transaminase activity invoked by the hormone. In most insects, the eggs develop in long ovarioles in a linear fashion, and the protein deposition thus would help to mature or ripen the eggs at the end of the ovariole proximal to the oviduct.

Another neurosecretory control over egg maturation occurs in flies. The medial neurosecretory cells of the brain stimulate egg maturation in these species by evoking the synthesis of proteases in the gut which are responsible for supply of amino acids for the synthesis of egg proteins (54). It has been shown that implantation of these cells into gravid females stimulates oviposition.

Increased efficiency in supply of amino acids cannot, however, explain all the gonadotropic effects of the corpora allata. Closely related mosquitoes of the genus *Culex* display both the autogenous type of ovarian development, which proceeds in the absence of feeding, and the anautogenous type, in which a blood meal is essential for egg development. Anautogenous ovaries transplanted into autogenous females develop without feeding; in the reciprocal transplantation, egg development does not occur. Implantation of the corpora allata of autogenous mosquitoes into anautogenous species, invokes egg maturation even in the absence of a blood meal (37). Ligation experiments indicate that a factor from the brain is also involved in these phenomena.

B. Ovulation in Insects

In most species little appears to be known about the subsequent stimuli for ovulation. In some of the cockroaches and in the milkweed bug, however, the ovulatory stimuli have been more carefully studied. In these species, inhibitory nerves from the brain block secretion by the corpora allata. Experimentally, egg maturation and ovulation occur when the inhibitory nerves are sectioned. Physiologically, effective neural stimuli vary: In cockroaches secretion by the corpus allatum appears to be invoked by mating, but inhibition is reimposed by the distension of the brood sac during the period when the animals are carrying their egg cases. In mosquitoes, it appears that the effective signal for ovulation is distension of the gut.

Rather surprisingly, no evidence has been obtained to indicate that the gonads exert an endocrine control over egg or sperm maturation or over ovulation in insects.

C. Gonad Development in Crustacea

In crustacea, ovarian development of immature forms appears to be inhibited by a secretion of the medulla terminalis X-organ. A better-studied situation exists in regard to the development of secondary sexual characters (11). Although it was known for years that certain crustacean parasites may cause sex reversal in male crustacea, all attempts to reproduce these effects by removal of the gonads failed. Endocrine control of secondary sexual characters was demonstrated when it was found that male isopod crustacea possess a strand of glandular cells associated with the vas deferens. Transplantation of this gland into females has the effect of initiating transformation of the ovary into a testis, and the male secondary sexual characters are progressively acquired over the next few molts. Similar glands have now been described in a variety of crustacea.

Pigmentary Controls in Crustacea

Two types of pigmentary changes are hormonally mediated in crustacea; body color is determined by expansion and contraction of hypodermal chromatophores, and adjustment for vision under scotopic or photopic conditions is determined by eye pigment migration. The former can be shown to be under the control of substances that can be extracted from the eyestalks in aqueous or dilute saline solutions. Since the variety of chromatophore colors and the responses of those of each color varies in crustacea from species to species, a brief description of the possible interactions is not easily made. Experiment 14–6 illustrates the techniques by which these changes may be studied. For a relatively complete account of the observations which have been made, see the monograph by Fingerman (14) on this subject. The active endocrine principles all appear to be polypeptides, and partial purification has been achieved by electrophoresis, column chromatography, and counter-current distribution.

Migration of the eye pigments is a less complex phenomenon, since only one pigment, melanin, is involved, and the pigment granules exist in only two sites, the proximal and the distal cells surrounding the ommatidia of the compound eye. This phenomenon is described in detail under Experiment 14–6.

Activity Rhythms

Cockroaches, like many other animals, show diurnal variations in rhythmic activity under dual neuroendocrine control (22). It has been noted that the hormone which regulates the rhythm is released from neurosecretory cells in the subesophageal ganglion, since transplantation of this organ between animals indicates that the rhythm follows closely the activity of the ganglion and is only slightly influenced by the rhythm of the recipient when the animals are kept in constant darkness. The rhythmic secretion of the ganglion of an intact animal is, in turn, controlled by rhythmic secretion by the corpora allata.

Pheromones

Control of behavior, and perhaps even of development, among social insects appears to be largely mediated by chemical substances transferred between members of the colony. The extension of the concept of hormones to these phenomena might not be justified were it not for the fact that, in some cases, endocrine glands seem to produce substances that are active both within and between individuals in the colony. The regulation of the number of reproductively competent individuals, of soldiers, and of workers in termite colonies is regulated by the transfer of substances between individuals of the colony (39). Similar effects may be produced by transplantation of the corpora allata. It seems likely that the same substances are involved in both types of communication (Experiment 14–11).

Other pheromones have been described which act as sexual attractants for cockroaches, honey bees, gypsy moths, and other insects (30, 66). Production of these sexual attractants may be under endocrine control, as has been shown for the cockroach *Byrsotria fumigata* (1). Most attractants, however, are not produced by glands that display endocrine functions in other contexts.

Regulation of Blood Carbohydrate Level

Several interesting analogies between the vertebrate mechanisms for the endocrine regulation of extracellular fluid glucose and the regulation of carbohydrates in the body fluids of flatworms and insects have been described. In the liver fluke *Fasciola hepatica*, 5-hydroxytryptamine has been shown to stimulate the conversion of glycogen to glucose by activating phosphorylase in a mechanism mediated by cyclic $3',5'$-AMP (41). In two species of cockroaches (6, 53), it has been demonstrated that a saline extract of the corpora cardiaca induces glycogenolysis and increases the blood concentration of trehalose, the predominant circulating carbohydrate of insects.

The effective substance in insects is reported to be a polypeptide, as is glucagon. A second analogy between glucagon and the corpus cardiacum factor is seen in the fact that both act by stimulation of phosphorylase activity. A third similarity is apparent when we recall that although glucagon and catechol amines both stimulate the phosphorylase of liver, glucagon does not act on this enzyme in muscle. Similarly, the polypeptide of the corpus cardiacum is without effect on the phosphorylase of muscle, or of the gut, and is effective only in stimulating the enzyme of the fat body, a tissue analogous to the vertebrate liver in a number of other respects. Neither epinephrine nor norepinephrine is active in stimulating insect glycogenolysis.

Saline extracts of crustacean eyestalks have also been shown to be diabetogenic (10).

Regulation of the Rate of Heart Beat

The contraction of cardiac muscle in most vertebrates is a property of the muscle cells themselves (myogenic hearts). The rate of beat, on the other hand, is accelerated by catechol amines released by the sympathetic nervous system or decelerated by acetylcholine from parasympathetic neurons. In the invertebrates, several other regulatory patterns are present (46). In adult arthropods, where the cardiac muscle cells contract only when stimulated by rhythmic impulses from the nerve cells of cardiac ganglia (neurogenic hearts) (42), the rate of beat appears to be regulated by different humoral mechanisms. Acetylcholine accelerates such hearts rather than slowing them.

In the crustacea the acetylcholine acceleration is a pharmacological effect. The naturally occurring accelerator is a peptide or group of peptides secreted by the pericardial organs (5). Earlier reports that 5,6-dihydroxytryptamine is the cardioaccelerator seem to have been in error.

In the insects, cardioacceleration results from administration of extracts of the corpora cardiaca. It is possible that the corpora cardiaca, in turn, act indirectly by regulating secretion of an o-dihydroxyindolalkylamine from the pericardial glands, but until further studies on the ramifications of the axons of the neurosecretory cells of the corpora cardiaca have been reported it seems dangerous to assign the function so precisely (28). Paranthetically, it should be noted that saline extracts of corpora cardiaca have many of the effects of catechol amines on mammalian uterine smooth muscle. Chemical and pharmacological examination of these extracts indicates that they are, however, different from epinephrine and norepinephrine (2).

Cardioinhibition has been less well studied. It can be shown (45) that, in *Limulus*, stimulation of nerves originating in the central nervous system and passing to the cardiac ganglion causes slowing of the heart, and that these effects are mimicked by 5-hydroxytryptamine (serotonin).

The search for the cardioregulatory substances acting on neurogenic hearts is complicated by the multiple sites at which humoral agents may act in these systems. Possible sites include the ganglia from which both the accelerator and inhibitory nerves arise, the nerves themselves, the junctions which their axons make with the neurons of the cardiac ganglia, and the myoneural junctions between the ganglionic neurons and the cardiac muscle. Since all these junctions may be excitatory or inhibitory, it is obvious that several quite different types of compounds may affect the rate of heart beat of intact animals. Indeed, it has been reported that approximately six different substances capable of accelerating the rate of beat of the cockroach heart and probably five causing deceleration can be isolated from the nervous system, gastrointestinal tract, heart, utricles, and hemolymph of this animal (47). The heat stability and sensitivity of the substances to proteases indicate that they are probably small polypeptides.

The molluscan heart has a certain pharmacological resemblance to that of vertebrates since acetylcholine, in low concentrations, also slows the rate of heart beat. In fact the heart of the quahog (*Mercenaria*

mercenaria or *Venus mercenaria*) is in frequent use as the most sensitive assay for cholinergic compounds (58). The strength and, in some species, the rate of beat of bivalve hearts are increased by 5-hydroxytryptamine and by higher concentrations of acetylcholine. It is not yet certain that either of these compounds are the natural transmitters for cardio-regulation in mollusks.

Regulation of Water Balance

Water metabolism has been extensively studied in many invertebrates, but endocrine participation has only recently been described (40). Following a liquid meal, the blood-sucking bug *Rhodnius* displays a diuresis. This diuresis can also be invoked in isolated malpighian tubules treated with blood from animals in the diuretic state. Further experiments have localized the diuretic hormone in neurosecretory cells of the meso- and metathoracic ganglia.

EXPERIMENT 14–1

Puparium Formation in Diptera

Puparium formation in *Diptera* (16, 29) is induced by a secretion from the ring gland. By means of a ligature the hormone may be confined to a region of the body containing the gland. Illustrative experiments are performed by isolating the abdomen of any of the larger species of flies by means of a ligature placed between the gland and the abdomen. Puparium formation in *Calliphora* has been used as an assay method for ecdysone. Other species are suitable for demonstration of the phenomenon, but are reported to be unsuitable for quantitative assay of purified hormone.

Procedure and Experimental

1. The internal anatomy of these flies may be visualized by placing between two microscope slides a maggot and a few drops of water, exerting slight pressure to flatten the animal and observing by transmitted light with sufficient magnification to see the internal anatomy (Fig. 14-3). Select last instar larvae, if possible, after they have ceased feeding and emptied their digestive tract.

2. Ligate the body posterior to the ring gland (a composite structure representing the thoracic gland, corpora allata, and corpora cardiaca).

3. Twenty-four hours later, the animals can be graded into three groups: The first group will have formed a tan or brown puparium both anterior and posterior to the ligature. The ring gland of such animals

had secreted a sufficient quantity of ecdysone to invoke puparium formation before the ligature was applied. The second group will not display puparium formation of either portion of the animals. Such results usually

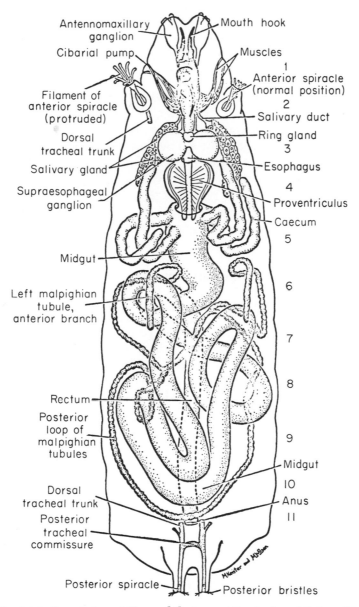

Fig. 14-3. Dorsal view of *Drosophila* larva. After Buck and Keister (9).

indicate damage to the ring gland during ligation. The third group, averaging about 10% of the total will display puparium formation in the anterior portion containing the ring gland, but not in the abdominal region.

4. Animals displaying only anterior pupation may be used to test for the presence of ecdysone. It has been reported that 0.0075 μg of α-ecdysone is sufficient to induce puparium formation in one *Calliphora* larva, but there seems to be considerable variation among test animals.

It is probable that the small number of animals which react in the expected fashion is due to the brief duration of the critical period during which the brain, but not the thoracic gland portion of the ring gland, has been activated. Once activated, the secretion and distribution of ecdysone seems to require only a few minutes, whereas the external signs (gut emptying and contraction of the body) of onset of the critical period are sufficient to stage animals only to within a period of 4–6 hours. It is wise, therefore, to plan to ligate approximately 1000 animals to provide a convincing demonstration. It has also been reported that animals fed on liver are less satisfactory than those reared on other diets.

EXPERIMENT 14–2

Removal of the Lepidopteran Brain*

The most detailed directions for the removal of lepidopteran brains are those of Williams (65), from which much of the following is paraphrased. The note in that reference should be consulted for a list of suitable species and for a brief discussion of the taxonomic difficulties in naming the species which have been used.

Procedures

General Surgical Procedures

1. Animals are anesthetized in flowing, humidified commercial carbon dioxide. When fully anesthetized after approximately 20 minutes, the pupae are flaccid, and muscular contractions cannot be elicited.

2. Operations are carried out under a binocular microscope with appropriate magnification. The following instruments and apparatus are useful: two No. 3 and two No. 5 watchmaker's forceps; a sharp scalpel with a pointed blade (Bard-Parker No. 11 detachable blades are convenient); iridectomy scissors (curved on the flat, in good condition);

* Cf. references (64, 65).

microscissors (convenient, but not essential); a dental probe or bent dissecting needle; and a syringe filled with a Ringer's solution (7.5 gm NaCl, 0.35 gm KCl, 0.21 gm $CaCl_2$ per liter has been used) and capped with a fine-gauge needle.

3. In general, rigid asepsis is not necessary. The instruments are soaked in 70% ethanol or other mild sterilizing solutions and wiped dry before the operation. If diseased insects are encountered, it is advisable to sterilize any instruments which have come in contact with them more stringently, and to treat the operating area with a germicide.

4. Add a few crystals of a mixture of equal parts of phenylthiourea (phenylthiocarbamide) recrystallized from ethanol, and streptomycin sulfate to the blood of the insect. In cases of apparently intractable infections, the most probable cause is fungal spores, and it is sometimes possible to avoid these problems with such antifungal agents as griseofulvin, nystatin, or amphotericin B.

5. After excision of the brain, a few crystals of the phenylthiourea-antibiotic mixture are added to the operation field and Ringer's solution is added from the syringe to bring the fluid level with the surface of the cuticle.

6. The excised cuticle is then replaced with a plastic window of appropriate size cut from a cellulose acetate cover slip (1 or 2 thickness).

7. This "window" is sealed in place with a paraffin wax which is melted on a bent dissecting needle over a micro flame or alcohol lamp. The melted wax will adhere to the cuticle and the underside of the cover slip if both are dry. If either has been wetted with blood, blotting with absorbent tissues may be necessary.

Ablation of Brains, Corpora Allata, and Corpora Cardiaca from Pupae

1. An anesthetized pupa is placed in a plasticine cradle shaped to fit the individual.

2. Under continuous carbon dioxide anesthesia the cuticle of the facial region is removed by making longitudinal incisions at the lateral margins, and an anterior transverse incision.

3. The flap may be removed by grasping it with forceps, lifting, and gently tearing it away.

4. The abdomen is pressed forward with a piece of plasticine and held so that the blood fills, but does not overflow, the opening. If the hypodermis is still in place it may be trimmed with scissors.

5. The exposed brain and endocrine glands are then visualized (Fig. 14-4). In general, it is difficult to remove the brain without simultaneously removing the corpora allata and corpora cardiaca. If it is

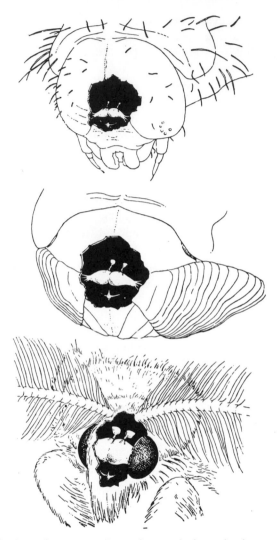

Fig. 14-4. Brain and corpora allata of cecropia larva (top), pupa (middle), and adult (bottom). For clarity, the other tissues are not shown. Taken from Williams (65).

desired to remove only one, the procedure of choice is to remove all, transfer them to a small black container (either black embryological watch glasses or black plastic bottle caps have been used), remove the corpora allata and corpora cardiaca from the brain, and reimplant them in the operation area. The greatest difficulties in removal of the organs are related to the ubiquitous tracheae. Large tracheae are best removed by grasping them with two pairs of forceps and pulling them apart.

Experimental

Preparation of "Dauer" Pupae

The pupal diapause state of developmental arrest occurs in many of the saturniid pupae. Removal of the brain of such animals results in continuation of the diapause state, and the pupa is referred to as a "Dauer" pupa. Initiation of renewed growth follows the implantation of secreting brains. In the cecropia moth (*Hyalophora cecropia*) and the cynthia moth (*Samia cynthia*) brains secrete following a period of exposure to 5–10°C *in situ* for 3–6 months. They may then be removed and implanted into previously prepared brainless animals and will evoke development at 25°C with a time course closely dependent upon the history of temperature exposure of both donor and recipient. Since the time and temperature interrelationships are complex, the original reference (64) must be consulted.

Studies may then be carried out relating time, temperature, and species to the onset of metamorphosis.

EXPERIMENT 14–3

Juvenile Hormone and Allatectomy of the Cockroach (Blattaria)*

Techniques for allatectomy, i.e., removal of the corpora allata, have been developed for the cockroach as well as many species of *Galleria*, *Bombyx*, *Calliphora*, *Rhodnius*, and others. The description given below is for the cockroach.

Procedures

General Surgical Procedures

1. Animals may be anesthetized with humidified tank carbon dioxide or ether. If the latter is used, care must be taken to ensure that the insects do not come in contact with the solvent.

2. Insects and instruments should be sterilized. (Benzalkonium chloride (Zephiran) or other similar compounds are satisfactory.)

* Cf. references (15, 59).

Instruments used are: 5, 7, and S watchmaker's forceps; small, curved-on-the-flat iridectomy scissors; and microscalpels constructed from broken fragments of double edge razor blades fixed to glass handles with cement.

3. Operations should be performed under 20- to 25-power magnification.

Allatectomy

1. Remove the anterior edge of the pronotum of a newly molted, anesthetized nymph.

2. Transfer the animal to a wax block where it can be continuously exposed to anesthesia and pin it by placing a No. 1 insect pin across the neck near its union with the thorax.

3. Arrange a second pin, bent in a Z-shape, to hold the free end of the restraining pin (Fig. 14-5, No. 1).

4. Place two No. 1 pins through the lateral edges of the pronotum and pull the roach posteriorly to stretch the neck.

5. Secure the pronotal pins to the wax block.

6. Make an incision between the epicranium and cervical sclerites. Pull the sclerites posteriorly and place them under the trimmed edge of the pronotum (Fig. 14-5, Nos. 2 and 3).

7. Blot excess hemolymph from the wound. The dorsal tracheae and cervical musculature can be identified.

8. After the dorsal tracheae are retracted, the opalescent blue corpora cardiaca will be evident (Fig. 14-5, No. 4). Tracing posteriorly along the esophagus from the corpora cardiaca, the translucent corpora allata may be visualized dorsal or slightly lateral to the esophagus.

9. Grasp the posterior portion of a corpus cardiacum with one pair of forceps and free the corpus allatum of nervous connectives, tracheae, and connective tissue with another pair of forceps (Fig. 14-5, Nos. 4 and 5).

10. Holding firmly to the corpus cardiacum, the homolateral corpus allatum (Fig. 14-5, No. 6) may now be removed to a dish with a black background. When both corpora allata have been removed, they should be examined under a magnification of 30 to 100 times to verify that each gland is intact. If either gland is not complete the cockroach should be discarded since it is virtually impossible to remove small fragments of corpus allatum tissue.

11. Return the cervical sclerites to their normal positions, and close the wound with a 1:1 mixture of petroleum jelly and beeswax (Fig. 14-5, Nos. 8 and 9).

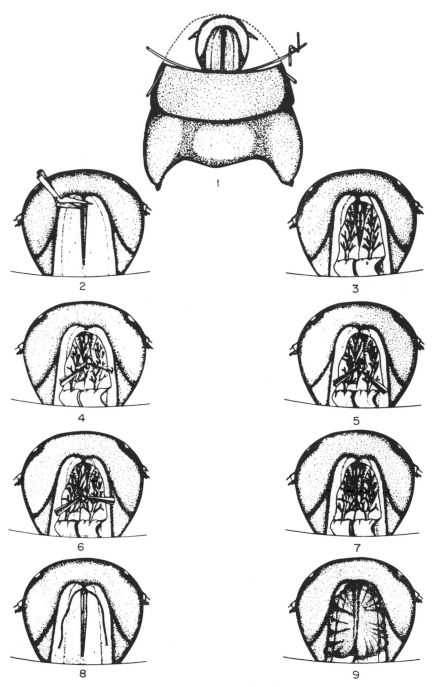

Fig. 14-5. Removal of corpora allata from *Periplaneta*. Taken from Fisher and Sanborn (15).

Experimental

Nymphs

When this operation is performed on nymphs, the operated animals molt prematurely to the adult stage. Scharrer has termed such premature adult forms "adultoids." Since the corpora allata are closely associated with the corpora cardiaca and the nervous system, it is appropriate to verify the endocrine nature of this control by reimplanting corpora allata in a fraction of the operated animals. Although most such reimplantations result in retention of juvenile characters, such as absence of wings and genital openings, the occurrence of cyclic secretion by the corpora allata may sometimes result in adultoids if only one pair of corpora allata are implanted. If two pairs are implanted, virtually no adultoids have been observed in more than 500 such operations.

The student should divide his animals into three groups. One group should be kept as controls, the second group should be allatectomized, and the third group should be allatectomized and implanted with several pairs of corpora allata.

Adults

Similar allatectomy performed on newly molted adult females can show the essentiality of the corpora allata for egg maturation. The student should remove ovaries from intact and allatectomized animals and observe the size of the ova and their nuclei in saline at a magnification of approximately 100 times. No histological preparation or staining is necessary. In intact females the ova mature as they pass from the terminal ends of the ovarioles to the oviducts; after allatectomy they are of uniform small size.

In general, it is not possible to show that implantation of corpora allata into females while they are carrying egg cases results in uterine contractions and expulsion of the case, since egg cases are always, in our experience, expelled during anesthesia.

EXPERIMENT 14–4

Preparation of Isolated Abdomens of Lepidoptera*

Isolated abdomen preparations are used to verify the observation that

* Cf. reference (65).

neither competent brains alone nor thoracic glands alone, nor any other single endocrine organ are capable of initiating molting and development. However, the implantation of thoracic glands and a competent brain result in resumption of development. It can also be shown that implantation of purified ecdysone initiates development and molting. Unfortunately, so little pure ecdysone is available that the last experiment will be possible only after synthesis of ecdysone or the development of more efficient sources of, and isolation procedures for, this hormone.

Procedures

The general procedures and instruments described for Experiment 14–1 are suitable for this experiment. Most of the difficulties may be avoided by performing this operation in the cynthia moth since the major problem with other lepidoptera is the avoidance of contamination with the contents of the digestive tract. In cynthia pupae the midgut contains a nearly solid rod of sodium pyrophosphate which may be readily removed without danger of contamination. The operation for the cynthia moth is described below; the necessary modifications for other species are apparent.

1. Under carbon dioxide anesthesia, the abdominal cuticle and underlying hypodermis is cut around the circumference of the abdomen at the level of the tips of the wings. Preferably, the incision should be made through the thin intersegmental membrane rather than in the middle of a segment.

2. After visualizing the internal anatomy, the muscle masses, the heart, and the nerve cord are sectioned.

3. The fat body and hindgut are transected and the tracheae pulled from the walls of the midgut. The midgut and associated malphigian tubules may be placed in the anterior or posterior fragment.

4. The cut surface of both fragments is then sealed with paraffin to a No. 1 or No. 2 cellulose acetate cover slip with a central hole.

5. After the phenylthiourea-antibiotic mixture has been added through the hole, Ringer's solution is added to displace *all* air. Organs, tissues, or other desired implants may also be made through the central orifice, which is finally plugged with melted paraffin.

Experimental

1. Prepare a number of isolated abdomens of pupae of the cynthia moth.

2. Transplant single endocrine glands and various combinations, including the brain.

3. Observe the abdomens for metamorphosis.

EXPERIMENT 14–5

Crustacean Eyestalks and Molting*

The ease of demonstrating that removal of the eyestalks of crustacea is followed by premature molting obscures, to some extent, the complexity of control of the molting process. The puzzling observation that eyestalk removal induces molting in only a fraction of the animals on which it is performed, rather than on all, is related to the intermolt stage of the experimental animals. If the eyestalks are removed from animals in appropriate stages of the intermolt cycle, all will molt. Since suitable intermolt stages occupy approximately one-third of the intermolt cycle, it is probably most expedient to perform initial experiments on randomly selected animals and expect that perhaps only 30% will molt.

Procedure

For many marine and freshwater species, molting follows rather promptly upon removal of the eyestalks, and the initial events of molting are apparent within a few hours to a few days. Following removal of the eyestalks, one need only provide aerated, cool water to observe the effects. In a few species, however, the relief of the eyestalk inhibition precedes the molt by several weeks. In such species as the fiddler crab, *Uca*, 4–6 weeks at ordinary temperatures are required. Under such circumstances, one must arrange to force feed the experimental animals in order to obtain analyzable experiments.

Since removal of entire eyestalks is a drastic change in the physiology of crustacea, involving loss of visual stimuli, a significant fraction of the central nervous system, and several of the optic ganglia, more refined studies of the inhibitory control of molting should be made by removal of only the endocrine glands concerned. Removal of the X-organ is extremely difficult. The more usual procedure involves the removal of the sinus gland (Fig. 14-7).

Removal of the eyestalks or of sinus glands should be followed by injection of aqueous or saline extracts of whole, ground eyestalk extracts to complete the proof of the endocrine nature of the effects. Karlson has

* Cf. references (44, 52).

extracted a substance from the Y-organs of crustacea which induces puparium formation in his *Calliphora* assay system for ecdysone. When sizeable quantities of ecdysone become available, it is probable that injection of the pure chemical will mimic the activity of the Y-organ in crustacea from which it has been removed.

Experimental

1. Distribute the animals into three groups.
2. Remove the eyestalks from two groups.
3. Inject one group of the eyestalkless animals with an extract of the eyestalk.
4. Observe time of molt in all groups.

EXPERIMENT 14-6

Eye Pigment Migration in Crustacea

The details of the structure of the compound eye of crustacea and the varying patterns of eye pigments and their movement have been amply reviewed (11, 34, 49). For present purposes, it should suffice to point out that the function of such movements is to screen the photosensory structures of the eye in bright light and to uncover them in darkness or in light of low intensity. The techniques for assay of hormones affecting the retinal pigments have been most carefully detailed. The most suitable animals for test appear to be such shrimp as the American *Palaemonetes* spp., and the European *Palaemon* spp.

Procedure and Experimental

Preparation of Extracts

Extracts are prepared by grinding whole eyestalks, sinus glands, optic ganglia, etc., of any readily obtained crustaceans with sand in sufficient seawater, or distilled water to give a final concentration of 10 units (i.e., 10 eyestalks, or 10 sinus glands) per milliliter. The resulting tissue brei is heated in a boiling water bath for 2–3 minutes to inactivate toxic substances and centrifuged to remove extraneous matter and coagulated protein.

The sinus glands, and ventral nerve cord of the European *Pandalus borealis* contain light-adapting hormone. In the other genera tested, such as *Libinia, Callinectes, Carcinus, Homarus, Orconectes,* and *Nephrops,* the sinus glands, the sensory-pore X-organ, medulla terminalis, and ventral nerve cord all displayed less activity than did whole eyestalks or eyestalks from which some or all of these organs had been removed.

Assay

1. Test animals, isolated in individual containers, are dark-adapted for 3–10 hours prior to injection.

2. The animals are injected through any intersegmental membrane with 0.05 ml of desired extracts using a 0.25 ml tuberculin syringe and a 27- to 29-gauge hypodermic needle.

3. Thirty to 45 minutes after the injection of test materials, the eyestalks are removed by traction exerted with forceps. Bleeding is slight, and ligation is rarely essential. The eyestalks are then oriented with the dorsal pigment spot uppermost in a water-filled cell on the stage of a compound microscope.

4. Two readings from the margin of the cornea are to be taken of each retina: one to the margin of the distal retinal pigment (a) and the second to the level of the dorsal pigment spot (b) (Fig. 14-6). From these readings the "distal retinal pigment index" $a:b$ is to be calculated.

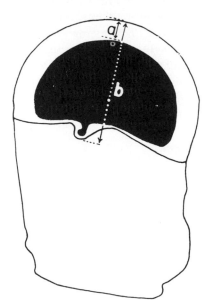

Fig. 14-6. Dorsal view of the eyestalk of *Palaemonetes vulgaris* showing measurements used for calculation of distal retinal pigment. Taken from Kleinholz *et al.* (34).

EXPERIMENT 14-7

Control of Chromatophores in Crustacea*

When changes in the coloration of crustacea were first noted, it was generally believed that they were regulated by nervous impulses. In the mid-1920's, it became apparent that humoral mechanisms were responsible. The injection of blood of animals in one color state modifies the color of the recipient toward the color pattern of the donor. Moreover, occlusion of the blood supply to a region of the body has more effect upon the chromatophore response in that region than does interruption of the nervous supply to the same region.

Although a number of classifications of chromatophores are possible, the most commonly used classification is an artificial one based upon their color. In such a scheme the usual types of crustacean chromatophores are: melanophores (dark brown or black), xanthophores (yellow), erythrophores (red), and guanophores (white). Few species possess all four types. The status of the chromatophores is usually specified in an arbitrary series (26; Ch. 11–43) in which the degree of dispersion is assigned a numerical value from 1 (punctate, least dispersed) to 5 (reticulate, most dispersed), as in Fig. 11-3.

In general, studies of chromatophorotropins have proceeded in three directions. Comparison of extracts from a large number of species treated in a number of ways, in an attempt to delimit the number of hormone compounds involved, has occupied many investigators. A second direction has been the attempt to find the sites of secretion of the hormones. Apparently, chromatophorotropins may be secreted, in varying amounts, from (a) the medulla terminalis X-organ, (b) the supracsophageal ganglion and circumesophageal connectives, (c) the sinus gland, (d) neurosecretory cells of the ventral ganglia, (e) eyestalk ganglia, and other parts of the nervous system.

The third approach has been directed to the nature and properties of the hormones, leading to their isolation and purification and the determination of their structure. Such properties as solubility, sensitivity to peptidases, and passage through dialysis membranes have gradually convinced most workers that the chromatophorotropins are moderately small polypeptides. It is probable that many of the questions regarding number of hormones, variety of sites from which isolation is possible, and species differences in both distribution and response may turn out to be the result of varying activities of a small number of peptides. In

---

* Cf. references (14, 26, 27, 33, 34, 48).

analogous fashion to the Melanocyte Stimulating Hormone activity of ACTH, various portions of the amino acid chains may exert different effects. Previous results probably reflect the varied procedures for preparation and administration as well as species differences.

Procedure and Experimental

Materials and Special Apparatus

1. *Palaemonetes* spp. are good experimental material since they are nearly ubiquitous in temperate fresh and salt water.

2. Equipment: watchmaker's forceps; iridectomy scissors; 0.25-ml tuberculin syringe; 27–gauge ½-inch hypodermic needle; black, white, yellow, and red dishes; dissecting microscope; darkroom or dark box; mortar and pestle.

Assay

1. Place 20–50 *Palaemonetes* overnight under illumination in each of the colored dishes and an equivalent number in the dark box or darkroom.

2. Examine two or three animals from each group. Identify the different types of chromatophores and score them according to their degree of dispersion. It is helpful to make a table showing the degree of dispersion of each type in animals in each colored dish and in those which have been dark adapted.

3. Remove the eyestalks from 10 animals and save both eyestalks and animals. What color changes follow such removal? To what chromatophores are the colors due?

4. Grind 10 eyestalks with mortar and pestle, using 1 ml of distilled or seawater.

5. After thorough trituration, heat the mixture in a boiling water bath for 2–3 minutes to precipitate extraneous protein, centrifuge, and inject 0.02–0.04 ml of the clear supernatant into each of five animals.

6. Examine the chromatophores under 10–20 times magnification and score the degree of dispersion of the chromatophores as a function of time. The first changes may be observed in 2 or 3 minutes after injection; the response will be maximal within 5 or 10 minutes. From the scores of five animals, construct a graph relating the average chromatophore score to the time after injection.

The techniques described above are generally used for assay of chromatophorotropins. Some workers find that the sensitivity of the assay is increased if one eyestalk is removed 12 hours prior to injection.

Other modifications of the test are necessary when other species are used as assay animals. Crustacea with dark exoskeletons have successfully been used by choosing an area of the body (frequently the limbs or tail fan) which is less heavily pigmented and/or by performing the assay on young animals. A major difficulty in using several species of test animals is the lack of correlation of results obtained with such a variety of species both as source and as test for the hormones. The safest procedure is to become familiar with the responses of one species before attempting comparative studies.

Advanced students will wish to attempt to localize the sites of production and secretion within the eyestalk. Figure 14-7 shows the location of the relevant structures in one species. Other species are generally similar.

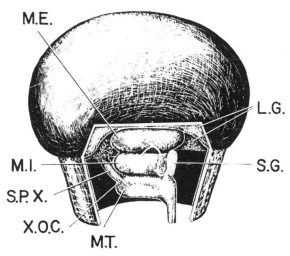

Fig. 14-7. Dissection of the eyestalk of *Pandalus borealis*. Only nerve tissue is shown. *L.G.*, lamina gangliaris; *M.E.*, medulla externa or second optic ganglion; *M.I.*, medulla interna; *M.T.*, medulla terminalis; *S.G.*, sinus gland; *S.P.X.*, sensory pore X-organ; *X.O.C.*, X-organ connectives. Taken from Kleinholz *et al.* (34).

EXPERIMENT 14–8

Endocrine Control of Rhythmic Activity in Blattaria*

Diurnal and circadian rhythms in cockroaches have been reviewed recently and shown to be under endocrine control. On a 12-hour light,

* Cf. references (19–21, 43).

12-hour dark cycle, *Periplaneta* displays locomotor activity beginning just before the onset of darkness and reaching a maximum during the first hours of darkness. Animals in continuous light display no measurable activity rhythm. Endocrine control of this phenomenon may be shown by joining an arrhythmic animal in parabiosis with an animal conditioned to the 24-hour cycle.

Procedures and Experimental

1. Condition one group of adult *Periplaneta* for at least 3 weeks to the light-dark cycle.

2. Condition another group to arrhythmia by exposure to constant light.

3. Under carbon dioxide anesthesia, make a 5×5 mm opening in the dorsal pronotal shield and hypodermis of several animals of each group.

4. Join rhythmic and arrhythmic animals in parabiosis using paraffin wax.

5. Use additional wax to immobilize the abdomen of the rhythm-conditioned animal, and remove its legs.

6. Rhythmic activity may then be followed (7). Under these conditions the activity rhythm of the mobile (initially arrhythmic animal) assumes a rhythmic pattern congruent to and in phase with the rhythm initially displayed by its immobile (initially rhythmic) partner.

EXPERIMENT 14–9

Control of Timing in the Rhythmic Activity of Blattaria

Selective removal and cautery of various organs have localized the control of activity in certain cells of the subesophageal ganglion. Fortunately, these cells are located peripherally on the ventral and lateral surface of the ganglion and may be selectively destroyed or removed. Such an experiment will demonstrate the participation of these cells in the activity rhythms. Sham operations on neighboring regions of the ganglion serve as controls.

Procedure and Experimental

1. Condition two groups of animals, one to 12 hours' light and 12 hours' dark and the other group to 24 hours' light (arrhythmic).

2. Subesophageal ganglia of rhythmic animals are implanted into arrhythmic specimens.

3. Observation of the rhythms for the next few days will demonstrate that the rhythm follows the timing and phase of the implanted ganglion.

EXPERIMENT 14-10

Role of the Subesophageal Ganglia in Rhythmic Activity*

The localized rhythmic activity of the subesophageal ganglion is the result of rhythmic neurosecretion in the operative cells.

Exposure of isolated ventral nerve cords of *Periplaneta americana* and *Blaberus craniifer* to saline extracts of corpora cardiaca depresses spontaneous activity. Exposure to extracts of other organs and tissues does not have a similar effect. Behavior patterns of animals injected with saline extracts of corpora cardiaca are also markedly altered. Treated animals display a stereotyped behavior pattern characterized by a continuous movement around the edges of their containers. The fullest development of the symptoms occurs in the first few hours and subsides gradually during the following 24-96 hours, depending upon the dosage administered. After administration of an extract of six corpora cardiaca, animals remain quiescent, even upon stimulation.

From neither Experiment 14-8 nor 14-9 is it possible to decide whether the cells of the subesophageal ganglion *initiate* the rhythm or whether they are merely storing information resulting from activity in some other part of the body. To resolve this dilemma, we may take advantage of the observation that rhythmic cycles are delayed by low temperatures.

Procedure and Experimental

1. Rhythmically conditioned cockroaches are kept at 3°C for 4 hours.
2. The animals are returned to room temperature, and rhythmic activity is observed.
3. A time lag equal to the duration of chilling should be noted.

EXPERIMENT 14-11

Caste Determination in Termites†

Students of social insects have long known that in addition to the control of the development of the individual exercised by the hormones

* Cf. references (8, 43).
† Cf. references (32, 39, 50).

within the *individual,* additional controls are exerted upon the development of the *colony* by chemical substances transferred among the members of the colony. It seems, therefore, appropriate to extend the concept of the hormone to these social hormones, emphasizing their separate status by referring to them as "pheromones." The control exerted by pheromones is clearly demonstrated in primitive termites.

The course of development in the dry-wood termite *Kalotermes*

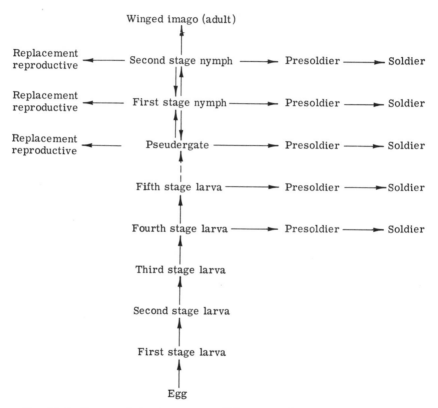

Fig. 14-8. Course of development in *Kalotermes flavicollis.* Each arrow indicates one molt; the broken line, the occurrence of several molts. The terms larva and nymph are used in the German sense, i.e., juvenile forms without wing pads are larvae; after the formation of wing pads, nymphs. In American terminology, all juvenile forms of hemimetabolous insects are nymphs. Adapted from Lüscher (39).

flavicollis is diagrammed in Fig. 14-8. In contrast to the complexities of some termite species, this species has only three fixed castes: winged adults (alates) which develop into primary reproductives ("queens and kings"), secondary or replacement reproductives, and soldiers. The functions of the workers, a separate caste in many social insects, are assumed by juvenile forms which are called pseudoworkers or pseudergates. Such pseudergates and nymphs have four or five possibilities at each molt rather than the single possibility open to most insect species. They can proceed toward adult forms (imagos), undergo stationary molts with no increase in size, differentiate into presoldiers and soldiers, regress, or differentiate into replacement reproductives. Additionally, nymphs may regress into pseudergates. The choice among possibilities is governed by pheromones, which may in some cases be identical with metamorphic hormones. The evidence for this identity is particularly strong in the case of juvenile hormone, as farnesol has been isolated from insect feces (50).

Although the experiments require very long times, several instructive experiments may be performed using colonies of 30–60 termites. Since such colonies require little care, and only about the same space as a package of cigarettes, they are among the easiest of laboratory animals to maintain. For identification, individual animals may be marked with spots of cellulose acetate laquers in various colors and on various parts of the dorsal head capsule.

Procedures and Experimental

Experiment a

In laboratory colonies, most molts are stationary (i.e., larval → larval, nymphal → nymphal, soldier → soldier), but if the nutrition is suddenly improved, progressive molts are induced. If, on the other hand, one transfers second stage nymphs from large to small colonies, they molt regressively.

Maintain one pair of colonies with adequate food, a second pair with minimal food, and observe molts of marked individuals.

Transfer about five marked second stage nymphs from a small colony to a large one and observe their molts.

Experiment b

Removal of adults from balanced colonies to leave "orphan" colonies induces a pair of the pseudergates to initiate a molt. The first sign of an approaching molt is emptying the gut, which occurs within 24 hours. Five days later they molt to replacement reproductives. Removal of soldiers results in similar differentiation to this pseudocaste, but, while the molt to form the white presoldier is relatively prompt, the sequential molt to a definitive soldier requires 11–17 days.

After two colonies are stabilized (about one month), remove the adults and note the effects.

Similarly, remove all the soldiers from a stabilized colony, and note the effect.

In both cases, record the time necessary for the changes.

Experiment c

To verify the hypothesis that the mechanism for maintenance of balanced colonies is regulated by pheromones rather than by crowding or nutritional factors, Lüscher (39) has performed the elegant experiment of maintaining two colonies separated by wire screening. Under these circumstances, the food available to the two colonies differs, but the colonies behave as a single unit. When reproductives are removed from one half-colony, there is no attempt at formation of replacement reproductives. If, however, the two half-colonies are separated by two screens placed far enough apart so that antennal contact is impossible the two colonies behave as separate entities.

Repeat Experiment b, above, but use two colonies separated by a wire screen. Remove the adults from one colony and note the molts in both colonies.

Now, repeat the experiment in two colonies separated by a double screen far enough apart so that antennal contact between individuals is impossible.

Experiment d

Second stage nymphs fed farnesol methyl ester molt into forms intermediate between nymphs and adults, rather than into winged adults.

Feed second stage nymphs on farnesol methyl ester (a juvenile hormone analog) and note the results of molts.

Experiment e

Among further, similar experiments advanced students may feed crude extracts with juvenile hormone activity to colonies and repress the differentiation of replacement reproductives in orphaned colonies. Feed honey bee queen substance, a corpus allatum inhibitor, and increase the number of replacement reproductives formed.

References

1. Barth, R. H., Jr. 1962. The endocrine control of mating behavior in the cockroach *Byrsotria fumigata* (Guerin). *Gen. Comp. Endocrinol.* 2: 53–69.
2. Barton-Browne, L., Dodson, L. F., Hodgson, E. S., and Kiraly, J. K. 1961. Adenergic properties of the cockroach corpus cardiacum. *Gen. Comp. Endocrinol.* 1: 223–236.

3. Beck, S. D., and Alexander, N. 1964. Hormonal activation of the insect brain. *Science* **143**: 478–479.

4. Beerman, W. 1963. Cytological aspects of information transfer in cellular differentiation. *Am. Zoologist* **3**: 23–32.

5. Belamarich, F. A. 1963. Biologically active peptides from the pericardial organs of the crab, *Cancer borealis*. *Biol. Bull.* **124**: 9–16.

6. Bowers, W. S., and Friedman, S. 1963. Mobilization of fat body glycogen by an extract of corpus cardiacum. *Nature* **198**: 685.

7. Brown, R. H. J. 1959. A simple activity recorder. *J. Insect Physiol.* **3**: 125–126.

8. Brown, R. J. H., and Harker, J. E. 1960. A method of controlling the temperature of insect neurosecretory cells *in situ. Nature* **185**: 392.

9. Buck, J. B., and Keister, M. L. 1950. *Drosophila melanogaster* (larva). *In* "Selected Invertebrate Types" (F. A. Brown, Jr., ed.), pp. 496–504. Wiley, New York.

10. Carlisle, D. B., and Knowles, F. 1959. "Endocrine Control in Crustaceans." Cambridge Univ. Press, London and New York.

11. Charniaux-Cotton, H. 1960. Sex determination. *In* "The Physiology of Crustacea" (T. H. Waterman, ed.), Vol. I, pp. 411–447. Academic Press, New York.

12. Clever, U. 1963. Gene activities and gene activations in the hormonal control of molting in insects. *Proc. 16th Intern. Congr. Zool.* Vol. 4, pp. 256–263.

13. Cottrell, C. B. 1962. The imaginal ecdysis of blowflies. Detection of the blood-borne darkening factor and determination of some of its properties. *J. Exptl. Biol.* **39**: 413–430.

14. Fingerman, M. 1963. "The Control of Chromatophores." Macmillan, New York.

15. Fisher, F. M., Jr., and Sanborn, R. C. 1964. *Nosema* as a source of juvenile hormone in parasitized insects. *Biol. Bull.* **126**: 235–252.

16. Fraenkel, G. 1935. A hormone causing pupation in the blowfly *Calliphora erythrocephala. Proc. Roy. Soc.* **B118**: 1–12.

17. Fraenkel, G., and Hsiao, C. 1963. Tanning in the adult fly: A new function of neurosecretion in the brain. *Science* **141**: 1057–1058.

18. Gabe, M. 1956. Histologie comparée de la glande de mue (organe Y) des Crustacés Malacostracés. *Ann. Sci. Nat. Zool. Biol. Animale* **18**(11): 145–152.

19. Harker, J. E. 1956. Factors controlling the diurnal rhythm of activity of *Periplaneta americana* L. *J. Exptl. Biol.* **33**: 224–234.

20. Harker, J. E. 1960a. The effect of perturbations in the environmental cycle of the diurnal rhythm of activity of *Periplaneta americana* L. *J. Exptl. Biol.* **37**: 154–163.

21. Harker, J. E. 1960b. Internal factors controlling the suboesophageal ganglion neurosecretory cycle in *Periplaneta americana* L. *J. Exptl. Biol.* **37**: 164–170.

22. Harker, J. E. 1960c. Endocrine and nervous factors in insect circadian rhythms. *Cold Spring Harbor Symp. Quant. Biol.* **25**: 279–287.

23. Hauenschild, C. 1959a. Zyklische Veränderungen an den inkretorischen Drüsezellen im Prostomium des Polychaeten *Platynereis dumerilii* als Grundlage der Schwärmperiodizität. *Z. Naturforsch.* **14b**: 81–87.

24. Hauenschild, C. 1959b. Hemmender Einfluss der Proventrikelregion auf Stoloisation und Oocyten-entwicklung bei dem Polychaeten *Autolytus prolifer. Z. Naturforsch.* **14b**: 87–89.

25. Highnam, K. C. 1961. The histology of the neurosecretory system of the adult female desert locust. *Schistocerca gregaria. Quart. J. Microscop. Sci.* **102**: 27–38.

26. Hogben, L. T., and Slome, D. 1931. The pigmentary effector system. VI. The dual character of endocrine co-ordination in amphibian colour change. *Proc. Roy. Soc.* **B108**: 10–53.

27. Hosoi, T. 1934. Chromatophore-activating substance in the shrimps. *J. Fac. Sci. Univ. Tokyo, Sec. IV* **3**: 265–270.

28. Johnson, B. 1962. Neurosecretion and the transport of secretory material from the corpora cardiaca in aphids. *Nature* **196**: 1338–1339.

29. Karlson, P. 1956. Biochemical studies on insect hormones. *Vitamins Hormones* **14**: 228–303.

30. Karlson, P. 1963. Chemistry and biochemistry of insect hormones. *Angew. Chem. Intern. Ed. Engl.* **2**: 175–182.

31. Karlson, P., Hoffmeister, H., Hoppe, W., and Hüber, F. 1963. Zur Chemie des Ecdysons. *Ann. Chem.* **662**: 1–20.

32. Karlson, P., and Lüscher, M. 1958. Experimentelle Auslösung von Hautungen bei der Termite *Kalotermes flavicollis* (Fabr.). *J. Insect Physiol.* **1**: 341–345.

33. Kleinholz, L. H. 1961. Pigmentary effectors. *In* "Physiology of Crustacea" (T. H. Waterman, ed.), Vol. 2, pp. 133–169. Academic Press, New York.

34. Kleinholz, L. H., Burgess, P. R., Carlisle, D. B., and Pflueger, O. 1962. Neurosecretion and crustacean retinal pigment hormone: Distribution of the light-adapting hormone. *Biol. Bull.* **122**: 73–85.

35. Kopeč, S. 1922. Studies on the necessity of the brain for the inception of insect metamorphosis. *Biol. Bull.* **42**: 323–342.

36. Kraus, E. 1960. Untersuchungen über die Neurosekretion im Schlundring von *Helix pomatia* L. *Z. Zellforsch.* **51**: 748–776.

37. Larsen, J. R. 1958. Hormone-induced ovarian development in mosquitoes. *Science* **127**: 587–588.

38. Lubet, P. 1956. Effets de l'ablation des centres nerveux sur l'émission des gamètes chez *Mytilus edulis* L. et *Chlamys varia* L. *Ann. Sci. Nat. Zool. Biol. Animale* **18**: 175–183.

39. Lüscher, M. 1963. Functions of the corpora allata in the development of termites. *Proc. 16th Intern. Congr. Zool. Washington, D. C., 1963*. Vol. 4, pp. 244–250.

40. Maddrell, S. H. P. 1963. Excretion in the blood-sucking bug, *Rhodnius prolixus* Stål. I. The control of diuresis. *J. Exptl. Biol.* **40**: 247–256.

41. Mansour, T. E., Sutherland, E. W., Rall, T., and Bueding, E. 1960. The effect of serotonin (5-hydroxytryptamine) on the formatiin of adenosine 3′,5′-phosphate by tissue particles from the liver fluke, *Fasciola hepatica*. *J. Biol. Chem.* **235**: 466–470.

42. Maynard, D. M. 1960. Circulation and heart function. *In* "The Physiology of Crustacea" (T. H. Waterman, ed.), Vol. 1, pp. 161–226. Academic Press, New York.

43. Ozbas, S., and Hodgson, E. S. 1958. Action of insect neurosecretion upon central nervous system *in vitro* and upon behavior. *Proc. Natl. Acad. Sci. U.S.* **44**: 825–830.

44. Passano, L. M. 1961. The regulation of crustacean metamorphosis. *Am. Zoologist* **1**: 89–95.

45. Pax, R. A., and Sanborn, R. C. 1964. Cardioregulation in *Limulus*. I. Physiology of inhibitor nerves. *Biol. Bull.* **126**: 133–141.

46. Prosser, C. L. 1961. "Comparative Animal Physiology," pp. 386–416. Saunders, Philadelphia, Pennsylvania.

47. Ralph, C. L. 1962. Heart accelerators and decelerators in the nervous system of *Periplaneta americana* (L.) *J. Insect Physiol.* **8**: 431–439.
48. Sandeen, M. I. 1950. Chromatophorotrophins in the central nervous system of *Uca pugilator*, with special reference to their origins and actions. *Physiol. Zool.* **23**: 337–352.
49. Scheer, B. T. 1960. The neuroendocrine system of arthropods. *Vitamins Hormones* **18**: 141–204.
50. Schmialek, P. 1961. Die Identifizierung zweier im Tenebriokot und in Hefe vorkommender Substanzen mit Juvenilhormonwirkung. *Z. Naturforsch.* **16b**: 461–464.
51. Schneiderman, H. A., and Gilbert, L. I. 1964. Control of growth and development in insects. *Science* **143**: 325–333.
52. Smith, R. I. 1940. Studies on the effects of eyestalk removal on young crayfish (*Cambarus clarkii* Girard). *Biol. Bull.* **79**: 145–152.
53. Steele, J. E. 1963. The site of action of insect hyperglycemic hormone. *Gen. Comp. Endocrinol.* **3**: 46–52.
54. Thomsen, E., and Moller, I. B. 1963. Influence of neurosecretory cells and of corpus allatum on intestinal protease activity in the adult *Calliphora erythrocephala* Meig. *J. Exptl. Biol.* **40**: 301–322.
55. Vander Kloot, W. G. 1960. Neurosecretion in insects. *Ann. Rev. Entomol.* **5**: 35–52.
56. Van Mol, J.-J. 1960. Phénomènes neurosecretoires dans les ganglions cérébroïdes d'*Arion rufus*. *Compt. Rend. Acad. Sci.* **250**: 2280–2281.
57. Wells, M. J., and Wells, J. 1959. Hormonal control of sexual maturity in octopus. *J. Exptl. Biol.* **36**: 1–33.
58. Welsh, J. H., and Twarog, B. 1960. Measurement of smooth muscle activity in invertebrate animals. *Methods Med. Res.* **8**: 187–199.
59. Wigglesworth, V. B. 1954. "The Physiology of Insect Metamorphosis." Cambridge Univ. Press, London and New York.
60. Wigglesworth, V. B. 1959. "The Control of Growth and Form." Cornell Univ. Press, Ithaca, New York.
61. Willey, R. B., and Chapman, G. B. 1960. The ultrastructure of certain components of the corpora cardiaca in orthopteroid insects. *J. Ultrastruct. Res.* **4**: 1–14.
62. Williams. C. M. 1946. Physiology of insect diapause: The role of the brain in the production and termination of pupal dormancy in the giant silkworm, *Platysamia cecropia*. *Biol. Bull.* **90**: 234–243.
63. Williams, C. M. 1956. The juvenile hormone of insects. *Nature* **178**: 212–213.
64. Williams, C. M. 1956. Physiology of insect diapause. X. An endocrine mechanism for the influence of temperature on the diapausing pupa of the cecropia silkworm. *Biol. Bull.* **110**: 201–218.
65. Williams, C. M. 1959. The juvenile hormone. I. Endocrine activity of the corpora allata of the adult cecropia silkworm. *Biol. Bull.* **116**: 323–338.
66. Wilson, E. O., and Bossert, W. H. 1963. Chemical communication among animals. *Recent Progr. Hormone Res.* **19**: 673–710.

Appendix

A-1. Guiding Principles in the Care and Use of Laboratory Animals*

1. All animals used for experimental purposes must be lawfully acquired and their retention shall be in strict compliance with Federal, State, and local laws and regulations.

2. Research projects involving live animals must be approved by the directors of the laboratory. When animals are used by students for their education or the advancement of science, such work shall be done under the direct supervision of an experienced teacher or investigator.

3. It is recommended that dogs and cats not be used in experimental work when, in the judgment of the investigator, other animals equally suitable for such work are readily and economically available.

4. It is earnestly recommended that the housing, care and feeding of birds and mammals be supervised by a veterinarian; that the care of other species be supervised by a biologist competent in such matters.

5. All laboratory animals must receive every consideration for their bodily comfort; they must be kindly treated, properly fed, and their surroundings kept in sanitary condition.

6. Rooms in which animals are to be housed shall be provided with an impervious floor, with adequate drainage, adequate light, adequate ventilation and temperature control, a separate cage for each animal (monkeys, dogs, cats, and rabbits) of sufficient size to permit the animal to stand or lie in a normal position, and for dogs, an exercise space equipped with an impervious floor.

7. The food supplied to all experimental animals must be palatable, of sufficient quantity and of proper quality to maintain the animals in good health. Water supplied to animals must be clean.

8. All major operative procedures must be done under a general anesthetic; minor operative procedures may be done under local infiltra-

* From "Principles of Laboratory Animal Care," National Society for Medical Research.

465

tion anesthesia. If the nature of the study is such as to require that the animal survive, sterile technic must be followed throughout operations on animals whose susceptibility to infection makes it necessary, as is the case with monkeys, dogs and cats. Clean technic alone may be used in animals highly resistant to infection such as chickens and rats. If the study does not require survival, the animal must be killed in a humane manner at the conclusion of the experiment. When for exceptional tests or investigations, it is necessary that the animals involved be not under the influence of any anesthetic or other drug, such experimentation shall be done only by persons skilled in such work and only after the project has had specific approval by the head of the department involved.

9. The postoperative care of experimental animals must be such as to minimize discomfort during convalescence. All conditions must be maintained for the animal's comfort in accordance with the practices followed in small animal hospitals or in accordance with the practices followed in human medicine and surgery.

A-2. Animal Hormones

Gland or structure	Hormone[a]	Action
Hypothalamus	CRF (Corticotropin releasing factor)	Stimulates release of ACTH
	Possible factors controlling the release of gonadotropins and TSH	Stimulates release of gonadotropins
	Source of oxytocin and vasopressin	See Hypophysis, posterior lobe
Pineal gland (epiphysis cerebri)	Adrenoglomerulotropin (?)	Stimulates release of aldosterone
	Antiadrenal gland factor (?)	Inhibits release of adrenal secretions, aldosterone and 17-hydroxycorticoids
	Pineal extract (?)	Inhibits precocious sexual development
Hypophysis, anterior lobe	Gonadotropins FSH, FRH (follicle stimulating hormone)	Follicle growth in ovary; spermatogenesis in testis
	LH, ICSH (luteinizing hormone, interstitial cell stimulating hormone)	Ovulation, corpus luteum formation in ovary; estrogen secretion, ovary (with FSH); androgen secretion, testis
	Prolactin (lactogenic hormone, LTH, luteotropin)	Crop sac growth, pigeon; milk secretion; corpus luteum function (some species)
	ACTH (adrenocorticotropin, corticotropin)	Stimulates secretion of adrenal cortex
	TSH (TTH, thyrotropin, thyroid stimulating hormone)	Stimulates secretion of thyroid gland
	STH (somatotropin, growth hormone)	Stimulates body growth, bone growth, carbohydrate metabolism
Hypophysis, intermediate lobe	Intermedin (MSH, melanophore stimulating hormone, chromatophorotropin)	Dispersion of pigment granules; melanin synthesis
Hypophysis, posterior lobe (neurohypophysis)	Oxytocin (Pitocin)	Contraction of uterus; ejection of milk
	Vasopressin (antidiuretic hormone, ADH, Pitressin)	Contraction of blood vessels; water retention

[a] ? indicates that the evidence for these factors is incomplete.

Gland or structure	Hormone[a]	Action
Thyroid gland	Thyroxine, triiodothyronine	Maturation; oxygen consumption (metabolism); metamorphosis
Parathyroid gland	Parathormone	Metabolism of calcium and phosphorus
	Calcitonin (?)	Bone metabolism
Pancreas, islets of Langerhans	Insulin	Carbohydrate, protein, and fat metabolism
	Glucagon (HGF, hyperglycemic factor)	Carbohydrate metabolism
Stomach	Gastrin	Stimulates gastric secretion
Duodenal mucosa	Secretin	Regulates flow of pancreatic fluids
	Cholecystokinin	Controls gall bladder function
	Enterogastrone	Inhibits gastric secretion and motility
	Pancreozymin	Secretion of enzymes from pancreas
Adrenal medulla	Epinephrine Norepinephrine	Increase in blood sugar, blood pressure, and effects similar to sympathetic stimulation
Adrenal cortex	Deoxycorticosterone	Salt and water balance
	Aldosterone	Salt and water balance
	11-Oxycorticoids (cortisone, hydrocortisone, corticosterone)	Carbohydrate metabolism, nitrogen metabolism, resistance to stress
	Sex steroids	See Ovary and Testis
Ovary, follicle	Estrogens	Stimulates female sex accessories, secondary sex characters, and sexual behavior
Ovary, corpus luteum	Progestogens	Maintenance of pregnancy, growth and development of uterus and mammary gland
	Relaxin	Separation of pubic symphysis, inhibition of uterine contractions, relaxation of uterine cervix
	Protein extract (?)	Water retention, pregnancy anemia

Gland or structure	Hormone[a]	Action
Testis	Androgens	Stimulates male sex accessories, secondary sex characters, and sexual behavior
	Inhibin (?)	Inhibits function of pituitary gland
Kidney	Renin (converts angiotensinogen to the active angiotensin)	Hypertension, aldosterone secretion
Placenta	HCG (human chorionic gonadotropin)	LH-like
	PMS (pregnant mare serum)	FSH-like
	LTH (luteotropin, in rat placenta)	Maintains function of corpus luteum
	Estrogen	See Ovary
	Progestogen	
	Relaxin	
	ACTH	Stimulate adrenal cortex
Nerve endings		
Adrenergic	Norepinephrine	Facilitate transmission of impulses at nerve endings
Cholinergic	Acetylcholine	

A-2a. Invertebrate Hormones

Gland or structure	Hormone	Action
	Insecta	
Brain	Prothoracotropic hormone	Stimulates the prothoracic gland to release ecdysone
Prothoracic gland	Ecdysone	Stimulates growth differentiation and enzyme synthesis
Corpus allatum	Juvenile hormone	Prevents metamorphosis A pheromone in social insects Stimulates growth and egg maturation
Neurosecretory cells in brain and thoracic ganglia	Darkening hormone	Hardening and darkening of cuticle
Epithelial cells of rectum	Proctodone	Stimulates release of prothoracotropic hormone

Gland or structure	Hormone	Action
Neurosecretory cells in subesophageal ganglion	Unnamed extract	Regulates activity rhythms of the organism
Corpus cardiacum	Cardioaccelerator (peptides) Cardioinhibitor (peptides) Unnamed polypeptide	Increases rate of heart beat Decreases rate of heart beat Regulates blood trehalose
Neurosecretory cells of meso- and metathoracic ganglia	Diuretic factor	Induces diuresis
Crustacea		
Sinus gland (probably secreted in the X-organ and stored in sinus gland)	Molt-inhibiting hormone Chromatophorotropins (may be four peptides) Diabetogenic factor	Inhibits the molt Movement of eye pigment Expansion and contraction of chromatophores Increase of blood sugar
Y-organ	Molt-stimulating hormone	Stimulates the molt
Androgenic gland	Androgenic hormone	Stimulates expression of male secondary sexual characteristics

Hormone	Amount equivalent to 1 IU
Androsterone	0.1 mg crystalline
Corticotropin (ACTH)	5 IU/ampoule containing 50 µg standard corticotropin preparation
Estradiol benzoate	0.1 µg crystalline
Estrone	0.1 µg crystalline
Human chorionic gonadotropin (HCG)	0.1 mg of standard preparation
Insulin	0.125 mg of standard preparation
Melanocyte stimulating hormone (MSH)	1.0 µg of standard preparation
Oxytocin	0.5 mg of standard preparation
Parathormone	0.01 of amount of solution required to induce an increase of 5 mg of calcium in the blood serum of the dog (20 kg) within 16 hours of injection (USP unit)
Pregnant mare serum gonadotropin (PMS)	0.25 mg of standard preparation
Progesterone	1.0 mg crystalline
Prolactin (LTH)	0.1 mg of standard preparation
Thyrotropin (TSH)	0.075 mg of standard preparation
Vasopressin (ADH)	0.5 mg of standard preparation

Hormones for Which Arbitrary Standards of Known Purity and/or Activity Are Used

Epinephrine
Follicle stimulating hormone (FSH)
Luteinizing hormone (LH)
Relaxin
Somatotropin (STH)
Thyroxine

A-4. Steroid Structures and Nomenclature

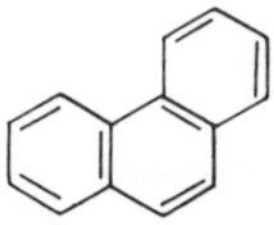

Phenanthrene

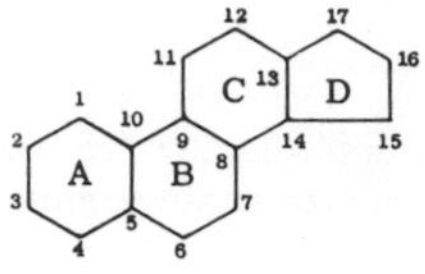

Steroid nucleus
(perhydrocyclopentanophenanthrene)

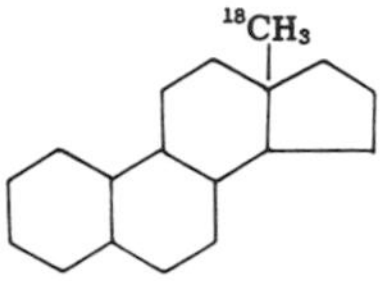

Estrane

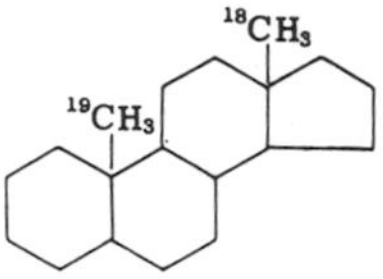

Androstane

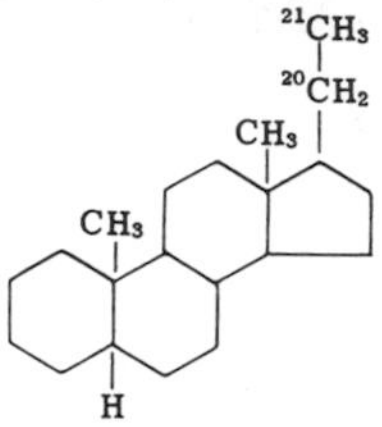

Pregnane

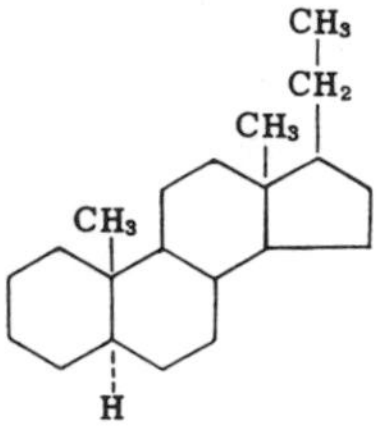

Allopregnane

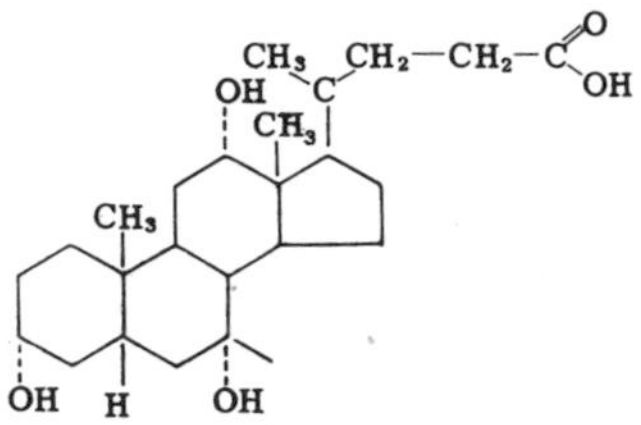

Cholane derivative
(cholic acid)

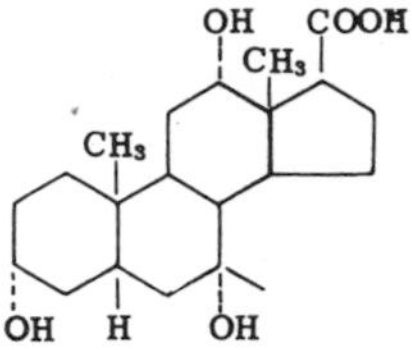

Etiocholic acid

<u>Cis</u> isomer	Both substituents on the same side of the ring. Usually in reference to the methyl groups, which are considered to be above the plane of the ring. Such substituents are indicated by a solid line, ———R
<u>Trans</u> isomer	Substituents on opposite sides of the ring, indicated by a broken line, -----R
Beta (β)	Substituents on same side of nucleus as methyl groups, indicated by solid line, ———H (see pregnane)
Alpha (α)	Substituents on opposite side of nucleus from methyl groups, indicated by broken line, -----R (see allopregnane)
Etio-	Indicates compound obtained from degradation of parent compound as etiocholic acid from cholic acid
-ol, and hydroxy-	Alcohol substituent (OH)
-one, keto-	Ketone substituent ($=O$)

472

-ane	Saturated compound
-ene, Δ-,	Double bond, C=C. Position of double bond indicated by delta superscript, as Δ^5 for double bond between carbons 5 and 6
-ynyl	Triple bond as in ethynyl, $-C\equiv C-$
Deoxy-, desoxy-,	One oxygen substituent less than parent or reference compound
Dehydro-	Two hydrogens less than parent or reference compound
Epi-, iso-	Isomers wherein substituents on one carbon atom differ in steric arrangement (androsterone and epiandrosterone)
Allo-	<u>Trans</u> isomer as in pregnane, 5(β)-H, and allopregnane, 5(α)-H

ESTRANE DERIVATIVES (A-RING UNSATURATED, ESTRATRIENE)

Estratrien-3β-ol-17-one
(Estrone)

Estratriene-3β,17β-diol
(Estradiol-17β)

ANDROSTANE DERIVATIVES (Δ^4 UNSATURATION)

Δ^4-Androsten-17β-ol-3-one
(Testosterone)

Androstan-3β-ol-17-one
(Epiandrosterone)

PREGNANE DERIVATIVES

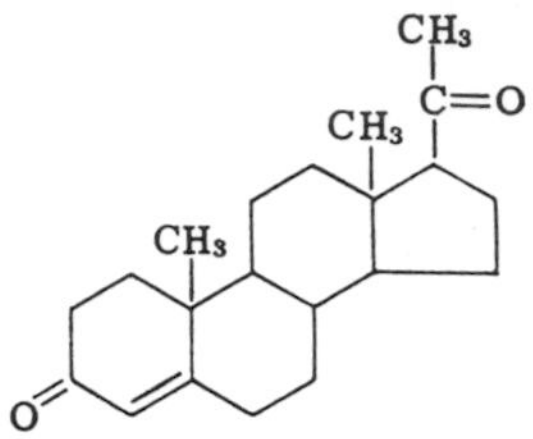

Δ⁴-Pregnene-3,20-dione
(Progesterone)

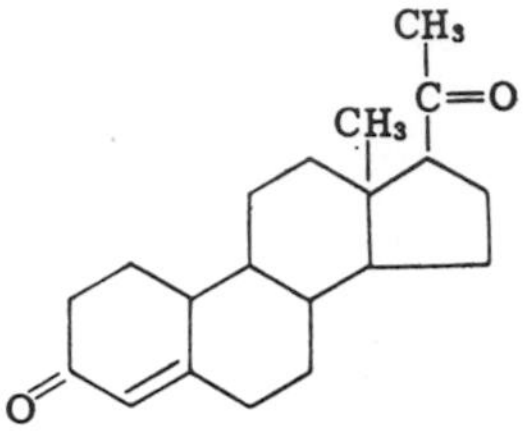

19-Norprogesterone

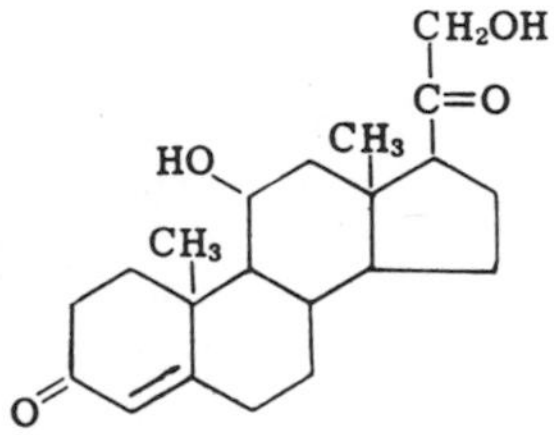

Δ⁴-Pregnene-11,21-diol-3,20-dione
(Corticosterone)
(other corticoids named as derivatives of corticosterone)

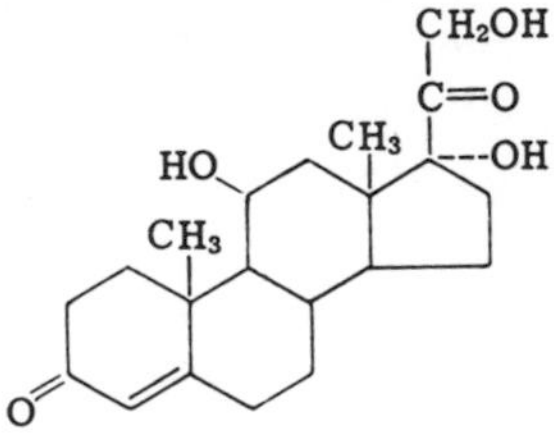

17α-Hydroxycorticosterone

A-5. Vehicles for the Administration of Hormones

I. *Saline or Water Solutions*

The protein and amino acid hormones are all soluble in water or saline. Physiological saline is often preferable. In the case of thyroxine, the hormone has to be dissolved in a slightly alkaline medium, i.e., a pH of about 8.0–9.0. Insulin is usually dissolved in acid medium, pH 4–6. All the protein and amino acid hormone solutions must be refrigerated.

II. *Oil Solutions and Suspensions*

The steroid hormones are usually insoluble in water and possess a varying degree of solubility in oil. Using a solubility table (see A–6), one may add the hormone directly to the oil and heat at 65°C for 24 hours, or dissolve the hormone in ether, add the oil, and remove the ether by *in vacuo* distillation. Solutions of many of these hormones are relatively stable and may be stored at room temperature.

It is frequently necessary to use a suspension in order to obtain an adequate concentration. Two vehicles for suspending steroid hormones are presented below:

Vehicle 1

Sodium chloride	0.9%
Polysorbate	0.4%
Sodium carboxymethylcellulose (120 medium)	0.5%
Benzyl alcohol	0.9%

Vehicle 2

A simple method for suspending the hormone is to prepare a saline solution containing 1 drop of Tween 80 per 5 ml of saline. The hormone can then be suspended in this material as indicated below. However, this suspension tends to break rapidly.

The steroids are weighed and transferred to a suitable size grinder (e.g., Ten Broeck grinder). A suitable volume of Vehicle 1 or 2, usually about 10% of the final volume, and the steroid are mixed and reduced to a fine suspension by grinding for 2 minutes. The resulting suspension is diluted with an additional 40% of the suspending fluid and, with a pipette, is transferred to a bottle. The grinder is then washed with the remaining fluid, which is also transferred with a pipette to the bottle. (PRECAUTION: suspensions of steroids should be examined carefully for contamination with molds.)

III. *Beeswax-Oil Suspension*

At times it is necessary to suspend hormones in a vehicle that will delay absorption and give a prolonged action to the hormone. Relaxin and ACTH have been used successfully in beeswax-oil vehicles.

1. Beeswax-oil vehicle is prepared by dissolving warmed beeswax in warmed peanut oil in a concentration of 5% (v/v). The vehicle is stored in the refrigerator when not in use.

2. All materials used in preparation of the vehicle, beeswax-oil, syringes, needles, bottles, vials, porcelain mortar and pestle, must be warmed in an oven to 50–60°C.

3. Weigh the hormone and place in a warmed mortar. Measure melted beeswax-oil using a warmed 10-ml syringe. Be sure to prepare an extra 20% of material to allow for overfill for injection requirements.

4. Add beeswax-oil very gradually (0.2–0.5 ml at a time) to the hormone powder, grinding continuously. Transfer the suspension with a warmed syringe to a vial or bottle.

5. At the time of injection, the hormone suspension, syringe, and needle must be warmed to 50–60°C before use. It is suggested that a needle size of at least 22 gauge be used. Although repeated heating is not harmful to the potency of relaxin or the steroid hormones, suspended material may tend to precipitate and make injection difficult.

A-6. Solubility of Some Common Steroid Hormones

Hormone	Vehicle	Maximum solubility (per ml)
Estradiol	Oil	1 mg
Estrone	Oil	0.5 mg
Estriol	Oil	30 μg
Estriol	Propylene glycol	0.5 mg
Progesterone	Oil	40–50 mg
Pregnanediol	Oil	0.9 mg
Testosterone propionate	Oil	25 mg
Testosterone	Oil	10 mg
Deoxycorticosterone	Oil	5.0 mg
Cortisone acetate	Propylene glycol	0.4 mg

A-7. Anesthetic Dosage Table for Laboratory Animals

Animal	Anesthetic	Route[a]	Dose (mg/kg body wt)
Rabbit[b]	Amytal	iv (ear vein)	45
	Nembutal	iv	25–30
	Nembutal	ip	30–40
	Urethan	ip	1550
	Chloretone (chlorobutanol)	Stomach tube (in 50% alcohol)	150–200
Dog	Amytal	iv (saphenous v.)	45–60
	Amytal	ip	60–70
	Nembutal	iv	25–30
	Nembutal	ip	45–55
	Sodium Barbital	iv	200–250
	Phenobarbital	ip	180
	Chloretone (chlorobutanol)	ip (in 50% alcohol)	350
Cat	Nembutal	iv (saphenous)	25–30
	Nembutal	ip	45–55
	Sodium Barbital	iv	200–250
	Amytal	ip	60–80
	Phenobarbital	ip	180
	Urethan	im	1800
Rat	Nembutal	ip	25–30
	Sodium Barbital	ip	200–250
	Amytal	ip	60
	Urethan	sc	1750
Guinea Pig	Sodium Barbital	ip	100
	Urethan	ip	1000
	Chloretone	ip	175 (in 50% alcohol)
Fowl	Nembutal	iv	25–100
	Phenobarbital	iv	100
	Dial	iv	60
Pigeon	Phenobarbital	im	12

	Analeptic		
Rabbit, rat	Metrazol	iv	10–50

[a] All intravenous injections should be given *very slowly*, while observing animal for level of anesthesia; im, intramuscular; ip, intraperitoneal; iv, intravenous; sc, subcutaneous.

[b] Excellent surgical anesthesia can be obtained in the rabbit by supplementing the Nembutal (25 mg per kilogram body weight) with a small amount of ether given by cone.

A-8. Physiological Fluids for Isolated Tissues

I. *Ringer (frog)*

NaCl	6.50 gm
KCl	0.14 gm
CaCl$_2$	0.12 gm
NaHCO$_3$	0.20 gm
glucose	2.00 gm
water	1000 ml

II. *Ringer-Locke (mammal)*

NaCl	9.00 gm
KCl	0.42 gm
CaCl$_2$	0.24 gm
NaHCO$_3$	0.20 gm
glucose	1.00 gm
water	1000 ml

III. *Modified Locke*

Oxytocin assay with rat uterus: same as II, but with 25% of the CaCl$_2$ and 50% of the glucose.

IV. *Tyrode (mammal)*

NaCl	8.00 gm
KCl	0.20 gm
CaCl$_2$	0.20 gm
NaHCO$_3$	1.00 gm
MgCl$_2$	0.10 gm
glucose	1.00 gm
water	1000 ml

V. *Krebs-Ringer Bicarbonate (mammal)*

NaCl	6.92 gm
KCl	0.35 gm
CaCl$_2$	0.28 gm
KH$_2$PO$_4$	0.16 gm
MgSO$_4 \cdot 7H_2O$	0.29 gm
NaHCO$_3$	2.10 gm
glucose	1.00 gm
water	1000 ml

Note: When glucose is used, it should be added just before use. All water should be glass distilled.

A-9. Miscellaneous Fluids

I. *Fluid for Visualizing the Thymus Gland: Carnoy's Fixative*

Ethyl alcohol	60 ml
Chloroform	30 ml
Glacial acetic acid	10 ml

II. *Antiseptic Solution*

These three solutions are used to sterilize instruments, cleanse incision areas, etc.

(a) Ethyl alcohol, 70%
(b) Zephiran (benzalkonium chloride) 1:1000 dilution
(c) Zephiran tincture 1:1000 dilution (Zephiran:ethanol:water, 10:640:630)

III. *Depilatory*

This depilatory for laboratory animals is prepared according to I. Pitesky and J. H. Last [*Science* **108**: 675 (1948)].

20 gm barium sulfide (yellow purified powder)
10 gm Tide

Mix with 50 ml of 10% glycerin in water to make a smooth creamy suspension.

Thoroughly wet area of body with water. Use a tongue depressor to apply the depilatory and work gently into the hair. Move the depressor carefully back and forth over the skin surface, especially where the action of the depilatory is slow. Add water to remove; rinse *thoroughly* with water to remove completely the sulfide residue.

IV. *Picric Acid Marking Solution*

Use for marking fur to identify animals; see scheme for marking animals by ear punch (A–10).

Saturated solution of picric acid in 70% ethyl alcohol or isopropyl alcohol

A-10. Scheme for Marking Animals by Ear Punch

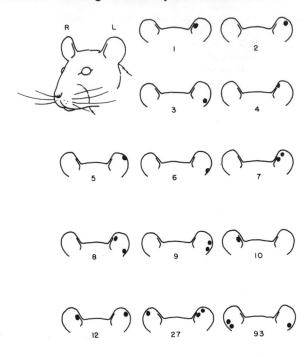

A-11. Sources and Maintenance of Invertebrates

Few laboratories maintain colonies of invertebrate animals; therefore, a word about sources and special techniques is in order. In addition to customary supply houses, local fishing bait dealers are a surprisingly good source for a variety of invertebrates. Most dealers stock or know of supplies of crayfish; additionally, many of them can supply grasshoppers, wax moth larvae, or other local species of insect larvae. In coastal areas, they are frequently able to supply one or more species of small Crustacea.

Interstate or postal shipment of insects is governed by special federal regulation in the United States. Permits must be obtained before shipping from the Bureau of Entomology and Plant Quarantine, U. S. Department of Agriculture, Washington, D. C. In general, permits are issued for legitimate scientific use of insects which are unlikely to become pests or which have already become common. It is sometimes worthwhile to contact the state entomologist to inquire whether a particular species may be imported into your area.

Maintenance of invertebrates is described in "Culture Methods for Invertebrate Animals" by F. E. Lutz, P. L. Welch, P. S. Galtsoff, and J. G. Needham. The first edition of 1937 [Cornell Univ. Press (Comstock), Ithaca, New York] has been republished, unaltered, in 1959 by Dover Publications, New York.

Author Index

Numbers in parentheses are reference numbers and indicate than an author's work is referred to although his name is not cited in the text. Numbers in italic show the page on which the complete reference is listed.

T

Tait, J. F., 183(24, 59), 187(24), 197 (59), *221*, *223*
Takahashi, Y., 355(46), *363*
Talbot, N. B., 80(83), *107*
Talmage, R. V., 25(72, 73), *63*, 72(38, 84), *104*, *107*, 110(26, 27), 111 (26), 112(36, 37), 115(12), 116 (1), *120*, *121*, *122*, 367(13), 370 (13), 372(8), *381*, *382*
Tanaka, A., 310(90), 311, *341*
Tanner, D. C., 393(88), *424*
Tata, J. R., *15*, 227, *261*
Taurog, A., 227(47), 249(47), *262*
Tausk, M., 67(1), 84(1), *103*
Thoehen, H., 143(39), *151*
Thomas, M., 84(66), *106*
Thompson, C. R., 21(14), 36(53), *61*, *62*
Thompson, L. M., 33(45), *62*
Thomsen, E., 435(54), *463*
Thomson, D. M., 130(12), 139(12), 140(12), *150*
Thorn, G. W., *222*
Thuline, H. C., 141(23), *151*
Tindall, J. S., 75(8), *103*
Törnblom, N., 371(28), *382*
Tolksdorf, S., 304(25), *337*
Tom, J., 31(44), *62*
Topel, W., 188(1), *220*
Treadwell, C. R., 389, 390(80), 406 (80), 417(80), *424*
Trippett, S., 344(19), *362*
Tschopp, E., 132, *151*
Turner, C. D., *15*, 402, *424*
.Turner, C. W., 235(19), 258(19), *260*, 273(5, 45), 286(5), *289*, *291*, 307 (50), 331(50), *339*, 369(29), *382*
Turpeinen, K., 299(24), *337*
Twarog, B., 440(58), *463*
Tyberghein, J. M., 398, 399(82), 420 (82), *424*

U

Uriac, D., 385(1), 390(1), *420*
Urist, M. R., 50(74), *63*
Urquhart, J., 185(64), *223*
Ussing, H. H., 349(25), *362*

V

Vallance-Owen, J., 391(85), 392, 396 (84), 397, 398(83), 399(86), 418 (83), 419, *424*
Vander Kloot, W. G., *463*
Vande Wiele, R. L., 33(75), *63*
Van Dyke, D. C., 318(91), *341*
van Dyke, H. B., 297(48), 300(48), 302 (47), 304(46), 305(47), 325(47), *338*, *339*, 344(66), 350(2, 65), 352 (1), *361*, *364*
Van Mol, J.-J., 427(56), *463*
van Tienhoven, A., 303(92), *341*
Velardo, J. T., *15*, 34(77), 36(76), 48 (76), *63*, 72(52), 80(85), 87(86), 89(37), *104*, *105*, *107*
Venning, E. H., 80(87, 90), 84(88, 89), *107*, 219(63a), *223*
vaz Ferreira, A., 166(13), *174*
Vilar, O., *152*
Villee, C. A., 34(41, 78), 36(79), *62*, *64*
Vogt, M., 162(42), *176*
von Berswordt-Wallrabe, R., 369(29), *382*
von Euler, U. S., 155(19), 158(43), 168 (19, 43), *175*, *176*
von Münstermann, A. M., 84(98), *107*
Vulpian, A., 153(44), *176*

W

Wada, H., 109(38), 111(38), *122*
Wagner, E. M., 394(70, 71), 406(70, 71), *423*, *424*
Wakeling, A., 127(37), *152*
Walker, J. M., 349(67), *364*
Wall, P. E., 164(3), *174*
Waltner, C., 113(7), *121*
Wang, G. H., 39(80), *64*, 86(91), *107*
Waring, H., 354, 355(43), 360(43), *363*
Warren, M. R., 234(48), *262*
Wasserman, P., 387(87), *424*
Weinstein, H. R., 385(28), 388(28), 398(28), *422*
Weisman, A. I., 332(93), 335(93), *341*
Weiss, P., 267(56), *292*
Welch, A. D., 163(25), *175*
Welch, P. L., *481*

Subject Index

A

Acetate
  androgen synthesis, and, 132, *133*
  corticoid synthesis, and, *193*
  estrogen synthesis, and, 33
Acetoacetic acid, test, 410
Acetone, test, 409
Acetylcholine
  acceleration of arthropod heart, 439
  action on smooth muscle, 169
  mollusc heart, 439
Acetyl Co A, 400, 404, *405*
Acidosis, in diabetes, 390
Activity rhythms, (*see* Circadian
  rhythms)
  cockroach, 437, 455
  running, 39
ACTH (*see* Corticotropin)
Adaptation, in stress, 187
Adenohypophysis (*see also* Pituitary
  gland)
  cell types, 263, 293
  diabetes insipidus and, 348
  location, 263, 293, *295*
  portal circulation, 3, 294, *295*
  transplantation of, 314
ADH (*see* Vasopressin)
Adrenal cortex
  ACTH, action, 184, 185, 269, 279, 281
  actions of, 181
  ascorbic acid, 188, 203, 208
  cholesterol, 188, 206
  determination of hormones in, 214
  embryogenesis, 178
  histology, 178, 208
  location, 177
  x-zone, 178, 179
Adrenalectomy
  diabetes mellitus, and 393, 394
  disturbances of, 181, *182*
  plasma corticoids after, *195*
  post-operative care, 196
  survival after, 197
    at low temperatures, 198

symptoms of, *182*, *195*
  technique of, 194, *196*
Adrenal medulla
  cell types, 154
  demedullation, technique, 166
  embryogenesis, 153
  location, 154
Adrenaline (*see* Epinephrine)
Adrenochromes, 156
Adrenocorticoids
  action, 181, *182*
  antagonists, 194
  antiestrogens, *36*
  assay, 187, *188*
  blood levels, *185*, 189, 190, 191
  carbohydrate metabolism, 181, *182*,
    216, 217, 219
  chemical determination, 189, 191, 212
  chromatography of, 189, 209
  diabetes mellitus and 183, 216, 394,
    395
  eosinophils, 199, *200*
  half-life, *185*, 192
  insufficiency, *182*, 194, *195*
  mechanism of action, 192
  muscle, 202
  nature of, 179, *180*
  protein, action on, 181
  sites of formation, 177
  and stress, 185, 186, 198
  survival, 197, 198
  synthesis and metabolism, 192, *193*
Adrenocorticotropin (*see* Corticotropin)
Aggressive behavior (*see* Behavior)
Alarm reaction, 160, 186
Aldosterone
  angiotensin secretion and, 179
  biogenesis, 193
  electrolyte regulation by, 183
  potency, *184*
  secretion of, 179, 186, 270
  sites of action of, 192
  source, 179
  structure, *180*